Property of Carl J. Yoder
212 Coffman Hall
Goshen College
Goshen, Indiana

Textbook of
BIOCHEMISTRY
Sixth Edition

By

BENJAMIN HARROW, Ph.D.

Professor of Chemistry, College of the City of New York

And

ABRAHAM MAZUR, Ph.D.

Associate Professor of Chemistry, College of the City of New York

Philadelphia and London

W. B. SAUNDERS COMPANY

Reprinted July, 1955

Copyright, 1954, by W. B. Saunders Company

Copyright, 1938, 1940, 1943, 1946 and 1950, by W. B. Saunders Company

Copyright under the International Copyright Union

ALL RIGHTS RESERVED. *This book is protected by copyright.*
No part of it may be duplicated or reproduced in any manner
without written permission from the publisher.

Made in the U.S.A.   Press of W. B. Saunders Company

Library of Congress Catalog Card Number: 54–5320

Preface

THE ACCELERATED development of biochemistry shows no abatement, and we believe this new edition is evidence for such a statement. Deletions, substitutions, additions, run through the book. Once again the stress has been to make the text present biochemistry in readable, thoroughly up-to-date terms.

A separate chapter on the metabolism of nucleoproteins has been introduced. The chapter on biological antagonists has been eliminated, but the essential facts have been incorporated in appropriate parts of the book, particularly within the material on the vitamin B complex. The chapter on the chemistry of the nervous system has been included under nerve tissue, in the chapter on the chemistry of the tissues. Some day "brain chemistry" will undoubtedly occupy a major portion of a text on biochemistry; but that day, we are afraid, is still distant.

It will be noticed that a considerable reshuffling of chapters has been done. This is the result of much discussion with a number of colleagues. For example, biological oxidations now precedes intermediate metabolism; but foods and vitamins follow metabolism. Further, the chapters dealing with detoxication and chemotherapy have been placed at the end of the text, as representing the transition stage from biochemistry to pharmacology and medicine.

Among the many topics that have been either enlarged or introduced, mention may be made of paper chromatography; countercurrent distribution of amino acids; determination of "end groups" in a protein; techniques for demonstrating enzyme activity; theory of the mechanism of enzyme action; the metabolism of bile pigments; a new table of blood values; blood plasma protein fractionation; shock; reorganization of chapters on intermediate metabolism of carbohydrates, lipids and proteins; coenzyme A; dynamic aspects of protein metabolism; peptide synthesis; urea synthesis; use of isotopes; intermediate reactions in photosynthesis; energy-rich phosphates.

For help in various directions our thanks are due to Dr. Oscar Bodansky (Sloane-Kettering Research Institute); Dr. Anne C. Carter (Cornell Medical College); Dr. O. H. Gaebler (Henry Ford Hospital, Detroit); Prof. S. Gurin (University of Pennsylvania); Prof. J. E. Jorpes (University of Stockholm); Prof. M. Karshan (Columbia University); Prof. J. B. Lucas (Virginia Polytechnic Institute); Prof. W. C. Rose (University of Illinois).

Our thanks are also due to our publishers, W. B. Saunders Company, for doing much to facilitate and ease our work.

BENJAMIN HARROW
ABRAHAM MAZUR

iii

Contents

Chapter 25

Abbreviations

(For general reviews consult the *Ann. Rev. Biochem.*, *Ann. Rev. Physiol.*, *Physiol. Rev.*, and *Harvey Lectures*. References to original papers are given. For further references see *Chemical Abstracts*.)

Adv. Enzym. = Advances in Enzymology
Adv. Protein Chem. = Advances in Protein Chemistry
Am. J. Physiol. = American Journal of Physiology
Annals N. Y. Acad. Sciences = Annals of the N. Y. Academy of Sciences
Ann. Rev. Biochem. = Annual Review of Biochemistry
Ann. Rev. Physiol. = Annual Review of Physiology
Arch. Biochem. = Archives of Biochemistry
Arch. Internal Med. = Archives of Internal Medicine
Biochem. J. = Biochemical Journal
Bull. N. Y. Acad. Med. = Bulletin of the N. Y. Academy of Medicine
Chem. Eng. News = Chemical and Engineering News
Chem. Rev. = Chemical Reviews
Federation Proceedings = Federation of American Society for Experimental Biology
Ind. Eng. Chem. = Industrial and Engineering Chemistry
J. Am. Chem. Soc. = Journal of the American Chemical Society
J. Am. Med. Assoc. = Journal of the American Medical Association
J. Biol. Chem. = Journal of Biological Chemistry
J. Chem. Educ. = Journal of Chemical Education
J. Gen. Physiol. = Journal of General Physiology
J. Nutrition = Journal of Nutrition
J. Physiol. = Journal of Physiology
J. Soc. Chem. Ind. = Journal of the Society of Chemical Industry
Nutr. Rev. = Nutritional Reviews
Physiol. Rev. = Physiological Reviews
Proc. Nat. Acad. Sci. U. S. = Proceedings of the National Academy of Sciences of the United States of America
Proc. R. S. (London), Series B = Proceedings of the Royal Society (London)
Proc. Soc. Exp. Biol. Med. = Proceedings of the Society for Experimental Biology and Medicine
Symp. Quant. Biol. = Symposia on Quantitative Biology

Chapter 1   *Introduction*

WITHOUT attempting a definition of biochemistry, we may say that it deals, among other things, with the chemical processes which go on in living matter. Chemical processes common to plants come under the heading of "plant biochemistry"; and this phase of the subject is barely touched upon in the present volume. A chapter on photosynthesis (Chap. 16) merely scratches the surface. For further information, see, for example, Bonner: *Plant Biochemistry;* Rabinowitch: *Photosynthesis.*

In this volume we devote ourselves to animal biochemistry, and when the word "biochemistry" (or "physiological chemistry") alone is used, we usually mean "animal biochemistry."

While it is difficult to trace origins, one is tempted to speak of Lavoisier (1743–1794) not only as the father of modern chemistry, but also as the father of biochemistry, for he was certainly one of the first, if not the first, to appreciate the true nature of respiration. His classic researches into oxidation, and the central role played by oxygen in the process, led him to investigate "burning" in the body, and he came to the conclusion that oxygen is consumed in the reaction, that carbon dioxide is eliminated, and that heat is evolved. He also realized that the temperature of the body is the result of the oxidation of foodstuffs. Later, in the hands of Voit, Pettenkofer, and Rubner in Germany, and Atwater and Benedict in this country, animal calorimetry (Chap. 11) became a science in the modern sense.

Liebig (1803–1873) and Wöhler (1800–1882), two organic chemists, had much to do with the further development of the subject; for their researches led them, from time to time, to analyze material of vegetable and animal origin. Liebig arrived at the conclusion that "the nutritive materials of all green plants are inorganic substances"; and Wöhler's dramatic synthesis of urea, the principal end-product of nitrogenous metabolism in the body, did much to destroy the notion that animal products were endowed with a "vitalism" which made them fundamentally different from "lifeless" substances. The work of Chevreul (1786–1889) on the chemical constitution of fats, and later the researches of Kossel and Emil Fischer on proteins, and of Emil Fischer on carbohydrates, gradually led to an understanding of the chemical composition of foods and the chemical composition of the cell.

Nor must the influence of the illustrious Pasteur (1822–1895) be overlooked. His extensive researches into the nature of fermentation led Buchner (1860–1917) to our modern conception of enzymes (Chap. 6), the cellular catalysts which are responsible for much of the activities within the body. Further, Pasteur's work on fermentation was a prelude to much activity in the field of muscle metabolism (Chap. 12), and, even more recently, to work dealing with the metabolism of nerve tissue (Chap. 21).

Researches by such pioneers as Arrhenius, van't Hoff, and Ostwald on

1

electrolytic dissociation and osmotic pressure led physical chemists, as well as organic chemists, to turn their attention to biological phenomena. The results were very fruitful; among others, Sörensen developed our concept of pH (Chap. 4), Loeb examined the colloidal behavior of proteins (Chap. 4), L. J. Henderson and Van Slyke developed their ideas regarding "body neutrality" (Chap. 10) and Schoenheimer and Rittenberg used isotopes for the development of the concept of the dynamic state of body constituents.

Side by side, physiologists and clinicians were contributing much of great value to the biochemist in such fields as digestion (Chap. 7), absorption (Chap. 8), blood (Chap. 9), and metabolism (Chaps. 12, 13, 14, 15, 17).

Nor can we overlook the impetus to further work given by the founding, in 1879, of the first journal devoted to biochemistry, the *Zeitschrift für physiologische Chemie*. In 1906 three other journals were started: the *Journal of Biological Chemistry* in this country, the *Biochemical Journal* in England, and the *Biochemische Zeitschrift* in Germany.

Present-day activity in biochemistry is quite varied. Especially fruitful have been the studies dealing with intermediary metabolism. These studies have been possible because, in a number of cases, enzymes have been obtained in the pure state; because of the introduction of isotopically labelled compounds; and because of the chromatographic separation techniques. It is now possible, for example, to describe the fate of ingested carbohydrate by a series of steps—some 25 individual reactions—until we reach the formation of carbon dioxide and water.

Now that many vitamins and hormones have been isolated, more and more attention is being given to the mechanisms of their action. The conception that many vitamins act as coenzymes, and that hormones may affect enzyme activity, is proving fruitful.

Nor can we overlook the more recent developments dealing with the biochemical explanations of muscle contraction and nerve impulse transmission.

The physico-chemical approach to reactions within the living cell deals, among other things, with the concept of the transfer of chemical bond energy and the storage of such energy in "high energy bonds." The "high energy bonds" make possible our acceptance of chemical reactions in the cell which, on theoretical grounds, would otherwise be impossible.

Microbiology—the field dealing with the chemical activity of microorganisms—has established itself as an important branch of biochemistry. Not only has it already yielded fundamental information concerning the biochemistry of unicellular organisms, but such information, when applied, has given answers to puzzling problems in mammalian biochemistry.

At the beginning of the present century there was already an active laboratory of biochemistry in this country. Chittenden was its founder at Yale. One of his pupils, Mendel, succeeded him, and another, Gies, became professor of the subject at Columbia. Folin was appointed to a chair of biochemistry at Harvard in 1907. The guiding spirits in the medical schools quickly recognized the importance of the subject, and chairs of biochemistry sprang up all over the country.

To such an extent has biochemistry developed, here and abroad, that a substantial portion of *Chemical Abstracts* is devoted to abstracts of biochemical articles. In the attempt to summarize a field which has become so extensive and diversified, the *Annual Review of Biochemistry* was founded in 1932.

The book leads off with a discussion of the organic constituents of the cell: carbohydrates, lipids, proteins and nucleic acids. A general description of enzymes and their mode of action precedes the discussion of digestion and absorption. This is followed by a study of blood (and respiration), the medium for transport, which, in turn, serves as an introduction to intermediary metabolism (of carbohydrates, lipids, proteins and nucleic acids).

A phase of intermediate metabolism in plants—photosynthesis, or biosynthesis in plants—is included at this stage, because the intermediate steps include compounds which appear in intermediate metabolism in general.

Specialized topics are reserved for the latter portion of the book: energy metabolism, inorganic metabolism, foods, vitamins, tissues, the kidney and urine, hormones. Detoxicating mechanisms and the chemical approach to immunology and therapeutics are the closing chapters of the book.

REFERENCES

Chittenden: The First Twenty-five Years of the American Society of Biological Chemists, 1945.

Von Meyer: History of Chemistry, 1891.
Lieben: Geschichte der physiologischen Chemie, 1935.

Chapter 2 *Carbohydrates*

THE CARBOHYDRATES include substances which are constituents of the cell, compounds which are important foods, and products which find industrial application. They include polyhydroxyaldehydes and polyhydroxyketones, and compounds which can be converted into such aldehydes or ketones by hydrolysis.

The simplest of these compounds is glycolaldehyde, $CHO.CH_2OH$, which exhibits many of the properties of carbohydrates. However, carbohydrates are all optically active, containing asymmetric carbon atoms, which makes glyceraldehyde, $CHO.CHOH.CH_2OH$, the more logical "mother" substance.

Classification. The more important of these carbohydrates may be classified as follows:

Monosaccharides	Pentoses, $C_5H_{10}O_5$ (ribose, xylose, arabinose, etc.)
	Hexoses, $C_6H_{12}O_6$ (glucose, mannose, galactose, fructose, sorbose, etc.)
Disaccharides	$C_{12}H_{22}O_{11}$ (sucrose, lactose, maltose, isomaltose, etc.)
Trisaccharides *	$C_{18}H_{32}O_{16}$ (raffinose, etc.)
Polysaccharides	$(C_6H_{10}O_5)_x$ (starch, glycogen, dextrin, cellulose, gum, mucilage, inulin, etc.)

The monosaccharides cannot be hydrolyzed into simpler sugars. By the use of the appropriate acid or enzyme, the higher saccharides can be hydrolyzed:

$$C_{12}H_{22}O_{11} + H_2O \longrightarrow C_6H_{12}O_6 + C_6H_{12}O_6$$

Sucrose	$\longrightarrow$ Glucose + Fructose
Maltose	$\longrightarrow$ Glucose + Glucose
Lactose	$\longrightarrow$ Glucose + Galactose

$$C_{18}H_{32}O_{16} + 2H_2O \longrightarrow C_6H_{12}O_6 + C_6H_{12}O_6 + C_6H_{12}O_6$$

Raffinose $\longrightarrow$ Fructose + Glucose + Galactose

A number of the polysaccharides, upon complete hydrolysis, yield glucose as the end-product (for example, glycogen, starch, dextrin, cellulose); some yield fructose (for example, inulin); and some yield galactose (for example, certain gums).

MONOSACCHARIDES

Structure of Glucose. The somewhat exceptional position occupied by glucose in carbohydrate metabolism (Chap. 12) and the impossibility, owing to limitations of space, of discussing the structure of each sugar individually make it desirable to describe glucose in some detail. Much of this discussion holds for other sugars.

* The term *oligosaccharides* is also used for compounds made up of two to five molecules of monosaccharides. Above this number we deal with polysaccharides.

A qualitative analysis of a purified sample of glucose shows the presence of the elements carbon and hydrogen; a quantitative analysis reveals the presence of oxygen also. The elements are in such proportion to one another that the formula (CH_2O) can be assigned to the compound. A molecular weight determination (by the freezing point depression method, for example) reveals that the formula assigned should be $(CH_2O)_6$, or $C_6H_{12}O_6$.

Glucose forms an oxime with hydroxylamine (p. 20), an osazone with phenylhydrazine (p. 20), and reduces Benedict's solution (p. 17);

all of these reactions point to the presence of a C=O group, and this

group may represent an aldehyde or a ketone.

Glucose forms a pentaacetyl derivative with acetic anhydride, indicating the presence of five free hydroxyl groups. It is reduced by means of sodium amalgam to an alcohol, hexahydroxyhexane, $CH_2OH.(CHOH)_4.CH_2OH$, which is sorbitol; and the latter compound, when treated with hydrogen iodide, is converted to a derivative of *normal* hexane, $CH_3.(CH_2)_3.CHI.-CH_3$. With hydrogen cyanide, glucose forms an addition compound which, when hydrolyzed, gives a straight-chain seven-carbon acid. All these facts

point to a straight-chain compound, with the C=O at one end (a com-

pound containing the aldehydic group).

```
        1. CHO
           |
        2. CHOH
           |
        3. CHOH
           |
        4. CHOH
           |
        5. CHOH
           |
        6. CH₂OH
```

Isomers of Glucose. An examination of the formula reveals that the compound has four asymmetric carbon atoms (at positions 2, 3, 4, and 5), each carbon being attached to four different atoms or groups of atoms. For example, the carbon at position 2 may be shown thus:

$$
\begin{array}{c}
R \\
| \\
H-C-OH \\
| \\
R^1
\end{array}
$$

where R stands for the CHO group and R^1 for everything below carbon 2. According to van't Hoff, the number of possible isomers is given by the formula $I = 2^n$, where n represents the number of asymmetric carbon atoms. Since glucose has four such asymmetric carbon atoms, the number of isomers equals 16 (2^4).

The Spatial Arrangement of the Isomers of Glucose. The exact proof for the stereochemical configuration of each isomer of glucose is beyond the scope of this book. Noller and also Fieser and Fieser (see references at the end of the chapter) give accounts of this phase of the work. All that can be said at this point is that the isomers are traced back to some simple compound, the constitution of which is beyond question. We may, for example, regard these isomers as being derived from glyceraldehyde:

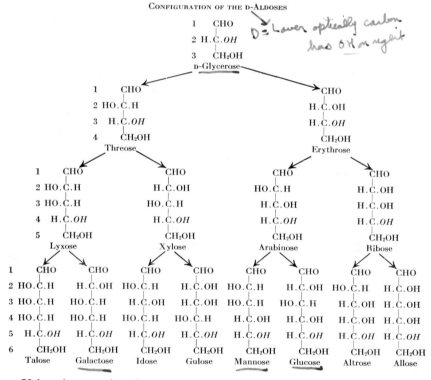

From each isomer of this aldehyde there are derived eight isomers of glucose. For example, the accompanying chart shows the derivation and configuration of eight aldohexoses:

Using the notation that

$$H.\overset{|}{\underset{|}{C}}.OH = + \text{ and } HO.\overset{|}{\underset{|}{C}}.H = -$$

* The symbols D- and L- refer to *configuration*, whereas dextro (+) and levo (−) refer to *sign of rotation*. D- and L- are always pronounced "dee" and "ell," *never* "dextro" and "levo." See also footnote, p. 55.

then D-glucose,

$$CHO$$
$$H.C.OH$$
$$HO.C.H$$
$$H.C.OH$$
$$H.C.OH$$
$$CH_2OH$$

can be represented in shorthand form as

[handwritten shorthand notation of the structure with plus/minus and OH groups, and a note "OH = +"]

Here the two end-carbon combinations are ignored in this notation. We can represent the sixteen possible isomers as follows:

```
 − +    + −    − +    + −    − +    + −    − +    + −
 − +    − +    + −    + −    − +    − +    + −    + −
 − +    − +    − +    − +    + −    + −    + −    + −
 + −    + −    + −    + −    + −    + −    + −    + −
 D   L
```

The first of each pair represents the D-series (related to D-glucose and D-glyceraldehyde), and the second, the L-series.

In this D-series, the hydroxyl group next to the primary alcohol group is written to the right; whereas the reverse is true with the L-series.

The Cyclic Structure for Glucose. However, the above formula for glucose still does not explain all the facts. To begin with, glucose, which is pictured as an aldehyde, falls somewhat short of certain common aldehydic properties. For example, glucose fails to give a Schiff's test (the formation of a reddish-violet color with magenta solution which has been decolorized with SO$_2$), nor does it form a stable addition compound with sodium bisulfite. Hydroxy acids of the γ- or δ-variety, similar in general structure to glucose, form lactones very readily, and these are cyclic in structure; for example, γ-hydroxybutyric acid, CH$_2$OH.CH$_2$.CH$_2$.COOH, is changed to γ-butyrolactone,

[structural diagram]
$$CH_2.CH_2.CH_2.CO$$

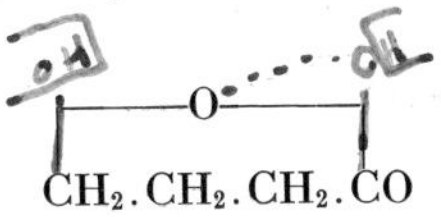

Mutarotation. But even more important is the problem of mutarotation or "change of rotation." A freshly crystallized sample of glucose has a specific rotation (in water) of +111° ([α]$_D$ = 111°); upon standing, this changes to +52°. Since the specific rotation of any compound is, as a rule, characteristic of the optically active compound in question (just as melting and boiling points are usually characteristic criteria), a change in rotation

[handwritten margin note: "Lactone — loss of H₂O in molecule"]

suggests a change in the structure of the substance. This appears all the more probable when it is shown that the compound with the rotation +111° (now known as α-glucose) can be dissolved in boiling pyridine and crystallized from this solvent to give an isomer with the specific rotation of +19° (now known as β-glucose), which, upon standing, also changes slowly to +52°. The β-form is the more stable one at temperatures around 100° C.

Another fact has to be recorded now. When an aldehyde is treated with methyl alcohol (using an acid to catalyze the reaction), an acetal is formed.

$$R.CHO + 2CH_3OH \longrightarrow R.CH(OCH_3)_2 + H_2O$$

Here two molecules of methyl alcohol react with one molecule of the aldehyde. When, however, glucose is treated similarly, the sugar combines with but *one* molecule of methyl alcohol:

$$C_6H_{12}O_6 + CH_3OH \longrightarrow C_7H_{14}O_6 + H_2O$$

The methyl glucoside which is formed can be resolved into two modifications: an α-methyl glucoside (rotation +159°) and a β-methyl glucoside (rotation −34°). The enzyme maltase hydrolyzes the former initially to α-glucose, and the enzyme emulsin hydrolyzes the latter initially to β-glucose, followed by mutarotation to give an equilibrium mixture of both forms of glucose.

The two modifications each of D-glucose and the corresponding methyl glucoside suggest the presence of an additional asymmetric carbon atom in the molecule, which can be shown if we assume a cyclic structure:

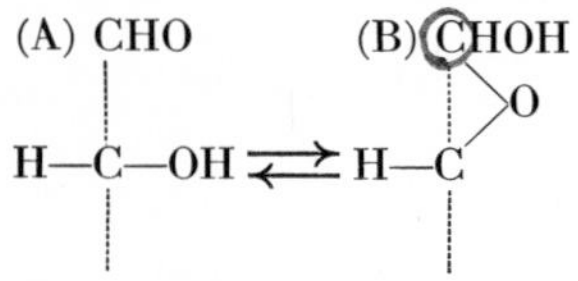

Here the carbon atom at (A), part of an ordinary aldehydic group, has been converted into an asymmetric carbon atom (B); so that now in glucose we have the possibility not of $16 (= 2^4)$, but of $32 (= 2^5)$ isomeric aldohexoses.

In the accompanying chart the structures and relationships of the compounds just discussed are given (the evidence for the oxygen bridge in the 1:5 position will be taken up presently).

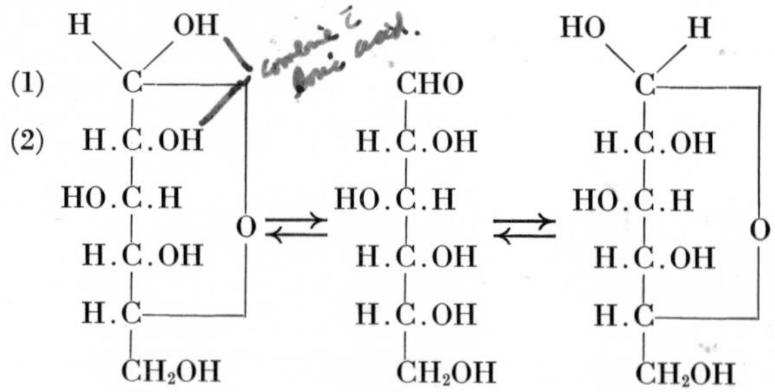

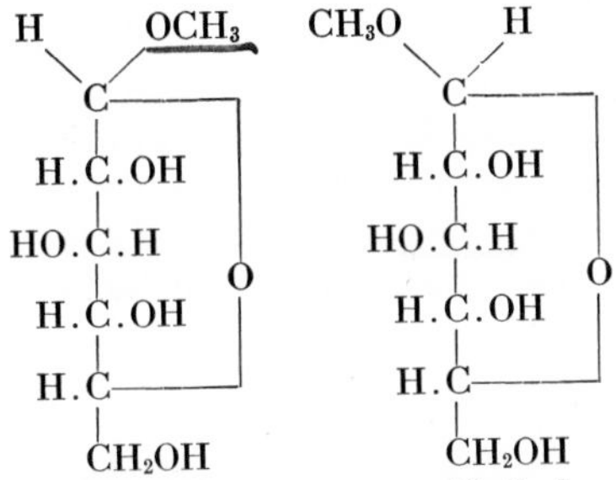

H   OCH₃   CH₃O   H

| | |
C   C
| |
H.C.OH   H.C.OH
| |
HO.C.H   HO.C.H
| O | O
H.C.OH   H.C.OH
| |
H.C   H.C
| |
CH₂OH   CH₂OH

α-Methyl   β-Methyl
glucoside   glucoside

It might be pointed out that there are reasons for writing the H and OH positions at carbon (1) in α- and β-glucose as shown. For example, α-glucose combines very readily with boric acid:

(1) H—C—OH   HO   H—C—O
| +   \B.OH → | \B.OH
(2) H—C—OH   HO   H—C—O
| /

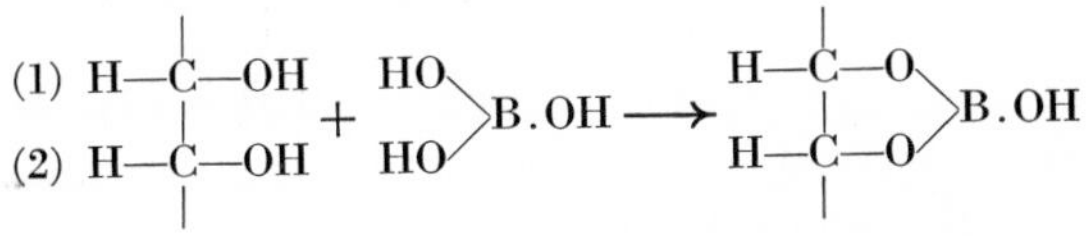

suggesting that the two OH groups in (1) and (2) are in the same plane. The β-form, however, does not combine so readily with boric acid until mutarotation has given some α-form.

Assuming, for the time being, a 1:5 oxygen bridge, glucose may be pictured as a derivative of pyran, the 5-carbon sugar, which would be a pentopyranose, and the 6-carbon sugar a hexapyranose:

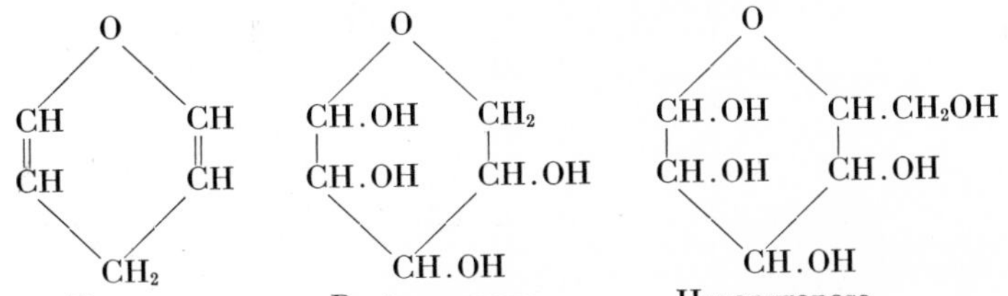

O   O   O

CH   CH   CH.OH   CH₂   CH.OH   CH.CH₂OH
‖ | | | | |
CH   CH   CH.OH   CH.OH   CH.OH   CH.OH

CH₂   CH.OH   CH.OH

Pyran   Pentapyranose   Hexapyranose
                     5 C   6 C

One such hexapyranose, glucose, can therefore be called glucopyranose.

Haworth shows this model in perspective, with the H and the OH groups above or below the plane of the ring:

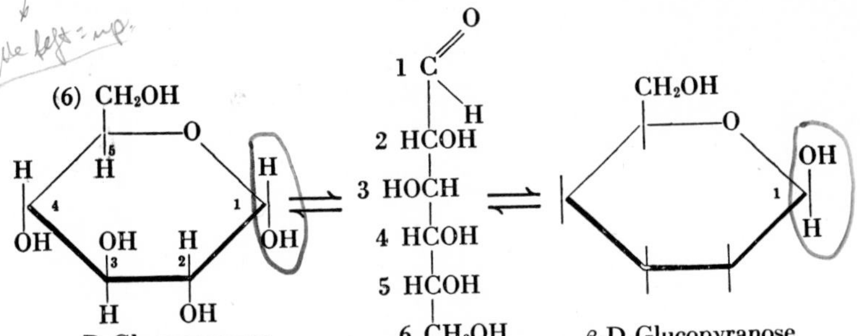

(6) CH₂OH   O   CH₂OH
O   1 C   O
H   H   H   \H   H   OH
| 2 HCOH
OH   OH   H   OH   3 HOCH ⇌ | | H
|3   2| 4 HCOH
H   OH   5 HCOH

α-D-Glucopyranose   6 CH₂OH   β-D-Glucopyranose
Aldehyde form

The ring is at right angles to the plane of the paper. The thin bonds of the ring are behind the plane of the paper, and the thick bonds in front of it. (H and OH attached to carbon atoms 1, 2, 3, 4, which are on the *right* side of the straight-chain formula, are here on the *bottom*.)

Methylation Studies. Evidence for the 1:5 Oxygen Bridge.   It has been assumed so far that the oxygen is attached to carbons 1 and 5.

```
              H     OH
               \   /
   1.           C----
                |      |
   2.    H.C.OH |
                |      |
   3.   HO.C.H  |
                |      | O
   4.    H.C.OH |
                |      |
   5.    H.C--------
                |
   6.      CH₂OH
```

There are obviously several other possible attachments. As a matter of fact, but two forms have been isolated: the 1:5 and the 1:4. Of these, the 1:5 is the more stable and the commoner variety.

After the methyl glucoside has been formed (with $CH_3OH + HCl$), the product is next treated with dimethyl sulfate. This results in complete methylation of the OH groups. Without using the stereochemical formulas, and still assuming the 1:5 oxygen bridge, the reactions are:

```
1. CH.OH              CH.OCH₃            CH.OCH₃
2. CH.OH    ─→        CH.OH      ─→      CH.OCH₃
3. CH.OH              CH.OH              CH.OCH₃
4. CH.OH              CH.OH              CH.OCH₃
          O                    O                    O
5. CH───              CH─               CH─
6. CH₂OH              CH₂.OH             CH₂.OCH₃
                   Methyl glucoside      Tetramethyl
                                         methyl glucoside
```

The glucosidic methoxyl group can be easily hydrolyzed, whereas the other methoxyls cannot—behaving, indeed, as true ethers. If, then, we hydrolyze the completely methylated compound, we get tetramethyl glucopyranose:

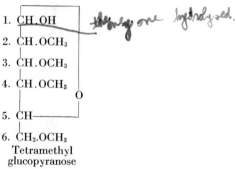

```
1. CH.OH         only one hydrolysed.
2. CH.OCH₃
3. CH.OCH₃
4. CH.OCH₃
                  O
5. CH───
6. CH₂.OCH₃
   Tetramethyl
   glucopyranose
```

which, upon oxidation with nitric acid, yields a trimethoxy derivative of glutaric acid:

1. COOH
2. CH.OCH₃
3. CH.OCH₃
4. CH.OCH₃
5. COOH

which indicates that the oxygen is attached to carbon atom 5 in the glucoside.

1:4 Oxygen Bridge.   Ordinarily, in the formation of methyl glucosides, hot alcoholic HCl is used. This forms the 1:5 oxygen bridge linkage, as we have already seen. If, however, cold alcoholic HCl is used, a far less stable compound is formed, and this differs from the more stable form by having a 1:4 linkage. Complete methylation and final oxidation with nitric acid lead to the production of a succinic acid derivative:

1. COOH
2. CH.OCH₃
3. CH.OCH₃
4. COOH

showing that this methyl glucoside has the structure

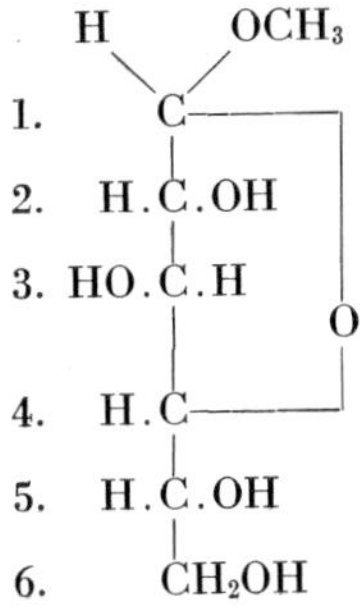

1. H   OCH₃
       C
2. H.C.OH
3. HO.C.H
                  O
4. H.C
5. H.C.OH
6.   CH₂OH

or a 1:4 oxygen bridge.

Just as the parent substance of the 1:5 sugars is pyran, so the parent compound of the 1:4 sugars is furan:

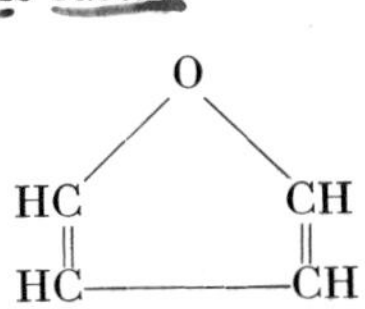

O
HC   CH
HC————CH
Furan

and the sugars derived from it are furanose sugars.

The Structure of Fructose.   From the physiological point of view, glucose, fructose, and galactose are the three important hexoses.

Fructose, a naturally occurring sugar, is levorotatory, but despite this fact, the sugar is known as D-fructose, because it is related, structurally, to D-glucose.* It has the same molecular formula as glucose ($C_6H_{12}O_6$), forms a pentaacetyl derivative, and shows the properties of a carbonyl

$(C{=}O)$ compound. When fructose is treated with HCN it forms an addition compound, which upon hydrolysis and subsequent reduction with HI gives methylbutylacetic acid:

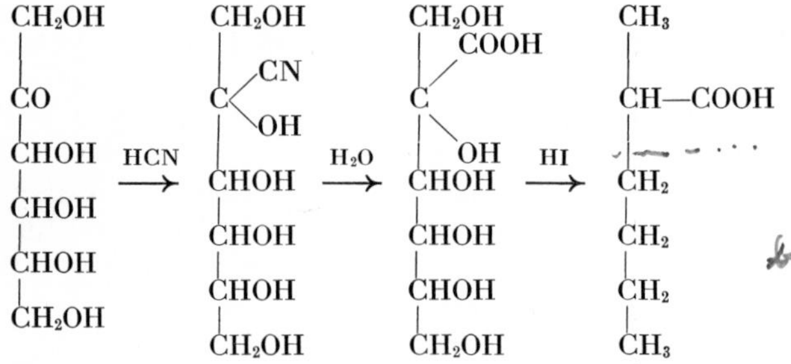

| CH₂OH | CH₂OH | CH₂OH | CH₃ |
| Fructose | | Methylbutyl-acetic acid |

and this means that fructose is a ketone and not an aldehyde. (Under similar conditions, glucose yields a 7-carbon straight-chain and not a branched-chain compound.)

The oxidation of fructose [with HgO and Ba(OH)₂] yields glycollic acid, $CH_2OH.COOH$, and trihydroxybutyric acid, $CH_2OH.(CHOH)_2.COOH$, indicating a splitting of the compound between carbons 2 and 3.

Both glucose and fructose give the same osazone (p. 20), and this, as we shall see (p. 21), points to the fact that in fructose, the groups at 3, 4, and 5 must be the same as those in glucose:

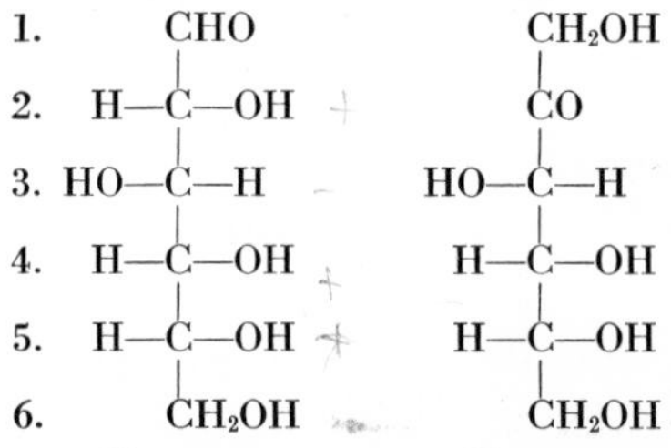

	Glucose	Fructose
1.	CHO	CH₂OH
2.	H—C—OH	CO
3.	HO—C—H	HO—C—H
4.	H—C—OH	H—C—OH
5.	H—C—OH	H—C—OH
6.	CH₂OH	CH₂OH

Like glucose, fructose exhibits the property of mutarotation, and normally forms a 2:6 oxygen bridge linkage, giving a fructopyranose. These structures may be summarized as follows:

* D (+) glucose is related structurally to D (−) fructose, for both give the same osazone (p. 21), but glucose rotates the plane of polarized light to the right, and fructose, to the left. The mirror images of these compounds are referred to as the L-series, quite regardless of whether the compounds are dextro- or levorotatory.

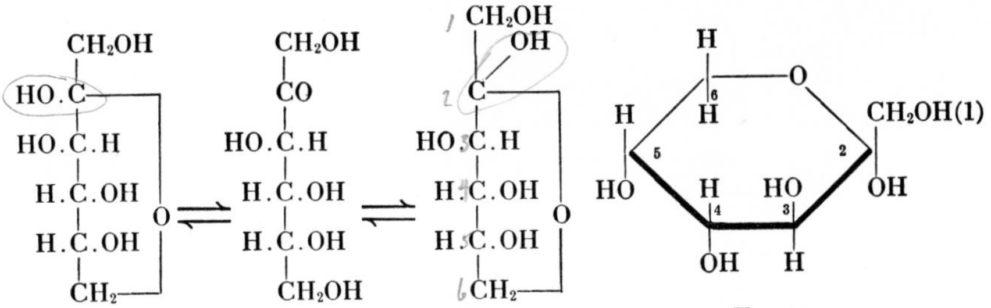

$$
\begin{array}{ccccc}
\text{CH}_2\text{OH} & \text{CH}_2\text{OH} & \text{CH}_2\text{OH} & & \\
\text{HO.C} & \text{CO} & \text{C}\!-\!\text{OH} & & \\
\text{HO.C.H} & \text{HO.C.H} & \text{HO.C.H} & & \\
\text{H.C.OH} & \text{H.C.OH} & \text{H.C.OH} & & \\
\text{H.C.OH} & \text{H.C.OH} & \text{H.C.OH} & & \\
\text{CH}_2\!- & \text{CH}_2\text{OH} & \text{CH}_2\!- & & \\
\beta\text{-Fructose} & \begin{array}{c}\text{Ketone}\\\text{formula of}\\\text{fructose}\end{array} & \alpha\text{-Fructose} & & \alpha\text{-Fructopyranose}
\end{array}
$$

β-Fructose $\rightleftharpoons$ Ketone formula of fructose $\rightleftharpoons$ α-Fructose

With O bridging in the ring structures. Labels: CH₂OH(1), positions 5, 6, 2, 4, 3; HO, OH, H groups. α-Fructopyranose.

Galactose. Mutarotation (β- and α-forms) with pyranose formation occurs here too.

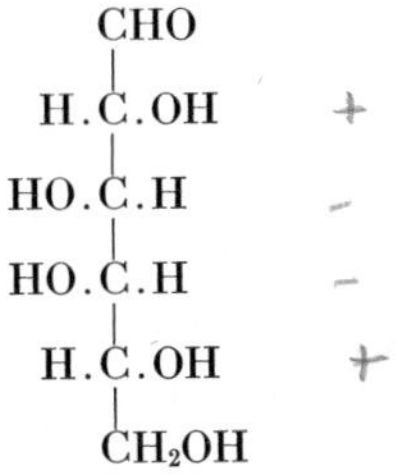

$$
\begin{array}{ll}
\text{CHO} & \\
\text{H.C.OH} & + \\
\text{HO.C.H} & - \\
\text{HO.C.H} & - \\
\text{H.C.OH} & + \\
\text{CH}_2\text{OH} & \\
\end{array}
$$
Galactose

DISACCHARIDES

The disaccharides may be regarded as glycosides of the form:

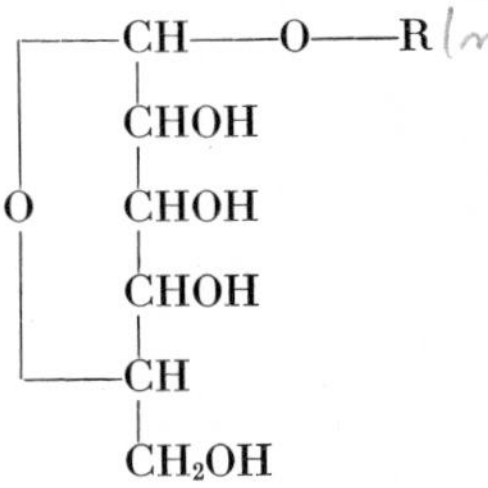

$$
\begin{array}{l}
\text{CH}\!-\!\!-\!\text{O}\!-\!\!-\!\text{R (monosaccharide)} \\
\text{CHOH} \\
\text{CHOH} \\
\text{CHOH} \\
\text{CH} \\
\text{CH}_2\text{OH}
\end{array}
$$

where R is a monosaccharide which (1) has a potential free aldehydic group (as in maltose and lactose), or (2) which has no such reducing group (see Sucrose, p. 15).

Where R is CH₃, we have the methyl glycoside which has already been discussed. In nature, important glycosides are known where R is a nonsugar, often a complicated group. For example, phlorhizin (also spelled *phloridzin* and *phlorizin*), found in the bark of Rosaceae, is a combination of glucose and phloretin; amygdalin, present in the seed of the bitter almond, is a combination of glucose and mandelonitrile; digitonin, found in the leaves and seeds of digitalis, is a combination of glucose, galactose, and digitogenin. In the cardiac glycosides (found in certain plants and possessing a characteristic action on the heart), the R is represented by a steroid. (According to Armstrong, *glycoside* is the general name for this group of compounds, irrespective of the sugar present; *glucoside* is the more specific name for those glycosides which contain glucose as the sugar constituent.)

As has already been pointed out, maltose, lactose, and sucrose, the three common disaccharides, are easily hydrolyzed to monosaccharides. The structures of these disaccharides, in turn, are dependent upon the monosaccharides they yield.

Maltose. This yields two molecules of glucose when hydrolyzed. Upon methylation and subsequent hydrolysis, we get 2,3,4,6-tetramethylglucose and 2,3,6-trimethylglucose. While these results lead to two possible structures, the following has been selected as more in accord with the facts:

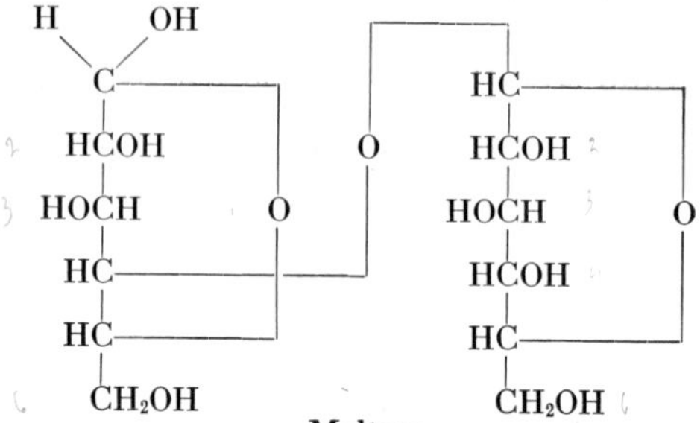

Maltose

or, using the Haworth model,

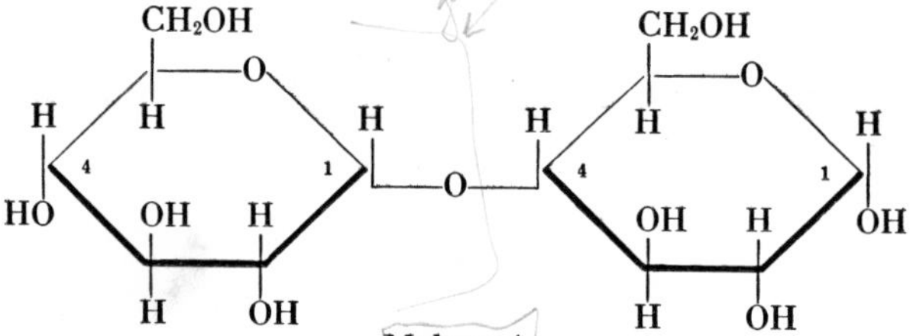

Maltose *

Lactose. Glucose and galactose are yielded on hydrolysis of lactose. When the lactose is methylated and then hydrolyzed, we get 2,3,6-trimethylglucose and 2,3,4,6-tetramethylgalactose, leading to the formula:

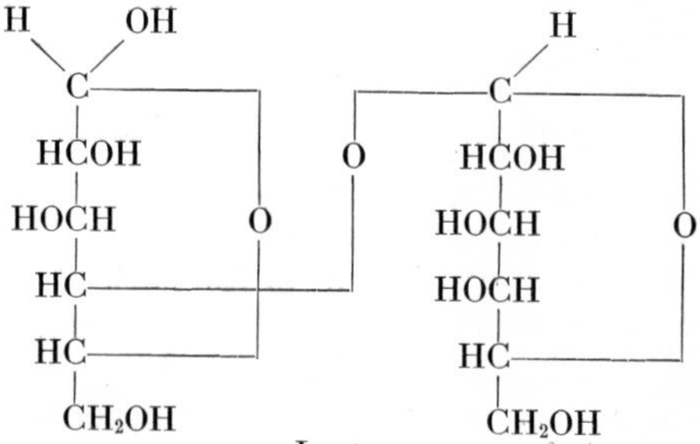

Lactose

---

* This is really α-maltose (or α-glucosido-α-glucose), where the active (aldehyde) group is at position 1 on the right side of the formula. There is also a β-maltose (or α-glucosido-β-glucose), in which the H and OH in position 1, on the right side of the formula, are

Here the Haworth representation would be

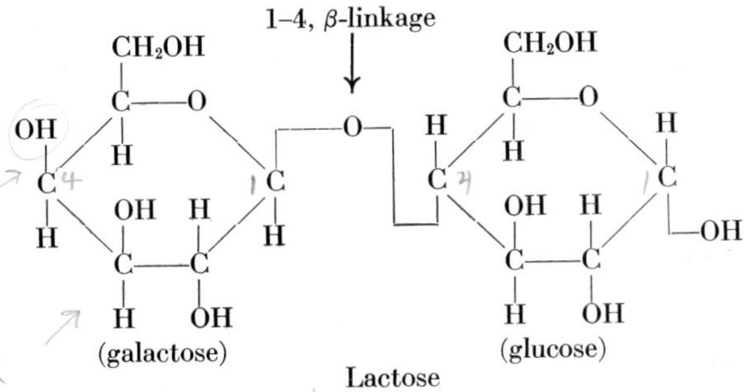

1–4, β-linkage

(galactose)   (glucose)

Lactose

showing a β-galactose unit on the left side and an α-glucose unit on the right side.

Sucrose.   Unlike maltose and lactose, sucrose does not reduce Benedict's solution (p. 17); it is a nonreducing sugar. When hydrolyzed, it yields glucose and fructose. Methylation and subsequent hydrolysis convert sucrose into a tetramethyl glucose and a tetramethyl fructose:

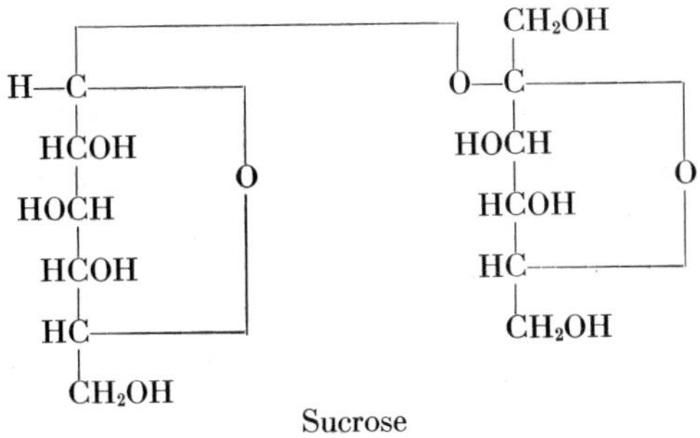

Sucrose

Sucrose has a pyranose structure for the glucose part, and a furanose structure for the fructose part. It is, therefore, a glucosido-fructofuranoside.

In the free form, fructose itself exists as a stable six-membered pyranose compound; but in the sucrose molecule the fructose exists as the more unstable five-membered furanose compound:

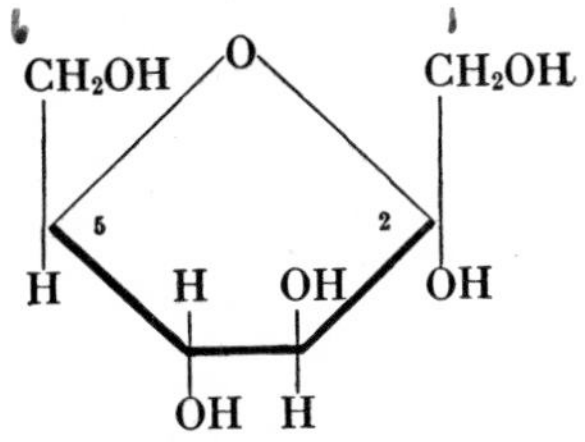

α-D-Fructofuranose

reversed. Cellobiose, obtained from cotton cellulose as its acetyl derivative, which is also made up of two glucose molecules, differs from maltose in being β-glucosido-α-glucose,

The Haworth representation for sucrose would be

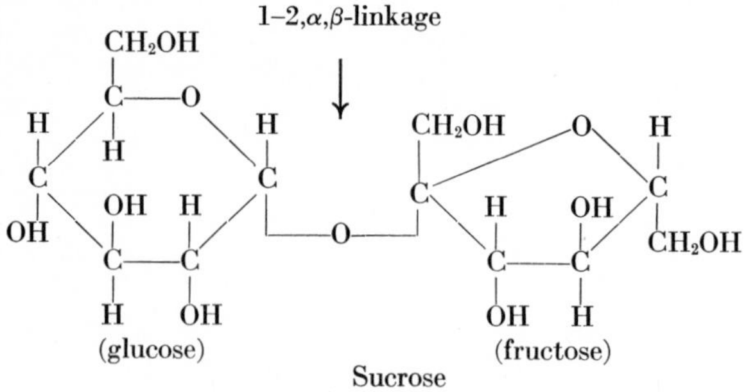

1–2,α,β-linkage

(glucose)   (fructose)

Sucrose

represented by an α-glucose and a β-fructose unit; or, to give it its full name, D-glucopyranosido-β-D-fructofuranoside.

SOME GENERAL PROPERTIES OF THE MONO- AND DISACCHARIDES

These substances are crystalline, soluble in water, and moderately soluble in dilute alcohol. They are practically insoluble in absolute alcohol, ether, and the usual organic solvents.

The Action of Nonoxidizing Acids.   Certain acids (like HCl) hydrolyze the disaccharides. (They also hydrolyze tri- and polysaccharides.) On the monosaccharides themselves, their action is negligible if the acid is dilute. In higher concentrations, and at the boiling point, such acids act on monosaccharides largely by dehydrating them, forming furfural derivatives. The pentoses form furfural:

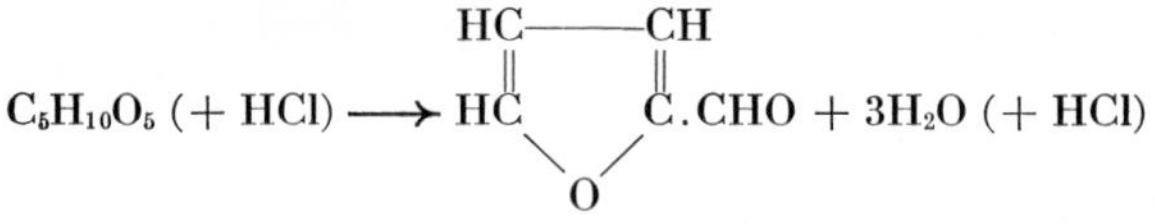

$$\text{C}_5\text{H}_{10}\text{O}_5 \ (+ \text{HCl}) \longrightarrow \text{HC} \underset{\text{O}}{\overset{\text{HC}{=\!=\!=}\text{CH}}{\diagup\diagdown}} \text{C.CHO} + 3\text{H}_2\text{O} \ (+ \text{HCl})$$

Furfural

The hexoses yield varying quantities of hydroxymethylfurfural:

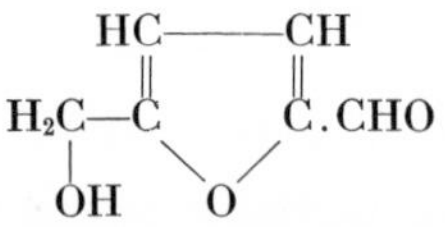

$$\text{H}_2\text{C}-\underset{\text{OH}}{\text{C}} \underset{\text{O}}{\overset{\text{HC}{=\!=\!=}\text{CH}}{\diagup\diagdown}} \text{C.CHO}$$

Hydroxymethylfurfural

The formation of such furfurals is the basis for a number of tests. One of the commonest is the *Molisch test:* The sugar mixed with α-naphthol

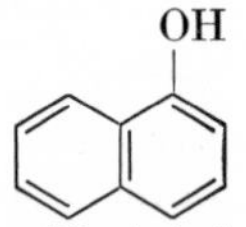

OH

α-Naphthol

and concentrated sulfuric acid gives a violet color. It is presumed that the concentrated sulfuric acid acts as a dehydrating agent, acting on the sugar to form furfural derivatives, which then combine with α-naphthol to form colored products of uncertain constitution. This is a very general test for carbohydrates.

Another very general test for carbohydrates is known as the *anthrone test*. Anthrone itself has the formula:

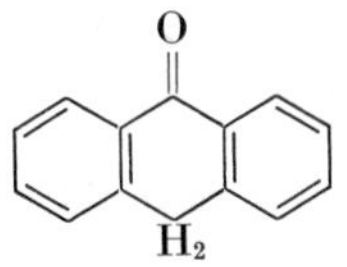

Anthrone

and, when mixed with concentrated sulfuric acid and the carbohydrate, it forms a blue or green color.

A more specific test is the *Seliwanoff test*, involving the action of resor-

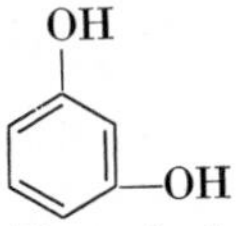

Resorcinol

cinol and HCl on the sugar. Here a red color is developed rapidly in the presence of a ketose sugar, such as fructose. The explanation of the test lies in the formation, first, of hydroxymethylfurfural and the condensation of this substance with resorcinol to form the colored product or products.

Two tests for pentoses, *Tollens' phloroglucinol test* and *Tollens' orcinol test* are based on the formation of similar intermediate furfural products and ultimate condensations to yield colored substances:

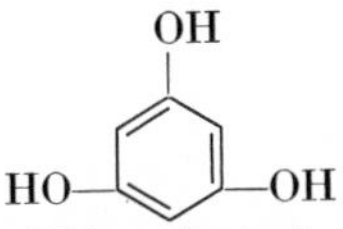

Phloroglucinol

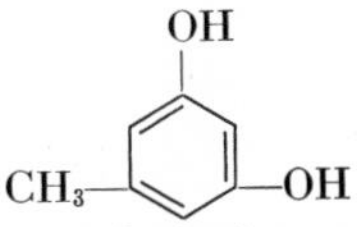

Orcinol

A test for desoxyribose (p. 22) is to mix the sugar with diphenylamine, glacial acetic acid and sulfuric acid, yielding a blue color (Dische). It is used to detect desoxyribose in nucleic acids (p. 78), where the sugar is linked to a purine (p. 85).

Oxidation.   Alkaline copper solutions readily oxidize the disaccharides (with the exception of sucrose) and the monosaccharides. The oxidation products are numerous, and not all of them have been identified. But, from a practical point of view, this reaction is important because with the oxidation of the sugar there is a simultaneous reduction of the cupric to insoluble, red cuprous oxide, which can be identified easily. The best-known reagents are *Fehling's solution* [an alkaline (NaOH) copper sulfate solution, with potassium sodium tartrate to keep the cupric oxide in solution] and *Benedict's solution* [an alkaline (Na_2CO_3) copper sulfate solution in the presence of sodium citrate]. An acid copper solution (copper acetate in acetic acid), known as *Barfoed's reagent*, is often used, though not always satisfactorily, to distinguish mono- from disaccharides. Under identical conditions, the monosaccharides are more rapidly oxidized.

With bromine water as the oxidizing agent, glucose forms gluconic acid:

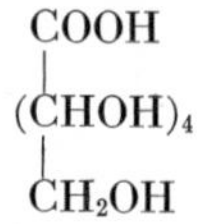

$$COOH$$
$$(CHOH)_4$$
$$CH_2OH$$

Gluconic acid

and with nitric acid, saccharic acid is formed:

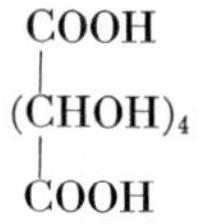

$$COOH$$
$$(CHOH)_4$$
$$COOH$$

Saccharic acid → *dicarboxylic*

With galactose, nitric acid yields an isomer, *mucic acid*, which, unlike saccharic, is highly insoluble. This mucic acid test is used to identify galactose (or lactose, which first hydrolyzes to form galactose as one of the products).

When saccharic acid is heated, it forms the corresponding lactone, which can be reduced to *glucuronic acid* with sodium amalgam:

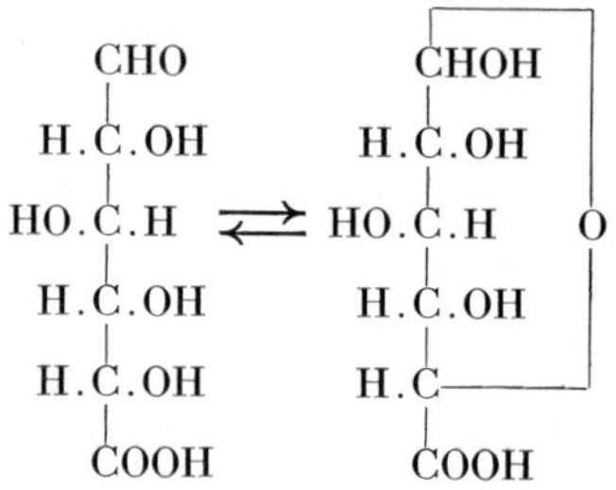

$$CHO \qquad CHOH$$
$$H.C.OH \qquad H.C.OH$$
$$HO.C.H \rightleftarrows HO.C.H \quad O$$
$$H.C.OH \qquad H.C.OH$$
$$H.C.OH \qquad H.C$$
$$COOH \qquad COOH$$

Glucuronic acid

This oxidation product of glucose is a physiologically important substance, since it acts as a detoxifying agent. It is combined in glucosidic linkage with poisonous substances * which find their way into the body, thereby making them nontoxic, the coupled products then being eliminated (see Chap. 24).

Examples of derivatives of glucuronic acid found in the body are heparin, the blood anticoagulant (p. 164), and chondroitin sulfate, a constituent of cartilage (Chap. 21).

Reduction.　Reduction (with sodium amalgam) converts the monosaccharides to the corresponding alcohols. Glucose, for example, gives sorbitol:

to alcohols

* Sometimes glucuronic acid combines with substances which can hardly be considered as poisonous. For example, the female hormones are eliminated by the body as glucuronides (see Chap. 23).

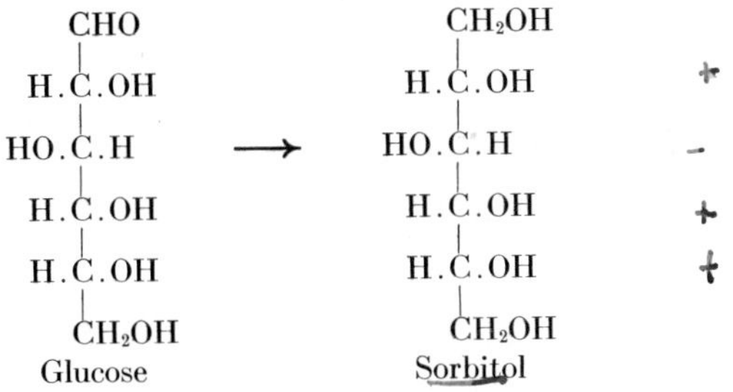

$$
\begin{array}{c}
\text{CHO} \\
|\\
\text{H.C.OH} \\
|\\
\text{HO.C.H} \\
|\\
\text{H.C.OH} \\
|\\
\text{H.C.OH} \\
|\\
\text{CH}_2\text{OH} \\
\text{Glucose}
\end{array}
\quad\longrightarrow\quad
\begin{array}{c}
\text{CH}_2\text{OH} \\
|\\
\text{H.C.OH} \\
|\\
\text{HO.C.H} \\
|\\
\text{H.C.OH} \\
|\\
\text{H.C.OH} \\
|\\
\text{CH}_2\text{OH} \\
\text{Sorbitol}
\end{array}
$$

Fructose yields a mixture of sorbitol and mannitol, since the carbon of the ketonic group now becomes asymmetric:

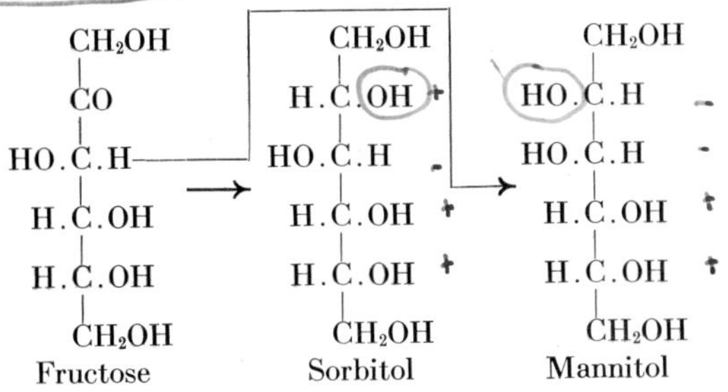

$$
\begin{array}{c}
\text{CH}_2\text{OH} \\
|\\
\text{CO} \\
|\\
\text{HO.C.H} \\
|\\
\text{H.C.OH} \\
|\\
\text{H.C.OH} \\
|\\
\text{CH}_2\text{OH} \\
\text{Fructose}
\end{array}
\;\longrightarrow\;
\begin{array}{c}
\text{CH}_2\text{OH} \\
|\\
\text{H.C.OH} \\
|\\
\text{HO.C.H} \\
|\\
\text{H.C.OH} \\
|\\
\text{H.C.OH} \\
|\\
\text{CH}_2\text{OH} \\
\text{Sorbitol}
\end{array}
\;\longrightarrow\;
\begin{array}{c}
\text{CH}_2\text{OH} \\
|\\
\text{HO.C.H} \\
|\\
\text{HO.C.H} \\
|\\
\text{H.C.OH} \\
|\\
\text{H.C.OH} \\
|\\
\text{CH}_2\text{OH} \\
\text{Mannitol}
\end{array}
$$

The Action of Weak Alkali. Using a saturated solution of barium hydroxide, and allowing the mixture to stand for some time, we can transform glucose into an equilibrium mixture of glucose, mannose, and fructose. The same holds true if instead of glucose we begin with fructose or mannose. This has been explained on the assumption that a reactive "intermediate" (enol) compound is formed:

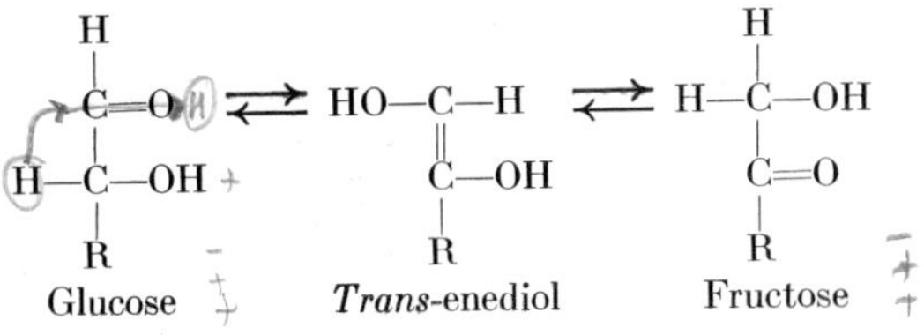

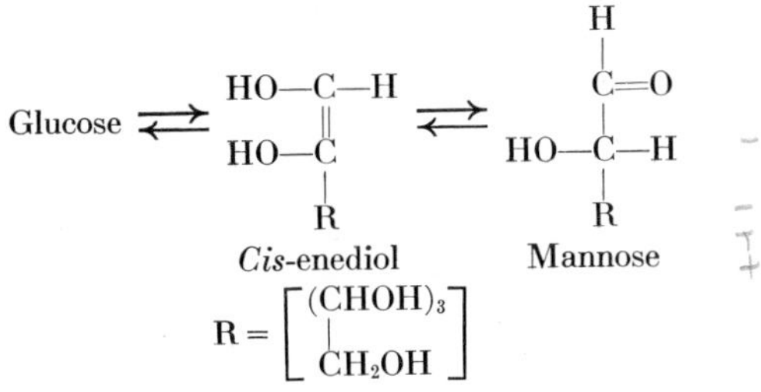

$$
\begin{array}{c}
\text{H} \\
|\\
\text{C}=\text{O} \\
|\\
\text{H—C—OH} \\
|\\
\text{R} \\
\text{Glucose}
\end{array}
\;\rightleftarrows\;
\begin{array}{c}
\text{HO—C—H} \\
\|\\
\text{C—OH} \\
|\\
\text{R} \\
\textit{Trans}\text{-enediol}
\end{array}
\;\rightleftarrows\;
\begin{array}{c}
\text{H} \\
|\\
\text{H—C—OH} \\
|\\
\text{C}=\text{O} \\
|\\
\text{R} \\
\text{Fructose}
\end{array}
$$

$$
\text{Glucose} \;\rightleftarrows\;
\begin{array}{c}
\text{HO—C—H} \\
\|\\
\text{HO—C} \\
|\\
\text{R} \\
\textit{Cis}\text{-enediol}
\end{array}
\;\rightleftarrows\;
\begin{array}{c}
\text{H} \\
|\\
\text{C}=\text{O} \\
|\\
\text{HO—C—H} \\
|\\
\text{R} \\
\text{Mannose}
\end{array}
$$

$$
\text{R} = \left[\begin{array}{c} (\text{CHOH})_3 \\ |\\ \text{CH}_2\text{OH} \end{array}\right]
$$

By the use of 1-deuterioglucose (glucose in which a hydrogen is replaced by deuterium), it has been shown that the deuterium is transferred from glucose to fructose to mannose.

Stetten has also shown that when galactose-1-C^{14} is fed to rats, and the glycogen from the liver is recovered, the polymer can be hydrolyzed to yield glucose in which the isotope is in position 1.

These tautomeric changes, known as the *Lobry de Bruyn transformation,* are of interest to biochemists since in the body all three of the natural monosaccharides—glucose, fructose and galactose—are converted to glycogen, but on hydrolysis this polysaccharide yields just glucose.

Osazones.   The monosaccharides and the disaccharides (with the exception of sucrose) combine with hydroxylamine to form oximes:

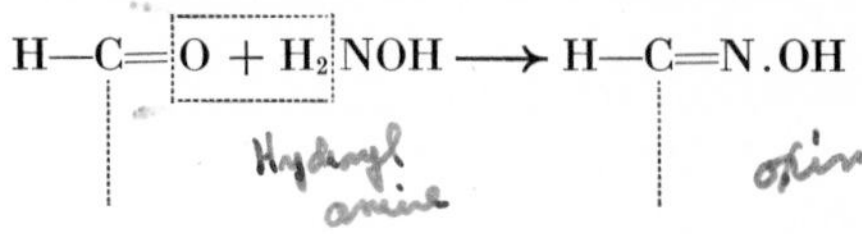

$$H—C{=}O + H_2NOH \longrightarrow H—C{=}N.OH$$

but from a practical standpoint, the more important reaction is the formation of osazones with phenylhydrazine, $C_6H_5NHNH_2$. At first, one molecule of the sugar combines with one molecule of the phenylhydrazine to form a hydrazone:

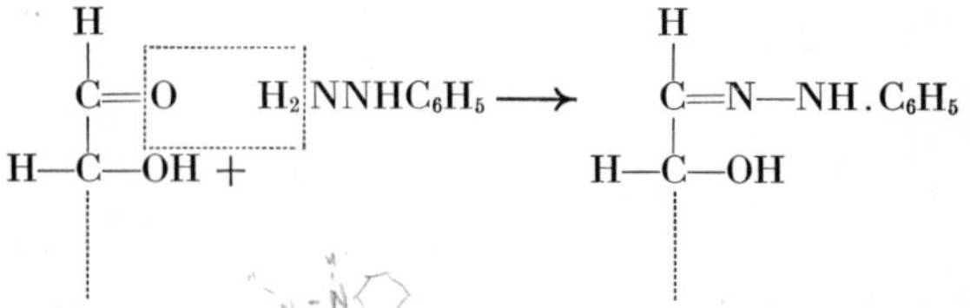

$$
\begin{array}{l}
\text{H} \\
| \\
\text{C}{=}\text{O} \quad H_2NNHC_6H_5 \longrightarrow \\
| \\
\text{H—C—OH} +
\end{array}
\qquad
\begin{array}{l}
\text{H} \\
| \\
\text{C}{=}\text{N—NH}.C_6H_5 \\
| \\
\text{H—C—OH}
\end{array}
$$

Glucose   Glucose phenylhydrazone

Next, in the presence of an excess of phenylhydrazine, another molecule of this reagent reacts with the sugar:

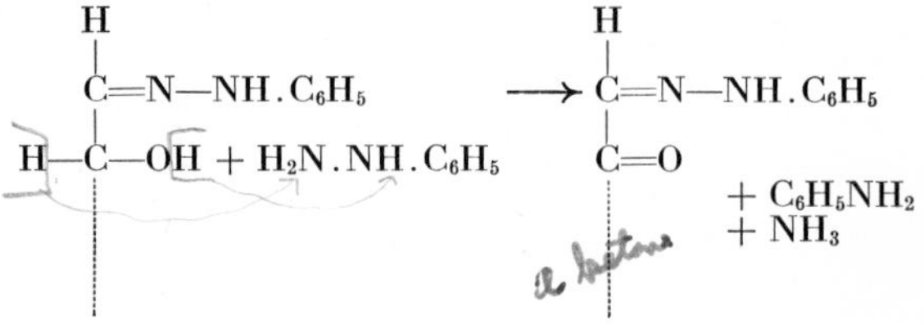

$$
\begin{array}{l}
\text{H} \\
| \\
\text{C}{=}\text{N—NH}.C_6H_5 \\
| \\
\text{H—C—OH} + H_2N.NH.C_6H_5
\end{array}
\longrightarrow
\begin{array}{l}
\text{H} \\
| \\
\text{C}{=}\text{N—NH}.C_6H_5 \\
| \\
\text{C}{=}\text{O} \\
\qquad + C_6H_5NH_2 \\
\qquad + NH_3
\end{array}
$$

converting the secondary alcohol group of the hydrazone into a ketone; and finally, a third molecule of the reagent enters the reaction, giving an osazone:

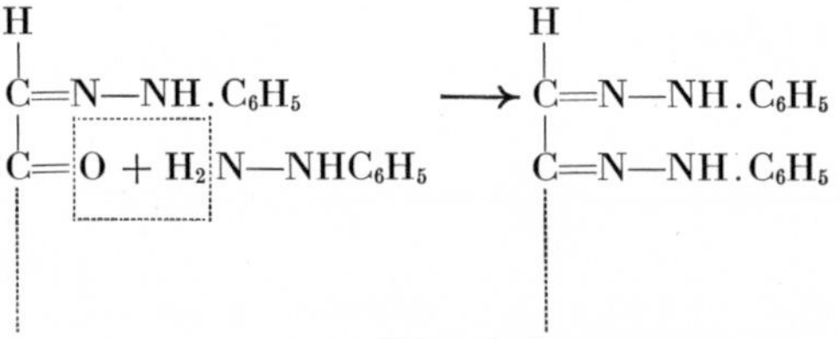

$$
\begin{array}{l}
\text{H} \\
| \\
\text{C}{=}\text{N—NH}.C_6H_5 \\
| \\
\text{C}{=}\text{O} + H_2N—NHC_6H_5
\end{array}
\longrightarrow
\begin{array}{l}
\text{H} \\
| \\
\text{C}{=}\text{N—NH}.C_6H_5 \\
| \\
\text{C}{=}\text{N—NH}.C_6H_5
\end{array}
$$

Phenyl glucosazone

These osazones are yellow, insoluble crystalline compounds, fairly characteristic in form (and other properties) for each individual sugar, so that the osazone test becomes an important one for purposes of identification.

Glucose, mannose, and fructose give the same osazone. This must mean that such sugars differ only in the first two carbon loadings:

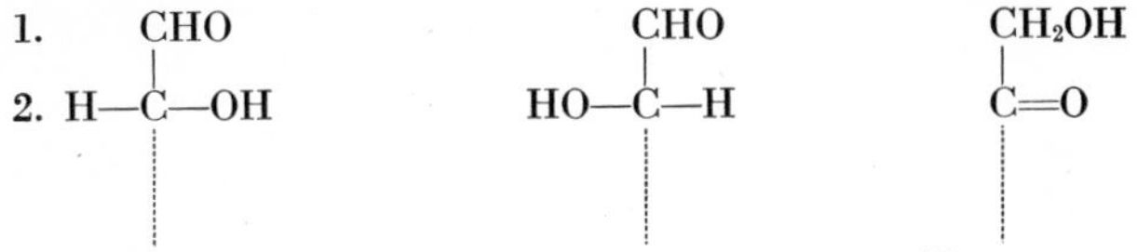

| 1. | CHO | CHO | CH₂OH |

1.   CHO   CHO   CH₂OH

2. H—C—OH   HO—C—H   C=O

Glucose   Mannose   Fructose

With fructose, the first molecule of the phenylhydrazine reacts with the carbonyl group; the second molecule is involved in the reaction which oxidizes the primary alcoholic group (next to the carbonyl group) to an aldehyde; and the third molecule of the reagent reacts with this aldehydic group to form the osazone.

Fermentation.   (See also Chap. 12.) The three hexoses which are fermented by yeast are glucose, mannose, and fructose; and they are fermented only when they are the naturally occurring D-forms (which means when they are structurally related to D-glyceraldehyde). The over-all equation for this reaction—which consists of many individual reactions—is:

$$C_6H_{12}O_6 \longrightarrow 2C_2H_5OH + 2CO_2$$

If a disaccharide such as sucrose is used, it is first hydrolyzed by an enzyme in yeast into a mixture of "invert sugar" (glucose + fructose), which then undergoes fermentation.

The enzyme system in yeast which is responsible for the over-all fermentation reaction was originally called *zymase*, which is, in reality, a general name for a mixture of many enzymes in yeast that take part in the fermentation reaction. A dialyzable factor which is needed, in addition to the various enzymes, has been called cozymase or coenzyme I and has been shown to be diphosphopyridine nucleotide (DPN) (p. 88).

Three important sugar derivatives of phosphoric acid which are involved in fermentation are

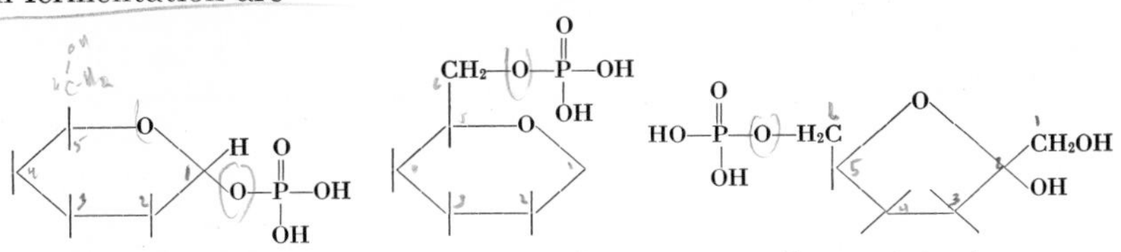

Glucose-1-phosphate   Glucose-6-phosphate   Fructose-6-phosphate

DESCRIPTIONS OF SOME MONO- AND DISACCHARIDES

Glucose ($C_6H_{12}O_6$).   Glucose is also called *dextrose* and *grape sugar*. It occurs with fructose in sweet fruits. It is the normal sugar present in blood. In diabetes the amount in the blood increases, and, very often, a considerable quantity of this sugar appears in the urine. Its preparation from cornstarch by acid hydrolysis is a commercial process. Glucose is surpassed in sweetness only by fructose and sucrose.

Fructose ($C_6H_{12}O_6$).   Fructose is also called *levulose* and *fruit sugar*, and is present in sweet fruits, together with glucose. It is now obtained on a commercial scale by the hydrolysis of inulin, a polysaccharide found in the Jerusalem artichoke.

Galactose ($C_6H_{12}O_6$).   Galactose is obtained when agar (an Asiatic seaweed) or lactose is hydrolyzed. It is found, in combination, in nerve tissue.

Mannose ($C_6H_{12}O_6$).   An aldohexose, mannose occurs in combination in mannans (found, for example, in the ivory nut from which buttons are made). While glucose, galactose, and fructose are common foodstuffs, mannose plays but a minor role.

Maltose ($C_{12}H_{22}O_{11}$).   This is also called *malt sugar*, and is obtained when starch is hydrolyzed by an enzyme (diastase or amylase) found in sprouting barley or malt. It is also a product formed when the enzyme in saliva (ptyalin) acts on starch. When hydrolyzed (by acid or by the enzyme maltase of the small intestine), glucose is formed. For each molecule of maltose we obtain two molecules of glucose.

Lactose ($C_{12}H_{22}O_{11}$).   Lactose, or *milk sugar*, is the sugar present in milk. It is sometimes found in the urine of women during lactation. When hydrolyzed (by acid or by the enzyme lactase of the small intestine), a mixture of glucose and galactose is obtained.

Sucrose ($C_{12}H_{22}O_{11}$).   Sucrose is also called *cane sugar* or *saccharose*, and occurs in abundance in sugar cane and sugar beets, and is the sugar commonly used for sweetening purposes. When hydrolyzed (by acid, by the enzyme invertase of yeast, or by the enzyme sucrase of the intestine), a mixture of glucose and fructose is obtained. This mixture is known as *invert sugar* because the sucrose is dextrorotatory, whereas the product obtained is levorotatory. The fructose molecule turns the plane of polarized light to the left more than does the glucose molecule to the right.

PENTOSES, $C_5H_{10}O_5$

The pentoses, the 5-carbon sugars, are common in the plant and in the animal kingdom. They are found in gums and pentosans (p. 26). The structural formulas for some of them, and their relations to the hexoses, are given on p. 6. *Arabinose* (obtained from gum arabic) and *xylose* (obtained from wood gums) are common examples. Ribose and desoxyribose (in which an OH is replaced by H) are part of the molecular configuration of nucleic acids (p. 78), substances of vital importance in cellular structure.

Ribose (β-D-ribofuranose)   Desoxyribose (β-D-2-desoxyribose)

POLYSACCHARIDES, $(C_6H_{10}O_5)_x$

Starch.   Starch, which occurs abundantly in grains, tubers, and fruits, is largely the source of carbohydrates for man. It consists of two types of molecules: a linear or nonbranched polymer of glucose (amylose) and a branched polymer of glucose (amylopectin). One method of separating the amylose from the amylopectin is to allow starch grains, soaked in water, to swell. The temperature should be 60–80° C. The amylose diffuses into the water. The residue, containing the amylopectin, is separated by centrifugation. Phosphorus and fatty acids are often found in starch. The amylose may be represented as:

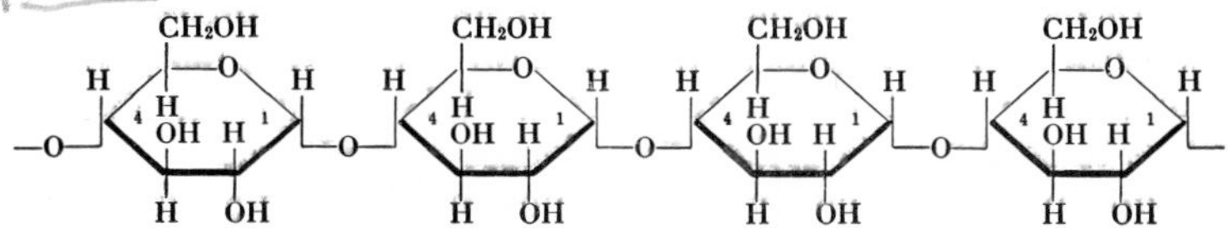

which shows nonbranched chains of glucopyranose units joined by the first and fourth carbon atoms. The amylopectin, the branched type, shows joining of branches at 1,6-glucosidic linkages (compare the numbering on p. 9 for formula for glucose):

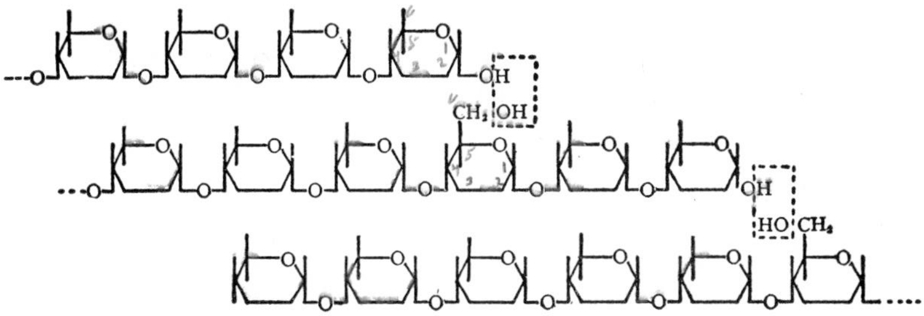

Amylose is slightly soluble in water, forms a slightly viscous solution, and is hydrolyzed to maltose by the enzyme, β-amylase. (The amylases obtained from saliva, pancreatic juice, and germinating seeds, and the diastase obtained from malt hydrolyze starch, as a whole, to maltose.) With iodine, amylose gives a more powerful blue color than does amylopectin.

Various theories have been advanced regarding the formation of a blue color when starch and iodine are mixed. Some investigators have advocated the idea that a starch-iodine complex is formed; others, that a process of adsorption is primarily the responsible factor.

Amylopectin itself constitutes some 80 per cent of many starches. It is highly viscous, and is incompletely hydrolyzed by β-amylase. Ignoring the phosphoric acid and the fatty acids, starch, or its two constituents, when hydrolyzed completely (by acid), yields glucose and nothing else. Like the other polysaccharides, and unlike the mono- and disaccharides, starch does not pass through a semipermeable membrane (dialysis).

When boiled with water, the starch granules swell and form a paste. A soluble starch can be obtained by a preliminary treatment of starch with cold dilute hydrochloric acid. The hydrolysis of starch by ptyalin or amylase (the enzyme in saliva) results in the production of a number of dextrins and, finally, maltose. Like the other polysaccharides, starch does not reduce Benedict's solution or form an osazone, so that free ketonic or aldehydic groups are absent.

Two enzymes are needed for the complete digestion of the branched polysaccharides (glycogen and amylopectin): (*a*) Phosphorylase, which specifically hydrolyzes the α1,4- linkages between glucose residues. The glucose units, in the presence of inorganic phosphate, are split off as glucose-1-phosphate until the enzyme approaches the α1,6- linkages at the branching points. This action may be referred to as *phosphorolysis*, in contradistinction to *hydrolysis*, which involves the introduction of a molecule of water instead of phosphoric acid. (*b*) The second enzyme—amylo-1-6-glucosidase—splits glucose units at the 1,6- linkage, permitting phosphorylase to continue its action; free glucose is produced.

The ratio of free to phosphorylated glucose which is produced is characteristic of the type of branched polysaccharide undergoing digestion and can be used for the determination of end groups (Fig. 1).

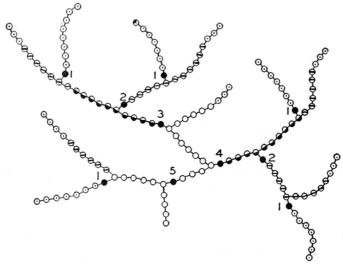

Fig. 1. Model of segment of muscle glycogen based on results obtained by stepwise enzymatic degradation. ⊙, ⊖, and ◔ glucose residues removed by first, second, and third degradation with phosphorylase, respectively. ●, glucose residues removed by amylo-1,6-glucosidase. Of five tiers three were degraded, corresponding to 122 out of 150 glucose residues. (*Larner, Illingworth, Cori and Cori: J. Biol. Chem., 199:* 641.)

More recently an enzyme, the "Q" enzyme, has been isolated which is concerned with the synthesis of starch. It functions to convert the linear amylose molecule to a branch molecule of the amylopectin type. Thus, the "Q" enzyme, together with phosphorylase and glucose-1-phosphate, yields a branched polysaccharide similar to starch.

When the source of phosphorylase is from animal tissue (liver), the polysaccharide which is synthesized resembles glycogen: it gives a reddish brown color with iodine rather than the blue color which is obtained with starch.

Glycogen.   *Animal starch*, or glycogen, is found in liver and muscle. It is soluble in water (unlike starch), and gives a red color with iodine (starch gives a blue color). It is hydrolyzed in vivo to glucose, and when hydrolyzed in vitro by acid, glucose is again the only product. Like starch, it fails to reduce Benedict's solution or to form an osazone. Haworth is of the opinion that, in structure, glycogen resembles the amylopectin of starch.

A substance resembling glycogen has been found in lower plants (fungi, yeasts, and bacteria); and glycogen, in addition to starch, has been isolated from the seed of the sweet corn. The isolation of glycogen from corn is important because it has always been assumed that this polysaccharide is a typical animal product, whereas now it is shown to be present in one of the higher plants as well.

Dextran. This is a polysaccharide of a molecular weight of approximately 50,000, closely related to starch and glycogen. It is synthesized from sucrose by certain bacteria and is a polymer of D-glucopyranose units.

The dextrans comprise chains of $\alpha1,6$- linked units with $\alpha1,4$- branching points. It may be recalled (p. 22) that starch and glycogen consist of $\alpha1,4$- linked units with $\alpha1,6$- branching points.

Dextran may prove of value as a blood substitute in situations involving extensive loss of blood.

Dextrins. Dextrins, such as erythrodextrin (which gives a reddish color with iodine) and achroodextrin (which does not give a color with iodine), are formed in the early stages of the hydrolysis of starch. They have the general formula $(C_6H_{10}O_5)_x$.

Cellulose. The constituent of the cell wall of plants, cellulose is a highly insoluble substance. It can be dissolved in Schweitzer's reagent (ammoniacal cupric hydroxide), in an acid (HCl) solution of zinc chloride and in a solution of sodium hydroxide and carbon disulfide, the last forming *viscose*, from which rayon is made. It is hydrolyzed with difficulty, the product formed being glucose. Unlike starch, glycogen, and the dextrins, which are readily digested, cellulose passes through the human digestive tract without being attacked by any of the digestive enzymes, though some bacterial decomposition probably takes place in the large intestine. In herbivorous animals, microorganisms (bacteria, yeasts, protozoa) in the digestive tract attack cellulose to form, among other products, lower fatty acids which the animal utilizes for energy purposes.

When hydrolyzed with acids, cellulose is converted to β-D-glucose (p. 9). The cellulose molecules appear to consist of unbranched chains of glucopyranose.*

Inulin. This is present in the Jerusalem artichoke, is soluble in hot water, gives a negative iodine test, and yields fructose on hydrolysis. It has been suggested that the molecule of this polysaccharide consists of thirty fructose units and has a molecular weight of about 5000.

---

* Cellulose is very widely distributed. Cotton, linen, and wood are rich in this substance. By changing the physical form of cotton (there are several methods available), rayon, known for a time as artificial silk, is produced. Cellulose acetate forms the basis for motion picture films and shatter-proof glass. From cellulose nitrate a number of important industrial products are also obtained; for example, guncotton, celluloid, collodion, lacquers, etc.

More than 80 per cent of the rayon manufactured is made by the viscose process. Spruce pulp or cotton linters are soaked in caustic soda, treated with carbon disulfide (to form "viscose") and forced through fine holes into an acid bath, thereby forming filaments of regenerated cellulose (rayon). These filaments can then be twisted to form threads.

When inulin is injected, it is excreted through the glomeruli of the kidney. The substance has been used as a test for kidney function.

Chitin.   The organic constituent of the skeletal material of the Insecta and Crustacea is chitin, which yields glucosamine on hydrolysis:

$$
\begin{array}{c}
\text{CHO} \\
| \\
\text{CHNH}_2 \\
| \\
(\text{CHOH})_3 \\
| \\
\text{CH}_2\text{OH}
\end{array}
$$

Glucosamine

Glucosamine is also obtained when the mucin of saliva and the mucoids of connective tissues are hydrolyzed.

One of the constituents of the molecule of streptomycin is glucosamine.

Hyaluronic Acid.   This polysaccharide—present in animal tissues—yields, when hydrolyzed, a hexosamine (glucosamine) and a uronic acid (glucuronic acid). The substance has been prepared from umbilical cord, skin, vitreous humor, synovial fluid, tumors, and hemolytic streptococci.

Pentosans.   The pentosans are polysaccharides which yield pentoses on hydrolysis. Examples of pentosans are found in gum arabic, from which arabinose is obtained, and in oat hulls and corn cobs, which yield xylose.

Galactans.   The galactans, such as agar-agar, another common plant product, yield galactose on hydrolysis.

Pectins.   The pectins, present in apples, lemons, etc., and which form fruit gels with sugar, give on hydrolysis some galactose and arabinose, but galacturonic acid—resembling glucuronic acid (p. 18)—is the principal product.

Agar.   A complex carbohydrate obtained from seaweed, agar may be mentioned here because of its wide use in bacteriological technique. Bacteria can be grown in agar because most of them neither digest nor liquefy this medium. Agar dissolves in boiling water and does not set until body temperature is reached.

PAPER PARTITION CHROMATOGRAPHY

A very ingenious method for the separation and identification of small quantities of biochemically important compounds has been developed by Martin, Consden and Gordon. It has been used for the separation of mixtures of sugars, amino acids (p. 54), purines (p. 86), etc.

The method is based on the partition of a compound between water (bound by the cellulose of the filter paper) and the solvent (which may be phenol, collidine, butyl alcohol, etc.).

A small quantity of the mixture in solution is placed as a spot near the top of a strip of filter paper. The paper is hung vertically from a trough containing the solvent in such a way that the edge is immersed in the solvent. The whole is enclosed in a jar whose atmosphere is kept saturated with respect to both the water and the solvent.

As the solvent moves down the paper, a sharp solvent front can be seen. When this "front" has traveled a sufficient distance, it is marked with a pencil, the paper removed, dried and sprayed with a reagent which will

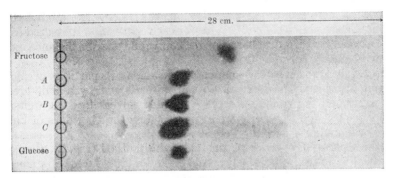

Fig. 2. Chromatogram of an extract of egg white in aqueous ethanol. A, extract treated with "Zeo Karb 215" and "Deacidite." B, extract treated with "Zeo Karb" only. C, untreated extract. The chromatogram was run 18 hr. in phenol-1% NH₃. (Partridge: Biochem. J., *42*: 238.)

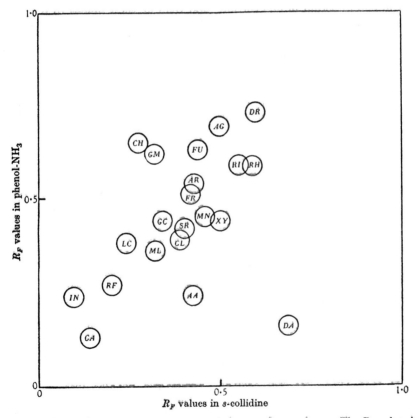

Fig. 3. Illustrating the separation obtainable by use of two solvents. The R_F values in phenol-1% NH₃ and s-collidine are plotted at right angles. AA, ascorbic acid; AG, acetylglucosamine; AR, arabinose; CH, chondrosamine; DA, dehydroascorbic acid; DR, deoxyribose; FR, fructose; FU, fucose; GA, galacturonic acid; GC, galactose; GL, glucose; GM, glucosamine; IN, inositol; LC, lactose; ML, maltose; MN, mannose; RF, raffinose; RH, rhamnose; RI, ribose; SR, sorbose; XY, xylose. (Partridge: Biochem. J., *42*: 238.)

produce a colored spot at those points along the paper where the individual compounds are present. The R_F value for each spot is now measured as the ratio between the distance moved by the compound and the distance moved by the advancing solvent "front."

The distance moved by the compound is related to its partition coefficient between water and the solvent—to the water bound by a unit area of filter paper and the volume of water-saturated solvent held per unit area of filter paper. The R_F values are compared with the R_F values of known compounds similarly treated.

In the separation of reducing sugars by this method (Fig. 2), the paper is sprayed with a solution of silver nitrate and a large excess of ammonia. Metallic silver is precipitated in the region occupied by the reducing sugar; and this shows itself in the form of a brown or black spot.

A one-dimensional strip may not be sufficient for an unknown containing a relatively large number of sugars. For this reason, the unknown is often placed near one corner of a filter paper square, and is chromatographed first in one direction in one solvent, and then at right angles to it in another solvent (Fig. 3). Since the R_F value of any one solute varies with the solvent, a better separation is achieved.

Various modifications of this technique have been suggested.

REFERENCES

Among organic chemistry texts which include chapters on the chemistry of carbohydrates, two may be mentioned: *Noller:* Chemistry of Organic Compounds, 1951; and *Fieser and Fieser:* Organic Chemistry, 1950.

More detailed discussions will be found in *Percival:* Structural Carbohydrate Chemistry, 1950; and *Pigman and Goepp:* Chemistry of the Carbohydrates, 1948.

Reviews of yearly progress are summarized in the Ann. Rev. Biochem., of which the first volume appeared in 1932. See, for example, *Wolfrom and Sugihara:* 19: 67, 1950; *Fischer and MacDonald:* 20: 43, 1951; *Montgomery and Smith:* 21: 79, 1952; *Isbell and Frush:* 22: 107, 1953. More extensive reviews are to be found in Advances in Carbohydrate Chemistry.

A fine review of Fischer's original method for determining the configuration of glucose is given by *Hudson:* J. Chem. Educ., 18: 353, 1941. See also Carbohydrate Nomenclature, in Chem. Eng. News, 26: 2, 1948 (May 31); and *Vickery:* Science, 113: 314, 1951.

The use of the anthrone reagent is discussed by *Seifter, Dayton, Novic, and Muntwyler:* Arch. Biochem., 25: 191, 1950; and by *Graff, McElroy, and Mooney:* J. Biol. Chem., 195: 351, 1952. *Devor:* J. Am. Chem. Soc., 72: 2008, 1950, describes a modified Molisch reaction.

Papers dealing with the Lobry de Bruyn conversions (of monosaccharides) are, among others, by *Topper and Stetten, Jr.:* J. Biol. Chem., 189: 191, 1951; 193: 149, (1951); and *Sowden and Schaffer,* J. Am. Chem. Soc., 74: 499 (1952).

The chemistry and biology of starch and related products are discussed by *Meyer:* Adv. Enzym., 12: 200, 1951; *Peat:* Ibid., 11: 339, 1951 (biological transformations of starch); *Nussenbaum and Hassid:* J. Biol. Chem., 190: 673, 1951 (enzymic synthesis of amylopectin); *Potter, Hassid, and Joslyn:* J. Am. Chem. Soc., 71: 4075 (1949) (structure cf apple starch); *Hehre:* Adv. Enzym., 11: 297, 1951 (enzymic synthesis of polysaccharides); *Gilbert and Patrick:* Biochem. J., 51: 181, 1952 (Q-enzyme); *Cori and Larner:* J. Biol. Chem., 188: 17, 1951 (amylo-1,6-glucosidase and phosphorylase on glycogen and amylopectin).

The separation of starch into its two constituents is described by *McCready and Hassid:* Ibid., 65: 1154, 1943.

For studies dealing with the nature of the starch-iodine complex, see *Rundle:* J. Am. Chem. Soc., 69: 1769, 1947; *Swanson:* J. Biol. Chem., 172: 825, 1948.

An excellent review article by *Hassid* dealing with the molecular constitution of starch (and glycogen), and the mechanism of its formation, may be found in *Gilman's* Organic Chemistry (1953), vol. 4, p. 901. See also *Meyer:* Experientia, *8:* 405, 1952 (in English).

Meyer: Advances in Enzymology, *3:* 109, 1943, is the author of an exhaustive article on the chemistry of glycogen.

A reference to dextran is the paper by *Hines, McGhee, and Shurter:* Ind. Eng. Chem., *45:* 692, 1953.

On the subject of cellulose, see *Siu:* Microbial Decomposition of Cellulose, 1951; and *Moyer:* Chem. Eng. News, *30:* 510, 1952 (cellulose research).

For a discussion of hyaluronic acid, see *Meyer:* Physiol. Rev., *27:* 335, 1947; *Haddian and Pirie:* Biochem. J., *42:* 260, 1948 (preparation and properties); *Meyer and Rapport:* Adv. Enzym., *13:* 5, 1952.

Articles illustrating experimental procedures are the following:
Partridge and Westall: Biochem. J., *42:* 238, 1948 (identification of sugars by the filter-paper chromatogram).
Dreywood: Ind. Eng. Chem., Analytical ed., *18:* 499, 1946; *Morris,* Science *107:* 254, 1948 (anthrone test for carbohydrates).

Swanson and Cori: J. Biol. Chem., *172:* 797, 805, 815, 825, 1948 (studies on the structure of polysaccharides).

For details regarding the life and work of *Emil Fischer,* who contributed so much to our knowledge of carbohydrates, see the biography (in German) by *Kurt Hoesch,* 1921, and the delightful autobiography entitled Aus Meinem Leben, 1922. A much shorter biography will be found in *Harrow's* Eminent Chemists of Our Time, 1927.

A historical description of the development of the chemistry of carbohydrates is to be found in *Lieben's* Geschichte der physiologischen Chemie, 1935, p. 460.

Papers dealing with chromotography are the following: *Partridge:* Biochem. J., *42:* 238, 1948; *Stein and Moore:* Scientific American, March, 1951, p. 35; *Patton:* J. Chem. Educ., *27:* 60, 574, 1950; *Bloch:* Analyt. Chem., *22:* 1327, 1950; *Dunn:* Experiments in Biochemistry, 1951, p. 84.

Plant Biochemistry, in contradistinction to animal biochemistry—which is the subject of this book—is splendidly outlined by *Bonner,* 1950.

Chapter 3   *The Lipids*

The LIPIDS include not only the true fats but substances which are (1) chemically related to fats (like lecithin), or (2) related to them because of common solubilities and possible biological relationships (like cholesterol). The true fats are not only of importance for energy purposes, but a number of the vitamins are often associated with them, and some of the fats contain unsaturated fatty acids which are needed by the organism (p. 33). The physiological significance of the lipids other than the fats is not always clear, but this matter will be discussed later.

The lipids include

1. Fats: esters of fatty acids and glycerol. (If liquid at ordinary temperature, the fats are known as "oils.")

2. Waxes: esters of fatty acids and higher alcohols (but *not* glycerol).

3. Phospholipids (phosphatides): fats containing, in addition, phosphoric acid and nitrogenous compounds (lecithin, cephalin, and sphingomyelin).

4. Cerebrosides (glycolipids): combinations of fatty acid, sugar and a nitrogenous substance (phrenosin, kerasin, etc.).

5. Steroids: partially or completely hydrogenated phenanthrene derivatives (cholesterol, ergosterol, etc.).

The lipids are soluble in alcohol-ether mixtures and allied solvents. The carbohydrates and the proteins (p. 45) are practically insoluble in such solvents.

THE FATS

The fats (and fatty oils like olive oil and cod-liver oil) contain mixtures of triglycerides: esters of glycerol and fatty acids (such as stearic, palmitic, or oleic acid). The general formula for such a fat or oil is

$$H_2C-O-CO-R_1$$
$$HC-O-CO-R_2$$
$$H_2C-O-CO-R_3$$

If $R_1 = R_2 = R_3$, then we have a simple glyceride; for example,

$$H_2C-O-CO-C_{17}H_{35}$$
$$HC-O-CO-C_{17}H_{35}$$
$$H_2C-O-CO-C_{17}H_{35}$$

Tristearin

($C_{17}H_{35}COOH$ = stearic acid)

If the R's are unequal, then we get a mixed glyceride; for example,

$$\alpha \quad H_2C\text{---}O\text{---}CO\text{---}C_{15}H_{31}$$
$$\beta \quad HC\text{---}O\text{---}CO\text{---}C_{17}H_{33}$$
$$\alpha_1 \quad H_2C\text{---}O\text{---}CO\text{---}C_{17}H_{35}$$

β-Oleo-α-α_1-palmitostearin
($C_{15}H_{31}COOH$ = palmitic acid)
($C_{17}H_{33}COOH$ = oleic acid)

Natural fats are largely mixed glycerides.

The fats, then, are typical esters. A simple ester would be formed by the combination of an acid and an alcohol: $CH_3COOH + C_2H_5OH \rightarrow CH_3COOC_2H_5 + H_2O$. A fat would be formed by the combination of an acid (usually of relatively high molecular weight) with the alcohol glycerol.

Being esters, the fats are readily hydrolyzed:

$$H_2C\text{---}O\text{---}CO\text{---}C_{15}H_{31} \qquad\qquad CH_2\text{---}OH$$
$$HC\text{---}O\text{---}CO\text{---}C_{15}H_{31} + 3H_2O \xrightarrow{acid} 3C_{15}H_{31}COOH + CH\text{---}OH$$
$$H_2C\text{---}O\text{---}CO\text{---}C_{15}H_{31} \qquad\qquad CH_2OH$$

Palmitin   Glycerol

Table 1   COMPOSITIONS OF TYPICAL VEGETABLE OILS

| No. of C atoms | Acid | Cottonseed oil | | Soybean oil, per cent | Corn oil, per cent |
		Sea island, per cent	Upland, per cent		
14	Myristic	0.3	0.5	. . . .	. . . .
16	Palmitic	19.1	20.9	6.5	7.3
18	Stearic	1.9	1.8	4.2	3.3
18	Oleic	33.15	29.2	32.0	43.4
18	Linoleic	39.35	42.8	49.3	39.1
18	Linolenic	. . . .	. . . .	2.2	. . . .
20	Arachidic	0.6	0.1	0.7	0.4
24	Lignoceric	. . . .	. . . .	0.1	0.2

This hydrolysis can be accomplished by using acid, alkali, superheated steam, or the appropriate enzyme (the lipase of the pancreas, for example). When acid is used, the free fatty acid is liberated. When alkali is used, a soap is formed, and the process is known as saponification:

$$C_3H_5(O.CO.C_{17}H_{35})_3 + 3NaOH \longrightarrow 3C_{17}H_{35}COONa + C_3H_5(OH)_3$$

Stearin   Sodium stearate   Glycerol
                            (A soap)

Fats and oils are, as a rule, more complex than mere mixtures of the triglycerides (stearin, palmitin, olein). For example, the composition of a number of vegetable oils is given in Table 1.

The fats we eat—the edible fats—are glycerides of even-numbered fatty acids, ranging from butyric (C_4) to lignoceric (C_{24}) and probably higher.

The composition of butter fat is as follows, the numbers representing the per cent of glyceryl ester: butyric acid, 3.0; caproic acid, 1.4; caprylic acid, 1.8; capric acid, 1.8; lauric acid, 6.9; myristic acid, 22.6; palmitic acid, 22.6; stearic acid, 11.4; oleic acid, 27.4.

Simple and mixed glycerides have also been prepared synthetically.

From 60 to 65 per cent of the total fat and oil production in the United States is used as food. These fats include butter, lard, cottonseed oil, and soybean oil. Fats and oils used in products other than foods are inedible tallow greases, and the oils of coconut, palm, linseed, tung, fish, soybean, and castor bean.

Glycerol. [$C_3H_5(OH)_3$].   Also called *glycerin*, glycerol is obtained in enormous quantities as a by-product in soap manufacture by the process of saponification. It is miscible with water and alcohol. When heated, either alone or in the presence of a dehydrating agent such as $KHSO_4$, acrolein is formed:

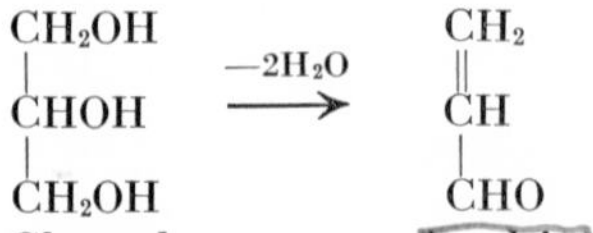

$$
\begin{array}{ccc}
CH_2OH & & CH_2 \\
| & -2H_2O & \| \\
CHOH & \longrightarrow & CH \\
| & & | \\
CH_2OH & & CHO \\
\text{Glycerol} & & \text{Acrolein}
\end{array}
$$

Acrolein has an acrid odor (the odor of burned fat), and the formation of this substance is used as a test for glycerol (and, indirectly, fat itself).

The Fatty Acids.   Table 2 lists some of the fatty acids found in fats which occur more or less commonly. Those found in nature have almost invariably an even number of carbon atoms. The most important and the most widely distributed are stearic, palmitic, and oleic acids. The highly unsaturated acids, such as linolenic acid, serve (*a*) as essential food constituents (Chap. 19) or (*b*) contribute to the "drying power" of oils in paint. Chaulmoogric acid, present in chaulmoogra oil (which is expressed from the seeds of certain trees found in Burma and nearby countries), has been used in the treatment of leprosy.

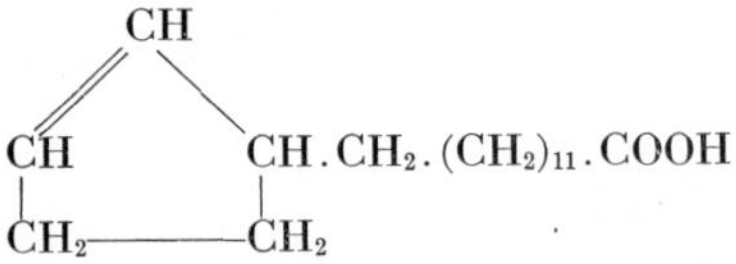

$$
\begin{array}{c}
CH \\
\diagup\diagdown \\
CH \quad\quad CH.CH_2.(CH_2)_{11}.COOH \\
| \quad\quad\quad | \\
CH_2\text{------}CH_2
\end{array}
$$
Chaulmoogric acid

Anderson and his associates have isolated a number of fatty acids from the human strain of tubercle bacillus. One of them, tuberculostearic acid, is probably 10-methylstearic acid. Another, phthioic acid, is a saturated fatty liquid with the formula of $C_{26}H_{52}O_2$.

As has already been mentioned, the fatty acids form soaps with metal ions and esters with alcohols. In the organism they undergo an extensive series of transformations, their ultimate oxidation being related to the oxidation of carbohydrate.

A number of the unsaturated fatty acids contain eighteen carbon atoms. They undergo oxidation when exposed to the air and become brown in color. Mild oxidation (with dilute $KMnO_4$) gives hydroxy acids. For example,

$$CH_3(CH_2)_7CH=CH(CH_2)_7COOH + O + H_2O \longrightarrow$$
Oleic acid

$$CH_3(CH_2)_7CHOHCHOH(CH_2)_7COOH$$
Dihydroxystearic acid

Table 2   COMMON FATTY ACIDS
(Reprinted by permission from Bull: The Biochemistry of the Lipids, John Wiley & Sons, Inc.)

		Occurrence
I. *Saturated fatty acids*		
Acetic	CH_3COOH	Vinegar
Butyric	C_3H_7COOH	Butter
Caproic	$C_5H_{11}COOH$	Butter, etc.
Caprylic	$C_7H_{15}COOH$	Butter, etc.
Capric	$C_9H_{19}COOH$	Coconut oil, butter, etc.
Lauric	$C_{11}H_{23}COOH$	Spermaceti, coconut oil, etc.
Myristic	$C_{13}H_{27}COOH$	Nutmeg butter, coconut oil, etc.
Palmitic	$C_{15}H_{31}COOH$	Animal and vegetable fats
Stearic	$C_{17}H_{35}COOH$	Animal and vegetable fats
Arachidic	$C_{19}H_{39}COOH$	Peanut oil
Lignoceric	$C_{23}H_{47}COOH$	Arachis oil; cerebrosides
Carnaubic	$C_{23}H_{47}COOH$	Carnauba wax
Cerotic	$C_{25}H_{51}COOH$	Beeswax, wool fat, etc.
II. *Unsaturated fatty acids*		
(a) One double bond		
Oleic	$C_{17}H_{33}COOH$	Animal and vegetable fats
Erucic	$C_{21}H_{41}COOH$	Rapeseed oil; etc.
(b) Two double bonds		
Linoleic	$C_{17}H_{31}COOH$	Linseed oil, cottonseed oil, etc.
(c) Three double bonds		
Linolenic	$C_{17}H_{29}COOH$	Linseed oil
(d) Four double bonds		
Arachidonic	$C_{19}H_{31}COOH$	Lecithin, cephalin
III. *Saturated monohydroxy acids*		
Cerebronic	$C_{24}H_{48}O_3$	Cerebron
IV. *Unsaturated monohydroxy acids*		
Ricinoleic	$C_{18}H_{34}O_3$	Castor oil
V. *Cyclic acids*		
Chaulmoogric	$C_{18}H_{32}O_2$	Chaulmoogra oil *, for leprosy*

The following list shows the position of the double bonds in other unsaturated fatty acids:

Erucic, $CH_3(CH_2)_7CH=CH(CH_2)_{11}COOH$
Linoleic, $CH_3(CH_2)_4CH=CHCH_2CH=CH(CH_2)_7COOH$
Linolenic, $CH_3CH_2CH=CHCH_2CH=CHCH_2CH=CH(CH_2)_7COOH$
Ricinoleic, $CH_3(CH_2)_5CHOHCH_2CH=CH(CH_2)_7COOH$

Owing to their unsaturated character, the unsaturated fatty acids combine not only with hydrogen but also with halogens. This is the basis for
the determination of the *iodine number*.

Two types of isomers are possible in the unsaturated acids. One of them
depends upon the position of the double bond. Taking oleic acid as the
example, 16 isomers are possible, and several have been actually isolated
(such as Δ2,3, Δ3,4 and Δ4,5 oleic acids).* Another type of isomerism,
geometrical isomerism, depends upon spatial arrangement. Oleic acid
(m. p. 13° C.) can be transformed into elaidic acid (m. p. 45° C.) by means

*   Δ = double bond.

of nitrous acid. Elaidic acid has the same empirical formula as oleic acid, and in each case the position of the double bond is 9,10. The difference is a difference in spatial arrangement, one (oleic) being the *cis* form, and the other (elaidic) being the *trans* form:

$$CH_3(CH_2)_7CH \qquad\qquad CH_3(CH_2)_7CH$$
$$\| \qquad\qquad\qquad \|$$
$$COOH(CH_2)_7CH \qquad\qquad HC(CH_2)_7COOH$$

Oleic acid
(*Cis* form)

Elaidic acid
(*Trans* form)

Ricinoleic acid, the unsaturated hydroxy acid present in castor oil, is optically active because the carbon attached to the hydroxyl group is asymmetric.

Fat Analysis.   Aside from physical methods (melting point, index of refraction, etc.), the usual analysis of a fat depends upon determining certain chemical constants. Among these are the following:

1. SAPONIFICATION NUMBER. This represents the number of milligrams of KOH needed to saponify completely 1 gm. of fat (or oil). Roughly speaking, this number varies inversely with the molecular weight of the fat. For example,

	M. W.	Saponif. No.
Tributyrin	302.2	557.0
Tricaprin	554.4	303.6
Tripalmitin	806.8	208.6
Tristearin	890.9	188.9
Triolein	884.8	190.2

2. REICHERT-MEISSL NUMBER. This is the number of milliliters of 0.1 N alkali required to neutralize the soluble volatile fatty acids from 5 gm. of fat. Butterfat has a particularly high Reichert-Meissl number.

Volatile fatty acids represent the acids which volatilize on steam distillation. They are confined, approximately, to the series ranging from butyric (C_4) to lauric (C_{12}) and are divided into two groups; those soluble in water and those insoluble in water. Butterfat and coconut and palm oils have a relatively high "volatile fatty acid" content; the reverse is true of most of the fats.

3. ACETYL NUMBER. This is the number of milligrams of KOH required to neutralize the acetic acid resulting from the hydrolysis of 1 gm. of the acetylated fat. A fatty acid containing a hydroxyl group will react with acetic anhydride to form the acetylated compound. Castor oil, for example, which contains the unsaturated hydroxy acid, ricinoleic acid, gives a high acetyl number (142–150); the common fats containing smaller quantities of hydroxy fatty acids yield a considerably smaller number (2.5–20).

4. IODINE NUMBER. The number of grams of iodine absorbed by 100 gm. of fat is the iodine number. From what has already been said, it is obvious that the iodine number will depend upon the extent of unsaturation in the molecule of fat. To accelerate the absorption process, "halogenating agents" are added; iodine monobromide (*Hanus'* method) or iodine monochloride (*Wijs'* method). A list of some iodine numbers of several fats and oils is given (Table 3).

The fats are soluble in ether. This is also true of the sterols (like choles-terol) which are closely associated with fats but, chemically, are not fats at all (p. 42). However, fats are readily saponified, whereas sterols are not. An ether fraction, then, which may consist of a mixture of fat and sterols, can be saponified and the product extracted with ether. Here the fat has been transformed into soap but the sterols remain unchanged, and the latter are now extracted by ether. This ether fraction represents the *unsaponifiable matter*. In such oils as cod-liver oil, it is this unsaponifiable matter which contains not only sterols but the vitamins A and D.

Rancidity.   The unpleasant (rancid) odor and taste of fats (including butter) which they acquire on standing are attributed to chemical changes due, largely, to the presence of unsaturated fatty acids. The fats in fish become rancid even more rapidly than do meat fats and butterfat.

Table 3   SAPONIFICATION AND IODINE NUMBERS OF SOME OF THE COMMON FATS
(From Winton and Winton: Analysis of Foods.)

Fat	Saponif. No. (mixture of glycerides)	Iodine No.
Butter	220–241	22– 38
Lard	193–203	54– 70
Mutton tallow	192–195	32– 50
Coconut oil	246–265	8– 10
Cottonseed oil	191–195	104–114
Linseed oil	190–196	170–202
Olive oil	190–195	74– 95
Peanut oil	186–189	83–105
Soybean oil	190–197	115–145

The change involves the oxygen of the air (which attacks the double bond) and is catalyzed by moisture, heat and light. Peroxides are probably first formed, which are then broken down to aldehydes. Ketones are also formed by the action of microorganisms. An enzyme, lipoxidase, often present in fatty material, accelerates the oxidation of unsaturated fatty acids.

To prevent fat spoilage, the substitution of oxygen by an inert gas, or the removal of oxygen by creating a vacuum, is possible. The more practical method is the use of "anti-oxidants," substances which prevent oxidation to a greater or less degree. Various such substances have been suggested; a number of them are phenolic in character. Gum guaiac and tocopherol (vitamin E) were among a number of compounds approved by the War Food Administration. Hydroquinone and salts of gallic acid have also been suggested.

Hydrogenation.   As has already been described, unsaturated fatty acids can be saturated by the addition of hydrogen. This process can be accelerated by using a catalyst, such as nickel. By this means, not only unsaturated fatty acids, but unsaturated fats can be made to add hydrogen. The method has its practical application, in that oils, such as cottonseed oil, can be "hardened" or solidified into edible products. Shortenings on the market are products of this process.

From 60 to 65 per cent of the fats and oils produced in this country are used as food. The remainder finds its way into various industries (soap, paint and varnish, oilcloth, printing ink, and the like), a little more than half being used for making soap. 20%

"Drying" Oils.   Somewhat associated with the process of rancidity are the changes undergone by certain oils when exposed to the air. These oils, of which linseed and tung oils are the most important, form a solid surface, which is strong and waterproof, when exposed to the air. The oils are apparently oxidized and polymerized. Such "drying" oils have an iodine number greater than 130 and contain large percentages of highly unsaturated fatty acids. For example, linseed oil contains nearly 50 per cent of linoleic acid and more than 30 per cent of linolenic acid.

The Separation of Fatty Acids.   The fat is saponified with alcoholic potassium hydroxide and extracted with ether. The ether-insoluble materials, the soaps, are acidified to form the free fatty acids, and distilled with steam. To each fraction, volatile and nonvolatile, hot alcohol and an alcoholic solution of lead chloride are added. The soluble lead salts are mostly unsaturated fatty acids (liquid), and the insoluble lead salts are, in the main, saturated fatty acids (solid).

The lead salts are next converted to their free acids by the addition of hydrochloric acid, extracted with ether and converted to their methyl esters for fractional vacuum distillation, in order to separate the esters and, eventually, the acids.

The fatty acids can also be separated by the method of *countercurrent* distribution. The name originates from a consideration of the distribution of a solute between two immiscible solvents as each phase (upper and lower) is moved in opposite directions on equilibration with fresh solvent. The solute distributes itself between the two immiscible solvents according to its partition ratio. Craig, the originator of the method, uses in actual practice some 220 specially designed "separatory funnels."

The choice of solvents depends upon the partition coefficients of the compounds to be separated by these solvents. Knowing such data, it is possible to calculate the degree of separation to be attained, and the numbers of the tubes in which to find the free fatty acids (Fig. 4). (K values represent partition coefficients in the solvent system which has been used.)

This countercurrent method has proved of value in the separation not only of fatty acids but of a mixture of other compounds of similar chemical composition (amino acids, etc.)

Identification Tests.   This has been discussed, in large measure, under fat analysis (p. 34), saponification (p. 31), and the acrolein test (p. 32). The formation of a soap, and the fact that this soap can be salted out of solution with salt and precipitated with the salts of metals (such as $CaCl_2$) is an excellent qualitative test. It should also be noted that the soap first formed is soluble in water, and that such soap can be transformed into the insoluble fatty acids by treatment with HCl.

WAXES

Waxes are esters of fatty acids with alcohols (not glycerol) of high molecular weight. A number of common waxes are given in Table 4.

Industrially, they have their uses in the manufacture of lubricants (sperm oil), polishes (carnauba wax), ointments (lanolin, which contains wool wax), candles (spermaceti), etc. In the body, waxes occur as cholesterol esters, in which the fatty acid is joined to the alcohol cholesterol. Anderson has shown that the tubercle bacillus contains a complex wax.

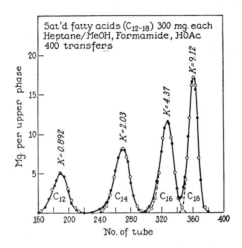

Fig. 4. Separation by countercurrent distribution of a mixture of saturated fatty acids (solid line curve) as compared with a theoretically calculated separation (dotted line curve) based on the partition coefficients (K) of the acids. (Ahrens and Craig: J. Biol. Chem., *195*:299, 1952.)

Aside from cholesterol, the common alcohols found in waxes are cetyl alcohol, $C_{16}H_{33}OH$, ceryl alcohol, $C_{26}H_{53}OH$, and myricyl alcohol, $C_{30}H_{61}OH$.

Table 4   A NUMBER OF COMMON WAXES

Wax	Iodine number
Sperm oil	81–90
Carnauba wax	13
Wool wax	30–35
Beeswax	8
Spermaceti	0–4
Chinese wax	0–1.4

PHOSPHOLIPIDS

The phospholipids are constituents of all animal and vegetable cells. They are present in abundance in brain, heart, kidney, eggs, soybeans, etc. The phospholipids have been separated into three distinct substances: lecithin, cephalin, and sphingomyelin. All three contain the elements nitrogen and phosphorus, besides carbon, hydrogen, and oxygen. In lecithin and cephalin, the nitrogen-phosphorus ratio is 1:1, and in sphingomyelin, it is 2:1.

Lecithin.   The formula for lecithin is

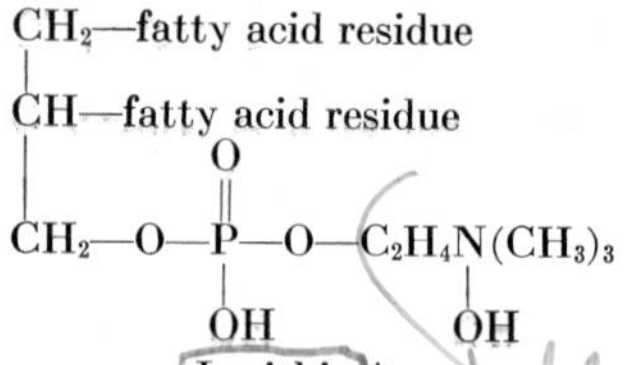

$$CH_2\text{—fatty acid residue}$$
$$CH\text{—fatty acid residue}$$
$$CH_2\text{—O—P—O—}C_2H_4N(CH_3)_3$$

with O above the P and OH below the P and OH below the right O.

Lecithin*

which means that the constituents of lecithin are fatty acids, glycerol, phosphoric acid, and the base, choline:

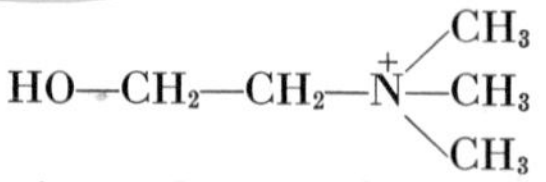

$$HO\text{—}CH_2\text{—}CH_2\text{—}\overset{+}{N}\overset{CH_3}{\underset{CH_3}{\diagdown}}CH_3$$

Choline (ethanoltrimethylammonium ion)

The common fatty acids in lecithin are stearic, oleic, and palmitic.

Lecithin is a common cell constituent and is considered to play a part in the metabolism of fat. It may be obtained from brain tissue or egg yolk. Crude lecithin from egg yolk is readily prepared by extracting the yolk with ether and precipitating out the lecithin with acetone. Fat and cholesterol, which are also present, remain in solution in acetone, but cephalin (p. 39) is also precipitated; so that the precipitate really consists of a crude mixture of lecithin and cephalin. To separate these two is not an easy problem. One method depends upon the fact that lecithin is more soluble in cold alcohol. The lecithin is finally purified by taking advantage of the fact that it forms an insoluble salt with cadmium chloride, which can be decomposed subsequently with ammonia.

When freshly obtained, lecithin has a waxlike appearance, but it readily turns brown on exposure, owing to oxidation. Lecithin is soluble in ether, alcohol, petroleum ether, benzene, carbon tetrachloride, carbon disulfide, and chloroform, and is insoluble in methyl acetate and acetone, but the presence of impurities has modifying influences. It can, of course, be saponified, and yields acrolein on heating; but unlike true fats, it contains nitrogen and phosphorus.†

The hydrolysis of lecithin results in choline, fatty acids, and *glycerophosphoric acid:*

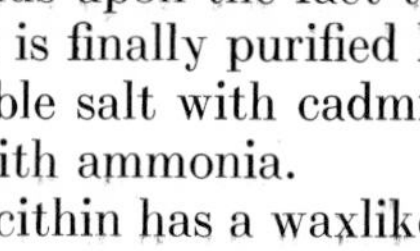

$$CH_2OH$$
$$CHOH$$
$$CH_2\text{—O—PO(OH)}_2$$

Glycerophosphoric acid

* It is more correct to write the lecithins thus:

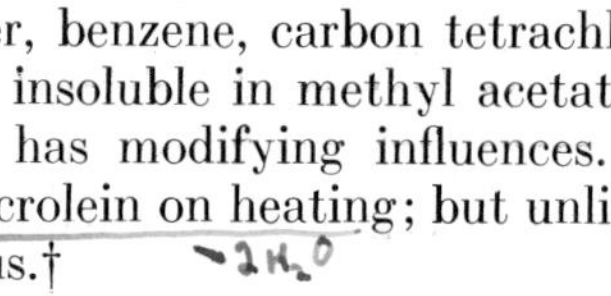

$$R\text{—O—P—OCH}_2CH_2\overset{+}{N}\overset{CH_3}{\underset{CH_3}{\diagdown}}CH_3$$

with O^- above the P and O below the P.

† In the industries, many thousands of pounds of lecithin, obtained from soybeans, are used as an emulsifier and in the manufacture of candies, chocolate, cocoa, margarine, medicines, and even in the dyeing of textiles.

The glycerophosphoric acid is not easily hydrolyzed. Bases have no action at all. Dilute acids do hydrolyze it slowly after boiling for a long time. It can, however, be readily hydrolyzed by an enzyme present in yeast and in animal material. Cobra venom contains an enzyme which splits off one molecule of fatty acid from lecithin (and cephalin, see below), giving a product called lysolecithin which is able to hemolyze red blood cells.

Enzymes capable of hydrolyzing lecithin—there are several varieties— are called *lecithinases*.

Choline.   This is a base comparable in strength to sodium hydroxide. It is important in preventing the accumulation of fat in the liver and is generally regarded as one of the B vitamins. Its acetyl derivative, acetylcholine, is the substance which is released at parasympathetic nerve endings when they are stimulated and is believed to be responsible for the transmission of nerve impulses (Chap. 21).

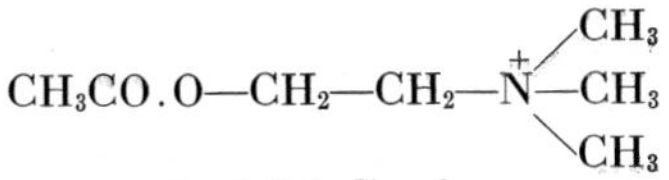

$$CH_3CO.O—CH_2—CH_2—\overset{+}{N}\underset{\diagdown CH_3}{\overset{\diagup CH_3}{—CH_3}}$$

Acetylcholine ion

2. **Cephalin,** also called "kephalin," is

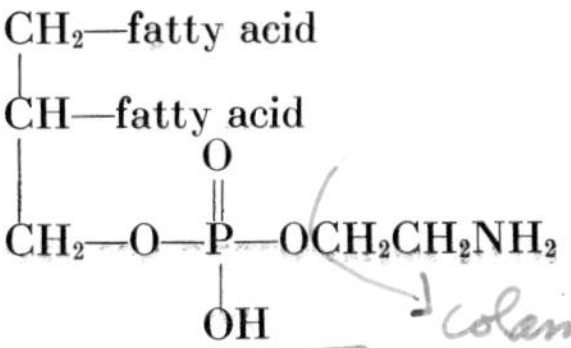

$$
\begin{array}{l}
CH_2—\text{fatty acid} \\
CH—\text{fatty acid} \\
\quad\quad\quad\quad O \\
\quad\quad\quad\quad \| \\
CH_2—O—P—OCH_2CH_2NH_2 \\
\quad\quad\quad\; OH
\end{array}
$$

Cephalin

which means that cephalin differs from lecithin in the kind of nitrogenous compound which it contains. This compound in cephalin may be β-aminoethyl alcohol, or *colamine*.

$$HO.CH_2.CH_2.NH_2$$
β-Aminoethyl alcohol (ethanolamine or colamine)

In ox brain, at least, the chief nitrogenous constituent of cephalin is serine (p. 55), though ethanolamine is also present (Folch).

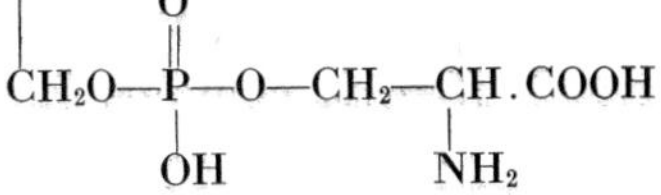

$$
\begin{array}{l}
CH_2—\text{fatty acid} \\
CH—\text{fatty acid} \\
\quad\quad\quad\quad O \\
\quad\quad\quad\quad \| \\
CH_2O—P—O—CH_2—CH.COOH \\
\quad\quad\quad OH \quad\quad\quad NH_2
\end{array}
$$

Phosphatidyl serine

Folch also finds that the ox-brain cephalin may contain inositol as a constituent. On hydrolysis, such cephalin yields fatty acids, glycerol, and inositol metadiphosphate.

$$\begin{array}{c} \text{H} \diagdown \qquad \diagup \text{O---PO}_3\text{H}_2 \\ \text{H} \diagdown \quad \text{C} \quad \diagup \text{H} \\ \text{C} \qquad \text{C} \\ \text{HO} \diagup \qquad \diagdown \text{OH} \\ \text{H} \diagdown \qquad \diagup \text{H} \\ \text{C} \qquad \text{C} \\ \text{HO} \diagup \qquad \diagdown \text{O---PO}_3\text{H}_2 \\ \text{H} \diagup \quad \diagdown \text{OH} \end{array}$$

Inositol metadiphosphate

Cephalin is believed to be concerned with the process of blood clotting (p. 235).

Sphingomyelin.   This yields, on hydrolysis, fatty acids, phosphoric acid, choline, and another nitrogenous base, sphingosine, with the probable formula $CH_3.(CH_2)_{12}.CH{=}CH.CHOH.CHNH_2.CH_2OH$, which means that it is an 18-carbon compound containing one unsaturated bond, one amino group and two hydroxyl groups. No glycerol is found in sphingomyelin.

The solubilities of the phospholipids may be summarized as follows (S = soluble, X = insoluble, and H = soluble in hot solvent):

Phospholipid	Ether	Alcohol	Acetone
Lecithin	S	S	X
Cephalin	S	X	X
Sphingomyelin	X	H	X

These differences in solubility are used for the separation of the phospholipids, although clearcut separations are rarely possible.

Sphingomyelin, like lecithin and cephalin, forms addition compounds with cadmium chloride. The cadmium salts of lecithin and sphingomyelin are insoluble in ether, whereas the corresponding cephalin salt is soluble in this solvent.

IV.   CEREBROSIDES

These substances, sometimes called *cerebrogalactosides*, or *galactolipids*, are found more particularly in the brain. Practically nothing is known as to their physiological function. They are readily distinguished from the phosphatides proper by the absence of the phosphoric acid group. They are composed of combinations of fatty acid, sphingosine (p. 40), and the sugar galactose,* and differ from one another only in the kind of fatty acid present. Two of the fairly well known cerebrosides are phrenosin (cerebron) and kerasin. Two others, nervone and oxynervone, have also been added to the list. *Phrenosin* is believed to yield a characteristic hydroxy acid, cerebronic acid, to which the formula $CH_3(CH_2)_7CH_2CH_2(CH_2)_{12}CHOH\text{-}COOH$ has been assigned. *Kerasin* contains lignoceric acid, $CH_3(CH_2)_7\text{-}CH_2CH_2(CH_2)_{12}CH_2COOH$. The acid in *nervone* is believed to be nervonic acid, $CH_3(CH_2)_7CH{=}CH(CH_2)_{12}CH_2COOH$, which is an unsaturated lignoceric acid. Oxynervonic acid, $CH_3(CH_2)_7CH{=}CH(CH_2)_{12}CHOH\text{-}COOH$, an unsaturated hydroxy lignoceric acid, is the acid which characterizes *oxynervone*.

A possible structure for a cerebroside is as follows (Carter):

* A cerebroside containing glucose instead of galactose has been reported.

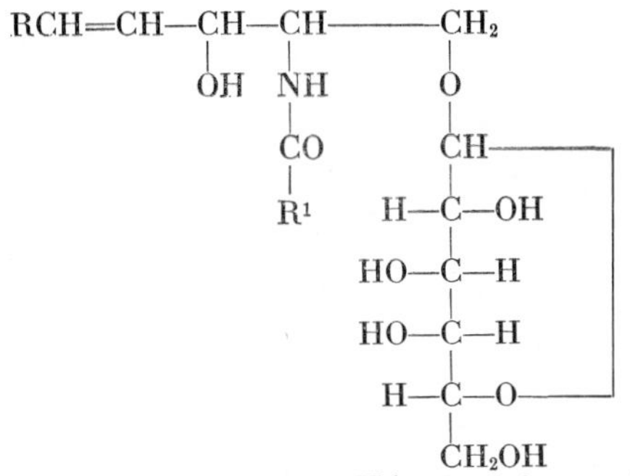

$$RCH=CH-CH-CH-\!\!\!-\!\!\!-CH_2$$

$$
\begin{array}{cccc}
& \underset{OH}{|} & \underset{NH}{|} & \underset{O}{|} \\
& & \underset{CO}{|} & \underset{CH-}{|} \\
& & \underset{R^1}{|} & H-C-OH \\
& & & HO-C-H \\
& & & HO-C-H \\
& & & H-C-O- \\
& & & CH_2OH
\end{array}
$$

$$[R = CH_3(CH_2)_{12}; R^1 = \text{fatty acid chain}]$$

Acetal Phosphatids. Thannhauser has isolated crystalline acetal phosphatids from the brain; that is, substances which are combinations of glycerol, phosphoric acid, ethanolamine and palmitic and stearic aldehydes.

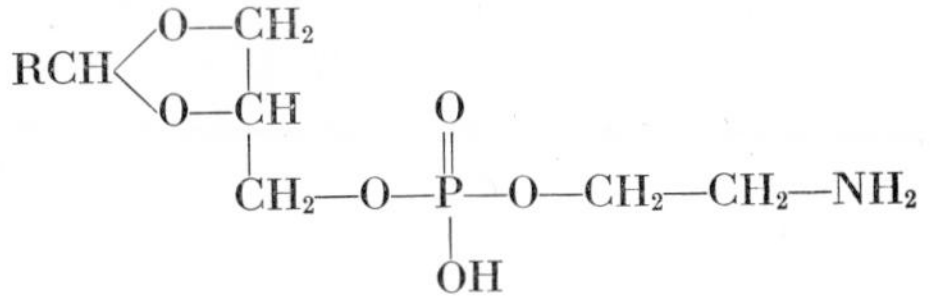

$$
RCH\begin{array}{l} O-CH_2 \\ \\ O-CH \end{array} \quad\quad O
$$
$$
CH_2-O-\overset{\displaystyle \|}{P}-O-CH_2-CH_2-NH_2
$$
$$
\underset{\displaystyle OH}{|}
$$

V. STEROIDS

The steroids may be classified into:

1. Sterols (cholesterol, ergosterol, etc.; see p. 42).
2. Bile acids (cholic acid, lithocholic acid, etc.; p. 132).
3. Substances obtained from cardiac glycosides (strophanthidin, etc.).
4. Substances obtained from toad poisons (bufotalin, etc.).
5. Substances obtained from saponins (digitogenin, obtained from digitonin; p. 42).
6. Sex hormones (estradiol, testosterone; Chap. 23).
7. Adrenal corticosteroids (desoxycorticosterone, etc.; Chap. 23).
8. Vitamins D (irradiated ergosterol, 7-dehydrocholesterol, etc.; Chap. 20).

These compounds are widely distributed in plant and animal tissues, either in the free state or in the form of esters (a combination with higher fatty acids). Chemically, they are known to be phenanthrene derivatives; or, more correctly, cyclopentanoperhydrophenanthrene derivatives.

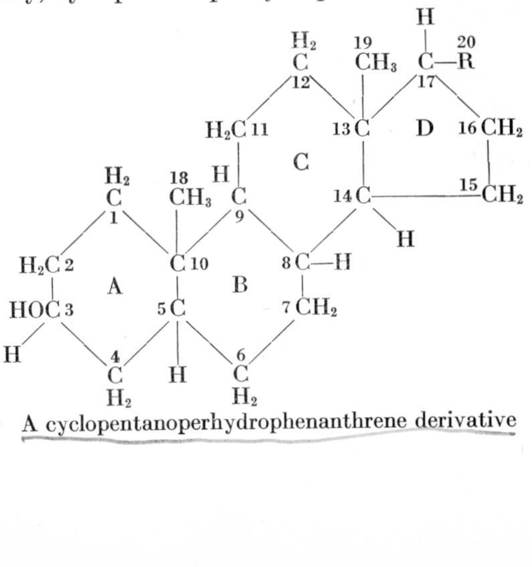

A cyclopentanoperhydrophenanthrene derivative

Cholesterol.   The best known of these steroids is cholesterol. It is present in all animal cells and is particularly abundant in nervous tissue. Varying quantities of this sterol are found admixed in animal, but not in vegetable, fats. Cholesterol has the following structure:

which means that it has a hydroxyl group in position 3 and a double bond connecting positions 5 and 6. The saturated hydrocarbon corresponding to cholesterol is known as *cholestane*.

In the cholesterol nucleus there are eight centers of asymmetry, and, theoretically, something like 240 isomers are possible. Fortunately for the problem, but two carbon centers seem to be involved, those at position 3 and position 5.

Cholesterol can be prepared from brain tissue, or, even better, from gallstones.* In either case, the essential point in the method is to extract the cholesterol with ether and, after evaporation of the ether, to recrystallize the sterol from hot alcohol. Unlike the fats or the phospholipids, cholesterol and other sterols cannot be saponified. They represent part of the "unsaponified fraction." [Hickman, using the molecular still, has been able to separate sterols from the natural oils in which they occur by distillation in vacuo.

Cholesterol gives a number of characteristic color tests. One of these is the *Liebermann-Burchard* test, in which a chloroform solution of the sterol is treated with acetic anhydride and concentrated sulfuric acid. The bluish-green to green color obtained varies in intensity with the amount of cholesterol present, and this color test is therefore the basis of a quantitative estimation. Another common test is the one developed by *Salkowski*, which consists in mixing the sterol with chloroform and concentrated sulfuric acid to give a bluish-red to purple color. These tests are not confined to cholesterol, but are given by a number of the sterols. However, in animal tissues one finds comparatively small quantities of sterols other than cholesterol. Saturated sterols (like dihydrocholesterol and coprosterol) fail to give these color tests.

Another test of importance is precipitation with *digitonin*, $C_{56}H_{92}O_2$, (a glycoside belonging to the saponin group and occurring in digitalis leaves and seeds). Cholesterol is readily precipitated with digitonin, forming cholesterol digitonide. This is not only a qualitative test, but it can be made the basis for a quantitative determination by weighing the digitonide. The combination with digitonin is possible only if the hydroxyl group in position 3 remains free. Cholesteryl acetate, for example, does not give the

* The need in comparatively large quantities for sex hormones and vitamin D_3—for both of which cholesterol is the starting point—has made it necessary to find a rich and economical source material. Much of the cholesterol is manufactured from the spinal cords and brains of cattle. Another method is the preparation of this sterol from wool grease.

test. Certain vegetable sterols, such as stigmasterol, sitosterol, and ergosterol, are also precipitated with digitonin.

As has been said, cholesterol is the most important sterol found in the animal body. There is abundant evidence to show that cholesterol can be synthesized in the animal organism, the liver being at least one organ where the synthesis occurs, and it is equally clear that plant sterols are not utilized by the body. Cholesterol is always present in cells, and present in abundance in nervous tissue. It is chemically related to bile acids, sex hormones, and a number of synthetic cancer-producing substances.

While the specific precursors from which the cholesterol is synthesized in the animal organism are unknown, Bloch and Rittenberg have shown that feeding acetic acid (in the form of deuterium-containing sodium acetate) to mice and rats made it possible to isolate cholesterol from the animal carcass, which contained a deuterium concentration over three times as high as that of the body fluids. Acetic acid may, therefore, be one precursor in the biological formation of cholesterol.

Recently Fieser isolated a substance closely related to cholesterol to which the name lathosterol (*latho* = undetected) has been given.

Ergosterol, originally isolated from ergot * and now more readily obtained from yeast, is of especial interest because when irradiated it gives rise to a compound with antirachitic activity—a vitamin D.

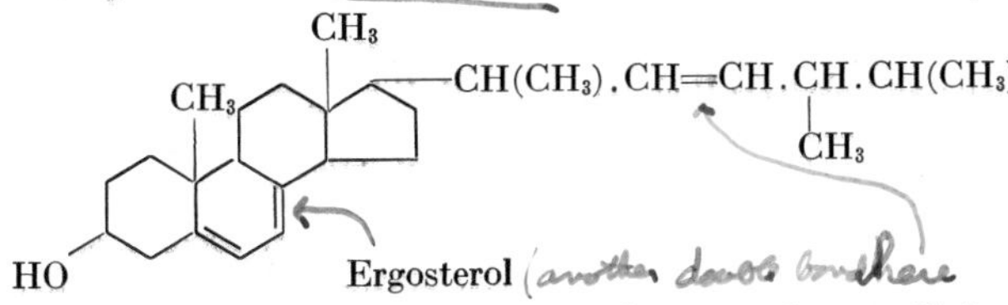

Ergosterol (another double bond here)

Stigmasterol, obtained most readily from soybean oil, has the formula

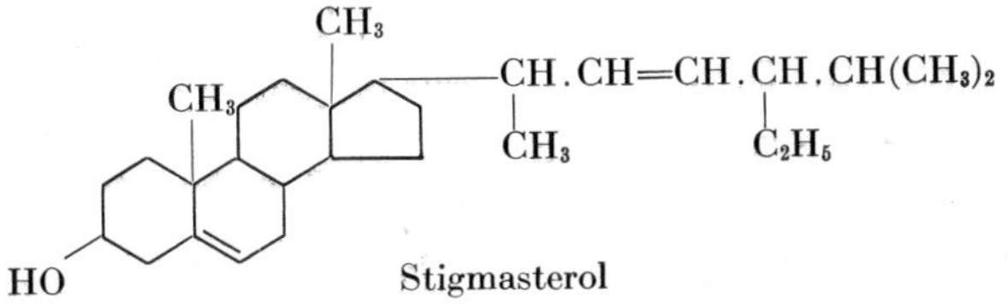

Stigmasterol

Sitosterol, most widely distributed sterol of the higher plants, differs in structure from cholesterol by having a different side chain attached to carbon atom 17:

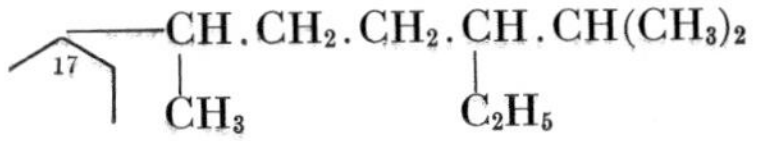

LIPOPROTEINS

Lipids are known to form complex compounds with proteins (p. 45); such compounds, lipoproteins, are found in the serum, etc. Being water-soluble, these lipoproteins act as transporters (by way of serum) of lipids and of some of the cholesterol. Certain functions of these lipoproteins—containing, among other things, some 10 to 15 per cent of the total serum

* Ergot—from which the name "ergosterol" is derived—is produced by a fungus growing on rye grains.

cholesterol—may be involved in the disease known as atherosclerosis, a form of arteriosclerosis in which there is a fatty degeneration of the connective tissue of the arterial walls.

In contradistinction to lipoproteins, which are soluble in water, there is a group of substances, the *proteolipids*, which are insoluble in water but soluble in organic solvents. These substances are present in a number of tissues (brain, heart, kidney, etc.) but are absent from blood plasma.

REFERENCES

A standard work of reference is by *Bloor:* Biochemistry of the Fatty Acids, etc., 1943. *Deuel's* The Lipids (vol. 1, 1951) promises to be a comprehensive work.

Hilditch, an eminent authority, is the author of The Chemical Constitution of Natural Fats, 1940. See also *Wittcoff:* Phosphatids, 1951.

For a thorough review of the chemistry of the phosphatids and cerebrosides, see *Celmer and Carter:* Physiol. Rev., *32:* 167, 1952.

For general reviews, see *Deuel:* Ann. Rev. Biochem., *19:* 89, 1950 (lipids); *Mattil:* Ibid., *20:* 87, 1951 (lipids); *Deuel and Alfin-Slater:* Ibid., *21:* 109, 1952 (lipids); *Lieberman and Dobriner:* Ibid. *20:* 227, 1951 (steroids); *Samuels and Reich:* Ibid., *21:* 129, 1952 (steroids); *Hilditch:* Ibid., *22:* 125, 1953 (lipids); *Cowan and Carter* in *Gilman's* Organic Chemistry (1953), vol. 3, p. 178 (lipids).

The steroids are discussed in masterly fashion by *Fieser* in his Natural Products Related to Phenanthrene, 1950.

Kenyon, Stingley and Young: Ind. Eng. Chem., *42:* 202, 1950, deal with the industrial development of chemicals from fats. See also *Harwood:* Chem. Eng. News, *30:* 1282, 1952.

Methods of separating fatty acids are described by *Hagdahl and Holman:* J. Am. Chem. Soc., *72:* 701, 1950. An account of the "countercurrent" method of separating substances—including fatty acids—is given by *Ahrens and Craig:* J. Biol. Chem., *195:* 299, 1952.

Cason and Sumrell: J. Am. Chem. Soc., *72:* 4837, 1950, contribute an article on the structural features of phthioic acid.

The determination of the saponification number is discussed by *Englis and Reinschreiber:* Analyt. Chem., *21:* 602, 1949.

Shearon: Chem. Eng. News, *29:* 4065, 1951, deals with the commercial development of vegetable oils.

See *Bailey:* Ind. Eng. Chem., *44:* 990, 1952, for details of nickel catalysts used in hydrogenation.

A report on the kinds of edible oils will be found in Ind. Eng. Chem., *42:* 1266, 1950, by *Shearon, Seestrom, and Hughes.*

A method of purifying lecithin is described by *Pangborn:* J. Biol. Chem., *188:* 471, 1951. *Baer and Kates:* J. Am. Chem. Soc., *72:* 942, 1950, report on the synthesis of α-lecithin.

For the chemistry of cephalin, see *Folch:* J. Biol. Chem., *177:* 495, 505, 1949; and *Hutt:* Nature, *165:* 314, 1950. *Baer, Maurakas, and Russell:* J. Am. Chem. Soc., *74:* 152, 1952, describe the synthesis of cephalin.

For the structure of cerebrosides, see *Carter and Greenwood:* J. Biol. Chem., *199:* 283, 1952.

For the acetal phosphatids of the brain, see *Thannhauser, Boncodo, and Schmidt:* J. Biol. Chem., *188:* 417, 423, 429, 1951.

Goffman: Circulation, *2:* 161, 1950, describes the lipoproteins; and *Folch and Lees:* J. Biol. Chem., *191:* 807, 1951, discuss the proteolipids.

Mason: J. Clinical Endocrinology, *8:* 190, 1948, outlines the system used for steroid nomenclature.

Fukushima, Lieberman and Praetz: J. Am. Chem. Soc., *72:* 5205, 1950, describe the preparation of deuterated steroids.

The use of paper chromotography for the detection of steroids is applied by *Kritchevsky and Kirk:* Arch. Biochem., *35:* 346, 1952.

For the synthesis of cholesterol, see *Woodward, Sondheimer, Taub, Heusler, and McLamore:* J. Am. Chem. Soc., *74:* 4223, 1952.

The synthesis of cholesterol in the liver is described by *Bloch, Borek, and Rittenberg:* J. Biol. Chem., *162:* 441, 1946. See also *Srere, Chaikoff, Treitman, and Burstein:* Ibid, *182:* 629, 1950.

For the isolation of lathosterol, see *Fieser:* J. Am. Chem. Soc., *73:* 5007, 1951.

Chapter 4   *Proteins*

THE PROTEINS belong to a group of the most complex of chemical substances. They are essential constituents of all protoplasm, and they provide amino acids, many of which are essential food constituents.*

The proteins are characterized by the fact that on hydrolysis they yield from twenty to twenty-five different α-amino acids. (Proline and hydroxyproline, hydrolytic products of proteins, are exceptions in that they are *imino* rather than *amino* acids.)

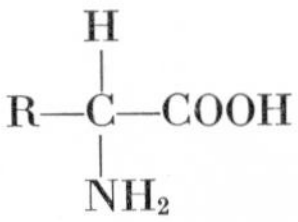

$$R—\overset{\displaystyle H}{\underset{\displaystyle NH_2}{C}}—COOH$$

An α-amino acid.

The differences among proteins are largely a matter of the number, the kind, and the arrangement of such amino acids within the protein molecule. Differences may also be due to the arrangement of chains of amino acids (polypeptide units) within the protein molecule. Since the protein molecule is often built up of hundreds, and even thousands, of these amino acids, the problem of determining protein structure is one of almost insuperable difficulty. We know, for example, that egg albumin, pepsin, and insulin are typical proteins, in that all three yield a variety of α-amino acids when hydrolyzed; but one of them (pepsin) is also a typical enzyme, and another (insulin) is a typical hormone. What is there in a protein molecule which endows it with enzymic or hormonic properties? We have no real answer as yet.

Stanley has isolated a crystalline protein from the mosaic-diseased Turkish tobacco plants. This protein apparently has the properties of the virus to which the disease has been attributed (p. 81). Why does this protein show the properties of the virus? We do not know. The antibodies (Chap. 25) are proteins. Perhaps even the specific properties of the gene may be due, in part at least, to the proteins present.

While we are on this discussion, a word should be said about "species specificity." The classification of proteins might indicate that an albumin is something very definite, irrespective of its source—in the same sense that sodium chloride is a very definite entity, irrespective of its source. This is not so. The albumin obtained from human blood is not the same as that obtained from beef blood. Nor, for that matter, is the casein obtained from cow's milk identical with that obtained from human milk. These differences apply to all proteins. While, chemically, it is well-nigh impossible to show these differences, yet immunochemical tests are not wanting to show that such differences do exist.

* For an elementary introduction to some properties of solutions, see Appendix.

45

The complexity of the problem makes a satisfactory classification of proteins impossible at present. However, based to a large extent upon more or less obvious differences in physical properties, the following crude classification has been adopted.

CLASSIFICATION OF PROTEINS

SIMPLE PROTEINS

These are proteins which on hydrolysis yield α-amino acids or their derivatives.

(a) *Albumins* are characterized by being soluble in water and being coagulated on heating. Examples are egg albumin,* serum albumin, lactalbumin (from milk), and leucosin (from wheat).

(b) *Globulins* are insoluble in water, coagulated by heating, soluble in dilute salt solutions and precipitated when the salt concentration is increased. NaCl, $MgSO_4$, and $(NH_4)_2SO_4$ are salts often used. Examples are myosinogen (from muscle), edestin (from hemp seed), ovoglobulin (from egg yolk), serum globulin, amandin (from almonds), legumin (from peas), and excelsin (from Brazil nuts).

(c) *Glutelins* are insoluble in neutral solvents but soluble in dilute acids and alkalies. Examples are glutenin (from wheat) and oryzenin (from rice).

(d) *Alcohol-soluble proteins* (*prolamins* or *gliadins*) are soluble in 70 to 80 per cent alcohol and insoluble in water and in absolute alcohol. Examples are gliadin (from wheat), hordein (from barley), and zein (from corn).

(e) *Albuminoids* (*scleroproteins*) are insoluble in neutral solvents. Examples are elastin (from ligament), collagen (from hide, bone, and cartilage), and keratin (from horn).

(f) *Histones* are soluble in water and insoluble in dilute ammonia. Solutions of other proteins precipitate histones. The coagulum formed on heating is soluble in dilute acids. Examples are globin (from hemoglobin), thymus histone, and scombrone (from mackerel).

(g) *Protamines* are polypeptides—a number of amino acids held together—which are less complex than the proteins so far considered, but are still more complex than proteoses and peptones (p. 47). They are soluble in water, are not coagulated by heating, precipitate other proteins from their aqueous solutions (for example, the insulin-protamine complex, Chap. 23), possess strong basic properties, and form stable salts with strong mineral acids. The few amino acids which are obtained from the protamines on hydrolysis are largely basic in character. Examples are salmine (from salmon), sturine (from sturgeon), clupeine (from herring), scombrine (from mackerel), and cyprinine (from carp).

CONJUGATED PROTEINS

These are substances made up of proteins combined with some other compound or compounds.

---

* As showing how even the so-called "simple" proteins may not be simple after all, Neuberger presents very strong evidence for the presence, in crystalline egg albumin, of a polysaccharide made up of a number of mannose and glucosamine groups.

(a) *Nucleoproteins* are combinations of proteins with nucleic acid. Examples are found in products obtained from glandular tissue and from the germ of grain.

(b) *Glycoproteins* are combinations of proteins with carbohydrate groups. Such groups may include hexoses, hexosamines, and hexuronic acids. Examples are mucin (from saliva), osseomucoid (from bone), and tendomucoid (from tendon).

(c) *Phosphoproteins* are combinations of protein with phosphorus-containing substances other than nucleic acid or lecithin. Examples are casein (from milk) and perhaps vitellin (from egg yolk).

(d) *Chromoproteins* are combinations of protein with various pigments. Examples are hemoglobin, the blood pigment, which is an iron pyrrole complex joined to protein; ferritin, an iron protein compound found in the liver and spleen; catalase, peroxidase and cytochrome *c*, iron-protein enzymes which play their part in biological oxidations; hemocyanin, a protein containing copper and found in lower invertebrates; laccase and tyrosinase, also enzymes containing copper, which are important in biological oxidations; chlorophyll-protein, the green pigment of plants, which has magnesium as a characteristic element and is combined with proteins in plant tissues.

(e) *Lipoproteins* are combinations of proteins with lipids. They occur in cell nuclei, blood, egg yolk, milk, serum, etc. These complexes, rather ill-defined, are believed to be present in the thromboplastic factor (p. 163), some viruses, and bacterial antigens.

DERIVED PROTEINS

These ill-defined substances are divided into (1) *primary protein derivatives* (proteans, metaproteins, and coagulated proteins) and (2) *secondary protein derivatives* (proteoses, peptones, and peptides). Primary protein derivatives represent a comparatively slight hydrolytic change in the protein molecule; secondary protein derivatives represent a more extensive hydrolysis of the protein.

(a) *Proteins* are insoluble products resulting probably from the action (for a comparatively short time) of water, dilute acids or enzymes. Examples are myosan (from myosin), edestan (from edestin).

(b) *Metaproteins* (infraproteins) are products of the further action of acids and alkalies which are soluble in dilute acids and alkalies but insoluble in solutions of neutral salts. Examples are acid metaprotein or acid albuminate and alkali metaprotein or alkali albuminate.

(c) *Coagulated proteins* are insoluble products resulting either from the action of heat or of alcohol.

(d) *Proteoses* are soluble in water and cannot be coagulated on heating. They can be precipitated by saturating their solutions with ammonium sulfate or zinc sulfate.

(e) *Peptones* are also soluble in water and are not coagulated on heating, but they are not precipitated by saturating their solutions with ammonium sulfate. Certain alkaloidal reagents—phosphotungstic acid, for example—do precipitate them.

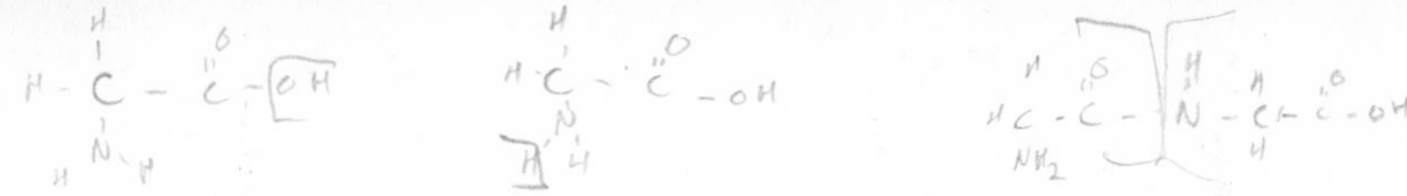

(f) *Peptides* are combinations of two or more amino acids, the carboxyl group of one amino acid being joined to the amino group of another (p. 68).

COLOR REACTIONS OF PROTEINS

The fact that proteins yield α-amino acids on hydrolysis characterizes them quite well, but to carry out such an operation, and to identify the products, is a time-consuming operation. For a preliminary survey, the protein color tests are extremely useful.

Biuret Reaction.   This consists in mixing the protein with sodium hydroxide solution and a very weak solution of copper sulfate. A violet color is obtained. The test depends upon the presence of two or more of the following groups (peptide linkages) in the protein molecule: $CONH_2$ with another $-CONH_2$, or one of the following groups in place of $-CONH_2$; $-CSNH_2$, $-C(NH)NH_2$, $-CH_2NH_2$, $-CRHNH_2$, $-CHOHCH_2NH_2$, $-CHNH_2CH_2OH$, $-CHNH_2CHOH$. Such simple compounds as oxamide, $CONH_2$, and biuret, $CONH_2.NH.CONH_2$

$$CONH_2$$

(from which the test takes its name), give positive biuret reactions.

Millon's Reaction.   When a protein is heated with Millon's reagent (a solution of mercuric nitrite and mercuric nitrate in a mixture of nitric and nitrous acids), a red color or precipitate is obtained. The test is due to the presence in the protein molecule of a phenolic group. The specific compound with this structure present in proteins is tyrosine.

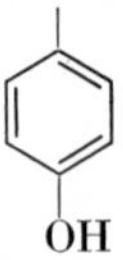

OH
Phenolic group

Hopkins-Cole (Glyoxylic Acid) Reaction.   A violet ring is obtained when concentrated sulfuric acid is added into a mixture containing the protein and glyoxylic acid, $CHO.COOH$. The tryptophan molecule containing the indole nucleus, present in proteins, is responsible for this test. It is believed that tryptophan condenses with the aldehyde to form the colored product. Gelatin gives a negative test. An actual hydrolysis of gelatin fails to yield any appreciable quantity of tryptophan among its hydrolytic products.

Xanthoproteic Reaction.   A yellow color is obtained when nitric acid and a protein are heated. The yellow color is changed to orange on the addition of alkali. The benzene ring is held responsible for the test. Compounds containing the benzene ring give yellow products on nitration. Among the amino acids, tyrosine and tryptophan (p. 59) give the test.

Ninhydrin (Triketohydrindene Hydrate) Reaction.   Protein solutions when heated with ninhydrin yield a blue color.

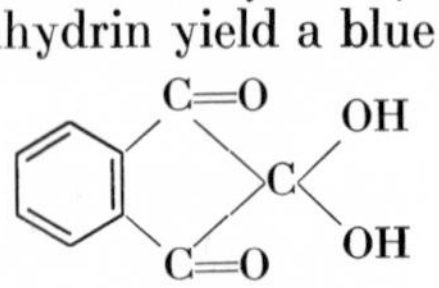

Ninhydrin

This reaction is due to α-amino acid groups in the protein molecule. Individual α-amino acids give a positive test, the shade of color varying with the particular amino acid.

SOME ADDITIONAL PROTEIN REACTIONS

Precipitation Reaction.   Proteins are precipitated by the salts of heavy metals (such as copper sulfate, lead acetate, mercuric nitrate, etc.). It is believed that, in many instances at least, these precipitates are metal proteinates (such as lead proteinate), formed on the alkaline side of the isoelectric point (p. 71) of the protein. Proteins are also precipitated by alkaloidal reagents (such as picric acid, phosphotungstic acid, tannic acid, etc.). This precipitation, in many cases at least, represents combinations on the acid side of the isoelectric point of the protein. Neutral salts (such as ammonium sulfate, sodium sulfate, and sodium chloride) are also used to precipitate or "salt out" proteins. Here, some believe, precipitation may be due to dehydration of molecular aggregates in solution. This may also explain precipitation with a dehydrating agent such as alcohol. However, on standing with alcohol at room temperature, proteins undergo other changes (see next paragraph) which affect their solubility.

Coagulation and Denaturation of Proteins.   The change which egg white undergoes when an egg is heated is an illustration of the kind of change undergone by a number of proteins when similarly treated. This change, spoken of as *coagulation*, is known to occur in two stages. In the first stage (brought about by heat, acid, alkali, alcohol, urea, ultraviolet light, high pressure, etc.) the protein is so changed that it is no longer as soluble at its isoelectric point as was the original protein. In addition to decreased solubility, the denatured protein may also differ from the native protein by being more readily digested by proteolytic enzymes, by loss of its enzymic properties if the protein is an enzyme, by differences in antigenic properties, and by an increase in the viscosity of the solution.

This change of *native* protein is called *denaturation*, and the protein which has undergone the change is a *denatured* protein (which, in this form, incidentally, cannot be crystallized).*

The second stage is the precipitation of the insoluble denatured protein, and this probably corresponds to the *coagulation* of colloids in general.

It is believed that the denaturation process corresponds to an unfolding of the peptide chains. This view is justified by the finding that a protein in the denatured state gives more intense reactions when tested for certain groups than the same protein in the native state. Such reactions involve the —SH group of cysteine, the —S—S— group of cystine, the phenolic —OH group of tyrosine, the guanido group of arginine and the *epsilon* (ε)-amino group of lysine. (For the chemical structures of these amino acids, see p. 54, etc.)

Using x-ray analysis, Astbury has shown that some denatured proteins are composed of extended peptide chains in parallel bundles; this change would account for decreased solubility.

* Denaturation has been more generally defined as "any nonproteolytic modification of the unique structure of a native protein, giving rise to a definite change in chemical, physical, or biological properties" (Neurath, Greenstein, Putnam, and Erickson).

Anson and Mirsky have presented evidence to show that the denaturation process, which has been looked upon as an irreversible change, can be a reversible one. Denatured hemoglobin, for example, has been reconverted into native hemoglobin which, in turn, is soluble, coagulable and crystallizable. Also, crystalline, soluble, native protein can be obtained from coagulated serum albumin.

Isolation and Composition of Some Proteins.   Proteins are so complex that it is difficult to determine whether the substance isolated is chemically pure. The aim is to obtain a crystalline compound and then to apply physico-chemical criteria for purity (see p. 50). The methods used in the purification procedure are designed to avoid denaturation. Too high a temperature, excessive shaking with air, exposure to water containing heavy metal impurities, chemical precipitating agents which markedly alter the pH—all these would tend to denature the protein.

The methods used for isolation involve extraction with a suitable solvent; precipitation of the protein (or of impurities) by changing the pH; precipitation of the protein (or of impurities) with ammonium sulfate (or some other salt) of varying strength; precipitation with alcohol at low temperatures; dialysis (to remove non-protein constituents); and adsorption and subsequent elution.

The composition of some of the proteins in terms of their amino acids is given in Table 5. These amino acids are obtained by hydrolyzing proteins by acids, alkalies, or enzymes (p. 91).

CRITERIA FOR THE PURITY OF PROTEINS

The fact that a protein is crystalline does not necessarily mean that it is pure. Several other tests are applied; these come under the headings of (*a*) electrophoresis, (*b*) sedimentation in the ultracentrifuge, and (*c*) constant solubility. Such tests are confirmatory rather than conclusive. For the time being, these (and other) tests tell us as much as we can know about the purity of the protein under consideration.

Electrophoresis.   This process is sometimes called *cataphoresis*, and it involves the movement of charged colloidal particles in solution under the influence of an electrical field. At a pH acid to its isoelectric point (p. 71), a protein migrates to the negative pole; at a pH alkaline to its isoelectric point, the protein will migrate to the positive pole. At its isoelectric point the protein has a net charge of zero and does not migrate to either electrode.

Assuming that the protein is impure and has for its impurity one other protein, at some particular pH (not, of course, their isoelectric points) these proteins will move at different speeds, because of the difference in net charge of the two species of molecules at that pH. In a suitable apparatus, the presence of an accompanying protein may thus be detected.

The results obtained by the electrophoretic method are best illustrated by Fig. 5 which gives the actual pictures obtained during the electrophoretic separation of the proteins from normal human plasma. The ability to get a picture of the separated protein fractions is based on the fact that there exists a difference in refractive index between the buffer solution acting as solvent and the protein solution. Using a suitable optical system these

Table 5

APPROXIMATE PERCENTAGE COMPOSITION OF SELECTED ANIMAL PROTEINS
(Hawk, Oser and Summerson, Practical Physiological Chemistry, 1947, Blakiston Co.)

	Gelatin	Elastin	Wool	Silk fibroin	Beef muscle	Casein	β-Lactoglobulin	Egg albumin	Human serum albumin	Human serum γ-globulin	Human fibrinogen	Human fibrin	Horse hemoglobin	Thymus histone	Salmine	Insulin	Pepsin
Arginine	9.2	1.0	10.6	0.7	7.2	4.3	3.4	5.9	6.0	4.8	7.9	7.9	3.7	12.9	88.4	3.3	1.3
Histidine	0.9	0.0	0.7	0.07	2.9	2.1	1.8	1.7	3.5	2.5	2.8	2.8	8.0	3.0	0	5.3	trace
Lysine	5.3	?	3.0	0.3	8.2	7.6	10.6	5.0	10.4	6.7	...	8.8	8.6	11.7	0	2.3	1.7
Tyrosine	0.3	1.6	5.8	13.2	4.4	6.7	4.5	4.3	5.3	6.8	5.8	5.8	2.7	4.4	0	12.7	10.4
Tryptophan	0.0	0.0	1.6	...	1.4	1.2	2.0	1.5	0.3	2.9	3.3	3.2	1.1	0.04	0	0.0	2.2
Phenylalanine	2.4	4.0	4.4	1.5	5.0	5.0	5.2	5.4	7.9	4.6	...	6.0	7.0	...	0	8.2	...
Cystine	0-0.2	0.2	14.3	0.0	1.1	0.35	3.5	1.9	6.5	3.1	2.7	2.4	0.7	0.5	0	12.7	1.4
Methionine	1.1	0.4	0.6	0.0	3.4	3.4	3.8	5.1	1.3	1.1	2.5	2.6	1.4	1.3	0	0.0	...
Threonine	1.7	...	(6.7)[b]	1.6	5.0	3.8	5.9	4	5.1	8.4	6.6	6.5	5.6[a]	5.7	0	2.7	...
Serine	3.7	...	...	13.5	5.5	7.7	5.0	7.4	3.7	11.4	8.3	9.8	5.5	3.8	7.0	3.5	9.5
Leucine	3.6	{ 31	11.7	0.9	7.7	9.7	13.6	10.0	11.9	7.9	7.1	7.1	17.3	7.4	0	14.0	...
Isoleucine	1.2		...	...	6.3	6.3	9.1	7.1	2	3.1	...	...	1.6	6.0	1.5	2.9	...
Valine	2.7	13.5	5.5	...	5.8	6.5	5.6	6.8	7	9.8	...	...	8.6	4.4	3.6	8.8	...
Glutamic acid	11.6	...	15.3	...	15.6	23.3	21.6	17.5	17.1	11.8	...	...	6.1	...	0	21	18.6
Aspartic acid	9.6	0.0	7.3	...	6.1	6.1	9.9	8.1	9.9	8.8	...	...	8.8	...	0	6.8	6.7
Glycine	26.6	29.4	7.1	44.4	5.1	0.5	1.4	3.2	2.0	4.2	...	...	0.4	...	0	4.6	...
Alanine	10.4	0	...	16.4	5	5.5	6.2	7.2	...	...	...	...	4	...	3.6	...	...
Proline	17.2	15.2	9.8	...	...	7-8	4.1	4-5	7.8	8.1	...	...	2	...	{ 7.9	2.9	...
Hydroxyproline	15	2	6-7	...	...	?	...	...	0	...	...	...	0	...		...	...

[a] Beef hemoglobin.
[b] Human hair.

differences are photographed after a suitable time during which an electric current has been passed through the solution contained in a special U-tube electrophoretic glass cell. In this way one obtains information regarding the number of electrophoretically different proteins in the mixture as well as the relative concentration of each protein fraction in the mixture.

Thus in Fig. 5 the rising boundary picture refers to the separation of proteins in that portion of the U-tube where the protein molecules are moving upwards towards one of the electrodes. The descending pattern is obtained from that limb of the U-tube containing the proteins which mi-

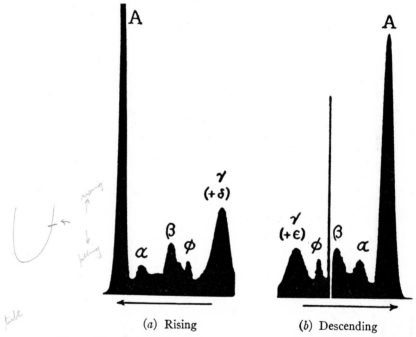

(a) Rising   (b) Descending

Fig. 5. Electrophoretic pattern of normal blood plasma. (Longsworth, Shedlovsky, and MacInnes, J. Exp. Med., *70:* 399).

grate downwards towards the same electrode. The area under each curve corresponds to the relative concentration of that protein fraction. One soon learns that in a complex mixture of proteins such as is present in plasma, each individual protein cannot be separated by this method; even those curves which look uniform can be further separated by removing it from the cell and repeating the electrophoresis again. Fraction A corresponds to the albumin fraction, α to the mixture of α-globulins, β to the mixture of β-globulins, ϕ to fibrinogen, γ to the mixture of γ-globulins and δ and ϵ represent salt boundary anomalies caused by an accumulation of salts during electrophoresis.

Where a single molecular species of protein is present, it would appear as a single sharp boundary throughout the period of electrophoresis and also when run at various values of pH, assuming that the pH itself does not cause a splitting of the protein molecule into several fragments.

Sedimentation in the Ultracentrifuge.   We owe to Svedberg the development of an apparatus, the ultracentrifuge, which is capable of giving rise to centrifugal forces 500,000 times those of gravity. This centrifugal force is capable of sedimenting protein molecules in solution. Since the sedimentation rate is a function, among other things, of the size of the molecule, the molecular weight of the protein may be determined. Here, too, a protein impurity could be detected because its molecular weight would be different.

The molecular weights and the isoelectric points of several proteins are here given:

Protein	Molecular Weight	Isoelectric Point
Egg albumin	42,000	4.9
Hemoglobin	67,000	6.7
Serum albumin	70,000	4.88
Apoferritin	465,000	4.4

Constant Solubility.   A sensitive test for the presence of a protein impurity is one based on the constant solubility of a protein regardless of the amount of substance present in the solid phase. Actually, one equi-

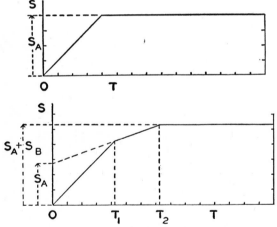

Fig. 6. Ideal relation between the solubility of one homogeneous substance (upper figure) and the total amount, T, of solid phase used per unit of solution. Lower curve same for a mixture of two substances that are not in solid solution. (Clarke: Topics in Physical Chemistry, 1948, 326.)

librates increasing amounts of the protein under test with the same amount of solvent (which may be water or some salt solution), and measures the amount of protein which has been dissolved. By plotting the amount of dissolved protein against the total protein, it becomes apparent whether we are dealing with one or more molecular species.

Figure 6 illustrates the theoretical curves obtained during the solubility test for purity of proteins. The lower curve indicates what would happen if two proteins, A and B were present in a solid mixture; S = total solid dissolved, S_A = solubility of A, S_B = solubility of B, T = total of A and B added to the whole system.

Figure 7 illustrates an experimental demonstration of the use of the constant solubility test to show the purity of crystalline trypsin. The curve corresponds to a theoretical curve for a single molecular species. A smooth curve indicates a solid solution and cannot be analyzed by this method.

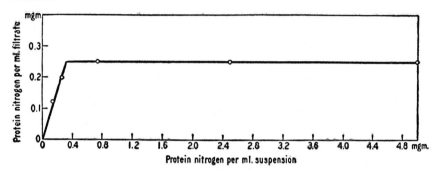

Fig. 7. Solubility of crystalline trypsin in saturated magnesium sulfate solution at pH 4.0 and 10° C., showing constant solubility in presence of increasing quantities of solid phase. (After Northrop, Crystalline Enzymes, 1939.)

AMINO ACIDS

Glycine.   The simplest of the amino acids is glycine, glycocoll, or

$$CH_2.COOH$$
$$|$$
$$NH_2$$

aminoacetic acid. It may be prepared from chloroacetic acid by the action of ammonia:

$$\begin{array}{ccc} CH_2Cl & \longrightarrow & CH_2NH_2 \\ | & & | & + HCl \\ COOH & & COOH \end{array}$$

A methyl derivative of glycine, sarcosine, is formed when creatine (Chap.

$$CH_2.COOH$$
$$|$$
$$H—N—CH_3$$
Sarcosine

14) is decomposed. A completely methylated glycine is betaine. Glycine

$$\begin{array}{ccc} CH_2COOH & CH_2.COOH & CH_2—CO \\ | & \longrightarrow & | & \text{or} & | & | \\ NH_2 & N(CH_3)_3OH & (CH_3)_3N——O \end{array}$$
Betaine

was among the first of the amino acids isolated from the hydrolysis of proteins.

Alanine. α-Aminopropionic acid, or alanine, is optically active. In

$$CH_3$$
$$|$$
$$CHNH_2$$
$$|$$
$$COOH$$
Alanine

fact, with the exception of glycine, all the amino acids derived from proteins show optical activity.*

Alanine may be synthesized from acetaldehyde by the action of hydrogen cyanide and ammonia:

$$\underset{\text{CHO}}{\overset{\text{CH}_3}{|}} + \text{HCN} + \text{NH}_3 \longrightarrow \underset{\text{CN}}{\overset{\text{CH}_3}{\underset{|}{\overset{|}{\text{CHNH}_2}}}} + \text{H}_2\text{O}$$

$$\underset{\text{CN}}{\overset{\text{CH}_3}{\underset{|}{\overset{|}{\text{CHNH}_2}}}} + 2\text{H}_2\text{O} \longrightarrow \underset{\text{COOH}}{\overset{\text{CH}_3}{\underset{|}{\overset{|}{\text{CHNH}_2}}}} + \text{NH}_3$$

Alanine is present in practically all proteins. Fibroin (from silk) contains 25 per cent of this acid.

Serine. β-Hydroxy-α-aminopropionic acid, or serine,

$$\underset{\text{OH}}{\overset{\text{CH}_2}{\underset{|}{}}}.\underset{\text{NH}_2}{\overset{\text{CH}}{\underset{|}{}}}.\text{COOH}$$
Serine

has been prepared, among others, by Dunn:

$$\underset{\underset{\text{Ethylene glycol monoethyl ether}}{\text{CH}_2\text{OH}}}{\overset{\text{CH}_2\text{OC}_2\text{H}_5}{\underset{|}{\overset{|}{}}}} \xrightarrow[\text{(CrO}_3)]{\text{oxid.}} \underset{\text{CHO}}{\overset{\text{CH}_2\text{OC}_2\text{H}_5}{\underset{|}{\overset{|}{}}}} \xrightarrow[+ \text{NH}_3]{\text{HCN}} \underset{\text{CN}}{\overset{\text{CH}_2\text{OC}_2\text{H}_5}{\underset{|}{\overset{|}{\text{H}-\text{C}-\text{NH}_2}}}} \xrightarrow{\text{Hydrolysis}} \underset{\underset{\text{Serine}}{\text{COOH}}}{\overset{\text{CH}_2\text{OH}}{\underset{|}{\overset{|}{\text{CHNH}_2}}}}$$

Threonine. β-Hydroxy-α-aminobutyric acid, or threonine, was isolated by Rose from protein hydrolytic products. It is an essential amino acid in nutrition.

$$\text{CH}_3.\underset{\text{OH}}{\overset{}{\underset{|}{\text{CH}}}}.\underset{\text{NH}_2}{\overset{}{\underset{|}{\text{CH}}}}.\text{COOH}$$
Threonine

An essential amino acid is one which the body cannot synthesize—at least, in adequate amounts—and which must therefore be supplied from the outside (as part of the food). The nonessential amino acid, on the other hand, is one which the body can synthesize, and at a rate to cover the needs of the animal.

The nonessential amino acids are the dispensable ones, whereas the essential amino acids are the indispensable ones (Chap. 19).

---

* Natural alanine is *configurationally* related to L (+) lactic acid (compare with footnote, p. 6). The naturally occurring amino acids belong to the L- series of configurationally related compounds.

When obtained synthetically, alanine is of the DL- variety. Krebs has shown that kidney tissue contains an enzyme (p. 189), called by him "D-amino acid oxidase," which oxidizes amino acids of the "unnatural" (D) configuration into ammonia and the corresponding α-keto acids. By allowing this oxidase to act on the DL-alanine, the D- form is destroyed and the L-alanine can be recovered.

Valine. α-Aminoisovaleric acid has the structure

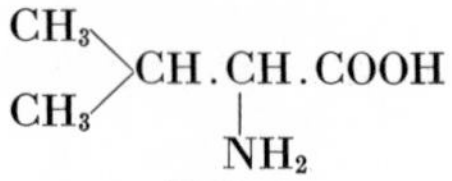

$$\begin{array}{c} CH_3 \\ \diagdown \\ CH_3 \diagup \end{array} CH.CH.COOH \\ \qquad\qquad | \\ \qquad\qquad NH_2$$
Valine

It is found to the extent of about 5 to 7 per cent in casein and is an essential amino acid.

Leucine. α-Aminoisocaproic acid is very widely distributed. It is an essential amino acid.

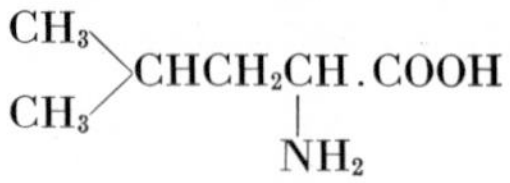

$$\begin{array}{c} CH_3 \\ \diagdown \\ CH_3 \diagup \end{array} CHCH_2CH.COOH \\ \qquad\qquad\quad | \\ \qquad\qquad\quad NH_2$$
Leucine

Isoleucine. α-Amino-β-methyl-β-ethylpropionic acid, like leucine, is considered an essential amino acid.

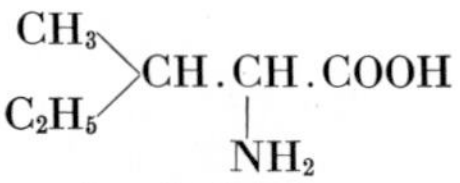

$$\begin{array}{c} CH_3 \\ \diagdown \\ C_2H_5 \diagup \end{array} CH.CH.COOH \\ \qquad\qquad | \\ \qquad\qquad NH_2$$
Isoleucine

Norleucine. α-Aminocaproic acid is found in a number of proteins, but only in traces.

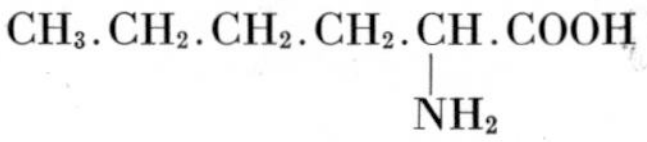

$$CH_3.CH_2.CH_2.CH_2.CH.COOH \\ \qquad\qquad\qquad\qquad | \\ \qquad\qquad\qquad\qquad NH_2$$
Norleucine

So far, we have listed monoaminomonocarboxylic acids. Now we shall list several monoaminodicarboxylic acids.

Aspartic Acid. α-Aminosuccinic acid is widely distributed.

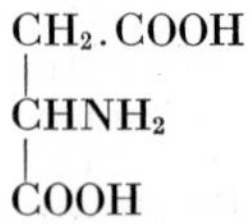

$$CH_2.COOH \\ | \\ CHNH_2 \\ | \\ COOH$$
Aspartic acid

Glutamic Acid. α-Aminoglutaric acid is also widely distributed, and is present in particularly large quantities in casein and gliadin (from wheat).

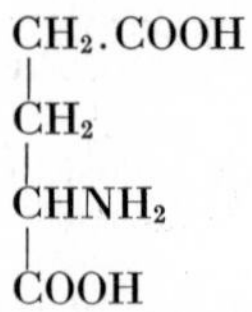

$$CH_2.COOH \\ | \\ CH_2 \\ | \\ CHNH_2 \\ | \\ COOH$$
Glutamic acid

It is probable that in the protein molecule as such glutamine rather than glutamic acid is present.

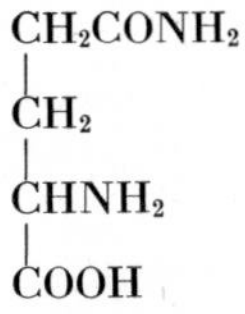

$$CH_2CONH_2$$
$$|$$
$$CH_2$$
$$|$$
$$CHNH_2$$
$$|$$
$$COOH$$

Glutamine

The following are diaminomonocarboxylic acids:

Lysine. α,ϵ-Diaminocaproic acid is an indispensable amino acid in nutrition. It occurs in most of the proteins.

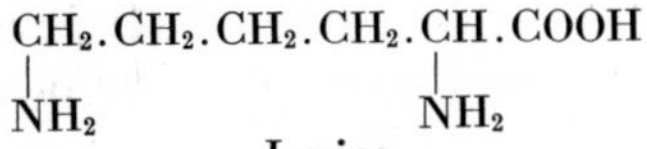

$$CH_2.CH_2.CH_2.CH_2.CH.COOH$$
$$|\qquad\qquad\qquad |$$
$$NH_2\qquad\qquad\quad NH_2$$

Lysine

Unlike any of the other common amino acids, lysine is unique in that the keto derivative ($R—CO—COOH$ instead of $R—CHNH_2COOH$), for example, cannot replace lysine in the diet. We speak of lysine as an amino acid which, unlike the other common amino acids, cannot be synthesized in the body from its immediate precursors.

Arginine. δ-Guanidyl-α-aminovaleric acid makes up more than two-thirds of the total amino acids in clupeine (from herring) and salmine (from salmon) and occurs, in smaller amounts, in most proteins. It is a strong base, forming stable carbonates. Within certain limitations, it is an essential amino acid.

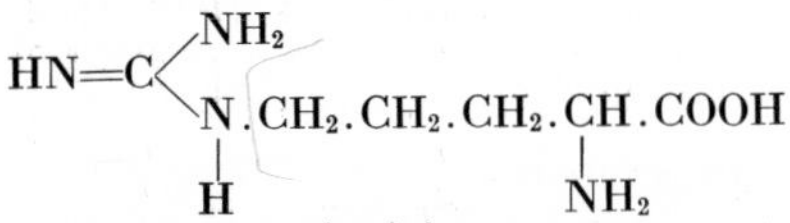

$$HN{=}C\diagup^{NH_2}_{\diagdown N.CH_2.CH_2.CH_2.CH.COOH}$$
$$\qquad\qquad |\qquad\qquad\qquad\quad |$$
$$\qquad\qquad H\qquad\qquad\qquad NH_2$$

Arginine

Arginine is needed by the body for the formation of creatine and urea (Chap. 14).

Histidine. β-4-Imidazolylalanine, β-4-imidazolyl-α-aminopropionic acid, contains one amino group in the side chain and one imino ($—NH—$) group in the ring. It is another of the amino acids which belong to the

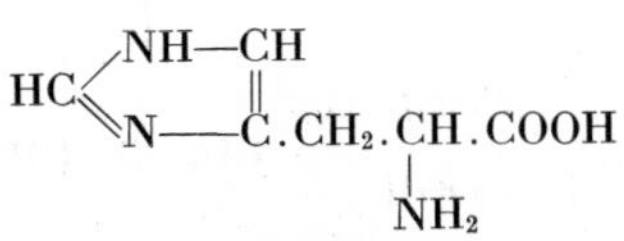

$$HC\diagup^{NH—CH}_{\diagdown N——C.CH_2.CH.COOH}$$
$$\qquad\qquad\qquad\qquad |$$
$$\qquad\qquad\qquad\qquad NH_2$$

Histidine

indispensable, or essential, group. It is present in many proteins.

Two amino acids are known to contain sulfur:

Cystine.   Dicysteine, di-(β-thio-α-aminopropionic acid),

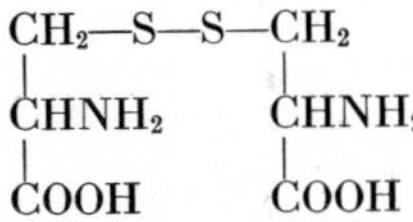

$$CH_2—S—S—CH_2$$
$$|\qquad\qquad\qquad |$$
$$CHNH_2\qquad CHNH_2$$
$$|\qquad\qquad\qquad |$$
$$COOH\qquad\quad COOH$$

Cystine

is the naturally occurring amino acid. A reduced form of this acid, cysteine, is of importance in biological oxidations.

$$CH_2—SH$$
$$CHNH_2$$
$$COOH$$
Cysteine

Cystine is obtained in large quantities from material containing keratin (hair, feathers, etc.).

Methionine.   γ-Methylthiol-α-aminobutyric acid. Mueller first isolated it and Barger and several other chemists have since synthesized it.

$$CH_2.SCH_3$$
$$CH_2$$
$$CHNH_2$$
$$COOH$$
Methionine

The following synthesis, making use of malonic ester, is due to Marvel:

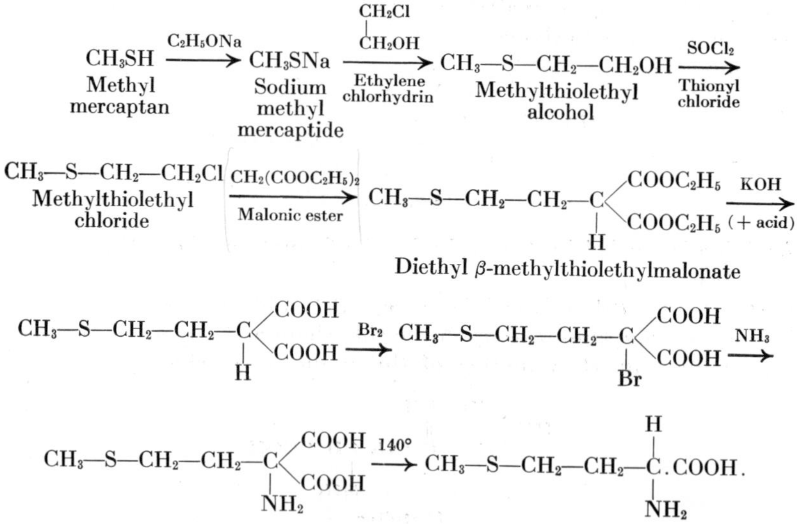

$$CH_3SH \xrightarrow{C_2H_5ONa} CH_3SNa \xrightarrow[\text{Ethylene chlorhydrin}]{\overset{CH_2Cl}{\underset{}{CH_2OH}}} CH_3—S—CH_2—CH_2OH \xrightarrow{SOCl_2}$$

Methyl mercaptan   Sodium methyl mercaptide   Methylthiolethyl alcohol   Thionyl chloride

$$CH_3—S—CH_2—CH_2Cl \xrightarrow[\text{Malonic ester}]{CH_2(COOC_2H_5)_2} CH_3—S—CH_2—CH_2—C\overset{COOC_2H_5}{\underset{\underset{H}{|}}{\diagdown}}COOC_2H_5 \xrightarrow[(+ \text{ acid})]{KOH}$$

Methylthiolethyl chloride

Diethyl β-methylthiolethylmalonate

$$CH_3—S—CH_2—CH_2—C\overset{COOH}{\underset{\underset{H}{|}}{\diagdown}}COOH \xrightarrow{Br_2} CH_3—S—CH_2—CH_2—C\overset{COOH}{\underset{\underset{Br}{|}}{\diagdown}}COOH \xrightarrow{NH_3}$$

$$CH_3—S—CH_2—CH_2—C\overset{COOH}{\underset{\underset{NH_2}{|}}{\diagdown}}COOH \xrightarrow{140°} CH_3—S—CH_2—CH_2—\overset{H}{\underset{NH_2}{C}}.COOH.$$

Methionine is an essential amino acid, whereas cystine is not.

There are several amino acids with aromatic nuclei:

Phenylalanine.   β-Phenyl-α-aminopropionic acid is found in many proteins, the protamines excepted. It is, according to Rose, an indispensable amino acid.

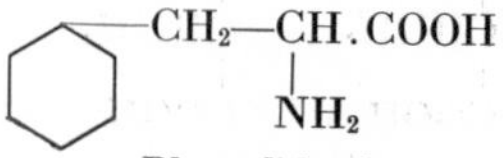

$$—CH_2—CH.COOH$$
$$NH_2$$
Phenylalanine

Marvel has synthesized this amino acid as follows:

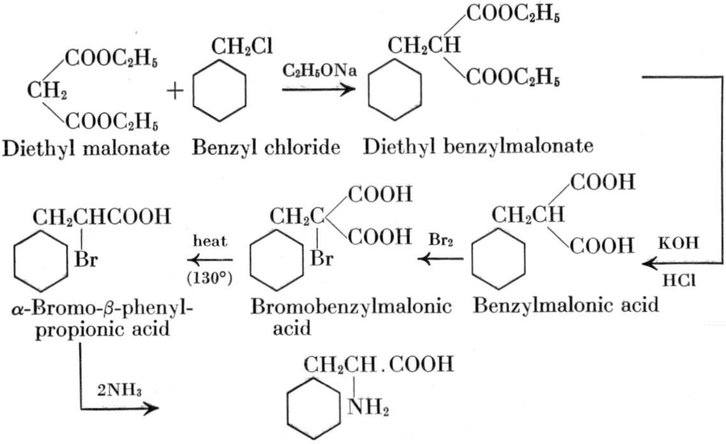

Diethyl malonate Benzyl chloride Diethyl benzylmalonate

α-Bromo-β-phenyl-
propionic acid

Bromobenzylmalonic
acid

Benzylmalonic acid

Tyrosine.   *p*-Hydroxyphenylalanine, β-*p*-hydroxyphenyl-α-aminopro-
pionic acid, is a common constituent of proteins (the Millon reaction depends upon its presence), though practically absent in gelatin.

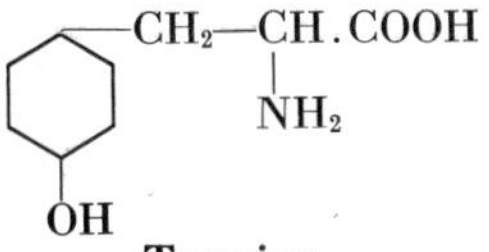

Tyrosine

Several amino acids have heterocyclic nuclei:

Tryptophan.   α-Amino-β-3-indolepropionic acid is an essential amino
acid. The Hopkins-Cole test (p. 48) is dependent upon its presence.
Nearly all proteins contain this amino acid in variable amounts. Zein, a

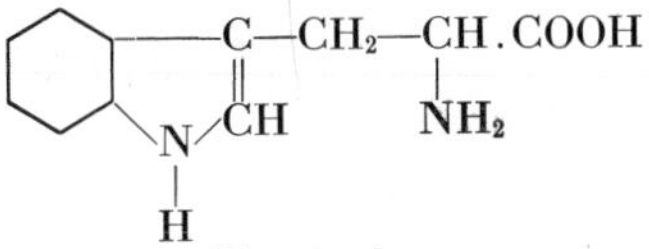

Tryptophan

protein obtained from corn, contains very little tryptophan, and gelatin
contains none of it.

Proline.*   Pyrrolidine-α-carboxylic acid is readily soluble in alcohol.
It is found in most proteins.

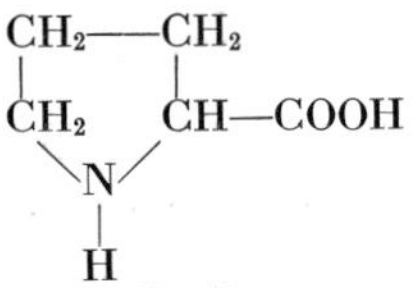

Proline

* Notice that proline and hydroxyproline contain the imino rather than the amino
group.

Hydroxyproline. γ-Hydroxypyrrolidine-α-carboxylic acid is present in small quantities in proteins.

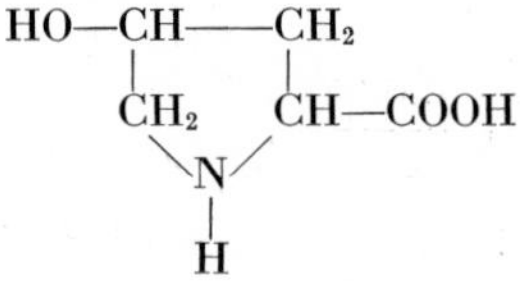

$$\begin{array}{ccc} \text{HO—CH} & & \text{CH}_2 \\ | & & | \\ \text{CH}_2 & & \text{CH—COOH} \\ & \diagdown \text{N} \diagup & \\ & | & \\ & \text{H} & \end{array}$$

Hydroxyproline

The following amino acids do not represent the usual hydrolytic products obtained from proteins:

β-Alanine, $\text{CH}_2.\text{CH}_2.\text{COOH}$, a constituent of carnosine and anserine

$$\begin{array}{c} | \\ \text{NH}_2 \end{array}$$

(Chap. 21), which are found in muscle, is also part of the pantothenic acid molecule, pantothenic acid being a vitamin (Chap. 20). So far, neither β-alanine nor β-amino acids in general have been isolated from proteins.

β-Alanine has been obtained synthetically in the following way, among others: First, ammonia is added to acrylonitrile:

$$\text{CH}_2\!\!=\!\!\text{CHCN} + \text{NH}_3 \longrightarrow \text{NH}_2\text{CH}_2\text{CH}_2\text{CN} + \text{NH}(\text{CH}_2\text{CH}_2\text{CN})_2$$

The primary amine, β-aminopropionitrile, is hydrolyzed to give the hydrochloride of β-alanine:

$$\text{NH}_2\text{CH}_2\text{CH}_2\text{CN} + 2\text{HCl} + 2\text{H}_2\text{O} \longrightarrow \text{NH}_2\text{CH}_2\text{CH}_2\text{COOH}.\text{HCl} + \text{NH}_4\text{Cl}$$

Liberation of β-alanine from its hydrochloride can be accomplished by using an anion-exchange resin (see reference at end of chapter).

Phosphoserine, $\text{CH}_2.\text{CH}.\text{COOH}$, is present in phosphoproteins such

$$\begin{array}{cc} | & | \\ | & \text{NH}_2 \\ \text{OPO}_3\text{H}_2 & \end{array}$$

as casein and vitellin.

Ergothioneine, the betaine of thiohistidine, is a derivative of histidine. It is found in ergot and in blood.

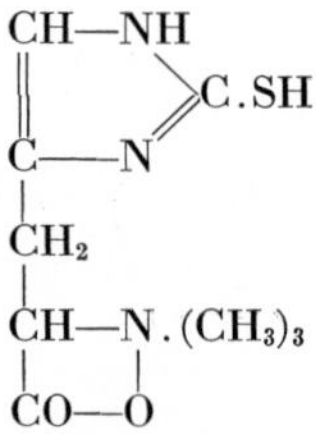

$$\begin{array}{c} \text{CH—NH} \\ \parallel \qquad \diagdown\!\!\!\text{C.SH} \\ \text{C——N} \diagup \\ | \\ \text{CH}_2 \\ | \\ \text{CH—N}.(\text{CH}_3)_3 \\ | \quad | \\ \text{CO——O} \end{array}$$

Ergothioneine

Ornithine, α, δ-diaminovaleric acid, is obtained by the hydrolysis of arginine (the action of alkali or the enzyme arginase).

$$\begin{array}{cc} \text{CH}_2.\text{CH}_2.\text{CH}_2.\text{CH}.\text{COOH} \\ | \qquad\qquad\qquad | \\ \text{NH}_2 \qquad\qquad \text{NH}_2 \end{array}$$

Ornithine

Citrulline, δ-carbamido-α-aminovaleric acid, as well as ornithine is considered to be of importance in the formation of urea in the body (Chap. 14).

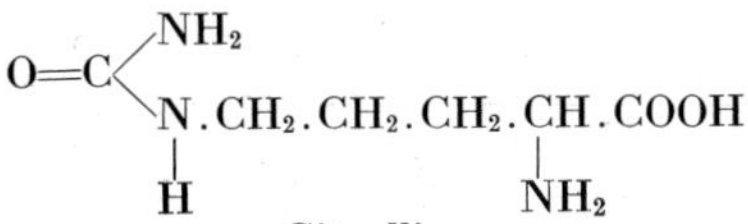

$$O=C\diagdown\begin{matrix}NH_2\\N.CH_2.CH_2.CH_2.CH.COOH\end{matrix}$$
$$\underset{H}{|}\qquad\qquad\underset{NH_2}{|}$$

Citrulline

Homocystine, the next higher homologue of cystine, has been obtained by du Vigneaud by heating methionine with sulfuric acid. It is converted into methionine in the body.

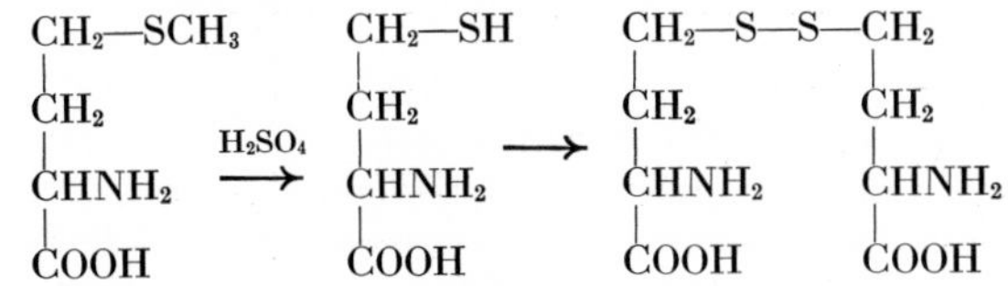

$$\begin{matrix}CH_2-SCH_3\\|\\CH_2\\|\\CHNH_2\\|\\COOH\\Methionine\end{matrix}\quad\xrightarrow{H_2SO_4}\quad\begin{matrix}CH_2-SH\\|\\CH_2\\|\\CHNH_2\\|\\COOH\\Homocysteine\end{matrix}\quad\longrightarrow\quad\begin{matrix}CH_2-S-S-CH_2\\|\qquad\qquad|\\CH_2\qquad\qquad CH_2\\|\qquad\qquad|\\CHNH_2\qquad CHNH_2\\|\qquad\qquad|\\COOH\qquad\quad COOH\\Homocystine\end{matrix}$$

Djenkolic acid, the cysteine thioacetal of formaldehyde, has been isolated from the djenkol bean (*Pithecolobium lobatum*). It does not belong to the amino acids found when proteins are hydrolyzed.

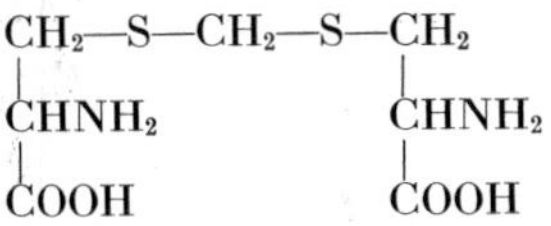

$$\begin{matrix}CH_2-S-CH_2-S-CH_2\\|\qquad\qquad\qquad|\\CHNH_2\qquad\qquad CHNH_2\\|\qquad\qquad\qquad|\\COOH\qquad\qquad COOH\end{matrix}$$

Djenkolic acid

Lanthionine, β-amino-β-carboxyethyl sulfide, is a product of the acid hydrolysis of wool (which, prior to hydrolysis, has been boiled for one hour with 2 per cent sodium carbonate solution). It is not a *direct* product of protein hydrolysis.

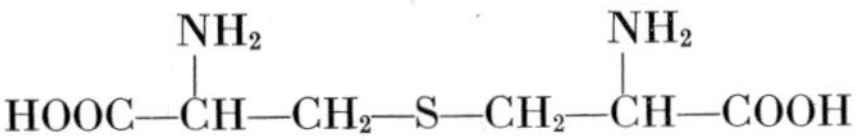

$$\underset{HOOC-CH-CH_2-S-CH_2-CH-COOH}{\overset{\displaystyle NH_2\qquad\qquad\qquad\quad NH_2}{\quad|\qquad\qquad\qquad\qquad\quad|}}$$

Lanthionine

Using a similar preliminary treatment with sodium carbonate, lanthionine can be obtained from any source of keratin (such as human hair and chicken feathers) and from lactalbumin.

3,5-Diiodotyrosine, iodogorgoic acid, has been obtained from the thyroid gland.

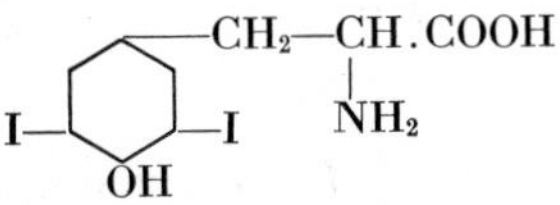

$$\underset{OH}{I-\bigcirc-I}\overset{-CH_2-CH.COOH}{\underset{NH_2}{|}}$$

3,5-Diiodotyrosine

Thyroxine,   3,5-diiodo-4-(3′,5′-diiodo-4-hydroxyphenoxy)-phenylalanine, is the physiologically active component of the hormone of the thyroid gland, about which more will be said presently (Chap. 23). It is found in the gland combined with protein, the combination being known as thyroglobulin.

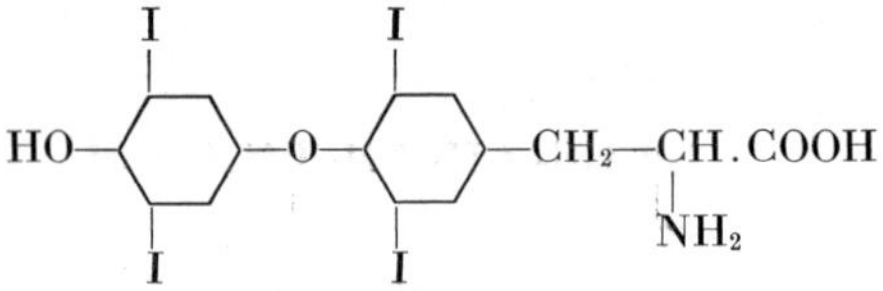

$$\text{HO} - \underset{I}{\overset{I}{\bigcirc}} - \text{O} - \underset{I}{\overset{I}{\bigcirc}} - \text{CH}_2 - \underset{\underset{NH_2}{|}}{\text{CH}} . \text{COOH}$$

Thyroxine

Neither iodogorgoic acid nor thyroxine are among the common products of protein hydrolysis.

SYNTHESIS OF AMINO ACIDS

The simplest procedure is that illustrated in the preparation of glycine: the action of ammonia on the halogenated acid. The principle has been used in the synthesis of a number of the amino acids (leucine, valine, aspartic acid, etc.). Another method involves the cyanohydrin synthesis, illustrated in the case of alanine: the action of ammonia and hydrogen cyanide on the appropriate aldehyde. Still a third method of synthesis involves malonic ester, illustrated in the preparations of methionine and phenylalanine. This does not exhaust the list.

SOME CHEMICAL REACTIONS OF AMINO ACIDS

These reactions apply to the proteins also since they contain free amino and carboxyl groups.

1. They form salts such as hydrochlorides with acids:

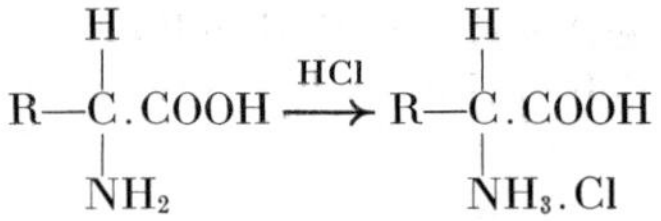

$$\underset{\underset{NH_2}{|}}{\overset{\overset{H}{|}}{R-C}} . \text{COOH} \xrightarrow{\text{HCl}} \underset{\underset{NH_3 . Cl}{|}}{\overset{\overset{H}{|}}{R-C}} . \text{COOH}$$

2. Methylation produces such compounds as

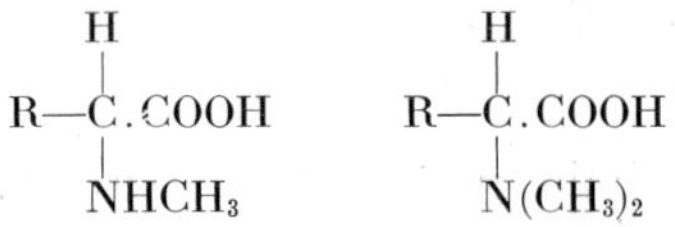

$$\underset{\underset{NHCH_3}{|}}{\overset{\overset{H}{|}}{R-C}} . \text{COOH} \qquad \underset{\underset{N(CH_3)_2}{|}}{\overset{\overset{H}{|}}{R-C}} . \text{COOH}$$

3. Acetyl chloride or acetic anhydride gives

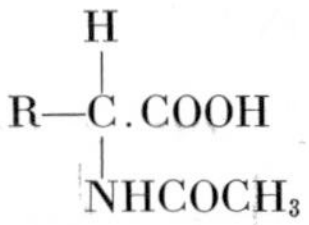

$$\underset{\underset{NHCOCH_3}{|}}{\overset{\overset{H}{|}}{R-C}} . \text{COOH}$$

4. Nitrous acid decomposes the amino group, liberating nitrogen.

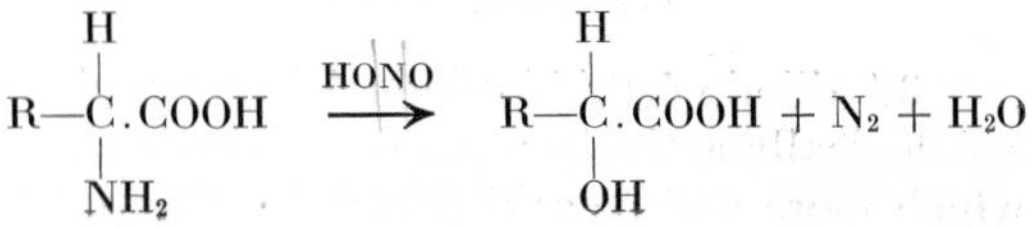

$$\underset{\underset{NH_2}{|}}{\overset{\overset{H}{|}}{R-C}} . \text{COOH} \xrightarrow{\text{HONO}} \underset{\underset{OH}{|}}{\overset{\overset{H}{|}}{R-C}} . \text{COOH} + N_2 + H_2O$$

This is the principle employed by Van Slyke in determining the rate of protein hydrolysis. If we assume, for the time being, linkages such as —CO—NH— in the protein molecule, then, as hydrolysis of a protein proceeds, more and more amino groups are set free; which means, in turn, a corresponding evolution of nitrogen when the products are treated with nitrous acid. Proline and hydroxyproline do not react with nitrous acid.

5. The amino acids often form characteristic crystalline combinations with Reinecke's salt, $[Cr(CNS)_4(NH_3)_2]NH_4$. Proline, histidine, and arginine, among others, form such combinations. This reaction is used in the isolation of amino acids. These metal complexes have been studied by Bergmann. He finds that a metal complex of the type $[Cr(C_2O_4)_3]K_3$ is a specific precipitant for glycine.

6. Owing to the presence of the carboxyl group, reactions with bases take place:

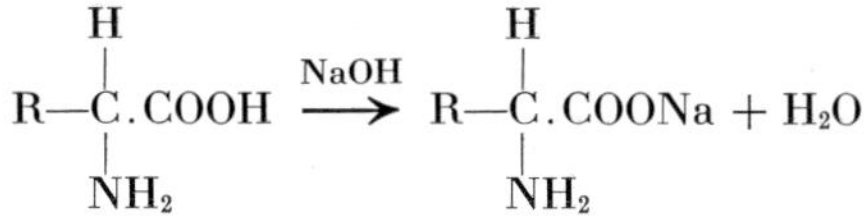

$$\underset{\substack{|\\ NH_2}}{\overset{\substack{H\\ |}}{R-C}}.COOH \xrightarrow{NaOH} \underset{\substack{|\\ NH_2}}{\overset{\substack{H\\ |}}{R-C}}.COONa + H_2O$$

7. The amino acids form copper salts which are also of use in their isolation.

8. With alcohol and hydrochloric acid, esters are formed:

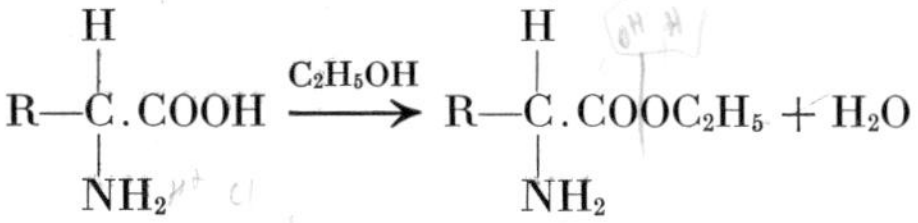

$$\underset{\substack{|\\ NH_2}}{\overset{\substack{H\\ |}}{R-C}}.COOH \xrightarrow{C_2H_5OH} \underset{\substack{|\\ NH_2}}{\overset{\substack{H\\ |}}{R-C}}.COOC_2H_5 + H_2O$$

Fischer's original method of separating a number of the amino acids was to distill fractionally their esters in a vacuum.

9. The acyl halides of the type

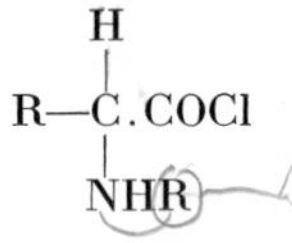

$$\underset{\substack{|\\ NHR}}{\overset{\substack{H\\ |}}{R-C}}.COCl$$

can be formed provided the amino group is first "protected" by being, for example, acetylated:

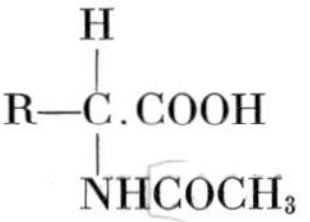

$$\underset{\substack{|\\ NHCOCH_3}}{\overset{\substack{H\\ |}}{R-C}}.COOH$$

Then treatment with thionyl chloride, $SOCl_2$, or phosphorus pentachloride gives

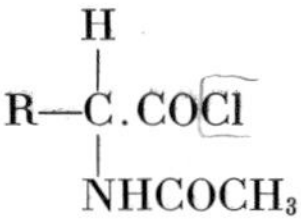

$$\underset{\substack{|\\ NHCOCH_3}}{\overset{\substack{H\\ |}}{R-C}}.COCl$$

The "protecting" group (—COCH₃) can later be removed with HCl after the reaction of the acyl chloride with another amino acid.

10. Heating with barium hydroxide removes CO_2 and gives the primary amines. In putrefactive processes, this change is brought about by certain enzymes in bacteria

$$R-\overset{\overset{\displaystyle H}{|}}{\underset{\underset{\displaystyle NH_2}{|}}{C}}.COOH \xrightarrow{-CO_2} R.\overset{\overset{\displaystyle H}{|}}{\underset{\underset{\displaystyle NH_2}{|}}{C}}.H$$

11. The amino acids form inner salts or dipolar ions (zwitterions):

$$R-\overset{\overset{\displaystyle H}{|}}{\underset{\underset{\displaystyle NH_2}{|}}{C}}.COOH \longrightarrow R-\overset{\overset{\displaystyle H}{|}}{\underset{\underset{\displaystyle H_3N-O}{|}}{C}}-CO \text{ or } R-\overset{\overset{\displaystyle H}{|}}{\underset{\underset{\displaystyle NH_3^+}{|}}{C}}.COO^-$$

12. The amino acids undergo dehydration to give diketopiperazines, which yield peptides (in this case dipeptides) on boiling with hydrochloric acid:

$$\underset{\underset{\displaystyle \text{Glycine}}{\overset{\displaystyle COOH}{\underset{\displaystyle CH_2-NH_2}{|}}}}{} + \underset{\underset{\displaystyle \text{Glycine}}{\overset{\displaystyle H_2N-CH_2}{\underset{\displaystyle HOOC}{|}}}}{} \longrightarrow \underset{\underset{\displaystyle \substack{\text{Diketopiperazine}\\ \text{(Glycine anhydride)}}}{\overset{\displaystyle CO-NH-CH_2}{\underset{\displaystyle CH_2-NH-CO}{|}}}}{}$$

$$\underset{\overset{\displaystyle CO-NH-\!-CH_2}{\underset{\displaystyle (H)\vdots(HO)}{\overset{\displaystyle |}{CH_2-NH-\!-CO}}}}{} \longrightarrow \underset{\underset{\displaystyle \substack{\text{Glycylglycine}\\ \text{(A dipeptide)}}}{\overset{\displaystyle CH_2.CO.NH.CH_2.COOH}{\underset{\displaystyle NH_2}{|}}}}{}$$

This was a method used by Fischer in his attempts to synthesize poly-peptides from amino acids.

13. The reaction of proteins with ninhydrin has already been mentioned (p. 48). Van Slyke finds that when α-amino acids are boiled in water with an excess of ninhydrin at pH 1 to 5, the CO_2 of their carboxyl groups is quantitatively evolved in a few minutes and can be determined gasomet-rically. In the place of CO_2, NH_3 can be determined.

$$\overset{\displaystyle O}{\underset{\displaystyle O}{\|}} \bigg\rangle C(OH)_2 + RCH(NH_2)COOH \longrightarrow \overset{\displaystyle O}{\underset{\displaystyle O}{\|}} \bigg\rangle CHOH$$
$$+ RCHO + NH_3 + CO_2$$

THE HYDROLYSIS OF PROTEINS AND THE SEPARATION OF THE AMINO ACIDS

Hydrolysis of a protein is brought about by boiling with acid or by allowing a proteolytic enzyme such as trypsin to act on the protein. Alkali is practically never used (except in the Folin method of estimating tryp-tophan), since it racemizes the amino acids and destroys arginine and cystine. Sulfuric acid is often favored as the hydrolytic agent because, after the necessary heating (from fifteen to twenty hours), the excess acid is conveniently removed with barium hydroxide. Hydrochloric acid is found more useful when the ultimate goal is the isolation of the monoamino acids.

The separation and the isolation of the various amino acids in the mixture after hydrolysis involves a complicated chemical procedure and is still not satisfactory. Only the briefest outline can be given here.

Usually, an attempt is made first to separate the amino acids into groups, such as the monoamino acids, the basic (two amino groups) amino acids and the dicarboxylic (two carboxyl groups) acids. Butyl alcohol will extract many of the monoamino acids. The dicarboxylic acids can be separated as their calcium salts, insoluble in alcohol (the calcium salts of the other amino acids are soluble). The basic amino acids are precipitated with phosphotungstic acid. Sometimes the separation into groups is accomplished by electrodialysis. Here the basic amino acids tend to migrate to the cathode, the dicarboxylic acids tend to proceed to the anode. The separation of individual amino acids, particularly in quantitative amounts, is difficult. Some of the monoamino acids can be separated by the fractional distillation of their methyl esters. Tyrosine and cystine may often be obtained directly from a protein hydrolysate, owing to their comparative insolubility. Tryptophan may be precipitated as the mercury salt, histidine as a silver salt, arginine as a flavianate, glycine as a double salt with potassium trioxalatochromiate.

THE QUANTITATIVE ESTIMATION OF AMINO ACIDS

Brief outlines are given of several methods in use.

Colorimetric Methods.   Specific color reactions for some amino acids can be utilized for their quantitative estimation. Tyrosine, for example, is determined by the application of the Millon's reaction (p. 48).

Microbiological Methods.   Many bacteria grow in a solution which includes adequate amounts of amino acids, vitamins, salts, purines (p. 85) and pyrimidines (p. 85). Some bacteria grow at a decreased rate when one of the amino acids is present in concentrations below the optimum. A set of growth rates may thus be determined experimentally for these bacteria in the presence of varying but known quantities of some particular amino acid. The sample of protein to be analyzed is hydrolyzed so as to yield a mixture of its amino acids. The bacteria are now suspended in a series of identical solutions complete in all respects for bacterial growth but lacking the amino acid to be determined. To each such suspension is now added a definite but varying quantity of the protein hydrolysate. By comparing the growth rate of the bacteria in these tubes with the growth rates of bacteria in the solutions containing known quantities of the amino acid, one can determine the quantity of the amino acid present in the protein hydrolysate, and thus in the original protein.

The growth rate of the bacterial suspension may be determined by measuring increased turbidity, or by the determination of some characteristic end-product of its metabolism (such as the production of lactic acid from lactobacilli).

The bread mold, *Neurospora*, may here be included. (For further details concerning this bread mold, see Chap. 20.) Irradiation of the wild variety of the mold has produced mutant strains which have lost their ability to synthesize some particular compound. One such variety may now need choline for growth, which gives the basis for the determination of choline in an unknown mixture. This method has been used for the determination of some vitamins, purines and pyrimidines.

Microbiological methods have the advantage, whenever they can be used, in that the amount of protein needed to run a determination is extremely small.

Isotope Dilution Method.   This is the most accurate method for the quantitative determination of amino acids in protein hydrolysates. It necessitates special equipment for the determination of the concentration of isotopes. The principle involved is that a compound which has an abnormal isotope content is inseparable by the usual laboratory procedures from its normal analogue. If, for example, the isotope-containing glycine is added to a hydrolytic mixture of normal amino acids, and then glycine is isolated, this will be a representative sample of the mixture of the added isotope-containing glycine and the glycine originally present.

From the amount of glycine added (x) and its content of N^{15} (C_0), as well as the N^{15} content of the isolated glycine (C), the amount (y) of glycine originally present in the mixture can be calculated from the equation

$$y = \left(\frac{C_0}{C} - 1\right) x$$

The importance of this technique lies in the fact that a quantitative yield of the amino acid is not necessary. What is important is that the sample which is isolated should be pure.

Chromatographic Analysis.   Tswett wrote (in 1906): "Like the light radiation in the spectrum, so is a mixture of pigments systematically separated on the calcium carbonate column into its constituents, which can then be qualitatively and quantitatively determined." Since then Tswett's method has been widely applied. The principle—as the above quotation makes clear—is the differential adsorption of a mixture on a column of adsorbing material.

The name "chromatography" originated because it was used to separate colored compounds; but the method has been extended so that colorless compounds can also be handled. Here the position on the adsorbing column can be determined by the use of reagents yielding characteristic color reactions.

By a judicious use of solvents, the separate bands on the column can be made to flow down into a receiver and recovered.

Stein and Moore have applied this technique for the analysis of the amino acids in a protein hydrolysate. Not more than 2.5 mg. of protein is needed for the entire analysis.

A column partially filled with an adsorbent such as starch or an ion-exchange resin is used. The substance to be analyzed (protein hydrolysate) is placed at the top of the column and slowly developed with a variety of solvents. Equal volumes of the effluent are collected in separate tubes and analyzed for amino acid content by reaction with ninhydrin (see p. 64) and estimated colorimetrically. Figure 8 illustrates the analysis of 2.5 mg. of bovine serum albumin by this method. The identity of the amino acids in each tube is determined by comparison with an analysis of a known mixture of amino acids run under identical conditions. The actual amount of each amino acid present is determined from the area under the individual curve. Where the resolution of two amino acids is not good, one can correct this by repeating the determination with different solvents.

Determination of End Groups in Proteins.   In connection with the structure of the protein molecule, one problem has been to discover the amino acids in the molecule whose functional groups are present in the free state (that is, not present in some peptide or other linkage). Among the methods proposed, one of the most useful is that of Sanger. The method determines the free amino groups which are present in the middle of the peptide chain and are part of a diamino acid (such as lysine, for example), and also the amino acids which are present at the terminal end of the polypeptide chain. Additional information is also obtained regarding the relationship of amino acids to each other in polypeptide chains.

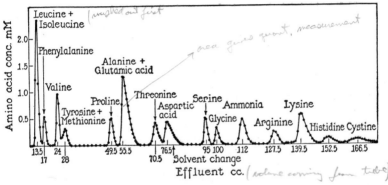

Fig. 8. Chromatographic fractionation of a hydrolysate of bovine serum albumin. Solvents, 1:2:1 n-butyl alcohol–n-propyl alcohol–0.1 N HCl and 2:1 n-propyl alcohol –0.5 N HCl. Column dimensions, 0.9 × 30 cm. Sample, an amount of hydrolysate corresponding to about 2.5 mg. of protein. (Stein and Moore: J. Biol. Chem., *178:* 79.)

The protein is coupled with 2,4-dinitrofluorobenzene at room temperature in the presence of sodium carbonate. In this way are formed the 2,4-dinitrophenyl derivatives of the amino acids in the chain whose reactive groups are free. The dinitrophenyl protein is subjected either to a complete or partial hydrolysis to yield a mixture of free amino acids and the dinitrophenyl amino acids, or free peptides, or dinitrophenyl peptides.

The dinitrophenyl derivatives are extracted by an organic solvent (in which the free amino acids or peptides are insoluble) and are fractionated and identified by the application of chromatographic methods (p. 26).

Sanger has shown that insulin, a hormone which is a protein (Chap. 23), contains six free amino groups: two attached to glycine, two to phenylalanine, and two to the ε-amino group of lysine (assuming a minimum molecular weight of 12,000 for insulin). Using a method of partial hydrolysis, Sanger has determined that the two terminal sequences in insulin are phenylalanine–valine–aspartic acid–glutamic acid, and glycine–isoleucine–valine–glutamic acid–glutamic acid. All the lysine in insulin is attached thus: threonine–proline–lysine–alanine.

The Synthesis of Polypeptides.   When two amino acids are coupled, a dipeptide is formed. The coupling of three such amino acids gives a

$$CH_2.CO\boxed{OH}\quad+\quad CH_2.COOH \longrightarrow CH_2.CO.NH.CH_2.COOH$$

$$NH_2 \qquad\qquad \boxed{H}——N—H \qquad\qquad NH_2$$

Glycylglycine
(A dipeptide)

tripeptide; etc. In general, these combinations of amino acids are known as polypeptides. It is believed that linkages found in polypeptide chains are similar to those found in protein molecules; and this makes the synthesis of such polypeptides a matter of importance. Several methods of synthesis are available:

1. This method can be illustrated by the following example:

$$CH_2.CO\boxed{Cl}+\qquad CH_3 \qquad CH_2.CO.NH.CH(CH_3).COOH$$

$$Cl \qquad \boxed{H} \qquad N—C—H \longrightarrow Cl$$

$$Chloroacetyl \quad H \qquad COOH \qquad Chloroacetylalanine$$
chloride

Alanine

$$+\ NH_3 \longrightarrow CH_2.CO.NH.CH(CH_3).COOH + HCl$$

$$NH_2$$

Glycylalanine

If in the place of chloroacetyl chloride we use α-bromopropionyl chloride, we provide the alanyl radical, and the resulting product would be alanylalanine. In other words, by using the appropriate halogen derivative, different dipeptides can be obtained. Obviously, the alanine itself can be replaced by some other amino acid. The method can be used to prepare tripeptides and polypeptides in general, within limitations.

$$CH(C_4H_9).CO.NH.CH_2CO.NH.CH(CH_3).COOH$$

$$NH_2$$

Leucylglycylalanine
(A tripeptide)

2. A practical method is one developed by Bergmann. The key to the method is the selection of the group used to "block" the amino group. The one selected is known as the "carbobenzoxy" group. Benzyl alcohol may be made to combine with phosgene to form the carbobenzoxy derivative:

$$C_6H_5CH_2O\boxed{H}\ +\ \boxed{Cl}\diagdown \qquad \longrightarrow C_6H_5CH_2.O.COCl$$

$$CO$$

$$Benzyl\ alcohol \quad Cl \diagup \qquad\quad Benzyloxycarbonyl\ chloride$$
$$(carbobenzoxy\ chloride)$$

Phosgene

which combines with an amino acid thus:

$$CH_2.COOH \longrightarrow CH_2.COOH$$

$$C_6H_5CH_2.O.CO\boxed{Cl\ +\ H}—N—H \qquad\qquad NH.CO.O.CH_2.C_6H_5$$

and this can be transformed into the corresponding acid chloride with phosphorus pentachloride:

$$CH_2.COCl$$
$$|$$
$$NH.CO.O.CH_2.C_6H_5$$

NH_2 group
will react with COCl
group of...
NH_2 blocked off.

The resulting compound can now be combined with an amino acid:

$$CH_2.CO\boxed{Cl} \quad + \quad CH_2.COOH \longrightarrow CH_2.CO.NH.CH_2.COOH$$
$$| \qquad\qquad\qquad | \qquad\qquad\qquad\qquad |$$
$$NH.CO.O.CH_2.C_6H_5 \quad \boxed{H}\!-\!N\!-\!H \qquad NH.CO.O.CH_2.C_6H_5 \qquad (A)$$

The carbobenzoxy group can be eliminated by treatment with hydrogen (in the presence of palladium black). The free peptide is formed by the removal of toluene and carbon dioxide:

$$CH_2.CO.NH.CH_2.COOH \longrightarrow CH_2.CO.NH.CH_2.COOH + CO_2 + C_6H_5CH_3$$
$$| \qquad\qquad\qquad\qquad\qquad\qquad | \qquad\qquad\qquad\qquad\qquad\qquad Toluene$$
$$NH\ CO.O.\ CH_2.C_6H_5 \qquad NH_2$$
$$H \qquad\quad H \qquad\qquad\qquad \underline{Glycylglycine}$$

Here no hydrolytic agent is needed to split off the carbobenzoxy group—a procedure which also tends to split the peptide linkage itself.

If a tripeptide is required, (A) is halogenated and coupled with another amino acid:

$$CH_2.CO.NH.CH_2.COOH \xrightarrow{PCl_5}$$
$$|$$
$$NH.CO.O.CH_2.C_6H_5$$

$$H$$
$$|$$
$$CH_2.CO.NH.CH_2.CO\boxed{Cl} + CH_3.C.COOH \longrightarrow$$
$$| \qquad\qquad\qquad\qquad\qquad \boxed{H}\!-\!NH$$
$$NH.CO.O.CH_2.C_6H_5$$
$$CH_2.CO.NH.CH_2.CO.NH.CH(CH_3).COOH \xrightarrow[(Pt)]{H_2}$$
$$|$$
$$NH.CO.O.CH_2.C_6H_5$$
$$CH_2.CO.NH.CH_2.CO.NH.CH(CH_3).COOH + CO_2 + C_6H_5CH_3$$
$$|$$
$$NH_2$$
$$Glycylglycylalanine$$

This method has the added advantage in that it can be applied to optically active amino acids, since the carbobenzoxy amino acids, in contrast to other acyl derivatives of amino acids, are not racemized.

3. Still another practical method of synthesizing polypeptides is that due to Boissonas. Here the amino acid is combined with ethyl chloroformate in the presence of tributylamine. The product is condensed with the amino acid (or peptide) to yield the polypeptide:

$$-CH-CO.O[H.N(C_4H_9)_3] + Cl.CO.OC_2H_5 \longrightarrow$$
$$|$$
$$N$$

$$-CH-CO.\boxed{O.CO}.OC_2H_5 + [H.N(C_4H_9)_3]Cl$$
$$|$$
$$N$$

$$+ HN-C- \longrightarrow -CH-CO.NH.C- + C_2H_5OH + CO_2$$
$$| \qquad\qquad\qquad | \qquad\qquad\qquad |$$
$$② \qquad\qquad\qquad N$$

A physiologically important tripeptide is glutathione

$$\begin{array}{cc} & \text{CH}_2\text{SH} \\ & | \\ \text{H}_2\text{N.CH.CH}_2.\text{CH}_2.\text{CO.NH.CH} \\ | & | \\ \text{COOH} & \text{CO.NH.CH}_2.\text{COOH} \end{array}$$

consisting of glutamic acid, cysteine and glycine (see p. 196).

It is possible, by a method developed by Katchalski, to prepare poly-peptide-like materials which represent the polymerization of some one or more amino acids (see references).

AMPHOTERIC NATURE OF PROTEINS

Proteins are amphoteric electrolytes (or ampholytes) due to the presence of amino and carboxyl groups:

$$\begin{array}{ccc} \text{R.CH.COOH} & \rightleftarrows & \text{R.CH.COO}^- + \text{H}^+ \\ | & & | \\ \text{NH}_2 & & \text{NH}_2 \end{array}$$

$$\begin{array}{ccccc} \text{R.CH.COOH} & \overset{\text{H}_2\text{O}}{\rightleftarrows} & \text{R.CH.COOH} & \rightleftarrows & \text{R.CH.COOH} \\ | & & | & & | \\ \text{NH}_2 & & \text{NH}_3.\text{OH} & & \text{NH}_3^+ + \text{OH}^- \end{array}$$

and in the presence of acids and alkalies they react as follows:

$$\begin{array}{ccccc} \text{R.CH.COOH} & \overset{\text{HCl}}{\longrightarrow} & \text{R.CH.COOH} & \rightleftarrows & \text{R.CH.COOH} \\ | & & | & & | \\ \text{NH}_2 & & \text{NH}_2.\text{HCl} & & \text{NH}_3^+ + \text{Cl}^- \end{array}$$

$$\begin{array}{ccccc} \text{R.CH.COOH} & \overset{\text{NaOH}}{\longrightarrow} & \text{R.CH.COONa} & \rightleftarrows & \text{R.CHCOO}^- + \text{Na}^+ \\ | & & | & & | \\ \text{NH}_2 & & \text{NH}_2 & & \text{NH}_2 \end{array}$$

A protein, then, is a substance of the type HPrOH. Its ionization as an acid is

$$\text{HPrOH} \rightleftarrows \text{H}^+ + \text{PrOH}^- \quad (1)$$

and its ionization as a base is

$$\text{HPrOH} \rightleftarrows \text{OH}^- + \text{HPr}^+ \quad (2)$$

Applying the law of mass action to (1) we find that

$$K_a = \frac{(\text{H}^+)(\text{PrOH}^-)}{(\text{HPrOH})} \quad (3)$$

and from (2) we get

$$K_b = \frac{(\text{OH}^-)(\text{HPr}^+)}{(\text{HPrOH})} \quad (4)$$

K_a (the dissociation constant for the acid) and K_b (that for the base) are rarely equal. Such a protein dissolved in water will not show equal con-centrations of H$^+$ and OH$^-$.

Hardy showed that in an electrical field the protein will migrate in one direction or in the other, depending upon whether acid or alkali is added. There must be some condition, however, where the tendency to migrate is at a minimum (or where there is the tendency to migrate equally in both directions). When this is reached we arrive at the *isoelectric* point of the protein.

At the isoelectric point the tendency of proteins to combine with acids or alkalies is at a minimum. On the acid side of the isoelectric point the proteins should combine with acids, and on the alkaline side of this point they should combine with bases. By a simple series of experiments, Loeb showed this theory to be correct.

Loeb's Experiment Illustrating the Isoelectric Point. Samples of gelatin were kept in contact with nitric acid of different concentrations. After pouring off the acid and washing the gelatin, each sample was added to a solution of silver nitrate. The gelatin was next filtered, washed, melted, brought to a known volume, and an adequate portion was used for a pH determination, while another was exposed to sunlight. (The experiments involving the silver nitrate were performed in a dark room.) After a time all solutions with a pH higher than 4.7 turned brown or black, while those of pH less than 4.7 remained colorless.

Michaelis had found quite independently and by other means (cataphoresis experiments—migrations in an electrical field) that the isoelectric point of gelatin is at a pH of 4.7. Loeb assumed that at pH greater than 4.7, gelatin combines with silver to form a salt of the type of silver gelatinate (which darkens on exposure); whereas below pH 4.7, gelatin combines with acid to form gelatin nitrate which does not react with silver salts; hence there is no change in color on exposure.

Using potassium ferrocyanide in the place of silver nitrate, where now the tendency would be to form combinations with the ferrocyanide ion, such combinations took place only below, but not above, pH 4.7; again presenting evidence in favor of Loeb's point of view.

"Zwitterions," or "Dipolar Ions." It has been assumed so far that when acids and alkalies combine with proteins (or amino acids), the following takes place:

$$Cl^- + {^+NH_3}.R.COOH \xleftarrow{\text{HCl}} NH_2.R.COOH \xrightarrow{\text{NaOH}} NH_2.R.COO^- + Na^+ \quad (1)$$

which means that the addition of hydrochloric acid causes the ionization of the amino (basic) group as hydrochloride, and the addition of sodium hydroxide causes the ionization of the carboxylic (acid) group as sodium salt. This implies that the protein (or amino acid) in aqueous solution is practically in an un-ionized condition. The "zwitterion," or "dipolar ion," theory, however, claims that the amino acid itself is in a completely dissociated form:

$$^+NH_3.R.COO^-$$

and that the reactions of acids and bases are to be formulated thus:

$$Cl^- + {^+NH_3}.R.COOH \xleftarrow{\text{HCl}} {^+NH_3}.R.COO^- \xrightarrow{\text{NaOH}} NH_2.R.COO^- + Na^+ \quad (2)$$

While the results in (1) and (2) are apparently the same, the interpretation is quite different. In (2), the amino group is already ionized. The addition of hydrochloric acid merely serves to depress the ionization of the carboxylic group, which is therefore displaced by the stronger mineral acid. Again, the addition of sodium hydroxide displaces the weaker amino group by the stronger base, leaving the ionization of the carboxyl group unchanged. According to the older view, adding hydrochloric acid measures the basic dissociation constant; according to the newer view, the reverse is true: we are really measuring the acid dissociation constant. According to the older view, adding sodium hydroxide measures the acid dissociation constant; the newer view means that that represents the measure of the basic dissociation constant.

The evidence in favor of the "dipolar ion" hypothesis is by now quite extensive, but only one example of the type of evidence can be given here. We have already seen (p. 71, equation 2) that the titration of an amino acid with acid is a measure of its reaction with the $—COO^-$ group, whereas the titration of the amino acid with alkali measures its reaction with the $—NH_3^+$ group, from which it removes a proton.

Figure 9 illustrates the results of the titration of an amino acid like

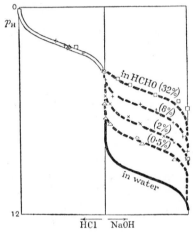

Fig. 9. Titration curves of glycine in presence of increasing concentrations of HCHO. (Harris: Biochem. J., *24:* 1080.)

glycine with acid and with alkali in the absence and in the presence of formaldehyde. The reaction of amino acids with formaldehyde yield a series of ill-defined compounds which are unstable but are best illustrated by the following:

$$R\begin{smallmatrix}COO^-\\ \\NH_3^+\end{smallmatrix} \rightleftarrows R\begin{smallmatrix}COO^-\\ \\NH_2\end{smallmatrix} + H^+$$

$$R\begin{smallmatrix}COO^-\\ \\NH_2\end{smallmatrix} + HCHO \rightleftarrows R\begin{smallmatrix}COO^-\\ \\NH.CH_2OH\end{smallmatrix}$$
(Methylol)

$$R\begin{smallmatrix}COO^-\\ \\NH_2\end{smallmatrix} + 2HCHO \rightleftarrows R\begin{smallmatrix}COO^-\\ \\N.(CH_2OH)_2\end{smallmatrix}$$
(Dimethylol)

From the above it can be seen that formaldehyde reacts only with the —NH$_2$ group and not with the —NH$_3^+$ group. As we titrate the amino acid in the presence of formaldehyde, only that portion of the curve which represents the reaction of alkali with the protons of the —NH$_3^+$ group is altered when compared to the titration with alkali in the absence of formaldehyde. Thus, in the presence of formaldehyde, the concentration of R.COO$^-$.NH$_2$ is diminished and the action of the alkali remains that of

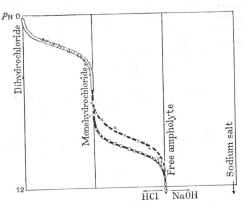

Fig. 10. Titration of arginine in water and HCHO. ○, in water. ✕, in HCHO (0.25%). (Harris: Biochem. J., *24*, 1087.)

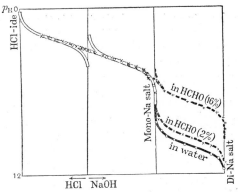

Fig. 11. Titration of aspartic acid in water and HCHO. ○, in water. ✕, in HCHO (2%). +, in HCHO (16%). (Harris: Biochem. J., *24*, 1089.)

stripping protons from the R.COO$^-$.NH$_3^+$ molecule, but the titration curve is displaced from its normal position towards lower values of pH, the greater the concentration of formaldehyde. These results confirm the hypothesis that HCl reacts essentially with the —COO$^-$ group, whereas NaOH reacts with the —NH$_3^+$ group. Similar results can be drawn from the titration of dicarboxylic and diamino amino acids (see Figs. 10 and 11).

Dissociation Constants and Isoelectric Points.   The variations in the isoelectric points (IEP) of different proteins can be understood by measuring the dissociation constants of those groups in amino acids which contribute to the value of IEP. For example, from Haurowitz (Chemistry and Biology of Proteins, 1950, p. 65) we obtain the following pK and IEP values for several amino acids:

Amino Acid	pK_1*	pK_2	pK_3	IEP
Aspartic acid	2.09 (COOH)	3.87 (COOH)	9.82 (NH$_3^+$)	3.0
Glutamic acid	2.19 (COOH)	4.28 (COOH)	9.66 (NH$_3^+$)	3.2
Tyrosine	2.20 (COOH)	9.11 (NH$_3^+$)	10.1 (OH)	5.7
Cysteine	1.96 (COOH)	8.18 (NH$_3^+$)	10.28 (SH)	5.07
Arginine	2.02 (COOH)	9.04 (NH$_3^+$)	12.48 (guanido)	10.8
Lysine	2.18 (COOH)	8.95 (α NH$_3^+$)	10.53 (ϵ NH$_3^+$)	9.7
Histidine	1.77 (COOH)	6.10 (imidazole)	9.18 (NH$_3^+$)	7.6

* (pK is equal to the negative log of K, the dissociation constant. Thus, pK_1 refers to the dissociation of the COOH group, and pK_2 and pK_3 to the corresponding dissociation constants for the other effective groups in the amino acid.)

A protein, then, high in aspartic and glutamic acids should have an IEP in the acid region; and one high in arginine and lysine should have an IEP in the alkaline region.

Donnan's Theory of Membrane Equilibria.   Loeb developed his theory of the colloidal behavior of proteins from two principles: one, that proteins are amphoteric substances (this subject has already been discussed); the other, that Donnan's theory of membrane equilibria (which is about to be discussed) furnishes an explanation of the influence of electrolytes on osmotic pressure and membrane potentials. Colloidal properties of proteins, according to Loeb, are associated with the presence of a non-diffusible ion.

Donnan's experiments and formulation of his theory have made a great contribution to our understanding of biochemical phenomena which were difficult to understand otherwise. His theory has helped to describe the important role of proteins as cellular constituents aside from their more specific action as enzymes. It explains how the cell finds it possible to maintain a difference in concentration of diffusible ions across a membrane, how by this mechanism water may be made to flow into or out of a cell, and even how an electrical potential is created across a membrane.

Assume a membrane permeable to inorganic ions but impermeable to protein ions. Place inside of this membrane (1) a solution of a protein (in the form of its chloride) together with a definite quantity of HCl. On the outside of this solution place an equal quantity of HCl (2). The situation at the beginning of the experiment will be:—

$$
\begin{array}{c|c}
\begin{array}{l} H^+ = y \\ Pr^+ = x \\ Cl^- = x + y \end{array} & \begin{array}{l} H^+ = y \\ Cl^- = y \end{array} \\
\hline
\text{M} &
\end{array}
$$

$$(1) \qquad\qquad (2)$$

There will now be a movement of H^+ and Cl^- so that at equilibrium n mols of HCl will have been moved from (1) to (2) and the concentration of the various ions will now be:

$$
\begin{array}{c|c}
\begin{array}{l} H^+ = y - n \\ Pr^+ = x \\ Cl^- = x + y - n \end{array} & \begin{array}{l} H^+ = y + n \\ Cl^- = y + n \end{array} \\
\hline
\text{M} &
\end{array}
$$

$$(1) \qquad\qquad (2)$$

The free energy (p. 112) required to transfer one mol of H^+ from (2) to (1) reversibly at constant temperature and pressure is:

(1)
$$\Delta F = RT \ln \frac{[H^+]_1}{[H^+]_2}$$

where R is the gas constant, T is the temperature, and the concentration of ions is denoted by brackets. In the same way for the movement of the Cl^- ion:

(2)
$$\Delta F = RT \ln \frac{[Cl^-]_1}{[Cl^-]_2}$$

By definition, at equilibrium the total change in free energy is zero; so that

(3)
$$RT \ln \frac{[H^+]_1}{[H^+]_2} + RT \ln \frac{[Cl^-]_1}{[Cl^-]_2} = 0$$

Therefore

(4)
$$\frac{[H^+]_2}{[H^+]_1} = \frac{[Cl^-]_1}{[Cl^-]_2}$$

or

(5)
$$[H^+]_2[Cl^-]_2 = [H^+]_1[Cl^-]_1$$

Since

(6)
$$[Cl^-]_2 = [H^+]_2$$

and

(7)
$$[H^+]_1 + [Pr^+]_1 = [Cl^-]_1$$

we get by substituting (6) and (7) in (5)

(8)
$$[H^+]_2[H^+]_2 = [H^+]_1 \left[[H^+]_1 + [Pr^+]_1 \right]$$

or

(9)
$$[H^+]_1^2 + [H^+]_1[Pr^+]_1 = [H^+]_2^2$$

and

(10)
$$[Cl^-]_1^2 - [Cl^-]_1[Pr^+]_1 = [Cl^-]_2^2$$

from which it follows that, at equilibrium,

$$[H^+]_1 \text{ is less than } [H^+]_2$$

and

$$[Cl^-]_1 \text{ is greater than } [Cl^-]_2$$

The Protein Molecule. The x-ray investigations of protein crystals often yield diffraction patterns which indicate "a regularity of spacing down to atomic dimensions" (Butler).

X-ray analysis of the protein fibroin suggests that it is composed of straight peptide chains lying parallel. In feather keratin the distance between two adjacent tails, R_1 and R_2, is reduced by slight folding of the chain; but the chain can be stretched until it is almost straight. In wool keratin —the wool can be stretched to double its length without tearing—it is believed that the unstretched form consists of chains coiled up into hexagons (Fig. 12).

Muscle fibers when relaxed resemble unstretched wool, though in muscle the fibers tear when stretched. This possibly means that the chains in muscle fibers resemble those of wool, "but that the hexagons so formed cannot be pulled out because they are fixed by some chemical combination" (Marrack and Astbury).

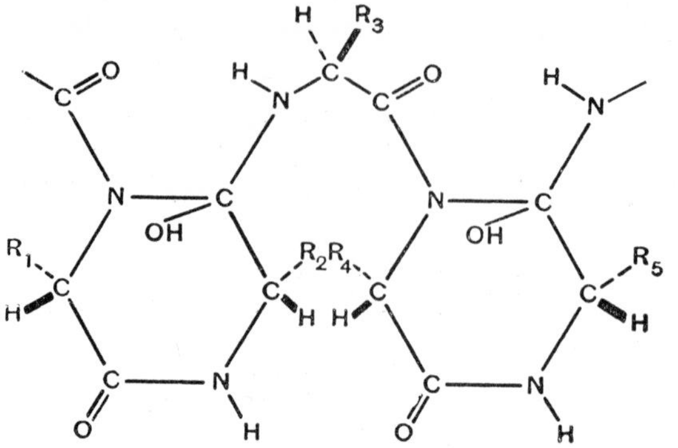

Fig. 12. Peptide chains of keratin in contracted state.

REFERENCES

General reference books are the following: *Greenberg:* Amino Acids and Proteins, 1951; *Edsall:* Advances in Protein Chemistry, 1951; *Haurowitz:* Chemistry and Biology of Proteins, 1950.

The advances in protein chemistry are reviewed in the Ann. Rev. Biochem. See, for example, *Cannan and Levy:* 19: 125, 1950; *Bailey and Sanger:* 20: 103, 1951; *Bull:* 21: 179, 1952; *Fromageot and Jutisz:* 22: 629, 1953; *Neurath and Bailey:* The Proteins, 1953.

The amount of copper bound by protein in the biuret reaction is given by *Mehl, Pacovska and Winzler:* J. Biol. Chem., 177: 13, 1949.

For the mechanism of the reaction of ninhydrin with α-amino acids, see *MacFadyen:* J. Biol. Chem., 186: 1, 1950; and *Moubasher and Othman:* J. Am. Chem. Soc., 72: 2666, 1950.

The question of the denaturation of proteins is discussed by *Haurowitz:* Chemistry and Biology of Proteins, 1950, p. 127; *Maurer and Heidelberger:* J. Am. Chem. Soc., 73: 2070, 1951; and *Porter:* Biochem. J., 46: 304, 1950.

The use of physico-chemical methods for the purification of proteins is described in Research Today (Eli Lilly), Spring, 1947, vol. 4, No. 2; *Gray:* Scientific American, Dec., 1951, p. 45; Ibid., June, 1951,

p. 43; *Mazur and Shorr:* J. Biol. Chem., 187: 473, 1950; *Bull:* Physical Biochemistry, 1951, p. 251.

See Chem. Eng. News, 25: 1364, 1947, for a report on the nomenclature of amino acids.

For an occurrence of the D- (or unnatural) amino acids, see *Wood and Gunsalus:* J. Biol. Chem., 190: 403, 1951; and *Stevens, Halpern, and Gigger:* Ibid., 190: 705, 1951.

A synthesis of serine is given by *King:* J. Am. Chem. Soc., 69: 2738, 1947; another, of lysine, is described by *Degering and Boatright:* Ibid., 72: 5137, 1950.

For articles on hydroxylysine, see *Bergström and Lindstedt:* Arch. Biochem., 26: 324, 1950; *Weisiger:* J. Biol. Chem., 186: 591, 1950.

Details regarding proline and hydroxyproline are given by *Hamilton and Ortiz:* J. Biol. Chem., 184: 607, 733, 1950; *Albertson and Fillman:* J. Am. Chem. Soc., 71: 2181, 1949.

The question of whether citrulline is present in proteins is discussed by *Wingo and Davis:* Proc. Soc. Exp. Biol. Med., 72: 415, 1949.

Abdel-Akher and Sandstrom: Arch. Biochem., 30: 407, 1951, discuss the abnormal behavior of glycine with nitrous acid.

For an explanation of the Sörensen's reaction, see *Levy:* J. Biol. Chem., *99:* 767, 1933; Ibid., *118:* 723, 1937.

Analysis of amino acid mixtures by paper chromatography is described by *Block, Le Strange, and Zweig:* Paper Chromatography, 1952; *Consden, Gordon, and Martin:* Biochem. J., *38:* 224, 1944. See also *Stein and Moore:* Cold Spring Harbor Symposium, *14:* 179, 1949; Scientific American, March, 1951, p. 35; *Keston, Udenfriend, and Levy:* J. Am. Chem. Soc., *72:* 748, 1950; *Rockland and Dunn:* Ibid., *71:* 4121, 1949; *Sober and Kegeles:* Science, *110:* 564 (1949).

Dunn: Physiol. Rev., *29:* 219, 1949, describes the determination of amino acids by microbiological assay.

For *Sanger's* work on the determination of end groups in proteins, see Biochem. J., *39:* 507, 1945; *44:* 126 (1949); *45:* 563, 1949.

The more recent methods of synthesizing polypeptides are described in the Annual Reports of the Chemical Society (London), 1951, p. 162.

Polyamino acids are described by *Katchalski and Spiturk:* J. Am. Chem. Soc., *73:* 3992, 1951.

For peptide synthesis using energy-rich phosphorylated amino acid derivatives, see *Sheehan and Frank:* J. Am. Chem. Soc., *72:* 1312, 1950.

Theories as to the structure of proteins are discussed by *Pauling, Corey, and Branson:* Proc. Nat. Acad. Sci. U. S., *37:* 205, 1951; *Meyer and Mark:* Nature, *167:* 736, 1951; *Pauling and Corey;* Ibid., *168:* 550, 1951; *Riley and Arndt:* Ibid., *169:* 138, 1952; *Astbury, Dalgliesh, Darmon, and Sutherland:* Ibid., *162:* 596, 1948.

Chapter 5   *Nucleoproteins and Nucleic Acids*

NUCLEOPROTEINS are essential constituents of the nuclei of animal and plant cells. They are present in chromosomes, in bacteria, and in viruses, many of the latter being, apparently, pure nucleoprotein.

A nucleoprotein may be regarded as *any* protein attached to nucleic acid. The linkage may be of a primary (nonpolar) or salt-like (polar) variety. In some cases, as in nucleohistone and in nucleic acid joined to prolamine, the nucleic acid can be separated by the addition of neutral salt. Here the linkage between nucleic acid and the protein is probably salt-like in character. Where the protein is of a more complex kind, such simple separation of nucleic acid and protein is not always possible.

The hydrolysis of nucleoprotein yields a series of successive products:

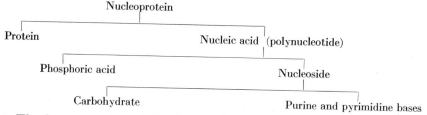

The Structure of Nuclei Acids.   The nucleic acid is a polynucleotide which on acid hydrolysis yields a mixture of phosphoric acid, a pentose sugar, purines and pyrimidines (p. 86). When isolated at low temperature, and without the use of strong reagents, the nucleic acid is highly polymerized. After mild hydrolysis (for example, with an appropriate enzyme, a nuclease), the viscosity of the nucleic acid solution decreases.

The nucleic acids, as Kossel pointed out, fall into two groups: one group is of a type derived from yeast (plant nucleic acid), and the other is represented by that obtained from the thymus gland (animal nucleic acid). All nucleic acids so far examined, no matter from what source, tend to resemble either the one group or the other. On complete hydrolysis, the two types of nucleic acid yield these products:

Yeast nucleic acid (ribonucleic acid)

1. Phosphoric acid
2. D-Ribose
3. Adenine
4. Guanine
5. Cytosine
6. Uracil

Thymonucleic acid (desoxyribonucleic acid)

1. Phosphoric acid
2. D-2-Desoxyribose
3. Adenine
4. Guanine
5. Cytosine
6. Thymine

Both contain phosphoric acid and both have two purines (adenine and guanine, p. 86) and one pyrimidine (cytosine, p. 86) in common. They differ in the sugar component (D-ribose, on the one hand, and D-2-desoxyribose,

78

on the other, p. 22) and in the nature of one pyrimidine (uracil, in the one case, and thymine, in the other, p. 86). The structure of these substances will be discussed presently.

It was supposed for a time that ribonucleic acid was exclusively a plant product, whereas desoxyribonucleic acid belonged to the animal world. This is not true. Ribonucleic acid has been isolated from the pancreas, for example, and desoxyribonucleic acid has been identified in plants. Furthermore, it is now pretty definitely believed that desoxyribonucleic acid is found in the *nuclei* of plant *and* animal tissues, whereas ribonucleic acid is confined to the cytoplasm.

Nucleic acids consist, it is believed, of ribosidyl- and desoxyribosidyl-purines and -pyrimidines linked together by phosphate groups and attached to sugar side chains. The points of attachment are still to be decided. The molecular weights of these nucleic acids may be in the neighborhood of 500,000 to 2,000,000.

Hydrolysis of Nucleic Acid.   Nucleic acid can be hydrolyzed by heating at 115° C. with very dilute ammonia for one hour. Under these conditions, a mixture of *nucleotides* is obtained, each nucleotide consisting of a combination of phosphoric acid, a sugar, and a purine (or pyrimidine) derivative. When, however, nucleic acid is heated at 180° C. with fairly dilute ammonia for three and one-half hours, phosphoric acid is split off and glycosides known as *nucleosides* are formed. The nucleoside is a combination of carbohydrate and purine or pyrimidine derivative. Hydrolysis with acid separates yeast nucleic acid into its fundamental components (phosphoric acid, a sugar, two purine, and two pyrimidine bases).

The Importance of Nucleoproteins.   The evidence is constantly increasing that the nucleoproteins are closely associated with the chromosome of cells, and, as we shall presently see (p. 81), with the characteristics of a number of viruses. Some even go so far as to assume that the genes themselves are largely nucleoproteins.

Caspersson, using ultraviolet spectrophotometry, has shown that desoxyribonucleic acid (DNA) is found in portions of the *chromosomes*, the carriers of the hereditary characteristics of the cell, and that the changes in concentration are related to mitosis. Caspersson has further shown that relatively high concentrations of ribonucleic acid (RNA) are found in the cytoplasm when the cell is active in the synthesis of protein.

The nucleus of the cell has an affinity for basic dyes. The material in the nucleus which can be easily stained is called *chromatin*.

During cell division, discrete units appear in the nucleus, and more particularly in the part where the chromatin is found. These units are the chromosomes, "the carriers of the hereditary characteristics of the cell." The number of these "characteristics" is greater than the number of chromosomes, a fact which led to the belief that these chromosomes could be further subdivided into smaller units, each unit "carrying" a single "characteristic." It is these units which are the *genes*.

Mirsky has isolated chromosomes from calf thymus, among other sources (see Fig. 13). Some 90 to 92 per cent of the mass of the chromosome is made up of desoxyribonucleic acid joined to a protein of the histone variety.

"The great accumulation of desoxyribonucleic acid in the chromosome," writes Mirsky, "strongly suggests that these substances are either the genes themselves or are intimately related to the genes." Ultraviolet radiation, among other means, induces gene mutation, and its efficiency, as Beadle

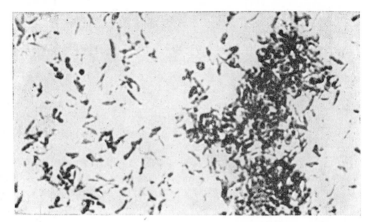

Fig. 13. Suspension of isolated thymus chromosomes. (Mirsky and Ris: J. Gen. Physiol., *31:* 1.)

points out, varies with wave length in the same way as does its absorption by nucleic acid, "strongly indicating that the energy effective in producing mutations in genes is absorbed by nucleic acid. The simplest assumption possible is that this is so because the nucleic acid is part of the gene."

Relatively enormous chromosomes are found in the salivary glands of insect larvae—big enough to be dissected by hand (see Fig. 14).

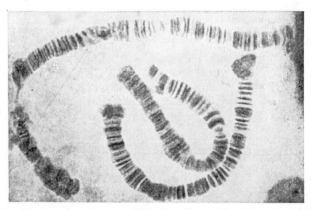

Fig. 14. Chromosomes from a cell in the salivary gland of an insect larva. [Monthly Science News (Britain), June, 1943.]

Striking evidence that the nucleoprotein and the gene are intimately related comes from the work of Avery on the pneumococcus. The core of the pneumococcus (protein) is nonspecific and harmless, but when surrounded by the capsule (polysaccharide) it becomes virulent. Each type of pneumococcus has its own variety of core and capsule. It is possible to make the core of the pneumococcus (R, nonvirulent) grow with the capsule of another type (S, virulent), and so continue reproducing. But some additional factor from S is needed for the reaction to proceed—a factor, in this case, capable of transforming the R-variant of type II pneumococcus into the virulent S-variant of type III. This factor Avery finds to be the sodium salt of desoxyribonucleic acid; so that, as Astbury puts it, "in the mechanism of biosynthesis and inheritance, the nucleic acids are indispensable."

Nucleic acid in the nucleus of the cell (in chromosomes, for example) is found joined to protein, such as a histone or a protamine. The nucleic acid–protein combination can often be extracted with 1 M sodium chloride solution and precipitated with physiological saline (0.9 per cent NaCl).

The Virus Is a Nucleoprotein. This important discovery, relating a protein to such diseases as smallpox, yellow fever, poliomyelitis, measles, mumps, influenza, virus pneumonia, and the common cold, as well as several mosaic and yellow diseases of plants, deserves discussion.

Viruses are submicroscopic,* infectious entities which are capable of causing disease in man, animals, plants, insects, and bacteria. In the past they have been characterized by their invisibility, by their ability to pass filters capable of holding back all ordinary living things, and by their inability to multiply or reproduce in the absence of living cells. However, because viruses may reproduce under certain conditions, because they are specific in that certain viruses occur or cause disease only in certain hosts, because they may change and adapt themselves to new conditions, and because of the lasting immunity which usually follows most virus diseases, many of the workers in the virus field chose to regard viruses as invisible living organisms.

A study of tobacco-mosaic disease, a virus which was discovered in 1892 and was the first of these agents to be described, was undertaken by Stanley in 1935. A high-molecular weight, crystalline protein possessing the properties of tobacco-mosaic virus was isolated from Turkish tobacco plants diseased with this virus. The following facts have since been brought out: The virus appears to be a conjugated protein containing about 95 per cent protein and 5 per cent nucleic acid. This nucleic acid belongs to the *ribonucleic* acid variety.

Bushy stunt virus appears to contain 83 per cent protein and 17 per cent of a nucleic acid similar to that found in tobacco-mosaic virus. Tobacco ring spot virus contains 40 per cent nucleic acid, which is the highest percentage yet found in a virus.

An analysis of the protein constituent of tobacco-mosaic virus shows the presence, among others, of tyrosine, tryptophan, proline, arginine, phenylalanine, serine, threonine, and cystine. Glycine appears to be absent.

The molecular weight of tobacco-mosaic virus is about 40,000,000.

These viruses, nucleoprotein in composition, can perpetuate themselves by reproduction within, and only within, certain specific living cells. Stanley emphasizes the similarities in properties between viruses and

* Viruses range in size from about 10 mμ—slightly smaller than some protein molecules—to about 300 mμ, which is somewhat larger than certain accepted living organisms (Stanley).

genes. In size and in composition (nucleoprotein), both resemble one another. Both reproduce within certain specific living cells. Both may undergo mutations, spontaneously or as a result of irradiation, changes which are reproduced in subsequent generations. But so far, unlike viruses, it has not been possible to isolate and study genes in vitro.

Unlike bacteria, viruses cannot be grown in a nutrient solution. They need certain specific cells as hosts. Tobacco-mosaic virus will grow in certain plant cells; yellow fever virus will grow in the cells of man, monkey, and the mouse; rabbit papilloma virus will grow in certain cells of rabbits, etc.

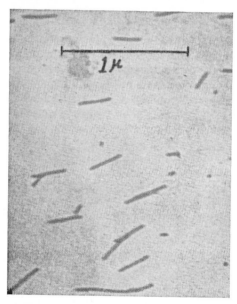

Fig. 15. Tobacco virus molecules. Micrograph of molecules of tobacco-mosaic virus taken by means of the RCA electron microscope. Magnification × 34,000. (Anderson and Stanley: J. Biol. Chem., *139:* 338.)

Some idea of the size of the molecules of the tobacco-mosaic virus may be obtained from Figs. 15 and 16.*

The effect on growth of a variety of plant virus, the bushy stunt virus, is shown in Fig. 17.

In Chapter 6, some details are given concerning the preparation of crystalline enzymes which are proteins. Stanley's original method of isolating the crystalline protein having virus activity may interest the reader.

The injured plants are cut, frozen, ground, and the juice is pressed out. The juice is adjusted to pH 6.7, filtered through a layer of Celite (a filter aid), and 30 per cent by weight of ammonium sulfate is added to the filtrate. The precipitate is dissolved in water, the solution adjusted to pH 7

* The electron microscope, which makes use of electrons instead of rays of light, and magnetic or electrostatic fields instead of glass lenses, gives magnifications up to 100,000 diameters. This means that the electron microscope is from 50 to 100 times more powerful than the strongest optical microscope.

and the precipitation with ammonium sulfate is repeated. The final precipitate is dissolved in water and the solution adjusted to pH 4.5, which precipitates the active protein. The precipitate is again dissolved in water, the solution adjusted to pH 7, and the protein in the filtrate is crystallized

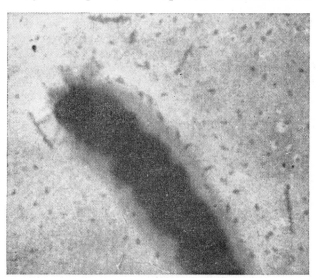

Fig. 16. Mixture of tobacco-mosaic viruses with normal rabbit serum. The contaminating bacterium serves to give a good idea of the relative size of the molecules of virus. Electron micrograph with magnification about × 37,000. (Anderson and Stanley: J. Biol. Chem., *139:* 344.)

Fig. 17. Left-hand, healthy tomato plant; right-hand, bushy stunt-diseased tomato plant of the same age. (Photograph by J. A. Carlile.) (Stanley: J. Biol. Chem., *135:* 452.)

by adding sufficient saturated ammonium sulfate to cause a slight cloudiness, then sufficient 10 per cent glacial acetic acid in one-half saturated ammonium sulfate is added to adjust the pH to 5.5, and finally sufficient saturated ammonium sulfate is added to bring all the protein out of solution.

Since Stanley's basic discovery, much work has also been done on animal viruses. Figure 18 is an electron photomicrograph of vaccinia virus—one of the pox group.

Several other viruses have been studied from the point of view of isolation, composition, etc.; these include rabbit papillomatosis, equine encephalomyelitis, influenza (human and swine types), and bacteriophages.

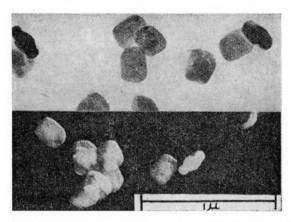

Fig. 18. Vaccinia virus purified by salt flocculation and fixed with osmic acid. Above, unshadowed; below, lightly shadowed with gold to reveal surface structure. (Dawson and McFarlane: Nature, *161:* 464.)

In the case of influenza, some practical results have been obtained. This virus will grow and multiply in chick embryos when these are infected. In this way relatively large quantities of the virus can be accumulated. After chemical purification, Stanley found that the material could be injected in small amounts into humans and would protect them against influenza.

How do viruses originate, reproduce or mutate? These are questions which cannot yet be answered. However, so far as the virus itself is considered, virus activity appears to be a property of its protein molecules. It is these protein molecules which show virus activity, the essence of which, as Stanley points out, is reproduction.

"There may be no sharp line of distinction between molecules and organisms," writes Stanley, "and the viruses may provide the transition between the two."

A chart showing relative sizes of viruses is given in Fig. 19.

Bacteriophage (Bacterial Virus).   Northrop has purified bacteriophage, a filtrable virus which destroys bacteria and which possesses the common "virus" property of increasing in the presence of living cells. Bacteriophage obtained from lysed cultures of staphylococcus shows the general properties of a nucleoprotein (Fig. 20).

The Purines and Pyrimidines.   Aside from the two sugars and phosphoric acid, the two nucleic acids are made up of several purines and pyrimidines. To a large extent we are indebted to Emil Fischer for our knowledge of the chemistry of these substances.

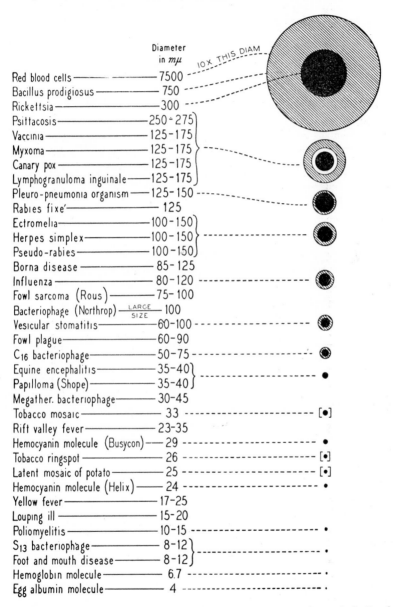

Fig. 19. A chart showing the relative sizes of several selected viruses including bacteriophages, as compared to those of the red blood cells, *Bacillus prodigiosus*, rickettsia, pleuropneumonia organism, and protein molecules. (Stanley: American Naturalist, 72: 112.)

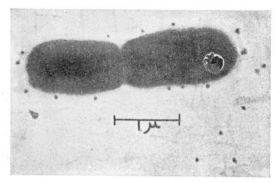

Fig. 20. Bacteriophage particles, α strain, attached to cells of *Escherichia coli*. Reduced from an electron micrograph with a magnification of 17,500 diameters. (Mudd and Anderson: J. Am. Med. Assoc., *126:* 561.)

Pyrimidine itself has the structure

$$
\begin{array}{ccc}
1 \text{ N} & =\!=\!= & \text{CH } 6 \\
| & & | \\
2 \text{ CH} & & \text{CH } 5 \\
\| & & \| \\
3 \text{ N} & \text{———} & \text{CH } 4 \\
\end{array}
$$
Pyrimidine

and the three pyrimidine compounds found in the two nucleic acids have the following formulas:

$$
\begin{array}{ccc}
\text{N} =\!= \text{C} - \text{NH}_2 \\
| \qquad | \\
\text{O} = \text{C} \qquad \text{CH} \\
| \qquad \| \\
\text{HN} \text{———} \text{CH} \\
\end{array}
$$
Cytosine
(6-amino-2-keto-
pyrimidine)

$$
\begin{array}{ccc}
\text{HN} \text{———} \text{C} = \text{O} \\
| \qquad | \\
\text{O} = \text{C} \qquad \text{CH} \\
| \qquad \| \\
\text{HN} \text{———} \text{CH} \\
\end{array}
$$
Uracil
(2, 6-diketo-
pyrimidine)

$$
\begin{array}{ccc}
\text{HN} \text{———} \text{C} = \text{O} \\
| \qquad | \\
\text{O} = \text{C} \qquad \text{C.CH}_3 \\
| \qquad \| \\
\text{HN} \text{———} \text{CH} \\
\end{array}
$$
Thymine
(2,6-diketo-5-
methylpyrimidine)
(5-methyluracil)

The purine base is

$$
\begin{array}{c}
\overset{6}{} \\
1 \text{ N} =\!= \text{CH} \qquad \text{H} \\
| \qquad | \qquad \overset{7}{\diagup} \\
2 \text{ HC} \quad 5 \text{ C} \text{———} \text{N} \\
\| \qquad \| \qquad \overset{8}{\diagdown} \\
\qquad\qquad\qquad \text{CH} \\
\qquad\qquad\qquad \diagup \\
3 \text{ N} \text{———} \text{C} \text{———} \text{N} \\
\quad\ 4 \qquad\quad 9 \\
\end{array}
$$
Purine

and adenine and guanine, the two purine compounds of interest here, have the following structures:

$$
\begin{array}{c}
\text{N} =\!= \text{C} - \text{NH}_2 \quad \text{H} \\
| \qquad | \qquad \diagup \\
\text{HC} \quad \text{C} \text{———} \text{N} \\
\| \qquad \| \qquad\qquad \text{CH} \\
| \qquad | \qquad\qquad \diagup \\
\text{N} \text{———} \text{C} \text{———} \text{N} \\
\end{array}
$$
Adenine
(6-aminopurine)

$$
\begin{array}{c}
\text{HN} \text{———} \text{C} = \text{O} \quad \text{H} \\
| \qquad | \qquad \diagup \\
\text{H}_2\text{N} - \text{C} \quad \text{C} \text{———} \text{N} \\
\| \qquad \| \qquad\qquad \text{CH} \\
| \qquad | \qquad\qquad \diagup \\
\text{N} \text{———} \text{C} \text{———} \text{N} \\
\end{array}
$$
Guanine
(2-amino-6-ketopurine)

Three other purines of importance physiologically are hypoxanthine, xanthine, and uric acid.

HN——C=O   H   HN——C=O   H   HN——C=O   H

HC   C——N   O=C   C——N   O=C   C——N

‖   ‖   CH | ‖   CH | ‖   C=O

N——C——N   HN——C——N   HN——C——N

                                                                           H

Hypoxanthine   Xanthine   Uric acid
(6-ketopurine)   (2,6-diketopurine) (2, 6, 8-triketopurine)
                                            (Also called 2, 6, 8-
                                            trioxypurine)

The Nucleotides.   Several nucleotides, which follow, are described briefly.

MUSCLE INOSINIC ACID.   This nucleotide was first isolated by Liebig from beef extract, and it is an important constituent of muscle (Chap. 17). Hydrolysis of inosinic acid with hydrochloric acid yields hypoxanthine and D-ribose 5-phosphoric acid. Its formula has now been established:

HN——C=O

HC   C——N
                        ┌————O————————————┐
‖   ‖   CH   OH OH   OH

N——C——N————CH——CH——CH——CH——CH$_2$——O——P——OH

                                             ‖
                                             O

Inosinic acid
(9'-hypoxanthine-5-phosphoribofuranoside)

MUSCLE ADENYLIC ACID.   This nucleotide is of importance in the metabolism of muscle (Chap. 12) as well as other tissues. It can be isolated from heart muscle and from brain. An enzyme in muscle is capable of transforming adenylic acid into inosinic acid, at the same time liberating ammonia. In fact, it is now known that the difference between the two acids is that in inosinic acid the base is hypoxanthine and in adenylic acid it is adenine. Adenylic acid has the formula

N=C.NH$_2$

HC   C——N
                        ┌————O————————————┐
‖   ‖   CH   OH OH   OH

N——C——N————CH——CH——CH——CH——CH$_2$——O——P——OH

                                             ‖
                                             O

Muscle adenylic acid
(9'-adenine-5-phosphoribofuranoside) (adenosine monophosphate, AMP)

Closely related *chemically* are the two:

N=C.NH$_2$

HC   C——N
                        ┌————O————————————┐
‖   ‖   CH   OH OH   OH   OH

N——C——N————CH——CH——CH——CH——CH$_2$——O——P——O——P——OH

                                             ‖   ‖
                                             O   O

Adenosine diphosphate (ADP)

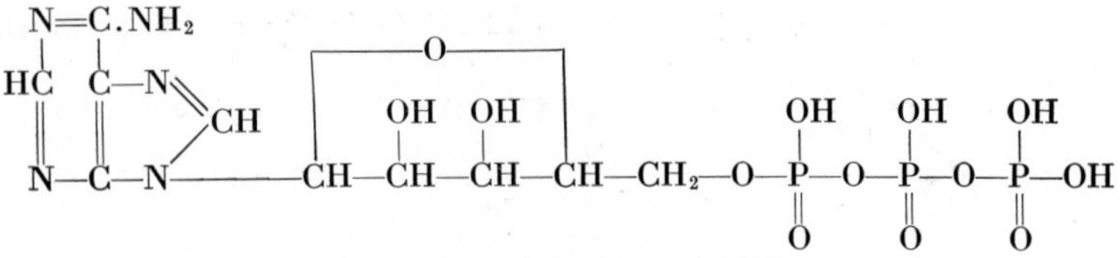

$$N=C.NH_2$$

Adenosine triphosphate (ATP)

Yeast adenylic acid differs from muscle adenylic acid by being a 3-phosphoribofuranoside.

GUANYLIC ACID. This has been isolated from animal tissues (pancreas, spleen, and liver) and from yeast. Aside from the presence of the base guanine, guanylic acid is also further characterized by the fact that the phosphoric acid–sugar combination is of the form 3-phosphoribose. The formula for guanylic acid is:

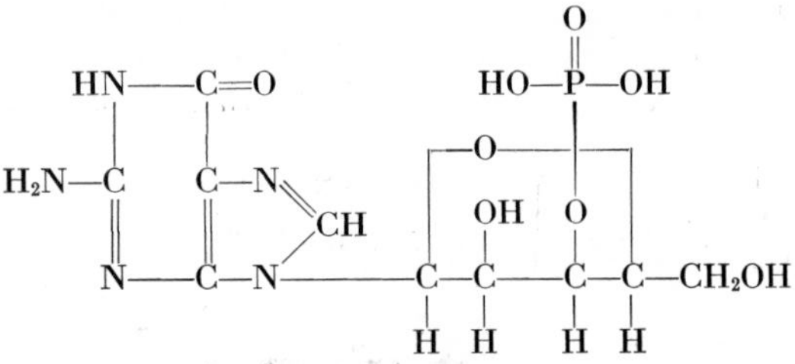

Guanylic acid
(9'-guanine-3-phosphoribofuranoside)

DIPHOSPHOPYRIDINE NUCLEOTIDE. Several purine or pyrimidine derivatives play an important part in biological oxidations. For example, diphosphopyridine nucleotide, also known as codehydrogenase I, coenzyme I, and cozymase, is an adenine-containing nucleotide and is important in yeast fermentation and in biological oxidations.

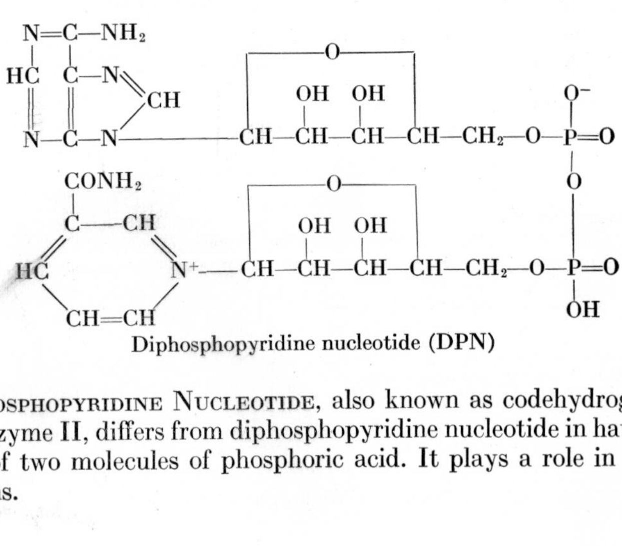

Diphosphopyridine nucleotide (DPN)

TRIPHOSPHOPYRIDINE NUCLEOTIDE, also known as codehydrogenase II, and coenzyme II, differs from diphosphopyridine nucleotide in having three instead of two molecules of phosphoric acid. It plays a role in biological oxidations.

$$O$$
$$O-P{\overset{OH}{\underset{OH}{<}}}$$

N=C—NH₂
HC C—N
         CH
N—C—N ——— CH—CH—CH—CH—CH₂—O—P=O

OH   OH

$$O$$

CONH₂
C——CH
HC   N⁺——CH—CH—CH—CH—CH₂—O—P=O
CH=CH

OH OH

O⁻

Triphosphopyridine nucleotide (TPN)*

REFERENCES

A good exposition of the subject is by *Davidson:* The Biochemistry of Nucleic Acids, 1950; also *Bowen:* Chemistry and Physiology of the Nucleus, 1952.

A review of nucleoproteins and related substances will be found in the Ann. Rev. Biochem., *19:* 149, 1950 (*Schmidt*); *20:* 149, 1951 (*Baddiley*); *21:* 209, 1952 (*Jordan*). See also *Chargaff:* Federation Proceedings, *10:* 654, 1951.

Greenstein: Federation Proceedings, *6:* 488, 1947, deals with the enzymic degradation of ribosenucleic acid and desoxyribosenucleic acid. See also *Kunitz:* J. Gen. Physiol., *33:* 349, 1950, for the isolation of crystalline desoxyribonuclease.

The methods used for the isolation of a nucleic acid—in this case, desoxypentosenucleic acid from yeast cells—are described by *Chargaff and Zamenoff:* J. Biol. Chem., *173:* 327, 1948.

Further references to nucleic acid, etc., are the following: *Chargaff, Vischer, Doniger, Green, and Misani:* J. Biol. Chem., *177:* 405, 1949 (composition of desoxypentosenucleic acids of thymus and spleen); *Neuberg and Roberts:* Arch. Biochem., *20:* 185, 1949 (properties of nucleic acids); *Markham and Smith:* Nature, *163:* 250, 1949 (chromatography of nucleic acids); *Davidson and Leslie:* Cancer Research, *10:* 587, 1950 (nucleic acid and tissue growth); *Chargaff:* Experientia, *6:* 201, 1950 (chemical specificity of nucleic acids); *Dische:* J. Biol. Chem., *181:* 379, 1949 (method of determining pentose in nucleotide); *Todd:* Harvey Lectures (1951–52), 1 (Chem-

istry); *Baddiley, Michelson, and Todd:* Nature, *161:* 761, 1948 (synthesis of ATP); *Loring, Fairley, and Seagran:* J. Biol. Chem., *197:* 823, 1952 (yeast ribonucleic acid).

For the isolation and composition of chromosomes, see *Mirsky and Ris:* J. Gen. Physiol., *31:* 1, 7, 1947. See further *Mirsky:* Harvey Lectures, 1950–51, p. 81.

For the possible connection of the gene with nucleoprotein, see Beadle in *Green's* Currents in Biochemical Research, 1, 1946. See also *Dobzhansky:* Scientific American, Sept., 1950, p. 55.

For a review of Avery's work on the transformation of pneumococcal types, see *Morgan:* Nature, *153:* 763, 1944. See also *Astbury:* British Science News, *1:* 3, 1947.

A large amount of work has been done on viruses, both plant and animal. For some general references, see the following: *Stanley:* Chem. Eng. News, *25:* 3786, 1947 (chemical studies on viruses); Stanley in *Green:* Currents in Biochemical Research, 13, 1946 (viruses); *Pirie:* Ann. Rev. Bioch., *15:* 573, 1946 (viruses); *Bawden:* Plant Viruses and Virus Diseases, 1950; *Pirie:* Nature, *166:* 495, 1950 (biochemical approach to viruses); *Luria:* Federation Proceedings, *10:* 582, 1951 (bacteriophage reproduction); *Burnet:* Scientific American; May, 1951, p. 43 (viruses).

Several individual papers are: *Sigurgeirsson and Stanley:* Phytopathology, *37:* 26, 1947 (electron microscope studies of tobacco mosaic virus); *Knight:* J. Biol.

Chem., *171:* 297, 1947 (chemical differences among strains of tobacco mosaic virus); *Knight:* J. Experimental Medicine, *83:* 11, 1946 (preparation of a purified influenza virus).

For an account of electron microscopy, see *Zworkin:* Ind. Eng. Chem., *35:* 450, 1943.

Delbrück: Harvey Lectures (1945–46), 161, discusses bacteriophages (bacterial viruses). See also *Price:* Scientific Monthly, *67:* 124, 1948; and *Luria:* Science, *111:* 507 (1950).

For purine and pyrimidine derivatives, see *Carter:* J. Am. Chem. Soc., *72:* 1466, 1950 (determination using paper chromatography); *Tinker and Brown:* J. Biol. Chem., *173:* 585, 1948 (determination by counter current distribution); *Shaw:* Ibid., *185:* 439, 1950 (synthesis of several purines); *Cavalieri, Blair, and Brown:* J. Am. Chem. Soc., *70:* 1240, 1948 (synthesis of uric acid containing isotopic nitrogen.

An excellent book on chromosomes, genes, etc., is by *Dunn and Dobzhansky:* Heredity, Race and Society, 1946. See also *Beadle:* Federation Proceedings, *9:* 512, 1950 (biochemical aspects of genetics); *Mirsky and Ris:* J. Gen. Physiol., *34:* 475, 1951 (composition of chromosomes).

Chapter 6   *Enzymes*

Enzymes are catalysts produced as a result of cellular activity "but independent of the presence of living cells in their operation" (Waldschmidt-Leitz). The name "enzyme" (from the Greek, "in leaven") is associated with the process of fermentation.

The Action of Catalysts on Equilibrium Reactions.   A chemical reaction which is reversible will attain a state of equilibrium when the velocity of the forward reaction is equal to the velocity of the reverse reaction. The factors which influence the equilibrium state are tempera-

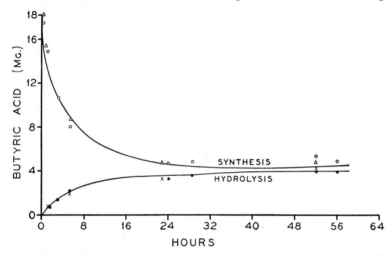

Fig. 21. Synthesis and hydrolysis of *n*-butyl-*n*-butyrate by hog pancreatic lipase. (Adapted from Rona, P., and Ammon, R.: Biochem. Z., *249*, 446, 1932.)

ture, pressure (when gases are present), concentration of the reacting substances and the presence of a catalyst. The catalyst speeds up both the forward and backward reaction and thus allows the system to attain a state of equilibrium in a shorter time. A catalyst will not make a reaction proceed unless that reaction can proceed of its own accord, no matter how slowly. As an example, ethyl acetate in water will hydrolyze very slowly to produce acetic acid and ethyl alcohol. The reverse reaction will also take place, but at a slow rate. However, the addition of acid speeds up both reactions and the equilibrium is achieved in a short time.

It should be stressed that at equilibrium the concentrations of the various compounds are not necessarily equal. The equilibrium may be entirely in favor of the reacting substances or of the products of the reaction.

Enzymes are catalysts of an organic nature. They act on biochemically important substances. Fig. 21 shows an example of the catalysis by hog pancreatic lipase of the hydrolysis of *n*-butyl butyrate. At equilibrium, approached from either side, the composition is the same for the final reaction mixture. For the synthetic reaction one would start with butyl alcohol and butyric acid; for hydrolysis, with butyl butyrate.

Here one essential difference must be stressed between inorganic catalysts, like platinum, which catalyzes many chemical reactions, and enzymes, which are extremely specific.

It is well known that most chemical reactions do not proceed entirely in one direction. Several reactions of the substrate (compound acted upon by the enzyme) are possible, depending upon the nature of the enzyme. Because of its specificity, the enzyme catalyzes only one of these reactions. For example, glucose-6-phosphate can yield (a) glucose + phosphate (p. 207), (b) phosphogluconic acid (p. 189), or (c) fructose-6-phosphate (p. 207). The product formed will depend upon the enzyme used.

Chemical Nature of Enzymes.   Pasteur believed that the fermentation reaction required the presence of living organisms (yeast cells). He showed that killing the organisms by heat (pasteurization), followed by subsequent incubation under sterile conditions, prevented the fermentation reaction. He was only partly correct in his interpretation. Buchner ground the yeast cells and extracted a clear solution which allowed the fermentation reaction to proceed even in the absence of live organisms. The mixture of enzymes in this extract was called *zymase*. Pasteur had not only killed the yeast cell but in doing so he had also denatured and inactivated the enzymes involved in fermentation.

The chemical properties of enzymes, as well as their stability and solubility characteristics, are closely related to those of proteins. As more and more enzymes have been isolated in a crystalline form and have proved to be single components (by a variety of tests), it has become more certain that enzymes are indeed proteins. So far, no enzyme has been isolated which is not a protein. It is also true, however, that, in many instances, for an enzyme to be active, some co-factor of a non-protein nature is required. Thus inorganic ions such as Ca^{++}, Mg^{++}, or Mn^{++} may be necessary, or organic compounds may be attached to the enzyme protein ("prosthetic groups"). The enzyme amino acid oxidase, for example, requires for its prosthetic group the compound iso-alloxazine dinucleotide (p. 191). The enzyme (protein) without its prosthetic group is referred to as the "apoenzyme."

CLASSIFICATION AND DESCRIPTION OF THE VARIOUS ENZYMES

Esterases.*   PANCREATIC LIPASE.   This enzyme is present in the pancreas and hydrolyzes fats into fatty acid and glycerol. Lipase is also found in gastric juice.

LIVER ESTERASE.   This enzyme, present in liver, hydrolyzes esters of simple alcohols and is an ester- rather than a fat-splitting enzyme.

RICINUS LIPASE.   This enzyme is found in the seeds of the castor bean and is similar to pancreatic lipase in activity.

---

* By general agreement, enzymes are so named that they end in "ase." Enzymes not named in accordance with this rule were known before the nomenclature was adopted.

CHLOROPHYLLASE. This is an enzyme present in green plants and hydrolyzes chlorophyll *a* into phytol ($C_{21}H_{39}OH$) and ethyl chlorophyllide *a*.

PHOSPHATASES. These enzymes are present in various tissues and hydrolyze various esters of phosphoric acid. The phosphatases, of which there seem to be quite a number, are divided into two groups: alkaline phosphatase, with an optimum *p*H of from 8 to 10, found in intestinal mucosa, kidneys, liver, etc., and acid phosphatase, with an optimum *p*H of from 4 to 5, present in blood serum, etc.

SULFATASES. These enzymes hydrolyze sulfuric esters: $ROSO_3K + H_2O \longrightarrow ROH + KHSO_4$. For example, phenolsulfatase hydrolyzes esters with an aromatic radical; glucosulfatase hydrolyzes esters with a carbohydrate radical; and chondrosulfatase hydrolyzes chondroitinsulfuric acid.

AZOLESTERASES. This name has been suggested for enzymes which hydrolyze nitrogen-alcohol esters. The best-known example is cholinesterase, the enzyme which hydrolyzes acetylcholine.

Peptidases. In the past the proteolytic enzymes were poorly classified because of the difficulty of identifying the specific groupings in the protein substrate which are hydrolyzed. Owing to the work of Bergmann and his group, these enzymes have been classified on the basis of the specific linkage which is split, using synthetic substrate models. While it is true that these small molecular weight substrates are quite different from the proteins which the enzymes attack in vivo, it is believed that the results with synthetic model compounds can be carried over to the large protein and polypeptide molecule.

ENDOPEPTIDASES. These act on large protein molecules although small synthetic molecules are also hydrolyzed.

PEPSIN. This enzyme is present in the gastric mucosa in the form of the inactive pepsinogen, which is converted to pepsin by the action of acid. It acts on substrates containing tyrosine and phenylalanine as well as on proteins.

TRYPSIN. This enzyme is secreted by the pancreas in the form of the inactive trypsinogen and is enzymatically changed to trypsin by the action of "enterokinase," the latter a poorly characterized substance present in the pancreatic secretion. It acts to only a slight extent on native proteins but more effectively on denatured proteins. Substrates which contain a free basic group but no free carboxyl group are split by trypsin. Thus, it will split arginine or lysine amides.

CHYMOTRYPSIN. This enzyme is found in the pancreatic secretion in the form of the inactive chymotrypsinogen. The latter is converted to chymotrypsin by the action of trypsin. It splits its synthetic substrates at the tyrosyl carboxyl group:

$$
\begin{array}{ccc}
\text{COOH} & & \\
| & & \\
\text{CH}_2 & \text{C}_6\text{H}_4\text{OH} & \\
| & | & \\
\text{CH}_2 & \text{CH}_2 & \\
| & | & \\
\text{C}_6\text{H}_5\text{CH}_2\text{OCO—NH.CH.CO} \!-\!\!\!\!-\!\!\!\mid\!\!- \text{NH.CH.CO} \!-\!\!\!\!-\!\!\!\mid\!\!- \text{NH.CH}_2.\text{CONH}_2 \\
& \quad \text{Pepsin} \quad\quad \text{Chymotrypsin}
\end{array}
$$

CATHEPSINS. These are a group of intracellular enzymes which are activated by cyanide, ascorbic acid, cysteine or glutathione. They have not been isolated in pure form but have been classified on the basis of their substrate specificity (Table 6).

Table 6   INTRACELLULAR PROTEOLYTIC ENZYMES OF ANIMAL TISSUES
(From Tallan, Jones, and Fruton: J. Biol. Chem., *194:* 793, 1952.)

Name	Typical Substrate
Cathepsin A	Carbobenzoxy-L-glutamyl-L-tyrosine
Cathepsin B	Benzoyl-L-argininamide
Cathepsin C	Glycyl-L-phenylalaninamide
Leucine aminopeptidase *	L-Leucinamide
Carboxypeptidase *	Carbobenzoxyglycyl-L-phenylalanine
Tripeptidase *	Glycylglycylglycine

* Exopeptidases.

EXOPEPTIDASES. This term was used by Bergmann to indicate an enzyme attacking a peptide linkage adjacent to a free polar group.

DIPEPTIDASE. These split dipeptides only. For example, there is present in many animal tissues a dipeptidase which specifically splits glycylglycine. The enzyme is activated by Co^{++}.

CARBOXYPEPTIDASES. These split acylated dipeptides where the amino group has been blocked. An example is pancreatic carboxypeptidase which split chloroacetyl-L-tyrosine. It requires Mg^{++} for its activity.

AMINOPEPTIDASES. These split dipeptides, dipeptide amides or amino acid amides. An example is leucine aminopeptidase from the intestinal mucosa, which splits L-leucylglycine and leucylamide.

TRIPEPTIDASES. These split tripeptides. An example is the tripeptidase from calf thymus which splits glycylglycylglycine, alanylglycylglycine and leucylglycylglycine.

For the enzyme rennin, see p. 125.

Amidases. These act on carbon-nitrogen linkages.

UREASE. This is an enzyme which is present in leguminous plants (soybeans and jack beans) and converts urea into ammonia. It was the first enzyme to be isolated in crystalline form.

ARGINASE. This enzyme is found in liver and converts arginine into ornithine and urea.*

PURINE AMIDASES. These represent a group of enzymes, present in the liver, which deaminize purines. The enzyme adenase is an example.

GLUTAMINASE. This is an enzyme which catalyzes the reaction: glutamine $\rightleftharpoons$ glutamic acid.

Phosphorylases. These enzymes can decompose polysaccharides as well as bring about the synthesis of the latter. For example, a phosphorylase obtained from muscle converts hexose-1-phosphate into a polysaccharide. The reaction is a reversible one. An x-ray diffraction pattern of this poly-

* There is evidence to show that maximum activity with arginase is obtained only in the presence of Mn^{++} ions.

saccharide shows it to be similar in structure to the amylose fraction of starch obtained from plants.

In contrast to this, when heart or liver phosphorylase is used in place of the one obtained from muscle, the polysaccharide obtained resembles glycogen.

Carbohydrases.   (See also enzymes under starch, p. 24.)

SUCRASE (saccharase, invertase).   This enzyme is present in animal and plant tissues and hydrolyzes sucrose into glucose and fructose.

MALTASE AND LACTASE.   These are found with sucrase in the small intestine, and hydrolyze maltose and lactose respectively.

EMULSIN.   This enzyme is present in bitter almonds and hydrolyzes the glucoside amygdalin into glucose, benzaldehyde, and hydrogen cyanide.

AMYLASES.   These enzymes are found in plant and animal tissues and hydrolyze starch and glycogen into maltose. The ptyalin found in saliva and the amylase present in pancreatic juice are examples.

Amylases are divided into α- and β- varieties. The α-amylase acts upon both amylose and amylopectin in starch, producing shorter chains (dextrins), the latter then being hydrolyzed to maltose. The β-amylase acts more readily on amylose, with the production of maltose; it also acts on amylopectin, but only approximately 50 per cent of the latter is converted to maltose, the remaining 50 per cent—a form of dextrin—not being acted upon any further. The β-amylase splits glucosidic linkages exterior to branching points, whereas the α-amylase splits linkages both inside and outside branching points.

CELLULASE.   This enzyme, which is found in the digestive secretions of invertebrates, and in extracts of some molds and bacteria, may break down cellulose to a reducing sugar, but usually a multiplicity of products are produced.

Oxidases.*   DEHYDROGENASES.   These are enzymes found in many tissues (muscle, for instance), which bring about oxidations by the removal of hydrogen from substances. For example, succinic dehydrogenase converts succinic acid into fumaric acid.†

CATALASE.   This enzyme is found in plant and animal tissues (liver, for example) and catalyzes the decomposition of hydrogen peroxide into water and molecular oxygen. Sumner has obtained the enzyme in crystalline form and states that it is a combination of a protein with an iron-pyrrole (heme) compound (compare with hemoglobin, p. 155).

PEROXIDASES.   These enzymes are present in many tissues (for instance, the spleen and horseradish) and they transfer peroxide oxygen to oxidizable substances.

TYROSINASE.   There is much confusion regarding this enzyme. Such various oxidation processes as the darkening of the potato on exposure and the formation of melanin (Chap. 14) are said to involve tyrosinase. The enzyme catalyzes the oxidation of various phenolic compounds [phenol, pyrocatechin (catechol), p-cresol, tyrosine, pyrogallol, etc.].‡

---

* Much of Chap. 11 is devoted to a discussion of these enzymes.

† Coenzymes are also needed (p. 190).

‡ Tyrosinase has also been called catecholase, cresolase, polyphenol oxidase, phenolase, etc.

LACCASE. This enzyme is found in plants and in bacteria and oxidizes both pyrocatechin and hydroquinone types of compounds.

The enzyme is a copper-protein compound.

CYTOCHROME OXIDASE (indophenol oxidase). This enzyme is present in various tissues and catalyzes the oxidation of a mixture of p-phenylenediamine and a-naphthol to indophenol. It acts in vivo by oxidizing reduced cytochrome C (p. 192).

URICASE. This enzyme is found in liver and kidney of animals that excrete allantoin. It oxidizes uric acid to allantoin.

LUCIFERASE. This enzyme is present in fireflies and acts on luciferin to produce light. Here some of the energy from the catalytic oxidation of an organic compound of unknown composition (luciferin) is emitted as light (bioluminescence).

Miscellaneous Groups of Enzymes. MUCOLYTIC ENZYMES. These enzymes act on polysaccharides containing hexosamine in their molecules. Hyaluronic acid is an example of such a polysaccharide. Lysozyme and hyaluronidase are examples of enzymes acting on these polysaccharides.

LYSOZYME, an enzyme which effects the lysis of some microorganisms, is found distributed in nasal secretion, saliva, tears, leukocytes, and eggwhite. Its lytic action is explained on the basis that the enzyme hydrolyzes a polysaccharide present in the bacterial membrane.

HYALURONIDASE acts on hyaluronic acid, a substance present in vitreous humor, umbilical cord, synovial fluid, skin, etc.

Both these enzymes may have a destructive effect on the body by disintegrating the mucoids in the lining of the skin, etc.

GLUCURONIDASE is an enzyme which catalyzes the hydrolysis of glucuronides. The reverse reaction, the formation of glucuronides in vivo, has also been postulated.

NUCLEOLYTIC ENZYMES. See Chap. 15.

THE DEMONSTRATION OF ENZYME ACTIVITY

Intact Organism. Using the whole organism made it difficult, and in many cases impossible, to follow the numerous steps in the metabolic transformations of compounds. Abnormal compounds—in so far as the body is concerned—such as Knoop's phenyl derivatives of fatty acids (p. 224) were also used in the attempt to identify the products formed in the organism. Such methods, in any case, revealed little about the enzymes involved, or about the intermediates of the reactions.

Perfused Organs. In order to eliminate the complications of a multi-organ system, a technique was perfected whereby an isolated organ was perfused with a solution whose contents approximated those of blood. The substance to be studied (some compound of physiological importance) was introduced into the circulation, and from time to time samples for analysis were withdrawn. This method is, of course, less physiological than using the intact organism.

Tissue Slices. Using a technique developed by Barcroft and by Warburg, very thin tissue slices of the organ—surrounded by a suitable salt solution (see Table 7) at optimum pH and at optimum temperature, and with a plentiful supply of oxygen—are used. Dissolved in the solution surrounding the slices is the substance whose metabolism is to be studied. The apparatus is of such a kind that tissue respiration (oxygen uptake and carbon dioxide output) can be measured, and the chemical change undergone by the substrate—the substance whose metabolism is being studied—may be determined by suitable means.

One difficulty with this method is that even with the thinnest of tissue slices, the cells which make them up contain not one enzyme but a multi-enzyme system, which increases the difficulty of isolating and identifying intermediate products. However, it does represent the simplest system for the study of metabolic reactions by intact cells with organized enzyme systems.

Table 7   COMPARISON OF THE KREBS MEDIUM AND
MAMMALIAN SERUM
(From Baldwin, E.: Dynamic Aspects of Biochemistry.)

	Mammalian Serum *	Krebs Solution *
Na^+	320	327
K^+	22	23
Ca^{++}	10	10
Mg^{++}	2.5	2.9
Cl^-	370	454
$PO_4^=$	10	11
$SO_4^=$	11	11.4
HCO_3^-	54 vols.%	54 vols.%
CO_2	2.5 vols.%	2.5 vols.%
pH	7.4	7.4

* All concentrations are in milligrams per 100 ml., excepting bicarbonate and CO_2, which are expressed as milliliters of CO_2 per 100 ml. Glucose (0.2 per cent final concentration) is sometimes added.

Tissue Homogenates.   This technique involves the mechanical breakdown of the cell wall, liberating the enzymes in solution or suspension. The problem of the passage of a compound across the intact cell wall is thus eliminated, and more data can be obtained concerning the specificity of enzymes and the effects of various agents on their activity. However, since the cellular enzyme is disorganized, co-factors needed for the complete functioning of many of the enzymes (such as ATP, for example; see p. 207) are rapidly destroyed; and it often becomes necessary to add such factors from the outside.

Cell-free Extracts.   By using a suitable extraction medium, and by making use of differential high speed centrifugation, cell-free extracts can be obtained from a tissue. Such an extract may serve as the starting point for the isolation and characterization of individual enzymes. Extracts can also be used for the identification of intermediate reaction products.

This type of extract is represented by Buchner's yeast extract (p. 92) and by Myerhoff's muscle extract with which he studied the reactions of fermentation (p. 207).

A drawback to this technique is that some enzymes are present in an insoluble form and are not found in the extract. Some of these insoluble enzymes have, to be sure, been brought into solution by suitable chemical treatment. In any case, in the intact cell, many enzymes appear to exist associated with insoluble particles.

Isotopes.   In the evolution of techniques for the study of enzymes, the pendulum has swung back again to the use of the intact organism. One great defect in this method as used earlier has been overcome. Instead of labelling compounds with unphysiological groups—as Knoop's *phenyl* fatty

Table 8   ISOTOPES OF IMPORTANCE IN BIOCHEMISTRY
(From Bull, H.: Physical Biochemistry, 2d ed.)

| | Stable Isotopes | | |
Element	Atomic No.	Mass No.	Relative Abundance
Hydrogen	1	1	99.99
Deuterium	1	2	0.003
Carbon	6	12	99.3
Carbon	6	13	0.7
Nitrogen	7	14	99.86
Nitrogen	7	15	0.14
Oxygen	8	16	99.81
Oxygen	8	17	0.16

| | Radioactive Isotopes | |
Isotope	Half-Life	Type of Radiation *
H^3	31 yrs.	β^-
C^{11}	20.35 min.	β^+
C^{14}	10^4 yrs.	β^-
Na^{24}	14.8 hrs.	β^-, γ
P^{32}	14.3 days	β^-
S^{35}	87.1 days	β^-
Cl^{38}	37 min.	β^-, γ
K^{42}	12.4 hrs.	β^-
Ca^{45}	180 days	β^-, γ
Fe^{59}	47 days	β^-, γ
I^{131}	8 days	β^-, γ

* β^- = negative beta-particles (electrons).
  β^+ = positive beta-particles (positrons).
  γ = gamma-rays (electromagnetic radiation).

acids, p. 224—for identification purposes, isotopically labelled compounds can now be prepared which are chemically indistinguishable by the organism from the non-isotopic compounds. An additional advantage is that relatively small quantities of the compound to be studied need to be administered.

The compound in question is so prepared that one or more of its elements contains either a radioactive isotope of that element, or a greater than normal amount of a stable isotope. (Table 8 lists some of the stable and radioactive isotopes of importance in biochemistry.)

The use of isotopically-labelled compounds will be illustrated throughout the book. Meanwhile, two examples will be given at this stage. The first (Fig. 22) demonstrates that choline causes an increased rate of incorporation of inorganic phosphate into the plasma phospholipids. In this experiment, P^{32}, in the form of inorganic phosphate, has been used.

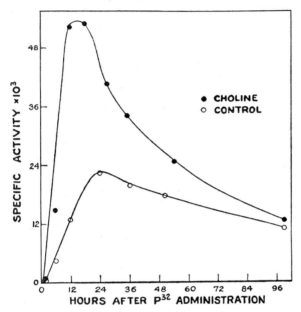

Fig. 22. The effect of choline on the extent of incorporation of P^{32} into plasma phospholipid in the dog. (Friedlander, Chaikoff and Entenman: J. Biol. Chem., *158*: 231, 1945.)

The second example (Table 9) illustrates the distribution in the egg, of administered P^{32} with time.

Table 9   LABELLED P^{32} CONTENT OF EGGS
(From Hevesy: Adv. Enzym., *7*: 159.)

Time Between Administration of Active P and Egg Laying	Per Cent of Labelled P Administered Found in			
	Shell	Albumin	Total Yolk	Yolk Lecithin
5 hrs.	0.24	0.0015	0.0014	0.000
1.0 day	0.052	0.032	0.109	0.014
3.0 "	0.036	0.030	0.42	0.17
4.5 "	0.026	0.027	0.95	0.34
6.5 "	0.022	0.020	0.85	0.35

Localization of Enzyme Activity in the Cell.   The biochemist has always been aware that during a water or saline extraction of ground tissue, much of the formed elements are disorganized and destroyed. In order to minimize such alterations, Schneider and Hogeboom developed a technique which allows for a separation of the homogenate into several uniform fractions. The tissue is subjected to mild homogenization in the cold with a solution of isotonic or slightly hypertonic sucrose.* The homogenate is next subjected to centrifugation at varying speeds. Each precipitate so obtained is suspended in fresh sucrose solution and again centrifuged. In this manner one obtains the following fractions (in the order of increasing speed required for their sedimentation: 1, nuclei; 2, mitochondria; 3, microsomes (submicroscopic particles); 4, supernatant.

Table 10   DISTRIBUTION OF ENZYME ACTIVITIES IN LIVER HOMOGENATE FRACTIONS OBTAINED BY DIFFERENTIAL CENTRIFUGATION
(From Schneider: J. Biol. Chem., *176*: 259, 1948; LePage and Schneider: Ibid., *176*: 1021, 1948; Schneider and Potter: Ibid., *177*: 893, 1949.)

Fraction	*Octanoxidase*	*Oxalacetic Oxidase*	*Glycolysis*
	(per cent of original homogenate activity)		
Nuclei (N)	2.8	10.5	12.6
Mitochondria (M)	81	44.5	0
Submicroscopic particles (P)	0	0	2.7
Supernatant (S)	0	0.5	52.7
M + P	95.0	81.5	
M + S		62.0	68.6
P + S			94.9

When the nuclei and mitochondria are examined microscopically, little change is apparent as compared to their appearance in the intact cell. Nor is any change apparent in their staining characteristics.

An analysis of the content of such fractions in terms of oxidizing and glycolytic enzymes is given in Table 10.

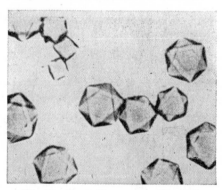

Fig. 23. Crystalline urease (Sumner).

It may be seen that the oxidizing enzymes appear to be associated with the mitochondrial particles, whereas the glycolytic enzymes are in solution in the supernatant. That co-factors (p. 102) are needed is seen by comparing the enzyme activity of any one fraction with the enzyme activity of the same fraction to which has been added a second fraction. Thus the mito-

* For an explanation of "isotonic" and "hypertonic," see p. 152.

chondria contain 81 per cent of the activity of the original homogenate in so far as its ability to oxidize octanoic acid is concerned; the submicroscopic particles show no activity at all. When the two fractions are mixed, the activity increases to 95 per cent.

Purification of Enzymes. The techniques involved in the isolation and crystallization of enzymes are the same as those used for proteins (p. 50). With enzymes there is the added advantage that the degree of purification can be followed by a quantitative estimation of enzyme activity. Again, the criteria of purity for enzymes are the same as those used for proteins: homogeneity upon sedimentation, electrophoresis, and solubility (p. 50). Figures 23, 24 and 25 are photographs of crystalline enzymes.

Fig. 24. Crystalline pepsin (Northrop).

Fig. 25. Crystalline trypsin (Kunitz and Northrop).

Table 11 lists molecular weights and isoelectric points for a number of enzymes.

Table 11   MOLECULAR WEIGHT AND ISOELECTRIC
POINT OF SOME ENZYMES
(From Sumner and Myrback: The Enzymes, article
by Moelwyn-Hughes, Vol. 1, Part 1, p. 28.)

Enzyme	Molecular Weight	Isoelectric Point
Catalase	248,000	5.58
Pepsin	37,000	2.85
Trypsin	34,000	7.50
Urease	483,000	5.05

Co-Factors for Enzymes.   Many enzymes show little or no activity unless supplied with some outside factor or factors. In some cases the factors may be inorganic ions, such as Ca^{++}, Mg^{++} or Mn^{++}; in other cases they may be organic compounds, such as DPN or TPN (p. 88). These factors, or *co-factors,* as they are called, may, in some cases, combine loosely with the enzyme to produce the active enzyme. In some cases the co-factor is found to be already present in the enzyme when the latter is isolated; here the co-factor is linked to the enzyme, and the former is known as the *prosthetic* group.

An example of an enzyme linked to a prosthetic group is a yellow enzyme which consists of a colorless protein (*apoenzyme*) in combination with flavin adenine dinucleotide (prosthetic group) (p. 191). The prosthetic group may be removed from the protein and recombined with it.

For examples of the function of these co-factors, see p. 193 under *Biological Oxidations.*

Amino Acid Groups Involved in Enzyme Activity.   In the action of an enzyme containing a prosthetic group, both the latter and the protein portion of the enzyme are necessary for activity. Enzymes, it would seem, combine with their substrates—the compounds acted upon by the enzymes —prior to their action (Michaelis-Menten, p. 108). The chemical alteration of specific groups in the protein molecule of the enzyme may lead to reduced enzymic activity. For example, one of the amino acids in pepsin is tyrosine. If the pepsin is acetylated—meaning the acetylation of the phenolic group in tyrosine—pepsin is inactivated. Again, if the cysteine —SH groups of urease are blocked by certain reagents, there is a marked decrease in urease activity; e.g.

$$Enz{-}SH + ICH_2CONH_2 \longrightarrow Enz{-}S{-}CH_2CONH_2 + HI$$

In many cases oxidation of these —SH groups to the disulfide (—S—S—) form by mild oxidizing agents can be reversed by the addition of an excess of a mild reducing agent with a reappearance of enzyme activity.

A good illustration of competition between two substances for a position on an enzyme, and one which has led to very practical results, involves the use of BAL (British antilewisite) as an antidote to the arsenical war gas, lewisite.

As a result of pioneer researches by Peters, the conclusion was reached that the toxic effects of lewisite were due primarily to a combination of this substance with the —SH group of one of the enzymes in the skin (the pyruvate oxidizing enzyme). The combination involved a linking of the arsenic in lewisite with the —SH groups in the enzyme:

$$\text{Tissue enzyme} \begin{array}{c} \diagup SH \\ \diagdown SH \end{array} + Cl_2As.CH:CHCl \longrightarrow \text{Lewisite}$$

$$\text{Tissue enzyme} \begin{array}{c} \diagup S \\ \diagdown S \end{array} As.CH:CHCl + 2HCl$$

Attempts were then made to obtain a compound which would act as an antidote by attracting away the arsenic from the tissue enzyme. BAL, a sulfhydryl compound, proved the answer:

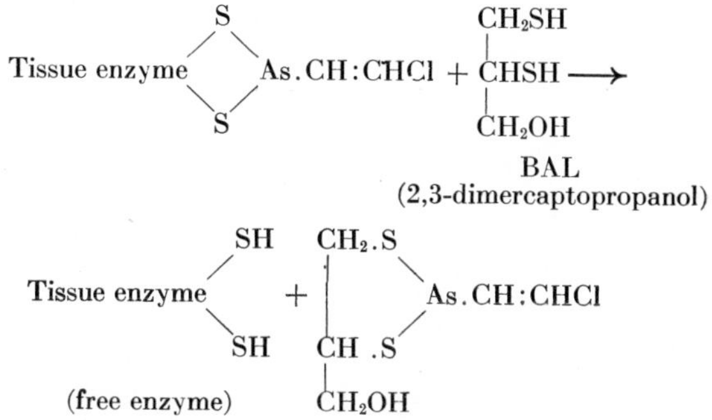

$$\text{Tissue enzyme}\diagup^{\displaystyle S}_{\diagdown\,\,S}\text{As.CH:CHCl} + \begin{matrix}CH_2SH\\|\\CHSH\\|\\CH_2OH\end{matrix} \longrightarrow$$

BAL
(2,3-dimercaptopropanol)

$$\text{Tissue enzyme}\diagup^{\displaystyle SH}_{\diagdown\,\,SH} + \begin{matrix}CH_2.S\\|\\CH.S\\|\\CH_2OH\end{matrix}\diagdown\diagup\text{As.CH:CHCl}$$

(free enzyme)

BAL will prevent skin blistering (vesication) if applied before the lewisite; and even if applied after the lewisite, the BAL will reverse the commencing reddening and swelling.

BAL has also been found to be effective in the treatment of poisoning by a number of heavy metals—mercury, for example. Here the —SH of BAL and the mercury combine to form a relatively undissociated complex which is rapidly eliminated.

KINETICS OF ENZYME ACTION

The equilibrium point of a chemical reaction is more rapidly reached in the presence of an enzyme capable of influencing the particular reaction. The enzyme is apparently unchanged at the end of the reaction and contributes no measurable energy to it. This may involve heterogeneous as well as homogeneous reactions; it may involve adsorption phenomena as well as reactions in solution. The enzymes are often inhibited in their activity by increasing the quantity of substrate—a phenomenon which has led to various theories of intermediate enzyme-substrate formation. The enzymes are further inhibited in their activity by the accumulation of the products of the reaction, the tendency here being toward a reversal of the reaction. They are very sensitive to changes in temperature and to pH changes; and they are easily "poisoned" by heavy metals, etc.

/, **Effects of Increasing the Concentration of the Enzyme.** According to the law of mass action, the velocity of a reaction is proportional to the concentration of the reacting substances. Assuming, for the sake of simplicity, a unimolecular reaction, involving but one type of molecule, the velocity of such a reaction can be expressed as

$$v = \frac{dx}{dt} = k(a - x)$$

in which a is the initial concentration, x the change in concentration during the time t, k is a constant (unimolecular velocity constant), and dx/dt is the velocity of the reaction. By integration we get

$$k = \frac{1}{t}\ln\frac{a}{a - x}$$

Plotting $a - x$ against t, we get a curve as shown (Fig. 26):

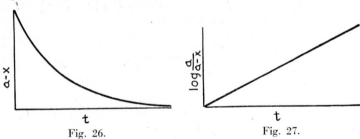

Fig. 26.   Fig. 27.

Figs. 26 and 27. [Hitchcock: Physical Chemistry for Students of Biology and Medicine (2d ed.). Charles C Thomas, Publisher.]

Plotting the log of $a/a - x$ against t gives us a straight line (Fig. 27).

These curves are typical of reaction velocity curves for a unimolecular reaction.

A simple example of a monomolecular reaction is the inversion of cane sugar by acid:

$$C_{12}H_{22}O_{11} + H_2O \longrightarrow C_6H_{12}O_6 + C_6H_{12}O_6$$

Table 12   REACTION COURSE OF CANE SUGAR INVERSION BY H IONS
(From Wilhelm)

Time (t), Minutes	Angle of Rotation, Degrees	$K = \dfrac{1}{t} \log_{10} \dfrac{a}{a - x}$
0	+46.75	
45	+38.25	0.001 34
120	+26.00	0.001 38
240	+11.50	0.001 40
450	− 4.50	0.001 47
630	−10.00	0.001 39
∞	−18.70	. . . .

Table 13   SACCHARASE QUANTITY AND REACTION VELOCITY
(From Hudson)

Relative Saccharase Concentration	Time, Minutes	Transformation (per cent) with Initial Concentration of Sugar of		
		4.55 per cent	9.09 per cent	27.3 per cent
2.00	15	73.2	45.3	11.2
1.50	20	73.2	44.8	11.2
1.00	30	72.9	45.3	11.5
0.50	60	72.9	45.2	11.4
0.25	120	73.1	45.2	10.9

Strictly speaking, this is a bimolecular reaction because of the presence of water; but the change in its concentration during the reaction is negligible. The acid in the reaction is the catalyst. The results of an experiment are given in Table 12.

By substituting an enzyme for the acid, we get results shown in Table 13.

In this case, the table shows the proportionality between the concentration of enzyme and the reaction velocity.

It would seem from Northrop's work that deviations from this rule must be attributed to the presence of impurities which inhibit the reaction.

Northrop also showed that where the enzyme is inhibited by the products of the reaction, the direct proportionality between enzyme concentration and reaction velocity is modified in accord with the *Schütz rule:* the amount of protein hydrolyzed is proportional to the square root of the concentration of the enzyme:

$$x = k \sqrt{ET}$$

where T = time (Fig. 28).

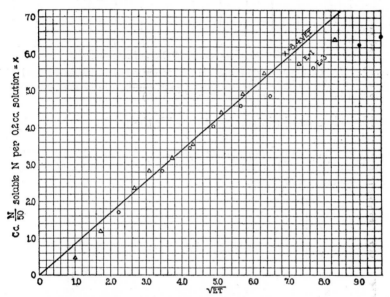

Fig. 28. Rate of digestion of casein solution plotted against the square root of the enzyme concentration × the time in days. (Northrop: Harvey Lectures. Williams and Wilkins Co.)

Effect of Concentration of Substrate.   Table 13 shows very clearly how the reaction velocity is influenced by the concentration of the substrate. Within a given time, a definite amount of saccharase (invertase) will hydrolyze a larger percentage of sucrose when the solution is dilute than when it is concentrated. This is illustrated in Figure 29.

To explain such retardation, Bayliss introduced his adsorption theory, wherein the colloidal enzyme particles became "saturated" and "a further increase in concentration will not result in more adsorption and therefore in no increase in the rate of reaction."

In at least one instance, that of pepsin, Northrop explains enzymic peculiarities on the basis that the reaction is between the ionized protein and the free enzyme. In the presence of acid the protein forms an ionized protein salt which varies by an amount depending upon the pH of the solution. The pepsin, on the other hand, is present as free pepsin, negatively

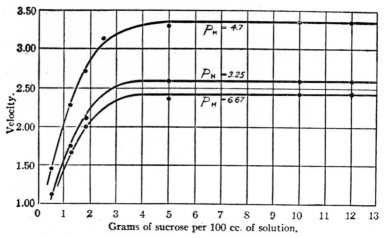

Fig. 29. Effect of substrate concentration on reaction velocity, illustrating the limiting or saturation value at higher concentrations. Experiments with sucrose and invertase. (Nelson and Bloomfield: J. Am. Chem. Soc., 46: 1027.)

charged, and as pepsin in combination with the products of hydrolysis of the protein.

Effect of Hydrogen Ion Concentration.   As has already been inti- mated, the activity of the enzyme is very much dependent upon the hydro- gen ion concentration of the solution.

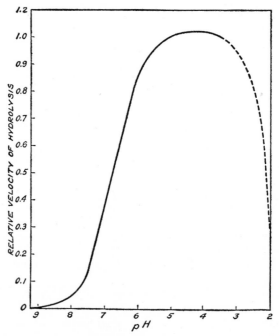

Fig. 30. Relationship between the pH and activity of a yeast invertase preparation. (Michaelis and Davidsohn: Biochem. Z., 35: 405.)

Another curve of this type we owe to Michaelis and Davidsohn (Fig. 30). Here we are dealing with the action of invertase (saccharase) on sucrose. The optimum pH is at 4.5. Both on the acid and the alkaline side there is a rapid decrease in activity. Between pH 4.5 and 9 the shape of the curve resembles the ionization curve of a weak acid, which suggests that invertase itself might be such a weak acid (within these pH limits), dissociating thus:

$$\text{Invertase acid} \xrightarrow{\text{Acid}} \text{Invertase anion} + \text{H}^+$$

and that it is the un-ionized portion which catalyzes the hydrolysis of sucrose. The shape of the curve from pH 2 to 4.5 resembles the ionization curve of a weak base.

Table 14, taken from the book by Waldschmidt-Leitz (see references at the end of the chapter), gives the pH optimum of a number of the enzymes.

Table 14 pH OPTIMUM FOR SEVERAL ENZYMES

Enzyme	pH optimum
Lipase (pancreas)	8
Lipase (stomach)	4–5
Lipase (castor oil)	4.7
Pepsin	1.5–1.6
Trypsin	7.8–8.7
Urease	7.0
Invertase	4.5
Maltase	6.1–6.8
Amylase (pancreas)	6.7–7.0
Amylase (malt)	4.6–5.2
Catalase	7.0

The Effect of Temperature.   Enzymic reactions are influenced by temperature changes in much the same way that chemical reactions in general are influenced by them. Very approximately, for an increase in temperature of 10° C. the velocity of the reaction is doubled or tripled. Between 20° and 30° C., then, the temperature coefficient (Q_{10}, or k_{30}/k_{20}) for many enzymic reactions is between 2 and 3. However, it must be remembered that enzymes are very susceptible to heat, and that temperatures from 50° C. and up for any length of time (and the time factor is very important) very rapidly destroy them. As the temperature is increased beyond body temperature, two forces come into play: the rate of destruction of the enzyme versus the increase in the rate of transformation of the substrate; and at comparatively high temperatures the first completely overshadows the second.

MECHANISM OF ENZYME ACTION

Michaelis and Menten proposed that an enzyme first combines with the substrate to form an intermediate complex. Experimental confirmation of this hypothesis has since been obtained by the actual identification of compounds of the enzyme-substrate complex. The enzyme next undergoes dissociation in such a way that the substrate is chemically altered, and the enzyme is liberated:

$$E + S \underset{k_2}{\overset{k_1}{\rightleftarrows}} ES \overset{k_3}{\longrightarrow} E + P$$

where $E =$ enzyme, $S =$ substrate, $ES =$ enzyme-substrate complex and $P =$ products.

The dissociation constant, K_m, of the enzyme-substrate complex is equal to $(E)(S)/(ES)$.

If E_o is the total concentration of enzyme, E is the concentration of free enzyme, and ES is the concentration of bound enzyme, then

$$K_m = \frac{(E_o - ES)(S)}{(ES)}$$

$$K_m(ES) = (E_o)S - (ES)S$$
$$K_m(ES) + (ES)S = (E_o)S$$
$$(ES)(K_m + S) = (E_o)S$$

$$(ES) = \frac{(E_o)S}{K_m + S}$$

The velocity of the reaction, v, is equal to $k_3(ES)$, so that

$$v = \frac{k_3(E_o)(S)}{K_m + S}$$

If the substrate concentration is increased to the point where the enzyme is saturated with the substrate, the maximum velocity of the reaction, V, is equal to $k_3(E_o)$; or v is equal to $(V)(S)/K_m + S$; or, taking reciprocals,

$$\frac{1}{v} = \left(\frac{K_m}{V}\right)\left(\frac{1}{S}\right) + \frac{1}{V}$$

If one plots $1/v$ against $1/S$ from the experimental values, a straight line is obtained whose value for the slope is K_m/V, and whose intercept is $1/V$. The Michaelis constant, K_m, which is the dissociation constant for the enzyme-substrate complex, can thus be evaluated. Actually, it is only when k_3 is very much smaller than k_2 that K_m becomes equal to the true dissociation constant of the complex.

The Mechanism of Enzyme Inhibitors.   The Michaelis formulation can be extended to provide an explanation for the action of enzyme inhibitors. Here the assumption is also made of an enzyme-inhibitor complex.

$$E + S \rightleftarrows ES \longrightarrow E + P$$
$$E + I \rightleftarrows EI$$

where I is the inhibitor.

$$K_m = \frac{(E)(S)}{(ES)} \text{ and } K_I = \frac{(E)(I)}{(EI)}$$

Combining, we get

$$EI = \frac{K_m(ES)(I)}{K_I(S)}$$

since $E = E_o - ES - EI$
we get

$$E = \frac{K_m(ES)}{S} = E_o - ES - \frac{K_m(ES)(I)}{K_I(S)}$$

Substituting $v = k_3(ES)$ and $V = k_3(E_o)$, we have

$$v = \frac{V}{\dfrac{K_m}{S} + 1 + \dfrac{K_m I}{K_I(S)}}$$

and taking the reciprocals,

$$\frac{1}{v} = \left(\frac{K_m}{V}\right)\left(\frac{1}{S}\right)\left(\frac{1}{\frac{I}{K_I}}\right) + \frac{1}{V}$$

By plotting $1/v$ against $1/S$, one gets a straight line whose slope is $(K_m/V)\left(\dfrac{1}{\frac{I}{K_I}}\right)$, which represents an increase of the slope over the uninhibited

slope of $\left(\dfrac{1}{\frac{I}{K_I}}\right)$.

For inhibition of the competitive type—which is the example just given—such inhibition can be overcome by increasing the concentration of the substrate. For noncompetitive inhibition, where the degree of inhibition is independent of the substrate concentration,

$$\frac{1}{v} = \left(1 + \frac{I}{K_I}\right)\left(\frac{1}{V} + \frac{K_m}{VS}\right)$$

If $1/v$ is plotted against $1/S$, both the slope and the intercept are increased by a factor $(1 + I/K_I)$.

Figure 31 gives an example of a plot of the reciprocal of the reaction velocity $(1/v)$ against the reciprocal of the substrate concentration $(1/S)$ for the enzyme which catalyzes the hydrolysis of acetyl choline to acetate and choline. Where the experimental lines intercept the vertical axis gives the value for $1/V$ whereas the slope of the experimental line gives the value for K/V, thus yielding the value for K, the Michaelis constant. It may be seen that in the case of the inhibitor eserine, the value for $1/V$ is the same as in the absence of inhibitor while the slope is altered upwards. This is an example of competitive inhibition and can be overcome by adding more substrate. In the case of the inhibitor diisopropyl fluorophosphate, the slope remains the same whereas the intercept, or $1/V$, is different. This is an example of noncompetitive inhibition where the experimental results can be interpreted as meaning that a portion of the enzyme is tied up in an inactive form and is unavailable for action on the substrate.

Example of a Reaction Mechanism.   Tagged compounds have been especially useful for the elucidation of the mechanism of enzyme action. An example is the action of phosphoglucomutase, an enzyme which converts glucose-1-phosphate to glucose-6-phosphate. One might assume, at first glance, that this reaction consists in the migration of the phosphate group from the 1 to the 6 position, on the same molecule of glucose. However, it was soon shown that in order for this reaction to occur, small amounts of glucose-1,6-diphosphate are required. The true mechanism of the reaction was uncovered by the use of glucose-1-phosphate in which the P was radio-active (P^{32}). The following scheme illustrates the mechanism:

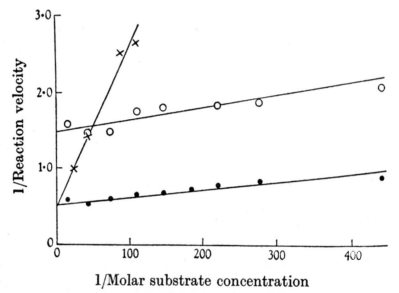

Glucose-1-$P^{32}O_4$ was incubated with non-isotopic glucose-1,6-diphosphate together with the enzyme phosphoglucomutase. After the reaction had

Fig. 31. Plot of reciprocal of reaction velocity against reciprocal of substrate concentration for horse serum acetyl choline esterase (ACh esterase) with and without inhibitors. ●—●, control, no inhibitor; ×—×, eserine; ○—○, diisopropyl fluorophosphate (see Chap. 21). (Mackworth and Webb: Biochem. J., 42: 91, 1948.)

proceeded for some time, the glucose-1,6-diphosphate was shown to be radioactive whereas the glucose-6-phosphate which was formed was not. These results could only be interpreted as a transfer of the phosphate group from position 1 of glucose-1,6-diphosphate to position 6 of the original glucose-1-phosphate resulting in radioactive glucose-1,6-diphosphate and non-radioactive glucose-6-phosphate.

The Action of Catalysts as Applied to Enzymes.   According to the modern concept of catalysis, before molecules can react they must pass through a configuration known as the "activated state." In this state the molecules have an energy content greater than that of the normal reactants. This is called the "activation energy."

The normal state of the reactants at an energy level corresponding to A (Fig. 32) is raised first to the activated state at an energy level B before it can go on to a decomposition of the activated complex to form the products at an energy level corresponding to C.

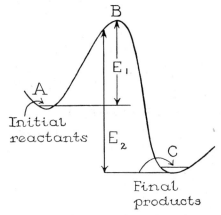

Fig. 32. The activation energy of a chemical reaction. (Adapted from Butler: J. Roy. Soc. Arts, Sept. 26, 1947.)

E_1 corresponds to the free energy of activation (see p. 112) of the forward reaction, and E_2 corresponds to the free energy of the opposing, or reverse, reaction. The function of the catalyst would appear to be that of "tunneling" under the energy pass and thus reducing the energy of activation. Table 15, collected by Lineweaver, gives figures to compare the energy of activation, E (Arrhenius), without and with catalysts.

Table 15   EXAMPLES OF ACTIVATION ENERGIES WITH VARIOUS CATALYSTS

Reaction	Catalyst	E *
H_2O_2 decomposition	None	18,000
	Colloidal Pt	11,700
	Liver catalase	5,500
Sucrose inversion	H^+	26,000
	Yeast invertase	11,500
Casein hydrolysis	HCl	20,600
	Trypsin	12,000
Ethyl butyrate hydrolysis	H^+	13,200
	Pancreatic lipase	4,200

* From $\ln k = -(E/RT) + C$, where E = Arrhenius' energy of activation, R = the gas constant, T = temperature, C = an integration constant, and k = reaction velocity.

ENERGETICS OF CHEMICAL REACTIONS

Chemical reactions follow the laws of thermodynamics. The second law, the law of conservation of energy, is of great importance in the study of metabolic reactions, involving, as they do, stepwise reactions intermediate between the foodstuff and its eventual end products. The metabolism of glucose to carbon dioxide and water, for example, takes place via a long series of intermediary steps allowing, perhaps, for a more efficient regulation of the expenditure of the energy resulting from this over-all reaction. It is necessary, therefore, to determine the energy relationships of these reactions, so that we may understand the manner in which the potential energy which resides in the chemical bond is transferred by way of a series of intermediate compounds.

A description, in mathematical form, of the energy which is available for useful work is given by:

$$\Delta F = \Delta H - T(\Delta S)$$

This statement describes the changes which the various factors involved in a reaction undergo when a system passes from its original state into a new condition (as in a chemical reaction). ΔF is the change in free energy (available energy for useful work), ΔH is the change in the total heat energy of the system, T is the absolute temperature, and ΔS is the change in entropy (the amount by which the total energy of the system is unavailable for the performance of useful work). Entropy may be thought of as those frictional forces which make for loss of energy—energy which cannot be converted into useful work. It may be noted that at $0°$ absolute, $\Delta F = \Delta H$, and that the value for ΔS will determine how nearly ΔF is equal to ΔH. In actual practice, ΔH can be measured and ΔF must be estimated.

For the chemist, the value in knowing ΔF is that it enables him to predict whether a chemical reaction can take place on its own or must be assisted by other reactions which furnish the energy. Thus, according to thermodynamic considerations, if $\Delta F = 0$, the system is in chemical equilibrium; if ΔF is $+$, the reaction cannot take place unassisted (free energy goes into the system and the reaction is called endergonic); if ΔF is $-$, the reaction can proceed on its own (free energy comes out of the system and the reaction is called exergonic).

In the cell, where reactions occur side by side under dynamic conditions, the idea of the coupling of reactions is considered of great importance by the biochemist. Thus, Bull illustrates this point by two reactions which together allow for the conversion of compound A to compound C in a series of two intermediary reactions:

$A \rightleftharpoons B$ $\Delta F = 2760$ calories $K_1 = 0.01$

$B \rightleftharpoons C$ $\Delta F = -4140$ calories $K_2 = 1000$

Thus, the second reaction will remove B as soon as it is formed even though the amounts are indeed very small in the first reaction, leading to the over-all reaction

$A \rightleftharpoons C$ $\Delta F = 2760 - 4140 = -1380$ calories

The free energy of the second reaction was transferred to the first reaction, enabling it to proceed in a forward direction. In this way, we can see how the free energy stored in a chemical bond may be utilized to make reactions proceed, and how this bond energy can be transferred.

The High Energy Chemical Bond. The mechanism whereby enzymes are able to cause the transfer of energy along a series of intermediate compounds has been clarified to a great extent by the studies of Lipmann and others. He points out that among biochemically important compounds there exist a group of phosphorylated substances which differ from other phosphorus-containing compounds in that the phosphorus is bound to the compound by means of a bond in which resides a relatively great amount of energy. This type of bond he called the *high-energy bond* or $\sim$ph. The following illustrate the two general types of phosphorylated compounds:

High Energy Bond

Acetyl phosphate	— 10,000 cal.
Phosphoenol pyruvic acid	— 11,000 cal.
1,3-Diphosphoglyceric acid	— 11,000 cal.
Creatine phosphate	— 10,000 cal.
Adenosine diphosphate (ADP)	— 10,000 cal.
Adenosine triphosphate (ATP)	— 10,000 cal.

Low Energy Bond

Glycerol phosphate	— 2300 cal.
Glucose-6-phosphate	— 3000 cal.
Glucose-1-phosphate	— 4800 cal.
3–Phosphoglyceric acid	— 3000 cal.
2-Phosphoglyceric acid	— 4050 cal.

The creation of a high energy bond from one of low energy is illustrated by the reaction catalyzed by the enzyme which transforms 1,3-diphosphoglyceric aldehyde to 1,3-diphosphoglyceric acid (p. 207). This oxidation reaction is coupled with the reduction of coenzyme I (DPN) (p. 88):

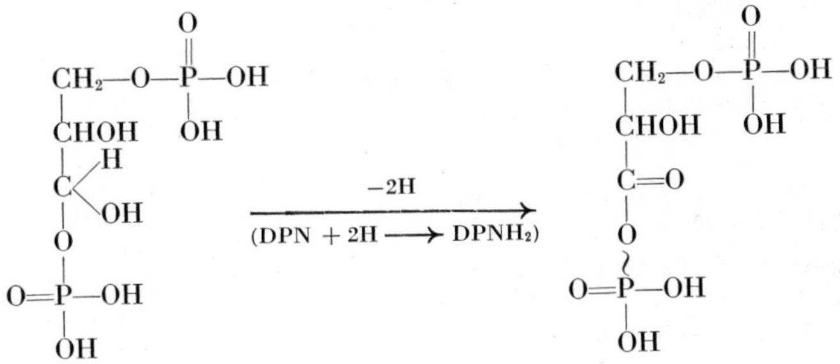

The transfer and utilization of this bond energy will be discussed in Chapter 12.

REFERENCES

Sumner and Myrbach, as the general editors, are responsible for a number of volumes on Enzymes: Chemistry and Mechanism of Action, 1951. Reviews may also be found in Adv. Enzym., edited by *Nord*. Selected topics are treated in Enzymes and Enzyme Systems, 1951, edited by *Edsall*.

See, further, *Lehninger:* Physiol. Rev., *30:* 393, 1950 (role of metal ions in enzyme systems); *Potter, Recknagel, and Hurlbert,* Federation Proceedings, *10:* 646, 1951 (intracellular enzymes); *Butler:* J. Roy. Soc. Arts, *95:* 715, 1947 (general review); *Pfeiffer:* Scientific American, Dec., 1948, p. 29 (a popular but scientifically sound outline).

For crystalline rennin, see *Baun, Connors, and Sullivan:* Arch. Biochem., *43:* 324, 1953.

A study of the terminal amino group of pepsin is by *Williamson and Passmann:* J. Biol. Chem., *199:* 121, 1952.

The catalytically active sites in the chymotrypsin molecule are discussed by *Loewus and Briggs:* J. Biol. Chem., *199:* 857, 1952.

Recent work in the field of enzymes is discussed by *Laskowski:* Ann. Rev. Biochem., *19:* 21, 1950; *Frisell and Hellerman:* Ibid., *20:* 23, 1951; *Balls, Jansen, Altman, and Dounce:* Ibid., *21:* 1, 29, 1952; *Linderstrom-Lang and Moller:* Ibid., *22:* 57, 1953; *Hestrin:* Ibid., *22:* 85, 1953.

References to enzymes more specifically active in biological oxidations are given at the end of Chap. 11. At this stage it may be sufficient to mention two volumes: Mechanisms of Biological Oxidations, 1940, by *Green*, and Respiratory Enzymes, 1942, Univ. Wisconsin Press.

Two papers by *Sumner* on crystalline urease are in the J. Biol. Chem., *69:* 435, 1926, and *76:* 149, 1928. An interesting autobiographical sketch may be found in the J. Chem. Educ., *14:* 255, 1937.

For the isolation and crystallization of enzymes, see *Northrop, Kunitz, and Herriott:* Crystalline Enzymes, 1948.

Anson's crystalline carboxypeptidase is described in the J. Gen. Physiol., *20:* 663, 1937. Crystalline catalase is discussed by *Sumner and Dounce* in the J. Biol. Chem., *115:* 417, 1937, and crystalline papain by *Balls and Lineweaver* in J. Biol. Chem., *130:* 669, 1939 and by *Balls*, Circular 631 (Dec., 1941), U. S. Dept. Agriculture.

For a review of the phosphatase enzymes, see *Gee:* Borden's Review of Nutritional Research, *11:* No. 6, 1950.

On the subject of the cellulase enzymes, see *Tracey:* Nature, *167:* 776, 1951; and *Levinson, Mandels and Reese:* Arch. Biochem., *31:* 351, 1951.

Peptidases have been studied extensively; here are some selections: Annals N. Y. Acad. Sciences, *54:* 143, 1951 (papain); *Casey and Laidler:* Science, *111:* 110, 1950 (pepsin); *Carroll:* Ibid., *111:* 387, 1950 (proteolytic activity); *Snoke and Neurath:* J. Biol. Chem., *187:* 127, 1950 (proteolyt. activity); *Tallan, Jones, and Fruton:* Ibid., *194:* 793, 1952 (intracellular enzymes); *Smith:* Ibid., *176:* 21, 1948 (dipeptidase); *Ellis and Fruton:* Ibid., *191:* 153, 1951 (tripeptidase); *Crook:* J. Soc. Leather Trades Chemists, *35:* 257, 1951 (mode of action); *Astrup and Alkjaersig:* Nature, *169:* 314, 1952 (classification); *Smith:* Proc. Nat. Acad. Sci. U. S., *35:* 80, 1949 (metal peptidases).

On phosphorylase, see *Sumner, Chou and Beuer:* Arch. Biochem., *26:* 1, 1950.

For amylases, see the following: *Schwimmer and Balls:* J. Biol. Chem., *179:* 1063, 1949 (crystalline α-amylase); *England and Singer:* Ibid., *187:* 213, 1950 (β-amylase); *Redform:* Wallerstein Lab., June, 1950, p. 89 (developments in amylase chemistry).

Cosby and Sumner: Arch. Biochem., *8:* 259, 1945, and *Watts and Peng:* J. Biol. Chem., *170:* 441, 1947, deal with the subject of lipoxidase.

For lysozyme, see *Jones:* J. Am. Chem. Soc., *68:* 854, 1946; and *Fraenkel-Conrat;* Arch. Biochem., *27:* 109, 1950.

Fishman, Kasdon, and Homburger: J. Am. Med. Assoc., *143:* 350, 1950, give a summary of the properties of β-glucuronidase.

For a study of physico-chemical relationships, see Annals N. Y. Acad. Sciences, *45:* 357, 1944 (energy relationships); *Frazer and Powell:* J. Biol. Chem., *187:* 803, 1950 (kinetics); *Chance:* Ibid., *194:* 471, 483, 1952 (effect of pH upon reaction kinetics); *Caputto, Leloir, Trucco, Cardini, and Paladini:* Arch. Biochem., *18:* 201, 1948; Ibid., *19:* 339, 1948; *Sutherland, Cohn, Posternack, and Cori:* J. Biol. Chem., *180:* 1285, 1949.

Rothen's experiments on "action at a distance" between enzyme and substrate are described in the J. Am. Chem. Soc., *70:* 2732, 1948. See also *Singer:* J. Biol. Chem., *182:* 189, 1950.

Chapter 7   *Digestion*

IN GENERAL, foods need to be hydrolyzed, to be simplified, chemically, before they can be assimilated by the body. This is true of the carbohydrates other than the monosaccharides, and of the fats and proteins. It is not true of water and most inorganic ions, for they pass through the digestive tract and are absorbed in their original form. The simplification

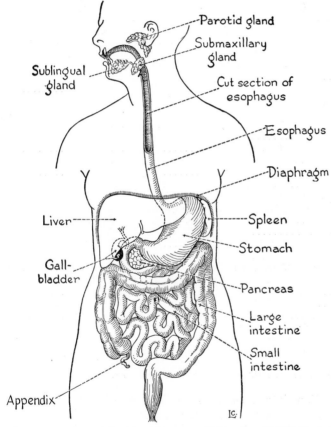

Fig. 33. Diagram of the digestive tract. (Etheredge: Health Facts.)

of the carbohydrates, fats, and proteins is accomplished by a series of hydrolytic changes brought about by enzymes. These changes are carried on in the digestive tract, which includes the mouth, the esophagus, the stomach, and the small and large intestines (Fig. 33). Secretions from the pancreas and the bile find their way into the small intestine, and, as we shall see, play important roles in the digestive process.

As so much of digestion deals with the activity of enzymes, the reader will do well to reread Chap. 6, which deals with the general properties of enzymes.

SALIVARY DIGESTION

Salivary digestion deals largely with the action of ptyalin, an amylase, on starch. The preliminary mastication, involving the breaking up of food particles by the teeth, is a desirable step. The ptyalin is found in saliva. Saliva represents a mixed secretion from the relatively large salivary glands, and also from accessory glands. The salivary glands consist of the parotid, the submaxillary, and the sublingual, and through their ducts they pour

Table 16   COMPOSITION * OF UNSTIMULATED AND STIMULATED † SALIVA (From Karshan; Values Are in Milligrams per 100 ml. Except as Noted.)

	Unstimulated		Stimulated	
	Range	Average	Range	Average
Calcium	4.6–11.0	6.2	3.5–9.2	5.6
Magnesium	0.2–1.3	0.7	. . . .	. . .
Sodium	20–55	40	18–88	55
Potassium	50–63	55	57–93	70
Ammonia	6–30	. . .	1.4–12	6
Chloride	30–63	55	31–63	42
Fluoride (parts per million)	. . . .	. . .	. . . .	0.1
Inorganic phosphorus	11–26	17	6–18	12.5
Thiocyanate	. . . .	15	. . . .	. . .
pH	6.0–7.4	6.8	7.1–7.8	7.3
CO_2 capacity (cc. per 100 cc.)	5–25	12	8–44	25
Titratable alkalinity‡	50–120	70	80–180	120
Lactic acid	. . . .	1.5	0.64–2.04	. . .
Total protein	214–525	320	208–565	280
Mucoid (as sodium mucinate)	. . . .	250	210–290	260
Reducing carbohydrate	11–28	. . .	14–30	. . .
Alcohol-ether soluble phosphorus	0.05–1.0	0.24	. . . .	. . .
Cholesterol	3–15	7.5	. . . .	. . .
Urea	. . . .	. . .	. . . .	10
Uric acid	. . . .	1.5	. . . .	. . .
Vitamin C	. . . .	. . .	. . . .	0.25

* These data are from a number of sources.

† Stimulated saliva refers here to the secretion produced while chewing paraffin.

‡ Titratable alkalinity is expressed as cubic centimeters of 1/50 N HCl needed to titrate 100 ml. of saliva with methyl orange as indicator.

their secretions into the mouth. The flow of saliva is regulated by a reflex stimulation of the secretory nerves. Approximately from 1 to 1½ liters of saliva may be secreted by an individual in the course of twenty-four hours.

Saliva.   This saliva contains about 99.5 per cent of water. The solid material includes the pytalin, several proteins (of which mucin is the most important) and a number of substances found in blood and urine (such as ammonia, amino acids, urea, uric acid, cholesterol, calcium, sodium, potassium, magnesium, phosphate, chloride and bicarbonate) (see Table 16).

The average pH of unstimulated saliva may vary considerably, although as a rule it is around 6.8.

The fact that saliva contains many of the constituents found in blood has suggested the possibility that the determination of such constituents in saliva may have diagnostic value; but the irregular fluctuation, and a failure to find any constant relationship between the constituents of blood and saliva, have not led to any practical results.

The calcium phosphate in enamel and dentin is less soluble in fluids which contain calcium and phosphorus, such as saliva, than it is in fluids which do not contain these elements. Therefore the presence of these elements is one of the most important features of saliva, because they prevent the enamel from dissolving at the normal pH of saliva.

Traces of thiocyanate ions are present in saliva (as well as in blood and urine). It is believed that the origin of the thiocyanate is traced to cyanides (products of protein decomposition) which are possibly detoxified in the liver, in the presence of sulfur compounds, to form thiocyanate. In this connection, it is of interest to note that the ingestion of sub-lethal doses of cyanide gives rise to an increased output of thiocyanate in the urine.

An enzyme system can be extracted from tissues which converts cyanide and thiosulfate into thiocyanate. A small quantity of the thiocyanate is excreted in the form of sulfate.

Action of Ptyalin.   The ptyalin (also known as salivary amylase) acts on starch * producing a series of ill-defined products: soluble starch, erythrodextrin, achrodextrins, and maltose. The starch and soluble starch give a blue color with iodine, the erythrodextrin gives a red color, and the achrodextrins and maltose give no color. Maltose is the only product which reduces Benedict's solution, unless some glucose is formed which would, of course, also reduce Benedict's solution.

Actually, the process of hydrolysis is more complex. Some maltose appears even at the erythrodextrin stage. This has been attributed to the complex nature of the starch itself (see p. 23).

The optimum for amylase activity is a pH of 6.6. The activity of the enzyme is stimulated by the presence of halide ions, particularly the chloride ion. The removal of this ion by dialysis renders ptyalin inactive. At a pH of 4 or below, the enzyme is rapidly destroyed. However, when the food reaches the fundus part of the stomach, salivary digestion may still proceed for fifteen to thirty minutes, owing to the slow accumulation of acid and to the partial neutralization of the acid by a temporary combination with the protein of the food.

Stark is of the opinion that the products of the action of ptyalin on starch include glucose, maltose, and "an array of nonfermentable copper-reducing polysaccharides."

The ptyalin of the mouth, like the amylase in pancreatic juice, belongs to the group of α-amylases. The primary action of these amylases on starch is liquefaction or lowering of viscosity, the amylose and amylopectin molecules being split by fission of α-1,4-glucosidic linkages into α-dextrins. The second process involves the breakup of 1,4-linkages which had so far escaped attack, yielding α-maltose as the main product and some glucose.

The pancreatic amylase, which finds its way into the small intestine, continues the hydrolysis of any undigested starch.

* The ptyalin can also act on glycogen.

In the tissues we find an enzyme, phosphorylase, which can also break down starch and glycogen. This action is not to be confused with the action of amylase on starch and glycogen—whether the amylase be ptyalin or pancreatic amylase or amylases which have their origin in the vegetable kingdom. The amylases act in the presence of water; the phosphorylases act in the presence of phosphate. These two actions may be termed "hydrolysis" and "phosphorolysis," respectively.

A number of the amylases—including ptyalin—have been isolated in crystalline form. As might be expected, they are proteins.*

Estimation of Ptyalin Activity.   The rate of starch hydrolysis (and the activity of the ptyalin) may be estimated by determining the achromic point—the point at which iodine fails to give a color with the substrate— or by determining the extent of reduction. A more carefully controlled estimation would include the achromic point, the residual polysaccharide, the total reducing power, and the reducing power after the precipitation of the dextrins by alcohol. Using such methods, Glock found that the relative rates of hydrolysis were different with different starches.

Mucin.   Mucin, the protein present in largest quantity, gives to saliva its "ropy" consistency. It is present as a soluble alkaline (probably potassium) salt and can be precipitated by the addition of acid. It has been classified as a glycoprotein, because on hydrolysis it yields glucosamine as one of its products. However, in addition to glucosamine, we also get glucuronic, acetic, and sulfuric acids.†

Tooth Decay (Dental Caries).   This disease deals with the disintegration of the enamel, the dentin and the pulp of the tooth. It has been suggested that in addition to its function as a digestive agent, saliva is also important in its influence on the possible development of dental caries. This well-nigh ever-present disease—85–95 per cent of people in civilized countries suffer from it—is of two kinds: in the one, common to young people, caries occurs in the pits and fissures of the crown or near points of contact of adjacent teeth; in the other, prevalent among older people, the smooth surfaces of the crown or exposed roots are attacked. The first variety is the more common, occurring very often during the period of eruption of the teeth.

The various centers of attack, the pits and fissures of the crown and the contact points, are precisely centers where food particles are likely to be deposited. The action of bacteria on such food particles may cause the production of acid. It is believed—and this is advanced as a theory of the origin of dental caries—that first the enamel on the surface of the tooth and then the dentin underneath are dissolved by such acids.

---

* As has been pointed out, amylases are found in the animal and vegetable kingdoms. A high concentration of amylase is found in the pancreas of higher animals. In some species (man, pig, rat), a fairly high concentration of the enzyme is found in the saliva. In herbivora, in general, the concentration of amylase in the saliva is low.

Amylases are also found in blood plasma, leukocytes, etc.

† The mucins have been classified into a number of groups, depending upon their chemical makeup: mucins proper, sulfomucins, chondroproteins and mucoproteins. The mucin of saliva comes more under the heading of the mucoproteins—glycoproteins whose prosthetic grouping is of the nature of mucoitin sulfuric acid (glucosamine, glucuronic, acetic, and sulfuric acids).

If such a theory is sound, then one might expect a difference between the neutralizing power of saliva derived from a patient suffering with caries and the saliva derived from a caries-free individual, assuming that saliva has some access to the regions where decay occurs. Furthermore, since the enamel is rich in calcium and phosphorus, an analysis of such elements in saliva may prove revealing.

Karshan and Krasnow did find that saliva, stimulated by chewing paraffin and obtained from individuals showing no caries, had a neutralizing power (as revealed by titration with acid), which, in group averages, was 10 per cent greater than that obtained from persons suffering with caries. A much greater difference in mean values between the two groups was found by Hubbell. However, when unstimulated saliva was used, no such difference could be noted.

This acid neutralizing power of saliva can be measured in another way: the carbon dioxide capacity of the fluid can be determined. As this topic is discussed under blood (p. 177), it will be enough to say at this point that the amount of carbon dioxide held in combination with sodium or potassium bicarbonate varies directly with the amount of alkali present. If, now, acid is added, and the amount of carbon dioxide which is evolved be determined, the greater the volume of such gas evolved, the larger the amount of alkali in the fluid. Using many subjects, and taking average values, the results with stimulated saliva were: caries-free, 31 (cubic centimeters of CO_2 per 100 ml. of saliva); arrested caries, 30.2; active caries, 19.5.

Turning next to studies dealing with the content of calcium and phosphorus in saliva, several observers showed that the mean values for total calcium and inorganic phosphate were higher in caries-free than in active-caries groups. This has been denied by others.

Apparently, there is some correlation between the penetration of enamel and the development of caries, on the one hand, and the composition of saliva, on the other. However, these studies tell us little, or nothing at all, as to possible methods of preventing such tooth decay. Attempts have been made, with indifferent success so far, to change the diet in the hope that it might influence the composition of the saliva. (For the effect of *fluorine* on tooth decay, see Chap. 21.)

Salivary Calculus.   This abnormal concretion—formed on the teeth and sometimes in a salivary duct—contains calcium phosphate as its principal inorganic constituent. The idea has arisen, very naturally, that the concentration of calcium and phosphate in saliva may be related to such deposits. Furthermore, the precipitation of calcium phosphate would be a function of the pH of the medium. Actual experiments indicated that the mean value for the amount of calcium in the calculus-free group was lower than that in the calculus group. To a certain extent, this was also true of the content of phosphate, which was lower in the calculus-free group. The studies in pH showed no such clearcut differences.

GASTRIC DIGESTION

Digestion in the stomach involves, primarily, the action of the enzyme pepsin and hydrochloric acid on protein, yielding hydrolytic products such as proteoses and peptones. The enzyme rennin is also present; its function is to curdle milk. Some lipase, a fat-splitting enzyme, may also be found. The food, mixed with saliva and formed into a bolus, passes through the pharynx and esophagus into the stomach (Fig. 34). There it gradually comes in contact with the pepsin and the acid. For some time, however, considerable starch digestion continues in the fundus part of the stomach.

As early as 1783, Spallanzani detected the acidity of gastric juice and also noted that it had the power of dissolving meat. He introduced food in perforated metal capsules into the stomach and recovered their contents

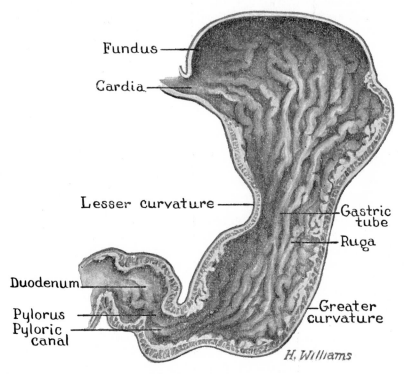

Fig. 34. Vertical section of stomach. (Francis: Fundamentals of Anatomy, C. V. Mosby Co.)

by strings attached to the capsules. In 1833 Beaumont, an American physician, published his "Experiments and Observations on the Gastric Juice and the Physiology of Digestion," in which he described various experiments performed on a patient who, as a result of a gunshot wound, found himself with an opening from the stomach to the exterior. This publication laid the foundation for much of our knowledge of gastric digestion. He described the digestibility of different foods in the stomach, confirmed the presence of hydrochloric acid (first noted by Prout), compared in vivo with in vitro experiments, and made an exhaustive study of the motions of the stomach.

Further contributions on the composition of normal gastric juice were made by Heidenhain, who cut away the fundic or pyloric end of the stomach and created an opening to the exterior. The secretion of this isolated sac was then studied. The experimental technique was subsequently vastly improved by Pavlov.

Gastric Juice. In the walls of the stomach one finds two types of cells, those at the pyloric end known as the chief cells, and those in the central part of the stomach and elsewhere, consisting of chief cells and parietal (border or oxyntic) cells. These cells secrete what ultimately appears as gastric juice. It is believed by some that the hydrochloric acid is produced by the oxyntic cells, while the chief cells throughout the stomach produce the other constituents.

The flow of gastric juice is controlled by nerve fibers. In one of his classic experiments dealing with "sham feeding," Pavlov divided the esophagus and brought the ends to the skin. The animal ate and discharged its food through this opening, without any of the food finding its way into the stomach. Nevertheless, an abundant flow of gastric juice was induced so long as the vagi were intact; but the flow was interrupted when the nerves were cut.

However, there is apparently a *chemical* as well as a psychical influence. It is possible to extract from the pyloric part of the gastric mucosa a substance to which the name *gastrin* has been given, which when injected into the blood causes a flow of gastric juice. The gastrin plays the role of a hormone. A similar effect is produced by histamine. Both gastrin and histamine stimulate the secretion of hydrochloric acid.

Composition of Gastric Juice. The stomach secretes some 2 to 3 liters of gastric juice in twenty-four hours. This juice, like saliva, usually contains water to the extent of more than 99 per cent. The material consists of mucin; the enzymes pepsin, rennin, and lipase; hydrochloric acid (around 0.5 per cent); and the chlorides of sodium and potassium, phosphates, etc.

Origin of Hydrochloric Acid. It is a remarkable fact that a mineral acid of the type of hydrochloric, with a concentration up to 0.5 per cent, should be made in the stomach from an approximately neutral fluid. No other secretion manufactured by the body approaches the gastric juice in such high acidity. What is the origin of this hydrochloric acid? It is not hard to assume that the chloride part of the acid has its origin in the chloride of the blood; but no satisfactory explanation has yet been offered for the origin of the comparatively high hydrogen ion concentration. The theories advanced are legion.

In forming the acid secretion, the cells of the gastric mucosa (of dogs) lower the pH from 7.4 (in blood) to pH 1–2 (acid secretion).

The chloride ion concentration is increased from 0.11 M in plasma to 0.17 M in the secretion.

A mechanism for the secretion of acid has been suggested by Davenport (Fig. 35). In the parietal cells carbonic acid is formed, which dissociates and is catalyzed in this reaction by the enzyme, carbonic anhydrase. Chloride ions pass from the plasma through the cells and into the secretion. These chloride ions which are removed from the plasma are replaced by the bicarbonate ions formed in the cells at the time when hydrogen ions are formed.

Davies is of the opinion that the reaction of fundamental importance in the production of HCl in gastric mucosa is

$$H_2O \longrightarrow H^+ + OH^-$$

The H^+ ions are secreted and the OH^- ions are neutralized by CO_2 and passed into the blood.

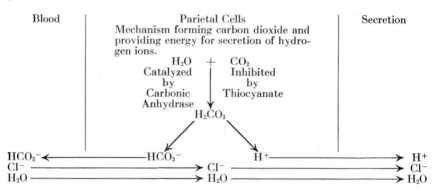

Fig. 35. Formation of hydrochloric acid in the stomach. (Davenport and Fisher: Am. J. Physiol., *131:* 165.)

Davies finds that there is a general correlation between acid secretion and the potential difference across the gastric mucosa ("the resistance of the latter and its ability to produce electrical power externally"). This indicates that the formation of HCl is an electrochemical phenomenon.

A summary of such reactions is given in Fig. 36.

Pepsin and Pepsinogen. The active proteolytic enzyme in the gastric juice is pepsin, which, however, is quite inactive except in acid solution.

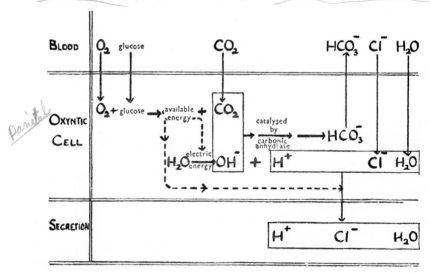

Fig. 36. Suggested over-all reaction elaborating hydrochloric acid in gastric mucosa. (Davies, Longmuir, and Crane: Nature, *159:* 468.)

Langley pointed out many years ago that in the gastric mucosa the enzyme existed in an inactive form which was more resistant to alkali than the pepsin. The inactive form of the enzyme was given the name *pepsinogen,* and the general name *zymogen* was given to an inactive form of an enzyme.

In the meantime, both pepsin and pepsinogen have been isolated in crystalline form, and both show the general characteristics of proteins. Pepsinogen has no proteolytic activity but is converted into active pepsin in slightly acid solution.

PEPSINOGEN.   Pepsinogen in crystalline form was isolated (Fig. 37) by Herriott from swine stomach mucosa by extraction with bicarbonate–ammonium sulfate solution, followed by the precipitation of the soluble pepsinogen at a higher concentration of ammonium sulfate. The precipitate was dissolved in water and treated with copper hydroxide at pH 6, which adsorbed the pepsinogen; the latter was eluted with phosphate buffer of

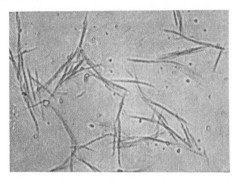

Fig. 37.   Pepsinogen crystals. $\times$ 340. (Northrop, Kunitz, Herriott: Crystalline Enzymes.)

pH 6.8. This treatment with copper hydroxide was repeated. To crystallize the pepsinogen, it was first precipitated with 0.7 saturated ammonium sulfate, then dissolved in nine volumes of 0.4 saturated ammonium sulfate at pH 6.3 (M/10 phosphate buffer), and kept for twenty-four hours at 10° C. (Table 17).

Pepsinogen is converted into pepsin at a pH below 6. At pH 4.6 the reaction is autocatalytic—pepsin, that is, catalyzes the reaction and so produces more of itself. Crystalline pepsin may be obtained in this way or from commercial pepsin, as described on p. 93.

The conversion of pepsinogen to pepsin at pH 1 to 5 is accompanied by the production of a number of polypeptides. One of these polypeptides has an inhibiting action on pepsin at pH 5–6. Herriott has isolated this inhibitor and finds it to have a molecular weight of about 5000, with an isoelectric point at pH 3.7. It contains arginine but no tryptophan and is destroyed by pepsin at pH 3.5.

PEPSIN.   That pepsin, like the other enzymes which have been isolated, is a protein is now well established. Northrop found that some samples of crystalline pepsin contained about 50 per cent of inert protein and all of them contained some other enzyme particularly active on gelatin. Herriott showed that pepsin prepared from different sources differed in activity. He proved that this difference was primarily due to the presence of at least two active proteins, with different solubilities. The more soluble and more active component Herriott and Northrop isolated by repeated extraction with 0.6 saturated magnesium sulfate at pH 5. The more insoluble (and less active) component was prepared by repeated precipitation with 0.45 saturated magnesium sulfate at pH 5. The homogeneity of this substance is still in doubt.

For the determination of peptic activity several methods are available, e.g., the use of the Van Slyke amino titration and the Sörensen formol titration. Northrop has introduced two others. One is based on the increase in conductivity as hydrolysis of the protein proceeds, and the other is based on the rate of change in viscosity of gelatin during digestion. A colorimetric method, using hemoglobin as a substrate, has been perfected by Anson and Mirsky. In this method—which, like many others, can be used for determining not only peptic activity but also the activity of other

Table 17   COMPARISON OF PROPERTIES OF SWINE PEPSINOGEN AND PEPSIN

Properties	Pepsin	Pepsinogen
Crystalline form	Hexagonal bipyramids	Needles
Catalytic activity	+	−
Isoelectric point	pH 2.7	pH 3.8
Molecular weight	38,000	42,000
pH stability	pH 2–6	pH 6–9
Analysis (per cent):		
Carbon	51.7	52.8
Hydrogen	6.8	6.9
Nitrogen	14.0	13.9
Sulfur	0.45	0.4
Phosphorus	0.09	0.08
Chlorine	0.00	0.00

proteolytic enzymes, like trypsin, papain, cathepsin—denatured hemoglobin is digested by pepsin under standard conditions; the undigested hemoglobin is precipitated with trichloroacetic acid; and the amount of unprecipitated protein split products (a measure of the amount of pepsin present) is estimated colorimetrically with Folin's phenol reagent—a phosphotungstic-phosphomolybdic acid—which gives a blue color with the tyrosine and tryptophan present in the hydrolyzed extract.

The great advantage of Anson and Mirsky's method is that "hemoglobin, unlike casein and gelatin, is a reproducible substrate. Different batches of hemoglobin are digested at the same rate by a proteinase solution."

The optimum pH for pepsin action is around 2. What is important, as Northrop has shown, is the hydrogen ion concentration, and not any particular acid. At equal pH's, the rate of peptic digestion of various proteins is the same in solutions of hydrochloric, nitric, sulfuric, oxalic, citric, and phosphoric acids.

The Products of Peptic Hydrolysis.   It is probable that during the few hours that the food stays in the stomach, peptic hydrolysis of proteins produces the rather ill-defined proteoses and peptones, but that no amino acids are produced. By incubating protein with an artificial pepsin-hydrochloric acid mixture for some twenty-four hours, it is possible to show the production of some amino acids; but this can hardly apply to gastric digestion in vivo.

The first product of peptic hydrolysis is said to be "acid-metaprotein," a soluble protein which precipitates on the careful addition of alkali, and which coagulates when the precipitate is heated. Further hydrolysis produces proteoses and peptones. Proteoses are precipitated with ammonium sulfate; one-half saturated ammonium sulfate precipitating the primary proteoses, and the fully saturated solution precipitating the secondary proteoses. In the filtrate we find peptones, which can be precipitated by certain alkaloidal reagents like tannic acid. These ill-defined stages of peptic hydrolysis differ somewhat in their reaction to the biuret reagent: the primary proteins give definite violet colors, whereas peptones mixed with the biuret reagent are rose-red in color.

Rennin (also known as *rennet*, or *chymosin*).   Another enzyme elaborated by the glands of the gastric mucosa * is one which coagulates milk. This enzyme, known as rennin, acts on the casein of the milk. It is believed that the rennin acts on the casein to change it to some soluble product, to which the name *paracasein* has been given. In the presence of calcium, the paracasein becomes the milk clot.

Commercial peptic preparations—and preparations of various proteolytic enzymes—show not only proteolytic properties, but also the property of clotting milk. This had led to a view that pepsin and rennin were one and the same enzyme, and that within the pepsin molecule certain groupings exhibited rennin properties. Tauber and Kleiner were able to separate the rennin from pepsin by a combination of isoelectric and fractional precipitations. This rennin has an activity of 1:4,550,000 when skim milk and calcium chloride are used as substrates, but shows no peptic activity at pH 2 (using the formol method). Crystalline pepsin, however, has a rennet activity of 1:800,000. Berridge has obtained a crystalline product capable of clotting ten million times its weight of milk in ten minutes.

The pH optimum (for the digestion of hemoglobin) of this crystalline rennin is 4, whereas the pH optimum for crystalline pepsin is 1.8.†

Lipase.   This is an enzyme which hydrolyzes fats. Its action at pH 1 to 2, the normal reaction of gastric juice, is very slight, but Willstätter has shown that its optimum pH is about 5, at which acidity hydrolysis becomes more apparent. In any case, it would seem that under normal conditions, gastric lipase is of little physiological importance. As we shall see presently, the important fat-splitting enzyme is found in the pancreas.

Gastric Analysis.   An analysis of gastric contents is of importance in clinical diagnosis.

The quantity of material found normally in the fasting stomach (interdigestive period) is about 50 ml. An increase above this amount may be due to retention or regurgitation from the duodenum.

* Probably present in relatively large quantities only in the stomach of young animals.

† Commercially, rennin plays its role in the making of cheese and in the preparation of junket.

Freshly secreted gastric juice is usually colorless. If yellow or green, it may indicate the presence of bile, due to intestinal obstruction. If red or brown, it may mean the presence of blood, which can be confirmed by the benzidine test (p. 166). Such blood may suggest lesions such as carcinoma of the stomach, peptic ulcer, etc.

Achlorhydria, the absence of free acid, together with the absence of pepsin, may suggest pernicious anemia, gastric carcinoma (cancer of the stomach), etc.*

To determine gastric acidity, we measure the number of milliliters of 0.1N NaOH required to neutralize 100 ml. of gastric contents. The *free* HCl may show an average value of 18.5; which means that 18.5 ml. of 0.1N NaOH are needed to neutralize 100 ml. of gastric contents. The free HCl may also be expressed as grams of HCl per 100 ml. of gastric contents; an average value would be 0.0675 gm.

By *total acidity* is meant free HCl, HCl combined with protein, acid salts (phosphates and carbonates), and organic acids (lactic, butyric, etc.). Its value averages 30; that is, 30 ml. 0.1N NaOH to neutralize 100 ml. of gastric contents; or an average of 0.1095 gm. of HCl.

The methods for free and total acidity are identical, except that different indicators are used. For instance, Töpfer's reagent (dimethylaminoazo-benzene), an indicator with a pH range of 2.9 to 4, is frequently used for the determination of free HCl; and phenolphthalein, with a pH range of about 8 to 9, is used for determining total acidity.

Stomach contents are withdrawn after stimulation by the introduction of foods (test meals), alcohol, or the injection of histamine.

Hypoacidity (hypochlorhydria) may suggest carcinoma of the stomach, chronic constipation, chronic gastritis (inflammation of the stomach), chronic appendicitis, etc.

Hyperacidity may suggest gastric ulcer (peptic ulcer), duodenal ulcer, cholecystitis (inflammation of the gallbladder), etc.

It has been shown experimentally that gastric ulceration can be produced in the rat in from seven to nine hours following ligation of the pylorus. Using this as an assay method, an anti-ulcer factor (enterogastrone or urogastrone?) has been obtained from normal urine which, when given to rats at the time of pyloric ligation, prevents the development of gastric ulceration.

That the bacteriolytic enzyme, lysozyme (which depolymerizes and hydrolyzes the mucopolysaccharide of mucus), may be involved in the development of peptic ulcer, has also been claimed.

PANCREATIC DIGESTION

After a time, the food in the stomach, now in more or less liquid form (chyme), passes into the small intestine. Here it is attacked by intestinal juice (*succus entericus*), pancreatic juice, and bile. The latter two find their way into the duodenum via the pancreatic and bile ducts, respectively, which open by a common orifice into the small intestine (Fig. 38). For purposes of convenience, we shall discuss these three secretions separately.

* *Achylia* connotes the absence of both HCl and the gastric enzymes.

Pancreatic Juice.   This is, in a sense, the most important of the digestive juices. It contains enzymes which split proteins, an enzyme which hydrolyzes starch, and another which hydrolyzes fats. As in the case of pepsinogen, the proteolytic enzymes as they first appear are in the inactive, or zymogen, condition. One of them, trypsinogen, is activated by a substance usually present in the intestinal juice and referred to as *enterokinase*. Another proteolytic enzyme, chymotrypsinogen, seems to be activated by trypsin. Carboxypeptidase, one of the constituents of erepsin, is also found in pancreatic juice.

There is evidence that the pancreatic juice also contains some factor which plays a part in the metabolism of lipids. The blood lipids (cholesterol,

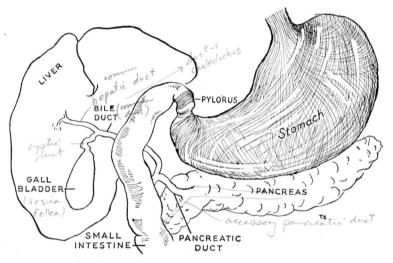

Fig. 38. The pancreas and related organs.

free and esterified, phospholipids, and total fatty acids) drop markedly when depancreatized dogs are given insulin and a normal diet. The same result is obtained by completely occluding the pancreatic ducts. The condition can be markedly improved by the administration of pancreatic juice or the addition of pancreas to the diet.

Enterokinase.   Trypsinogen can be autocatalytically transformed into active trypsin at pH 7 to 9 (refer to Chap. 6). However, this is not the only way in which the inactive zymogen can be transformed into the active enzyme. Pavlov discovered a substance in intestinal juice (which he called *enterokinase*) which could transform trypsinogen into trypsin. Pavlov was of the opinion that enterokinase itself was an enzyme. A careful study by Kunitz has confirmed this point of view. He finds that crystalline trypsinogen is transformed into trypsin by enterokinase in the range of pH 5.2 to 6.

The process of conversion by enterokinase, Kunitz finds, follows the course of a catalytic unimolecular reaction, "the rate of formation of trypsin being proportional to the concentration of enterokinase added, and the ultimate amount of trypsin formed being independent of the concentration of enterokinase."

By fractional precipitation with ammonium sulfate, using the proper pH conditions, Kunitz has prepared some highly concentrated solutions of enterokinase.

Secretin.* In 1902 Bayliss and Starling showed that the stimulation of pancreatic juice was due to a substance in the lining of the intestinal wall, to which they gave the name of *secretin*. An extract containing the substance could be obtained from the intestinal mucosa which, when injected, caused a copious flow of pancreatic juice. This chemical messenger, acting via the blood, was given the general name of *hormone* ("to excite") (see Chap. 23).

The discoverers claimed that the hormone was present in an inactive (prosecretin) condition, and that the acid coming from the stomach converted the inactive into the active (secretin) form. Once produced, this secretin finds its way into the blood and then stimulates the pancreas.

Hammarsten, Ågren, and Wilander isolated secretin and found it to be a polypeptide with a molecular weight of 5000.

At the time when secretin stimulates pancreatic secretion, the gallbladder empties (of its bile). This is due to a contraction of the musculature of the gallbladder by a hormone, cholecystokinin.

Ivy, in confirmation of Raper's work, states that there are two hormonal factors controlling the external secretion of the pancreas: one is secretin, which stimulates the production of pancreatic fluid and bicarbonates; and the other is another hormone, to which the name *pancreozymin* has been given, which stimulates enzyme production by the pancreas.

The Proteolytic Enzymes. It has been the custom to refer to two proteolytic enzymes, trypsin and erepsin. Trypsin, it was said, attacked native proteins and hydrolyzed them down to the amino acid stage. Erepsin, it was said, was an enzyme which acted primarily on proteoses (and peptones?), hydrolyzing them to amino acids. Erepsin was regarded as completing the work of pepsin. (See further p. 93.)

The situation has changed considerably. The erepsin which is found both in the pancreas and in the small intestine is certainly a mixture of enzymes, one of them, the carboxypeptidase, being normally present in pancreatic juice.

Besides trypsin there is another proteolytic enzyme in pancreatic juice, chymotrypsin. Trypsin and chymotrypsin together act on proteins to produce polypeptides, but they are distinguished in two ways: first, chymotrypsin has a much greater milk-coagulating power than trypsin; second, whereas trypsinogen is activated by enterokinase to form trypsin, the chymotrypsinogen is activated by trypsin to form chymotrypsin.†

The further hydrolysis is undertaken by a mixture of enzymes—carboxy-

---

* See also Chap. 23.

† According to Kunitz, the pancreas and the soybean contain a protein which has been isolated and acts as a trypsin inhibitor.

Brown, Shupe, and Laskowski: J. Biol. Chem., *173:* 99, 1948, present evidence which indicates more than one chymotrypsin.

peptidase in the pancreatic juice, and aminopeptidase and dipeptidase mainly in intestinal juice.*

Pancreatic Amylase.   This enzyme is, in general, similar to the ptyalin of saliva. It has been isolated in crystalline form and is then stable at a pH of 6.9 at 2° C. There is some evidence to point to inositol as a constituent of this enzyme.

Lipase.   This important enzyme hydrolyzes fats into fatty acid and glycerol. Enzyme activity may be estimated by titrating the free fatty acid produced with standard alkali. Using protein-precipitating agents, King has succeeded in purifying a sample sufficiently to regard it as protein.

Pathology of the Pancreas.   The two lesions commonly observed are duodenal ulcer and obstruction.

The methods of determining pancreatic function (other than that of its internal secretion, which contains insulin, and which is discussed elsewhere (Chap. 23) are in an unsatisfactory condition. They center around tests for its enzymes in duodenal and gastric contents, as well as in feces, urine, and blood.

The absence of pancreatic enzymes from duodenal juice may suggest pancreatitis (inflammation of the pancreas) or some abnormality of the pancreatic ducts.

Gastric contents usually show the presence of bile and pancreatic enzymes during digestion; and while pancreatic disease might be supposed to change the picture, little of a definite nature can be deduced.

The determination of fat in the feces, particularly when the disturbance may be traced both to the pancreas and the gallbladder, is of value. Here large masses of undigested fat—due to lack of lipase and lack of efficient support from bile—are encountered. Sometimes as much as 70 per cent of the total dry matter is fat.

The examination of the nitrogen content of the feces may sometimes be of value. Normally some 5 to 10 per cent of the nitrogen of the food fails to be absorbed and finds its way into the feces. Abnormally, in pancreatic disease, with an increased loss of effective proteolytic action, the amount of nitrogen in the feces may increase considerably. This is on the assumption that such an impairment does not involve absorptional facilities.

In obstruction of the pancreatic duct, the amylase (also called diatase) in the urine may be increased. In pancreatic disease, as in pancreatitis, the amount of amylase in the blood may increase considerably; this is often of marked diagnostic significance. This may also be true of serum lipase.

INTESTINAL JUICE

The small intestine itself secretes a juice which contains a number of enzymes of importance to digestion. Aminopeptidase and dipeptidase have already been mentioned. Several additional proteolytic enzymes are un-

---

* Why is not the living stomach digested by proteolytic enzymes, since they so readily digest the dead stomach? No clearcut answer to this question has yet been given. Osterhout's extensive researches on the permeability of the cell membrane lead to the conclusion that the permeability changes with the injury or death of the cell; which may mean, as Northrop points out, "that the permeability to enzymes is also greatly different in the living and the dead cell."

doubtedly also present. In addition, there are enzymes which hydrolyze three of the disaccharides. Sucrase converts sucrose into glucose and fructose; maltase converts maltose into two molecules of glucose; lactase hydrolyzes lactose into galactose and glucose. Phosphatases—largely alkaline phosphatase—split several of the compounds of phosphorus (nucleotides, hexosephosphate) yielding, as one of the products, inorganic phosphate. Enterokinase, which is perhaps an enzyme, though not a digestive one, is also found in intestinal juice. The intestine also contains a lecithinase which hydrolyzes lecithin into fatty acid, glycerol, phosphoric acid, and choline.

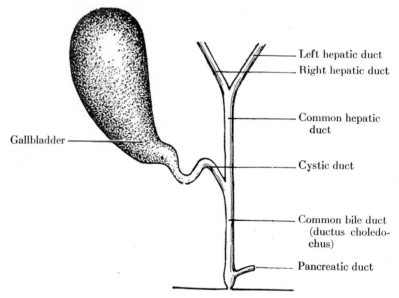

Fig. 39. Diagram of bile ducts. (From Pitzman: Fundamentals of Human Anatomy. C. V. Mosby Co.)

BILE

The formation of bile is one of the many activities of the liver. The bile is stored in the gallbladder, which is attached to the liver. During fasting, the bile accumulates in the gallbladder; and during digestion, especially during a meal rich in fats, bile leaves the bladder to enter the small intestine (see Figs. 39 and 40). The hormone cholecystokinin instigates the contraction of the gallbladder and, probably, the relaxation of the common duct sphincter.

Bile is alkaline in reaction (pH 7.8–8.6) and is composed of bile salts, bile pigments, lecithin, cholesterol, inorganic salts, etc. It is, in reality, both a secretion and an excretion, the secretory substances being represented by the bile salts and the excretory ones by the bile pigments, cholesterol, etc.*

Bile Salts.   The value of bile in digestion is largely due to these salts which are formed in the liver. They aid in the digestion of fat and fat-

* There is evidence that protein stimulates the formation of bile and bile salts.

soluble vitamins, A, D, E, and K. How this is brought about is now fairly clear. In the first place, mixed with fats, these bile salts lower the surface tension and increase the emulsification of fats, which makes them more easily digested by lipase. In the second place, they combine with fatty acids, produced as a result of lipolytic action, giving rise to a complex which is more soluble and more easily absorbed.

The evidence points to some value of bile salts in promoting intestinal absorption of fats and fat-soluble vitamins on those occasions when there is a lack of bile in the intestine.*

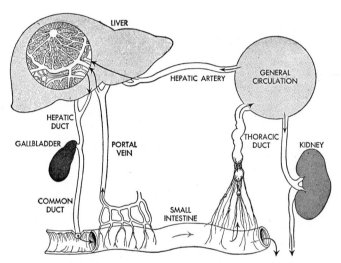

Fig. 40. Circulation of bile. Precursors of bile acids are supplied by protein (glycine and taurine) and sterols (cholic acid). Formation of bile acids occurs in the polygonal liver cells. From these cells, the bile acids are secreted into bile canaliculi that lead to the intrahepatic ductal system.

Bile acids are absorbed along with fats. Most enter the portal circulation, are carried to the liver, and again secreted in the bile. Bile acids traverse this cycle repeatedly unless lost through the intestine, kidneys, or from biliary fistula. Some bile acids enter intestinal lymphatics, are carried to the general circulation, and return to the liver in the hepatic arteries. (Therapeutic Notes, by courtesy of Parke, Davis & Co.)

The bile salts are made up of sodium taurocholate and sodium glycocholate. The former is the sodium salt of taurocholic acid, a combination of taurine and cholic acid. Sodium glycocholate is the sodium salt of glycocholic acid, a combination of glycine and cholic acid.

Taurine, $CH_2.CH_2.SO_3H$, or aminoethylsulfonic acid, is probably de-

|

NH_2

rived from cystine.

Cholic acid is related to cholesterol in structure; the carbon skeleton is similar, but the side chain is somewhat different, and the relationship of the first two rings, configurationally speaking, is also different. However,

* When bile is excluded from the intestine, excessive amounts of fat appear in the stools (steatorrhea).

Bloch and Rittenberg have shown that the administration of cholesterol containing heavy hydrogen to the dog gives rise to a cholic acid which contains as much of the deuterium as the cholesterol in the blood and bile. This strengthens the biological relationship.

Besides cholic acid, several other closely related compounds are found in bile, all of them, presumably, metabolic products of the "mother" sterol, and all of them showing a characteristic steroid configuration; examples are desoxycholic acid and lithocholic acid.

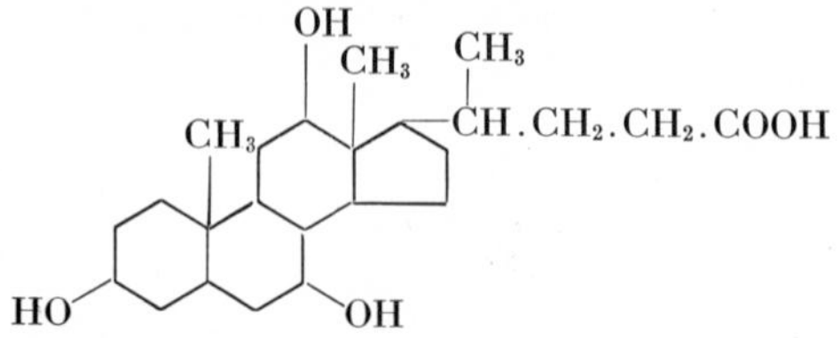

Cholic acid

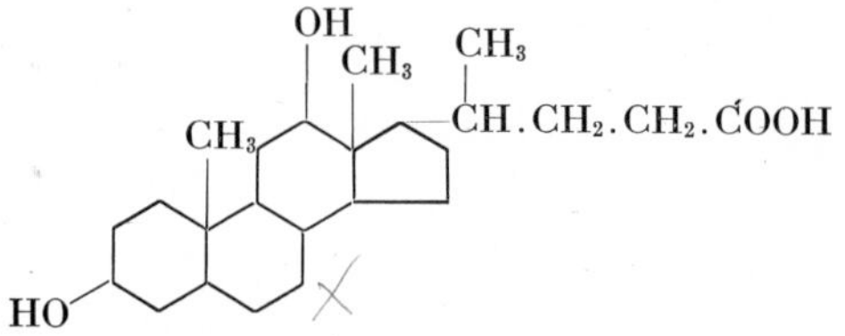

Desoxycholic acid

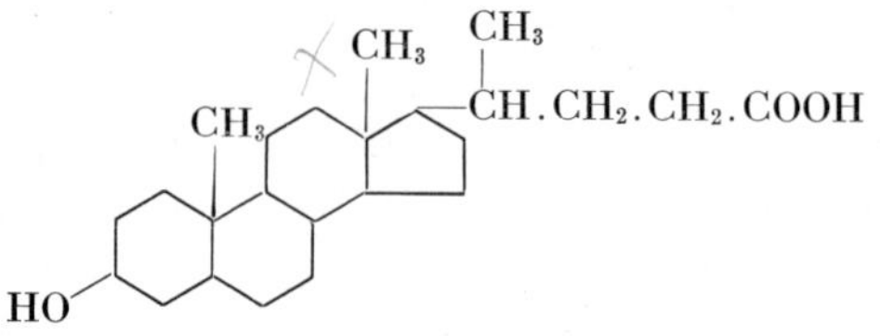

Lithocholic acid

Dehydrocholic acid, an oxidation product of cholic acid

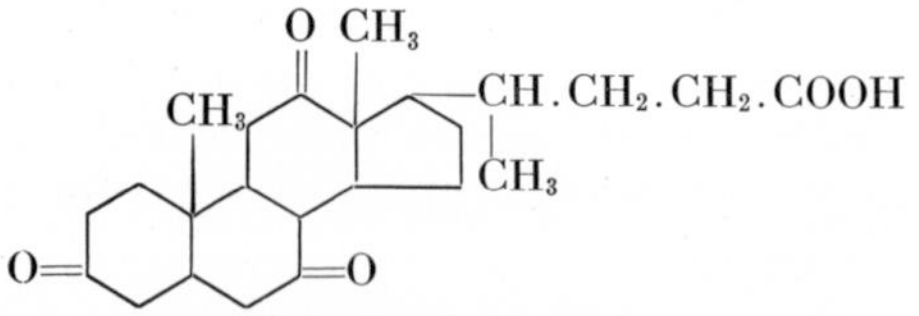

Dehydrocholic acid

(from which it is prepared), is used to increase the volume of the bile. It may be of some value in inflammatory conditions of the gallbladder.

Bile acids are synthesized by the animal (from cholesterol). The amount of these acids excreted is less than that formed. Nor do these acids accumulate in the animal body. By studying the fate of cholic acid in the guinea-pig, it can be shown that when the acid is injected intravenously it disappears from the body and is not eliminated in the excreta. However, the disappearance is due largely to decomposition within the cecum through the action of bacteria.

Bile Pigments.   The bile pigments have their origin for the most part in the decomposition of hemoglobin of the red cell. Possibly the first stage in this decomposition is a compound present to a very small extent inside the red cell, called *choleglobin*, one of a group of altered hemoglobins (*verdoglobins*). The next step in the breakdown of the hemoglobin molecule is the splitting of the iron-protoporphyrin (heme) from the protein, globin, and the opening of the porphyrin ring with a removal of iron. The new structure, a tetrapyrrane, is the basic structure of the bile pigments:

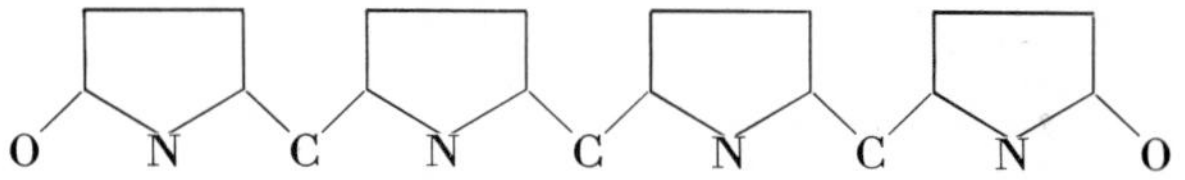

Bile pigment skeleton

The bile pigment most closely resembling the protoporphyrin structure is the green biliverdin:

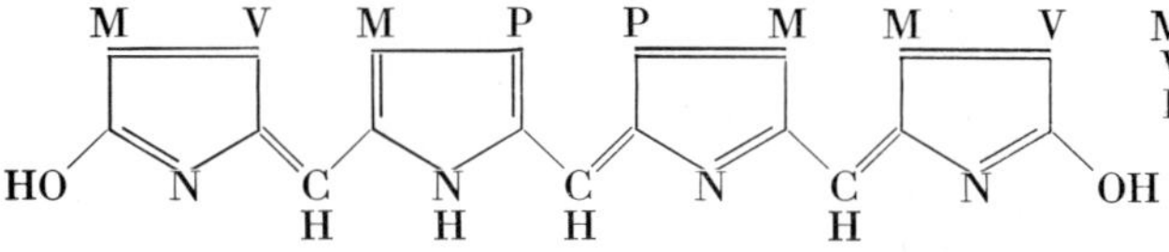

M = methyl (CH$_3$)
V = vinyl (CH=CH$_2$)
P = propionic acid
    (CH$_2$CH$_2$COOH)

Biliverdin

This is presumably converted to bilirubin, the major bile pigment, which is orange in color and is a partially reduced form of biliverdin:

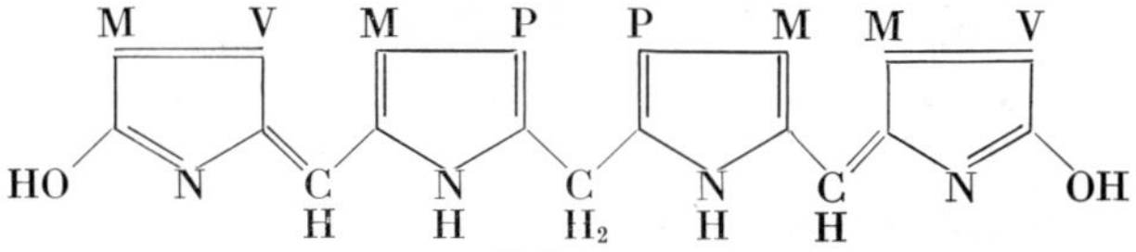

Bilirubin

Reduction of bilirubin yields the colorless mesobilirubinogen:

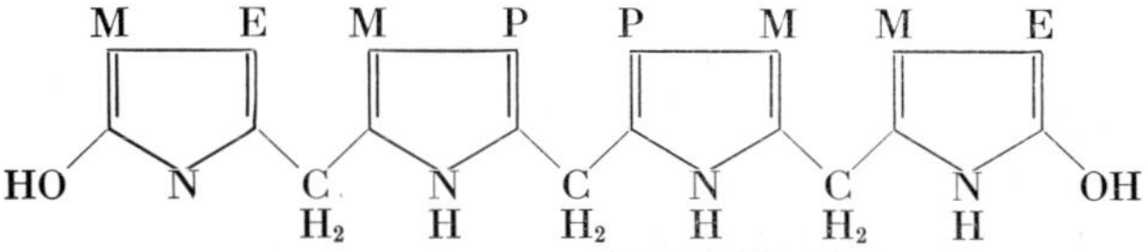

E = ethyl (CH$_2$CH$_3$)

Mesobilirubinogen

The bile pigments are excreted for the most part in the feces in the form of the colorless stercobilinogen which, on exposure to air, is transformed into the yellow stercobilin. Some of the bile pigment is re-absorbed into the circulation, where most of it is re-excreted via the bile into the intestinal tract. Some of it, however, is excreted in the urine, where it is known as urobilinogen; and this, on exposure to air, is converted to urobilin. These latter two compounds are identical with stercobilinogen and stercobilin, respectively:

Stercobilinogen (urobilinogen)

Stercobilin (urobilin)

Not all of the stercobilin originates in hemoglobin. London (and co-workers) fed N^{15}-glycine to a dog and analyzed for the isotope in both the heme of the circulating hemoglobin and the stercobilin of the feces. It had been shown by Shemin and Rittenberg that the N of glycine is incorporated into heme and remains inside the circulating red cell during its lifetime (see p. 154). Had all the stercobilin originated in the circulating hemoglobin, the former would not have incorporated the isotopic label

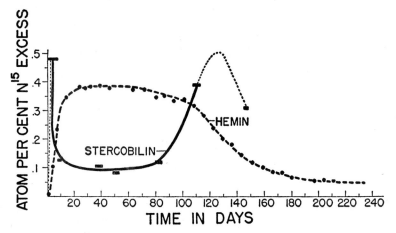

Fig. 41. N^{15} concentration in hemin and stercobilin of a normal man after the start of feeding N^{15}-labelled glycine for 2 days. (London, West, Shemin, and Rittenberg: J. Biol. Chem., *184:* 351, 1950.)

during the first six weeks of the administration of glycine (N^{15}), because the life of the red cell precludes earlier destruction.

Figure 41 shows that N^{15} appears at a very early stage in stercobilin; which means that its predecessor could not have been the hemoglobin of circulating mature red cells.

Whereas, under normal conditions, 11 per cent of the stercobilin is attributable to a non-hemoglobin precursor, in pernicious anemia some 40 per cent is so attributable (Fig. 42).

Tests for Bile.   One test depends upon the presence of the pigments. With an oxidizing reagent, such as nitric acid, a series of colored products are obtained (*Gmelin's test*). Another test depends upon the presence of the bile salts. With sucrose and concentrated sulfuric acid, a red color is obtained (*Pettenköfer's test*). This is probably not unlike the Molisch test for sugars, involving the intermediate production of furfural.

Biliary Pathology. GALLSTONES. Gallstones (biliary calculi) are found largely in the bile ducts and in the gallbladder in pathological conditions, and they may prevent bile from entering the intestines. They consist of cholesterol or cholesterol mixed with the calcium salts of bilirubin, carbonate, or phosphate (Fig. 43).

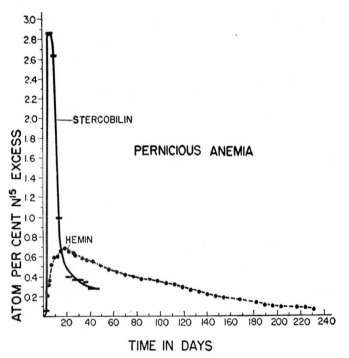

TIME IN DAYS

Fig. 42. N^{15} concentration in hemin and stercobilin after the start of feeding N^{15}-labelled glycine for 2 days to a patient with pernicious anemia. (London and West: J. Biol. Chem., *184:* 359, 1950.)

The calculi in the gallbladder and the bile ducts (cholelithiasis) are often associated with inflammation of the gallbladder (cholecystitis) and of bile passages (cholangitis).

Pure gallstones probably originate when the gallbladder is unable to handle the cholesterol reaching it. Mixed gallstones are often due to infection and inflammation of the gallbladder.

Diagnosis of gallbladder disease is often helped by an x-ray examination of the gallbladder after administration of tetraiodophenolphthalein (radiopaque substance).

JAUNDICE (icterus). When bile pigments get into the blood the skin and secretions become yellow in color. In a common form of the disease, obstructive jaundice, this is due to complete or partial obstruction of the common duct (see Fig. 39). In another form, hemolytic jaundice, the disease is due to an extensive destruction of hemoglobin.

Various clinical tests are used. Among them are tests for bile pigments and bile salts in the urine; the icterus index, a test depending upon the increase in bilirubin which in turn increases the intensity of the yellow color of the blood plasma; test for urobilinogen in urine; and the van den Bergh test for bilirubin in plasma (or serum), which is said to distinguish obstructive jaundice (in which bilirubin has passed through the liver) from hemolytic jaundice (in which the bilirubin has not passed through the liver).

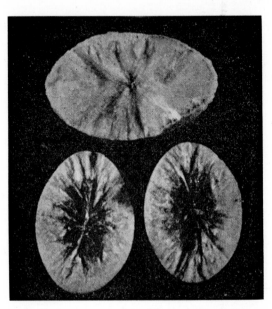

Fig. 43. Varieties of biliary calculi. The majority of the calculi contain cholesterol. (Merck Report, Jan., 1948.)

PUTREFACTION

As we shall see presently (Chap. 8), most of the absorption of foodstuffs occurs in the small intestine. What is not absorbed passes on to the large intestine, where gradual loss of water occurs by absorption, and from where the products are evacuated finally as feces.

The normal stool is a mixture of water, undigested food, products of the digestive tract (bile pigments, enzymes, mucus), products of putrefaction (indole, skatole, fatty acids, gases, etc.), epithelial cells from the walls of the intestine, bacteria, etc.

In the large intestine active bacterial action takes place. Gases (hydrogen, carbon dioxide, ammonia, hydrogen sulfide, methane), acids (acetic, lactic, butyric), various toxic substances (indole, skatole, phenol, etc.) are formed. The acids are largely products of the bacterial decomposition of carbohydrates. Some special substances, such as choline, neurine, and muscarine, have their source in lecithin.

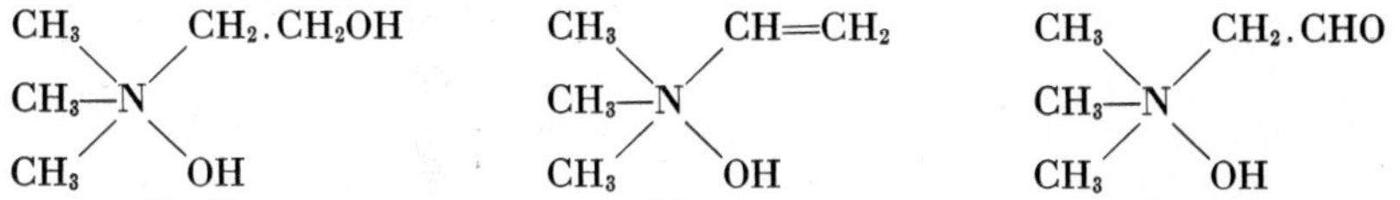

$$
\begin{array}{ccc}
\text{CH}_3 \qquad \text{CH}_2.\text{CH}_2\text{OH} & \text{CH}_3 \qquad \text{CH}=\text{CH}_2 & \text{CH}_3 \qquad \text{CH}_2.\text{CHO} \\
\text{CH}_3\!-\!\text{N} & \text{CH}_3\!-\!\text{N} & \text{CH}_3\!-\!\text{N} \\
\text{CH}_3 \qquad \text{OH} & \text{CH}_3 \qquad \text{OH} & \text{CH}_3 \qquad \text{OH}
\end{array}
$$

Choline   Neurine   Muscarine

The most characteristic group of substances are derived from the proteins. After a preliminary hydrolysis into their respective amino acids, the latter undergo a series of reactions involving deamination and decarboxylation. These reactions can be illustrated as follows:

$$
\begin{array}{l}
\text{R.CH.COOH} \xrightarrow[\text{(deamination)}]{-\text{NH}_3} \text{R.CH}_2.\text{COOH} \\
\quad | \qquad\qquad\qquad\qquad\qquad \text{(Fatty acid)} \\
\quad \text{NH}_2
\end{array}
$$

$$
\begin{array}{l}
\text{R.CH.COOH} \xrightarrow[\text{(decarboxylation)}]{-\text{CO}_2} \text{R.CH}_2 \\
\quad | \qquad\qquad\qquad\qquad\qquad\quad | \\
\quad \text{NH}_2 \qquad\qquad\qquad\qquad\quad\ \text{NH}_2 \\
\qquad\qquad\qquad\qquad\qquad\qquad \text{(Amine)}
\end{array}
$$

giving rise in the amines to some highly toxic substances.

To illustrate the process, we will select a number of amino acids which produce characteristic products.

Tryptophan forms, among others, indole and skatole, substances partially responsible for the odor of feces:

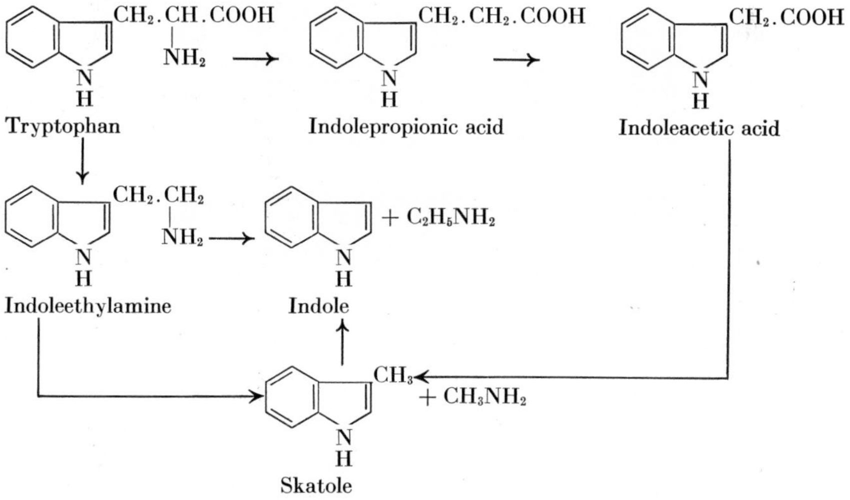

Tryptophan   Indolepropionic acid   Indoleacetic acid

Indoleethylamine   Indole

Skatole

Mercaptans are formed from the sulfur-containing amino acid cystine:

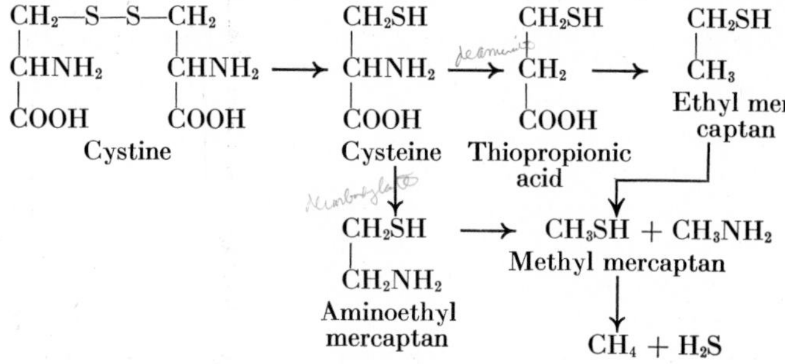

$$
\begin{array}{cccc}
\text{CH}_2\!-\!\text{S}\!-\!\text{S}\!-\!\text{CH}_2 & \text{CH}_2\text{SH} & \text{CH}_2\text{SH} & \text{CH}_2\text{SH} \\
| \qquad\qquad | & | & | & | \\
\text{CHNH}_2 \qquad \text{CHNH}_2 \rightarrow & \text{CHNH}_2 \xrightarrow{\textit{deamin't}} & \text{CH}_2 \rightarrow & \text{CH}_3 \\
| \qquad\qquad | & | & | & \text{Ethyl mer-} \\
\text{COOH} \qquad \text{COOH} & \text{COOH} & \text{COOH} & \text{captan} \\
\text{Cystine} & \text{Cysteine} & \text{Thiopropionic} & \\
& & \text{acid} &
\end{array}
$$

$$
\begin{array}{l}
\text{CH}_2\text{SH} \longrightarrow \quad \text{CH}_3\text{SH} + \text{CH}_3\text{NH}_2 \\
| \qquad\qquad\qquad \text{Methyl mercaptan} \\
\text{CH}_2\text{NH}_2 \\
\text{Aminoethyl} \\
\text{mercaptan} \qquad\qquad\qquad \text{CH}_4 + \text{H}_2\text{S}
\end{array}
$$

The so-called "ptomaines," substances obtained from putrefying flesh, may be formed by the decarboxylation of lysine and arginine, giving rise to cadaverine and putrescine, respectively:

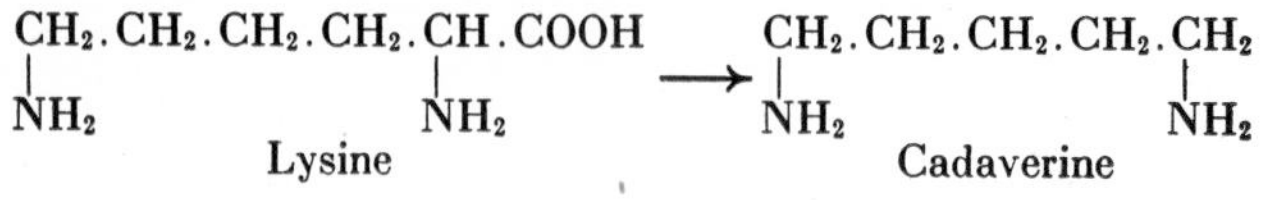

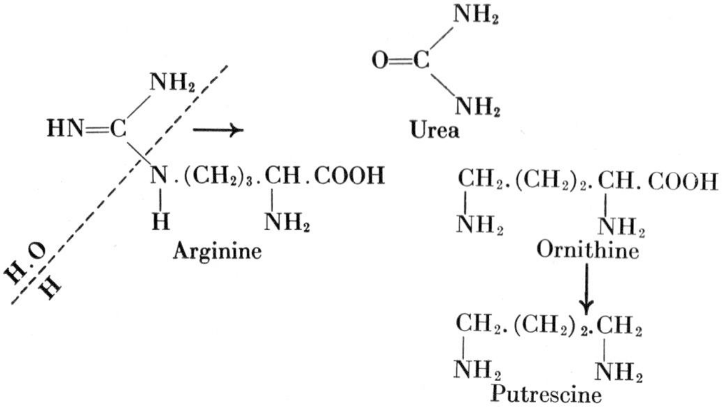

$$CH_2.CH_2.CH_2.CH_2.CH.COOH \qquad CH_2.CH_2.CH_2.CH_2.CH_2$$
$$\quad NH_2 \qquad\qquad\qquad NH_2 \longrightarrow \quad NH_2 \qquad\qquad\qquad NH_2$$

Lysine   Cadaverine

$$HN{=}C\overset{NH_2}{\diagup}\ \longrightarrow$$

$$O{=}C\overset{NH_2}{\diagup}_{NH_2}$$

Urea

$$\diagup N.(CH_2)_3.CH.COOH \qquad CH_2.(CH_2)_2.CH.COOH$$
$$\quad H \qquad NH_2 \qquad\qquad NH_2 \qquad\qquad NH_2$$

Arginine   Ornithine

$$CH_2.(CH_2)_2.CH_2$$
$$\quad NH_2 \qquad\qquad NH_2$$

Putrescine

Histamine, obtained from histidine by decarboxylation, is a highly toxic substance when injected, and some have claimed it to be identical with the gastrin of the stomach, and also to be responsible for allergic reactions (Chap. 25):

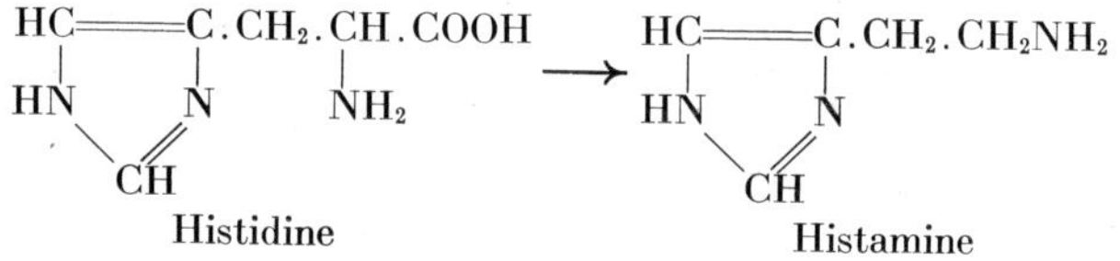

$$HC{=\!\!=}C.CH_2.CH.COOH \qquad HC{=\!\!=}C.CH_2.CH_2NH_2$$
$$HN \quad N \quad NH_2 \qquad\qquad HN \quad N$$
$$\quad CH \qquad\qquad\qquad\qquad CH$$

Histidine   Histamine

Tyramine, obtained from tyrosine, is somewhat similar to epinephrine in raising blood pressure:

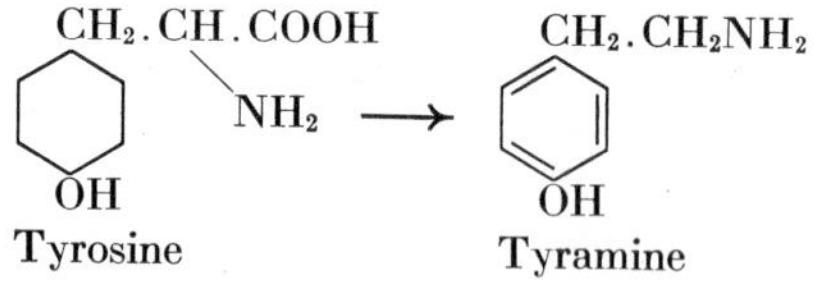

$$CH_2.CH.COOH \qquad CH_2.CH_2NH_2$$
$$\qquad NH_2 \longrightarrow$$
$$OH \qquad\qquad\qquad\qquad OH$$

Tyrosine   Tyramine

Intestinal Flora.   Probably 25 per cent of the dried feces represents bacteria, mostly of the nonpathogenic variety. Bacterial decomposition of whatever foodstuffs remain in the large intestine is of particular importance to herbivora, for in this way much of their food is utilized. The colon bacillus is the commonest organism found in man, and we have seen how the putrefactive products—toxic substances—are thereby produced. An organism present in much smaller quantity belongs to the aciduric group. Such bacteria produce lactic acid from carbohydrates. The addition of dextrin or lactose to the diet brings about a greater production of the aciduric group, and the acid produced as a result of their metabolic activity tends to establish a medium which is unfavorable to the colon bacillus.

The more favorable medium, containing an optimum of the aciduric organisms, is also supported by a well-balanced inorganic diet, particularly by the addition of both calcium and phosphorus.

Despite the fact that with fruits and vegetables, for example, we ingest cellulose, there is little evidence for any digestion of it by man (though it facilitates proper digestion). Herbivorous animals and insects do utilize cellulose. This is due to the action of various microorganisms in their digestive tracts.

Normally the stool contains water, undigested foods, material which cannot be digested (vegetable cells and fibers), products of the digestive tract (changed bile pigments, enzymes, mucus), products obtained through bacterial decomposition (indole, skatole, etc.), and bacteria, mainly harmless. Under abnormal conditions, we may find blood, pathogenic bacteria, etc.

From the point of view of nutrition in general, intestinal flora play an important role. Some of these microorganisms have the ability to synthesize a number of vitamins, some amino acids, and possibly even some fatty acids; so that our needs of these nutrients depend, to some degree at least, upon the microflora.

REFERENCES

For advances in the physiology of the digestive system, see Ann. Rev. Physiol.

Saliva. The problem of taste and smell is discussed by *Baradi and Bourne:* Nature, *168:* 977, 1951.

For activity and stability of salivary amylase, see *Bauer and Svedres:* J. Amer. Pharmaceutical Assoc., *40:* 545, 1951.

On the subject of dental caries, see Merck Manual (1950), 301; Nutr. Rev., *10:* 304, 1952 (relation of cereals and sugars to experimental dental caries); *McClure:* Science, *116:* 229, 1952 (dental caries in relation to processed cereal foods and low sugar content); *Shaw:* J. Nutrition, *41:* 13, 1950 (effect of dietary composition); *Constant, Phillips, and Elvehjem,* Ibid., *43:* 551, 1951 (natural versus refined sugars); *Shaw:* Sugar Molecule (Sugar Research Foundation), *5:* No. 3, 1951 (review); Ibid., *6:* No. 4, 1952–53.

For the connection of fluorine to tooth decay, see Chap. 21 of this text.

For a discussion of the chemistry of starch, see p. 23 of this text.

The origin of thiocyanate in saliva is described by *Himwich and Saunders:* Am. J. Physiol., *153:* 348, 1948, and *Wood, Williams, Jr., and Kingsland:* J. Biol. Chem., *170:* 251, 1947.

Gastric Juice. The pioneer experiments by Beaumont on gastric juice and the physiology of digestion have been reprinted in book form by the 13th International Physiological Congress, held in Boston in 1929 (Harvard University).

Pavlov has described his experiments in his book, The Work of the Digestive Glands, 1902.

A method of preparing gastrin is described by *Jorpes, Jalling, and Mutt:* Biochem. J., *52:* 327, 1952. See also *Hawk and Hundley:* Proc. Soc. Exp. Biol. Med., *78:* 318, 1951 (vitamin B deficiences and gastric secretion); *Hollander:* Rev. Gastroenterol. *18:* 651, 1951 (gastrointestinal hormones).

Regarding the origin of HCl in the stomach, see *Conway:* Biochemistry of Gastric Acid Secretion (1952); *Hollander:* Science, *110:* 57, 1949; *Bradford and Davies:* Biochem. J., *46:* 414, 1950; *Rehm, Hokin, de Graffenfried, Bajandas, and Coy, Jr.:* Amer. J. Physiol., *164:* 187, 1951; *Teorell:* J. Physiology, *114:* 267, 1951; *Patterson and Stetten, Jr.:* Science, *109:* 256, 1949; Nutr. Rev., *8:* 199, 1950; *Hollander:* Federation Proceedings, *11:* 706, 1952 (gastric secretion of electrolytes).

For the determination of lipase activity —using water-soluble esters of sorbitan and fatty acids as substrate—see *Archibald:* J. Biol. Chem., *165:* 443, 1946.

For a discussion of digestive tract disorders, see *Golden:* Bull. N. Y. Acad. Med.,

March, 1950, p. 163; Scope (Upjohn), *3:* No. 4, 1951.

Papers dealing with pernicious anemia, vitamin B_{12}, extrinsic and intrinsic factors are the following: Nutr. Rev., *8:* 85, 165, 1950 (vitamin B_{12} and intrinsic factor); Ibid., *10:* 229, 1952 (nature and mode of action of intrinsic factor); *Beerstecher, Jr., and Altgelt:* J. Biol. Chem., *189:* 31, 1951 (apoerythein); *Murphy:* J. Am. Med. Assoc., *149:* 907, 1952 (treatment of pernicious anemia). See also references to vitamin B_{12} (Chap. 20) and blood (p. 156).

For crystalline rennin, see *Berridge:* Nature, *151:* 473, 1943.

Dotti and Kleiner: Am. J. Physiol., *138:* 557, 1943, claim that rennin is absent from adult human gastric juice.

For gastric analysis, see *Cantarow and Trumper:* Clinical Biochemistry, 1949, 465; *Todd and Sanford:* Clinical Diagnosis, 1948; *McLester:* Nutrition and Diet, 1952, 394.

Proteolytic enzymes, etc., are discussed by *Northrop, Kunitz, and Herriott,* in their book Crystalline Enzymes, 1948.

Pancreatic Juice. Northrop, Kunitz, and Herriott, in their Crystalline Enzymes, 1948, discuss the isolation and properties of proteolytic enzymes.

Methods for preparing secretin are the following: *Friedman and Thomas:* Proc. Soc. Exp. Biol. Med., *73:* 345, 1950; *Jorpes and Mutt:* Biochem. J., *52:* 328, 1952; *Gershbein and Krup:* J. Am. Chem. Soc., *74:* 679, 1952.

Papers dealing with pancreatic enzymes are the following: *Fraser and Powell:* J. Biol. Chem., *187:* 803, 1950 (kinetics of tryptic digestion); *Kunitz:* J. Gen. Physiol., *32:* 265, 1948 (chymotrypsinogen and chymotrypsin); *Putnam and Neurath:* J. Biol. Chem., *166:* 603, 1946 (carboxypeptidase); *Meyer, Fischer, Bernfeld, and Duckert:* Arch. Biochem., *18:* 203, 1948 (pancreatic amylase); *Caldwell, Adams, Kung, and Toralballa:* J. Am. Chem. Soc., *74:* 4033, 1952 (pancreatic amylase).

Wirts and Snape: J. Am. Med. Assoc., *145:* 876, 1951, discuss the evaluation of pancreatic functional tests.

Enterokinase and its relation to trypsingen are reviewed critically by *Bates and Koch* in the J. Biol. Chem., *111:* 197, 1935; and *Kunitz:* J. Gen. Physiol., *22:* 429, 447, 1939.

The purification of lipase is described by *Glick and King* in the J. Am. Chem. Soc., *55:* 2445, 1933; its mode of action has been studied by *Ball and Matlack:* J. Biol. Chem., *123:* 679, 1938.

For a study of the factor in the pancreas which influences lipid metabolism, see *Entenman, Chaikoff, and Montgomery:* J. Biol. Chem., *130:* 121, 1939. See also *Beazell, Schmidt, and Ivy:* J. Am. Med. Assoc., *116:* 2735, 1941.

Intestine. Florey, Wright, and Jennings: Physiol. Rev., *21:* 36, 1941, review the work on the secretions of the intestine.

For a study of intestinal phosphatase, see *Schmidt and Thannhauser:* J. Biol. Chem., *149:* 369, 1943. See, also, *Kosman, Kaulbersz, and Freeman:* Am. J. Physiol., *138:* 236, 1943.

A study of the pH of the small intestine has been made by *Bucher, Flynn, and Robinson:* J. Biol. Chem., *155:* 305, 1944.

Bile. Reviews of liver and bile may be found in Ann. Rev. Physiol.

The chemistry of the bile acids is reviewed by *Fieser:* The Chemistry of Natural Products Related to Phenanthrene, 1936, p. 123.

For bile salts, see *Haslewood and Wootton:* Biochem. J., *47:* 584, 1950 (comparative studies of bile salts); *Trickey:* J. Am. Chem. Soc., *72:* 3474, 1950 (separation of the acids of bile).

Lemberg and Legge: Hematin Compounds and Bile (1949), discuss the bile pigments. See also *Watson:* Harvey Lectures, 1948–49, p. 41 (urobilin and stercobilin); J. Am. Med. Assoc., *144:* 1098, 1950 (origin of bile pigments).

The following are clinical articles: *Buxton, Ray, and Coller:* J. Am. Med. Assoc., *146:* 301, 1951 (acute cholecystitis); *Thorek:* Ibid., *141:* 767, 1949 (jaundice); *Steigmann:* Ibid., *144:* 1076, 1950 (jaundice).

For the formation of amines from amino acids, see *Blaschko, Holton, and Stanley:* J. Physiol., *108:* 427, 1949.

The conversion of cholesterol to bile acids is described by *Bloch, Berg, and Rittenberg:* J. Biol. Chem., *149:* 511, 1943.

Teeter: J. Am. Med. Assoc., *131:* 1482, 1946, is the author of an article on bile physiology and therapy.

Lederer: Ann. Rev. Biochem., *17:* 495, 1948, is the author of a review of natural pigments including bile pigments (p. 512).

The study of calculi—stones of the body —is reviewed in Merck Report for Jan., 1948.

Feces. Martin and Wilkinson: Arch. Biochem., *12:* 95, 1947, describe the use of ion exchange materials to adsorb putrefactive materials.

The bacterial amino acid decarboxylases are discussed by *Gale:* Adv. Enzym., *6:* 1, 1946.

For the mode of formation of indole from tryptophan, see *Baker, Happold, and Walker:* Biochem. J., *40:* 420, 1946; *Dawes, Dawson, and Happold:* Ibid., *41:* 426, 1947.

The nutritional significance of the intestinal microflora is discussed by *Elvehjem:* Federation Proceedings, *7:* 410, 1948.

For the clinical examination of the feces, see *Todd and Sanford:* Clinical Diagnosis, 1948, p. 479.

Marston: Biochem. J., *42:* 564, 1948, is the author of an article on the fermentation of cellulose by organisms from the rumen of the sheep.

Chapter 8   *Absorption*

BEFORE being absorbed, foods must be in a relatively simple (chemically speaking), soluble form. The action of the digestive juices converts much of the foodstuffs into amino acids, hexoses (glucose, fructose, and galactose), glycerol, and fatty acids. If pentosans and mannans are present, pentoses and mannose may be formed. Some pentose is also formed from animal nucleic acid. The cellulose in the diet remains largely unchanged and passes into the large intestine, acting as "roughage." Some bacterial decomposition of cellulose probably does take place. This is particularly true of herbivorous animals.

In general, absorption through the stomach wall is slight. By occluding the pylorus, 99 per cent of sugar can be recovered from the stomach several hours after feeding. Not even water is absorbed to any appreciable extent. In a particular experiment on a dog with a fistula in the duodenum just beyond the pylorus, of 500 ml. of water offered by mouth, 495 ml. appeared through the duodenal fistula in twenty-five minutes. However, experiments involving the use of heavy water suggest that there may be an appreciable change in the water between the time it enters the gastric contents and the time it enters the body fluids.

Alcohol, on the other hand, seems to be absorbed quite readily.

"While the stomach is definitely not an absorptive organ in the sense of the intestine," writes Karel, "and cannot be considered of especial importance in supplying the nutritional needs of the normal organism, its absorptive ability, particularly as regards substances physiologically active in minute quantities, has been grossly underestimated."

The absorption of food—which includes much, but not all of the water—takes place most readily through the walls of the small intestine. The tube is some 25 feet long, and its surface area is considerably increased by the villi, finger-like projections some 1 mm. in length (Fig. 44). Using a fistula at the end of the small intestine, it has been shown that, on the average, some 90 per cent of the protein is absorbed. This applies equally well to the carbohydrates and fats. Water is absorbed here too, but its loss is apparently made up by diffusion of liquid into the intestine, for the food at the ileocecal valve is still very fluid.

In the large intestine there is considerable absorption of water, resulting in a residue which eventually appears as feces. As we have already seen, bacterial action resulting in putrefactive processes is here very pronounced.

For the general plan of absorption, see Fig. 45.

ABSORPTION OF CARBOHYDRATES

The villi of the small intestine contain blood vessels, nerves, and lymphatics, and it is through these villi that absorption takes place. There are two possible paths. One is absorption through the capillaries, the absorbed
142

material passing via the portal system into the liver before entering the
general circulation. The other is absorption through the lacteals, the material then passing via the lymph into the thoracic duct and finally into the
blood. The weight of evidence is that the absorption of carbohydrates takes
place through the capillaries of the villi. These carbohydrates in order to
be absorbed must be in the form of hexoses—glucose, fructose, galactose,
and mannose. Pentoses, if present, are also absorbed, though more slowly
than the hexoses.

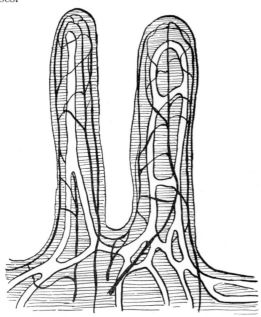

Fig. 44. Diagram of villi of human intestine. Lacteals are white and blood vessels are
dark. (From Christian: Anatomy for Nurses, C. V. Mosby Co.)

Hexoses are absorbed at rapid rates only through the living membrane.
Since the rate of absorption of glucose is not affected by its concentration
in the blood, the process of absorption must involve a force other than that
of simple diffusion. An explanation of the source of such energy required
for the process of active absorption involves a phosphorylation of the
hexoses before absorption can take place (p. 207).

In this connection, it has been shown that the hexosephosphate content
of the intestinal mucosa increases during the absorption of sugars. Furthermore, two substances which prevent the formation of such phosphates,
phlorizin and iodoacetic acid, prevent the absorption of sugars from the
small intestine.

There is a difference in the rate of absorption of different hexoses, indicating a selective action on the part of the intestinal mucosa. The order is
galactose > glucose > fructose > mannose. Another somewhat puzzling
feature in terms of a simple diffusion process is that the rate of absorption
remains the same over a comparatively long period—in fact, until most
of the sugar is absorbed.

In this connection, it is of interest to point out that normally glucose is more rapidly absorbed than a pentose. However, if a dead mucous membrane is used, or if the membrane is first poisoned with iodoacetic acid, the absorption is in the reverse order; first the smaller pentose molecule, and then the hexose.

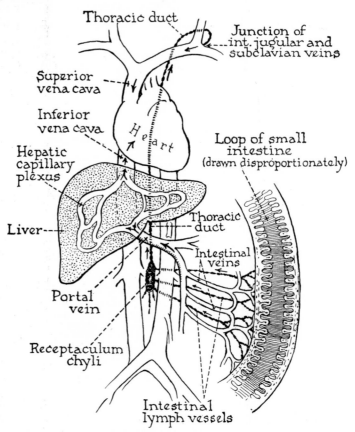

Fig. 45. Routes by which the absorbed foods reach the blood of the general circulation. Intestinal veins converging to form in part, the portal vein, which enters the liver and by repeated branchings assists in the formation of the hepatic capillary plexus; the hepatic veins carrying blood from the liver discharging it into the inferior vena cava; the intestinal lymph vessels converging to discharge their contents, chyle, into the receptaculum chyli, the lower expanded part of the thoracic duct; the thoracic duct discharging lymph and chyle into the blood at the junction of the internal jugular and subclavian veins. (Modified scheme of G. Bachman.)

The hexoses are changed largely to glycogen in the liver and stored there as such until needed by the body. Preliminary phosphate combinations are necessary. (The further fate of carbohydrates is discussed under the metabolism of these substances, Chap. 12.) The problem has arisen whether, prior to the synthetic formation of glycogen, hexoses other than glucose are first transformed into the latter, or whether each hexose is polymerized into glycogen (p. 200). In any case, when glycogen itself is hydrolyzed, glucose and glucose alone is the product. Nor is it clear as to just what happens to such pentoses as xylose and arabinose when they are absorbed. The weight of evidence at present is that they are not glycogen-formers and that they are not utilized by the body.

ABSORPTION OF LIPIDS

Absorption of Fats. It is believed by many investigators that fat has first to be hydrolyzed to glycerol and fatty acid before any absorption can take place. There are some investigators, however, who are of the opinion that an appreciable amount of fat as such can be absorbed, provided it is at first thoroughly emulsified by bile.

The fats can be hydrolyzed by the lipase in the intestine into glycerol and fatty acids. The glycerol is quite soluble and is easily absorbed. This is not true of the fatty acids, which are insoluble in the aqueous medium. For a time a favorite theory was to suppose that the fatty acids were largely converted into soaps, and that the latter, being soluble, were absorbed. Unfortunately for this theory, the formation of such soaps would require the pH of the intestinal contents to be around 9; actually, it is often less than 7. More recent evidence points to an actual combination of the bile salts with the fatty acids, producing products which are soluble and which can be absorbed even at a pH below 7.

How important the bile is in the process involving fat absorption becomes apparent when the bile duct is occluded. Under such conditions, relatively large quantities of undigested fat appear in the feces.

The glycerol and the complex of fatty acids are absorbed through the lacteals and are resynthesized into fat. Combination with phosphoric acid (phosphorylation) is perhaps a preliminary to actual resynthesis. However, phospholipids (lecithin, etc.) are not intermediates in the passage of fats through the intestinal wall. There is some evidence that this resynthesized fat is not quite the same as the original fat in the food. In any case, this resynthesized fat passes into the lymph and finally into the venous circulation via the thoracic duct.

During a meal rich in fat, the lymphatics of the mesentery are filled with fat in a finely emulsified form; this also becomes true of the blood itself. By collecting and estimating the fat absorbed from the intestines through the lacteals—this can be done by means of a cannula inserted into the thoracic duct at the point of its connection with the subclavian and jugular veins—it was shown originally that some 60 per cent of the fat is absorbed through the lacteals.

According to Chaikoff, this figure is too low. Even odd carbon fatty acids, which are rarely present in nature, are absorbed via the lymph to the extent of from 84 to 93 per cent.

Frazer has claimed that any free fatty acids are absorbed by way of the portal blood, whereas unhydrolyzed glycerides are absorbed via the lymphatics. This has been denied: free fatty acids are absorbed by the same route as the triglycerides.

While it would seem that the absorption of fat, whether free fatty acid or otherwise, takes place via the lymph, the question is still somewhat an open one as to whether hydrolysis is a prerequisite to fat absorption.

The fat which finally appears in the blood is either stored (in adipose tissue, etc.) or metabolized. The details will be discussed in the chapter devoted to the metabolism of fats (Chap. 13).

Absorption of Lecithin.   It is generally believed that lecithin—and phospholipids in general—is hydrolyzed in the small intestine, and that such hydrolysis is necessary before any absorption can take place. Enzymes which can split phospholipids are found in intestinal mucosa and pancreatic juice, among other places. Pancreatic juice, for example, contains an enzyme which partially hydrolyzes lecithins and cephalins, liberating fatty acid groups; and it is believed that this enzyme is not identical with lipase.

Using labeled phospholipids—prepared from the liver of animals after they had been injected with radioactive phosphate—Artom concludes that while part of the phospholipid is split in the small intestine, removing phosphate or glycerophosphate (which is absorbed as such), a portion can also be absorbed as the intact molecule.

Absorption of Cholesterol.   Cholesterol is absorbed to some extent depending upon the amount of fat (the kind of fatty acids?) absorbed at the same time. A factor in the absorption may be the solubility of the cholesterol in bile.

Cholesterol is absorbed through the lacteals. The fact that cholesteryl esters have been detected in the chyle suggests that there is esterification of the sterol during absorption. In the blood we find cholesterol as well as cholesterol esters (cholesterol plus fatty acids); and this has led Bloor to suggest that cholesterol may act as a transporter of fatty acids.

To show the delicate responses of the tissues, we know that whereas cholesterol is absorbed by the animal, sitosterol, the sterol in the plant kingdom, is not. Ergosterol is also not absorbed, although it is absorbed when irradiated—when it has become a vitamin D.

ABSORPTION OF PROTEINS

The proteins are absorbed as amino acids; these, like the hexoses, pass directly into the portal circulation. (Hepatic)

Folin and Van Slyke have shown that the blood always contains amino acids, and that after a meal rich in protein there is a definite increase in the amino acid content of the blood. Abel, using his "vividiffusion" technique, arrived at the same result. Here the blood from the portal vein of a dog was passed through collodion tubes immersed in Ringer's solution, and then the blood was returned to the body. What diffused out through the collodion tubes contained, among other things, amino acids, some of which were actually isolated.

This evidence that the absorption of protein takes place in the form of amino acids is further strengthened by the fact that the injection of foreign protein directly into the blood gives rise to antibodies which can be detected; but no such antibody formation results from the oral ingestion of protein. In fact, there is evidence to point to the view that absorption of even traces of protein through the walls of the intestine may give rise to allergic symptoms.

This problem of sensitivity needs emphasis. Where chemical methods fail, immunological methods do lead to the view that very small quantities of protein—what would usually be called "traces"—are absorbed as such by some persons, and in these cases, such absorption may not be unrelated to sensitivity to special protein foods (such as egg white).

The amino acids pass into the liver and thence into the general circulation. The further changes which they undergo will be discussed in the chapter on the metabolism of protein (Chap. 14).

A study has been made of the rate of absorption of various D- and L-isomers of amino acids, and in every case the L-isomer disappeared faster than the D-isomer. Since the rates of diffusion of both isomers are the same, a mere diffusion process would not explain this difference in the rates of absorption; and it is necessary to assume a specific mechanism for the absorption of the L-amino acids.

ABSORPTION OF SALTS AND WATER

Active absorption of salts and water takes place in the intestine via the blood capillaries. Unlike the three principal foodstuffs, no preliminary treatment would appear to be needed before absorption takes place. Here again, if one elects to study the absorption of iron, for example, the evidence that the intestinal mucosa is not just a diffusion membrane but rather made up of actively metabolizing cells which regulate absorption, is quite striking (see Chap. 18).

REFERENCES

The mechanism of absorption is reviewed by *Verzar and McDougall* in their book Absorption, 1937.

For a critical review of gastric absorption, see *Karel:* Physiol. Rev., *28:* 433, 1948.

Karel and Fleisher: Am. J. Physiol., *153:* 268, 1948, describe experiments dealing with the gastric absorption of ethyl alcohol in the rat.

That the absorption of sugars involves a preliminary phosphorylation is emphasized by *Beck:* J. Biol. Chem., *143:* 403, 1942.

The absorption of fat is discussed in detail by *Bloor:* Biochemistry of the Fatty Acids, 1943, p. 85. See also *Zilversmit, Chaikoff, and Entenman:* J. Biol. Chem., *172:* 637, 1948; *Frazer:* St. Bartholomew's Hospital J., Feb., 1950; *Frazer, French, Sammons, Thomas, and Thompson:* British J. Nutrition, *3:* 358, 1949; *Tidwell:* J. Biol. Chem., *182:* 405, 1950; *Bloom, Chaikoff, Reinhardt, Entenman, and Dauben,* Ibid.,

184: 1, 1950; Nutr. Rev., *8:* 300, 1950; *Reiser and Bryson:* J. Biol. Chem., *189:* 87, 1951; *Mead, Bennett, Decker, and Schoenberg:* J. Nutrition, *43:* 477, 1951; *Chaikoff, Blum, Stevens, Reinhardt, and Dauben:* J. Biol. Chem., *190:* 431, 1951; Nutr. Rev., *9:* 211, 1951; *Reiser, Bryson, Carr, and Kuiken:* J. Biol. Chem., *194:* 131, 1952; Nutr. Rev., *10:* 54, 1952.

The absorption and transport of cholesterol is discussed by *Biggs, Friedman, and Byers:* Proc. Soc. Exp. Biol. Med., *78:* 641, 1951.

Gibon and Wiseman: Biochem. J., *48:* 426, 1951, are responsible for a study of the selective absorption of stereo-isomers of amino acids.

For the absorption of phospholipids, see *Artom and Swanson:* J. Biol. Chem., *175:* 871, 1948.

Two historical papers dealing with the absorption of proteins are by *Folin and Denis:* J. Biol. Chem., *12:* 253, 1912; and *Van Slyke and Meyer:* Ibid., *16:* 213, 1913.

Chapter 9 *Blood*

THE PRODUCTS of digestion are carried by the blood to the various tissues of the body. The blood also carries the waste products away from the tissues. The hemoglobin of the blood carries oxygen to the cells and is involved in the elimination of carbon dioxide from the cells. Hormones, the chemical regulators of the body, are also carried by the blood. Transportation within the body, then, is one of the outstanding functions of the blood. (For diagram of the circulation of the blood, see Fig. 46.)

The blood consists of a solution (plasma) in which are suspended solid

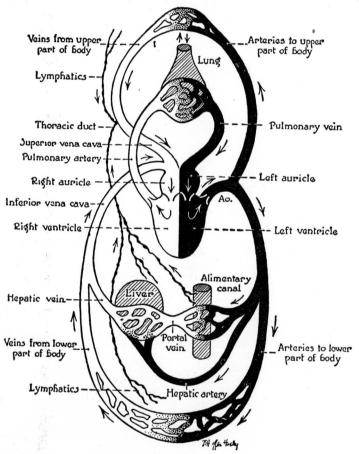

Fig. 46. The circulation of the blood. The arterial, or oxygenated, blood is shown in black; the venous blood, in white. The lymphatics are black knotty lines. (Pettibone: Physiological Chemistry. C. V. Mosby Co.)

148

components. The suspended materials include the red corpuscles (erythrocytes), the white corpuscles (leukocytes)—of which there are several kinds—and the thrombocytes (blood platelets).* The liquid portion, the plasma, is practically colorless, the red color of blood being due to the red corpuscles suspended in it. By centrifuging blood, the corpuscles can be made to separate; and then it can be observed that they occupy some 45 per cent of the total volume (hematocrit).

When the blood is allowed to clot, the clear liquid which separates is the serum. Roughly speaking, serum is plasma from which fibrinogen has been removed. If blood is whipped as it is freshly drawn, the fibrin clings to the rod, and a product is obtained which does not clot and which is called "defibrinated blood"; and this is, essentially, blood serum together with corpuscles. This defibrinated blood serves quite well for many of the experiments on blood carried out in the laboratory.

FUNCTION

We have already referred to the blood as a transporting medium for food material, waste, gases, hormones. Blood has a number of other functions of importance. It helps to maintain a delicate osmotic pressure relationship between blood and tissues; it plays a part in the acid-base equilibrium within the body; it aids in regulating the temperature; and, through its white cells and chemical defense mechanisms, it is of importance in immunological reactions (Chap. 25).

CHEMICAL COMPOSITION

The many substances in the blood, with their approximate quantities, are summarized in Table 18. Hemoglobin, fibrinogen, albumin, and globulin are among the chief proteins. Fatty acids (fat), phospholipids, and cholesterol (free and esterified) represent the lipids. The sugar that is normally present is glucose. The nonprotein-nitrogen (NPN) constituents—substances derived from proteins—include urea, uric acid, creatinine, creatine, ammonia, and amino acids. The inorganic material includes chloride, bicarbonate, phosphate, and sulfate, combined in various ways with sodium, potassium, calcium, and magnesium. There may be present small quantities of still other substances, such as the acetone bodies, bile pigments, lactic acid, phenol, iodine, etc. All of these substances are kept in some sort of solution by water, which constitutes about 80 per cent by weight of the blood. The pH of the blood is in the neighborhood of 7.4 and its specific gravity is about 1.06.

Clinically, changes in the composition of the blood are of great importance. Being the purveyor of materials to and from the cells, a marked deviation from the normal composition of blood may indicate (a) a subnormal or abnormal supply of foodstuff from the outside, (b) the presence of toxic substances, (c) one or more organs which are diseased, etc.

---

* On the average there are some 5 liters of blood in the individual. In each cubic millimeter of blood there are 5,000,000 red cells, 10,000 white cells, and 300,000 thrombocytes.

Table 18 NORMAL VALUES FOR HUMAN BLOOD AND SPINAL FLUID CONSTITUENTS [1]

Determination [2]	Mean	Units	Standard deviation [3]	Examples of abnormal values [4]
Albumin (S)	5.2	gm./100 ml.	0.25	Low in nephrosis
Amino acids (P)	4.4	mg.N/100 ml.	0.48	High in acute atrophy of liver
Amylase (S)	105	units [5]	26	High in acute pancreatitis
Ascorbic acid (P)	0.75	mg./100 ml.	0.40	Low in scurvy
Bilirubin (S)	0.54	mg./100 ml.	0.25	High in biliary obstruction
Calcium (S)	10.0	mg./100 ml.	0.36	High in hyper-, low in hypoparathyroidism
CO_2 content, venous (S)	28.4	mMol./liter	2.7	Low in diabetic acidosis
Chloride (S)	104	mEq./liter	2.6	Low in pernicious vomiting, diarrhea
Cholesterol, free (S)	26.9	% of total	1.4	High in biliary obstruction
Cholesterol, total (S)	210	mg./100 ml.	50	High in nephrosis
Copper (P)	114	µgm./100 ml.	16	High in anemia of infection
Creatinine (P)	1.0	mg./100 ml.	0.15	High in renal insufficiency
Fat, total (P)	735	mg./100 ml.	216	High in nephrosis
Fat, neutral (P)	225	mg./100 ml.	137	High in nephrosis
Fat, phospholipid (P)	181	mg./100 ml.	71	High in biliary obstruction
Fibrinogen (P)	0.2–0.4	gm./100 ml.	.....	Low in severe liver disease
Globulin (S)	2.0	gm./100 ml.	0.27	High in multiple myeloma
Glucose (B)	90	mg./100 ml.	9.6	High in diabetes; low in steatorrhea
Hemoglobin, male (B)	15.9	gm./100 ml.	1.12	High in polycythemia; low in iron deficiency anemia
Hemoglobin, female (B)	13.9	gm./100 ml.	0.86	Same as for male
Iodine, protein-bound (S)	5.0	µgm./100 ml.	0.68	High in hyperthyroidism; low in myxedema
Iron (S)	105	µgm./100 ml.	30	Low in iron deficiency anemia, infection
Iron-binding capacity (S)	200	µgm.Fe/100 ml.	.....	High in iron deficiency anemia; low in infection
Ketone bodies, as acetone (B)	0.2–0.7	mg./100 ml.	.....	High in diabetes, starvation
Lactic acid (B)	11.5	mg./100 ml.	30	High in exercise
Nitrogen, non-protein (B)	29	mg.N/100 ml.	4.4	High in renal insufficiency
O_2 content, arterial (B)	19.6	ml./100 ml.	1.2	High in polycythemia; low in emphysema
O_2 content, venous (B)	12.6	ml./100 ml.	1.3	Same as for arterial
pH (S)	7.36	pH units	0.034	Low in diabetic acidosis
Phosphatase, acid (S)	2.8	Gutman units [6]	0.6	High in carcinoma of the prostate

Determination[2]	Mean	Units	Standard deviation[3]	Examples of abnormal values[4]
Phosphatase, alk. (S)[7]	2.6	Bodansky units[8]	0.59	High in bone diseases with osteoblastic activity
Proteins, total (S)[7]	7.2	gm./100 ml.	0.35	High in multiple myeloma; low in nephrosis
Phosphorus (S)[7]	3.6	mg./100 ml.	0.42	High in hypoparathyroidism; low in rickets
Potassium (P)	4.26	mEq./liter	0.43	High in adrenal insufficiency
Pyruvic acid (B)	1.04	mg./100 ml.	0.36	High in thiamine deficiency
Sodium (S)	140	mEq./liter	1.7	Low in adrenal insufficiency
Thiamin (B)	3.4	μgm./100 ml.	1.2	
Urea nitrogen (B)	13.6	mg.N/100 ml.	3.3	High in renal insufficiency
Uric acid (S)	4.4	mg./100 ml.	1.1	High in gout
Vitamin A, male (P)	128	I.U./100 ml.	29	Low in vitamin A deficiency
Vitamin A, female (P)	91	I.U./100 ml.[9]	22	Same as in male
Volume, plasma	45.3	ml./kg.	5.5	Low in shock
Volume, RBC	34.8	ml./kg.	5.1	High in polycythemia; low in nutritional edema
Volume, whole blood	80.1	ml./kg.	10.5	Low in dehydration
Spinal Fluid:				
Albumin	17	mg./100 ml.	4.9	See protein
Chloride	709	mg./100 ml.	25	Low in tuberculous meningitis
Globulin, gamma	3.4	mg./100 ml.	1.1	See protein
Glucose	57	mg./100 ml.	13	Low in bacterial meningitis
Protein	37	mg./100 ml.	8	High in brain tumors

[1] Most of these values are taken from a comprehensive table prepared by O. Bodansky, in Bodansky and Bodansky: Biochemistry of Disease (1952). For references to methods see this text. Unless otherwise noted, venous blood was used for the determinations.

[2] S = serum, P = plasma, B = whole blood, RBC = red blood cells.

[3] Bodansky calls a value abnormal when it is different from the mean by 2 to 3 times the standard deviation. It should be remembered that most values will vary depending on the method used.

[4] The degree of alteration will vary with the severity as well as with the stage of the disease. The alteration does not always occur in the disease and there are many other diseases in which it will occur.

[5] Somogyi amylase unit = mg. reducing substance liberated from standard sodium chloride–starch mixture by 100 ml. serum in 30 min. at 40°.

[6] Gutman acid phosphatase unit = mg. phenol liberated at pH 5.0 from standard phenylphosphate-citrate mixture by 100 ml. serum in 1 hr. at 37°.

[7] In children these values are higher.

[8] Bodansky alkaline phosphatase unit = mg. inorganic phosphate liberated at alkaline pH from standard glycerophosphate-Veronal mixture by 100 ml. serum in 1 hr. at 37°.

[9] I. U. = International Units.

151

ERYTHROCYTES

These are the red blood cells. In appearance, they are biconcave circular disks devoid of a nucleus (human). Normally, there are some 5,000,000 per cubic millimeter. The erythrocyte is made up of protoplasmic material (stroma) which encloses the pigment hemoglobin. The pigment accounts for more than three quarters of the total solids.

The mature erythrocyte, after it comes from the bone marrow, where it is manufactured, has a life span of some 120 days. At the end of this period, the dying erythrocytes are removed from the circulation by cells in the spleen.

When first formed, the erythrocyte is relatively large, and contains a nucleus but no pigment. When finally ready to leave the bone marrow and enter the circulation, the cell has become smaller, it has incorporated the pigment, and has lost its nucleus.

In various types of anemias there is a notable decrease in the red blood count; and under certain conditions—in fevers, at high altitudes, after severe muscular exercise—there may be a marked increase in the number of red blood cells (polycythemia).

If the red cells are injured, hemoglobin may pass out into the surrounding medium. This process is known as *hemolysis*, or "laking of the blood." A simple experimental procedure accomplishes such a result. Add water (or a solution less concentrated in electrolytes than blood—a *hypotonic* solution) to blood. Under these conditions, water will pass into the cells, which may burst. By using a solution more concentrated in electrolytes than blood —a *hypertonic* solution—water will pass out of the erythrocytes and the cells will shrink. By using a solution of sodium chloride containing 0.9 per cent of the salt, no contraction or expansion of the erythrocytes occurs. Such a solution is spoken of as *isotonic;* and the osmotic pressure of this solution is equal to the osmotic pressure within the cell.

Hemoglobin.   The physiological role of hemoglobin involves its oxygen-carrying capacity and its property as a buffer. These properties will be discussed later (Chap. 10). At this stage we are more concerned with its chemistry.*

Hemoglobin is made up of a protein, globin (which is a histone), and an iron-containing compound known as reduced *heme* (Anson and Mirsky). This heme is also called *hematin.* The chloride of heme (the unreduced form), *hemin,* has been known for many years. It can be easily obtained in crystalline form by evaporating a small quantity of blood and a little acetic acid on a microscope slide (a trace of salt is also added) and examining the crystals under the microscope. The characteristic brownish rods obtained serve as an excellent test for blood.

---

* See also under Iron, Chap. 18.

Hemoglobins are universally distributed throughout the animal kingdom. Hemocyanins, copper-containing proteins, occur only in invertebrates.

Keilin and Wang (Nature, *155:* 227, 1945) point out that hemoglobin is present in the root nodules of leguminous plants. In animals outside of vertebrates hemoglobin has an irregular distribution. "The limiting factor in the distribution of hemoglobin in nature," they write, "is the ability of cells to synthesize the highly specific proteins which, when combined with heme, impart to it the remarkable property of reversible oxygenation."

Hans Fischer has succeeded in synthesizing hemin. Its essential structure involves four pyrrole groups (compare the structure with that of chlorophyll, Chap. 16).

The hemin may be considered as a chloride compound of heme. Both are iron-porphyrin combinations. Porphyrins are substituted porphins and iron-free compounds. The porphin is the "mother substance" containing four pyrrole nuclei.

The heme itself is derived from an iron-free compound known as protoporphyrin IX * (p. 155), and together with globin forms the hemoglobin.

Reduced heme not only combines with native (not denatured) globin to form hemoglobin, but has the property of combining with many nitrogenous compounds to form *hemochromogens.* For example, heme combines with proteins other than globin, with pyridine, with ammonia, etc. Hemoglobin, in this sense, is merely one of a number of possible hemochromogens. These hemochromogens have, as a rule, characteristic absorption spectra, which makes their identification relatively simple. We shall presently see that cytochrome, Warburg's respiratory ferment, peroxidase (Chap. 11), etc., are all examples of hemochromogens.†

Hemoglobin combines readily with oxygen to form oxyhemoglobin, and the gas is removed when the pressure is decreased.

$$HbO_2 \rightleftharpoons Hb + O_2$$

This property of hemoglobin is of fundamental importance in respiration (Chap. 10). Approximately, 1 gm. of hemoglobin will combine with 1.36 cc. of oxygen. If hemoglobin iron is oxidized with an oxidizing agent (such as potassium ferricyanide), the oxygen is driven off and *methemoglobin* is formed.

Methemoglobin can also be produced from the blood pigment by the action of chlorates, nitrites, acetanilid, nitrobenzene, etc. The condition of methemoglobin in the blood is known as *methemoglobinemia.*

Hemoglobin also combines with carbon monoxide to form a more stable compound than with oxygen. The affinity of carbon monoxide for hemoglobin is over 200 times that of oxygen. Poisoning due to carbon monoxide may result from exposure to gasoline motors, illuminating gas, gas heaters, and defective stoves and furnaces.

Hemoglobin combines with carbon dioxide to form a carbamino compound, HbNHCOOH, wherein the union is between the NH_2 of the hemoglobin and the CO_2. Hemoglobin also combines with nitric and nitrous oxides.

The state of the iron in these compounds, ferric (Fe^{+++}) or ferrous (Fe^{++}), is affected by oxidizing and reducing agents, such as potassium ferricyanide or sodium hydrosulfite.

Using the nomenclature of Peters and Van Slyke, we shall call hemin from which the iron has been removed the "porphyryl" group; and we can

---

* Among the precursors of iron porphins in nature, this protoporphyrin IX is the most widespread.

† The names "porphin" and "porphyrin" are often used interchangeably. "Heme" may stand for ferrous or ferric porphin; and "hemochromogen," therefore, is a ferric or ferrous porphin joined to the nitrogen-containing compound.

then summarize the various hemoglobin combinations, with their approximate structures, as follows:

Porphyryl group.....................................Por
Hemin (formed by action of acetic acid and NaCl on oxy-
  hemoglobin).......................................Por:Fe^{+++}—Cl
Heme (sometimes called "hematin") (formed by action of
  NaOH on hemin)...................................Por:Fe^{+++}—OH
Reduced heme (sometimes called "reduced hematin")
  (formed by reduction of heme with $Na_2S_2O_4$)...........Por:Fe^{++}
Reduced hemoglobin (formed by lowering oxygen tension or
  by reducing methemoglobin with $Na_2S_2O_4$).............(Globin) (Por:Fe^{++})
Oxyhemoglobin (formed by the combination of oxygen with
  hemoglobin)......................................(Globin) (Por:Fe^{++})O_2
Carboxyhemoglobin (the combination of CO and hemo-
  globin)..(Globin) (Por:Fe^{++})CO
Methemoglobin (by the action of ferricyanide on hemo-
  globin)..(Globin) (Por:Fe^{+++}—OH)
Cyanmethemoglobin (action of KCN on methemoglobin)..(Globin) (Por:Fe^{+++}—CN)

Just how the globin is attached to the heme portion of the molecule is not known.

Iron is present in hemoglobin to the extent of 0.33 to 0.34 per cent. Assuming one atom of iron in the molecule, the smallest molecular weight would be in the neighborhood of 16,000. Svedberg with his ultracentrifuge has determined the molecular weight to be 66,800; which means that we are dealing here with four atoms of iron per molecule.

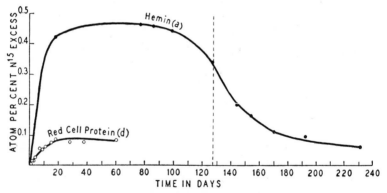

Fig. 47. N^{15} concentration in hemin after feeding N^{15}-labelled glycine for 3 days. The dotted line indicates the calculated life span for the average red cell, 127 days. (Shemin and Rittenberg: J. Biol. Chem., *166:* 627, 1946.)

BIOSYNTHESIS OF HEME. A discussion of the role of various amino acids in the biosynthesis of proteins in general will be found in Chap. 14. At this stage emphasis will be placed upon the precursors needed for the synthesis of that portion of hemoglobin known as heme. Using isotopically labelled compounds, Shemin and Rittenberg fed them to the animal, and the heme of the circulating red cell hemoglobin was isolated and analyzed for isotopes.

For example, N^{15}-glycine was administered and from time to time, samples of blood were removed and analyzed. While a certain amount of the isotope was incorporated into the globin molecule, a relatively high concentration of N^{15} was found in the heme molecule (Fig. 47).

The hemoglobin of the circulating red cell appears to stay inside of the cell for the duration of its lifetime. If, therefore, the concentration of N^{15} in the circulating heme is plotted against time, it becomes possible to calculate the life span of the average red cell. This was found to be 127 days for man—a value which is in good agreement with that found using other methods.

Shemin and co-workers studied the source of the various elements in the heme molecule in an attempt to account for each of the four nitrogen atoms and the 34 carbon atoms of its structure:

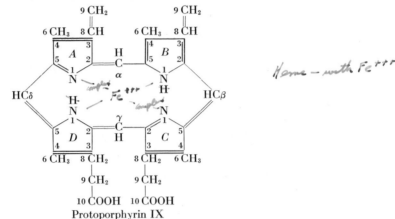

Protoporphyrin IX

These are the conclusions:

(a) All four nitrogen atoms are derived from the nitrogen of glycine.

(b) All four carbon atoms at position 2 of rings A, B, C and D are derived from the alpha carbon atoms of glycine. This is also true for the four methene carbon atoms labelled α, β, γ and δ. The carboxyl carbon of glycine is not utilized for heme synthesis.

(c) The remaining 26 carbon atoms are derived either from methyl or carboxyl groups of acetate by means of an intermediate four-carbon compound arising from the tricarboxylic acid cycle (see further Chap. 14).

The Anemias.   In anemia there is a decrease in the amount of hemoglobin per unit volume of blood; this results in a reduction in the oxygen-carrying power of the blood. Since under normal conditions, the amount of hemoglobin in the blood remains fairly constant despite the decomposition of the pigment, pigment formation must roughly equal pigment destruction.

The intake depends upon the activity of the marrow organ in supplying red blood cells. The elimination is brought about by the reticulo-endothelial system—particularly in the spleen—which removes and decomposes the erythrocytes. When this "balance of forces" fails, anemia is likely to result.

The normal amount of hemoglobin in male adult blood is 15.9 gm. per 100 ml. of blood. This is considered 100 per cent. The content within the normal range may decrease to 85 per cent for men and 77 per cent for women. From 70 per cent downwards, the symptoms of anemia usually appear.

Below 4.7 million per cubic millimeter (males) and 4.13 million (females), the red blood cell count indicates abnormality.

There are many forms of anemia, and no attempt will be made to treat the subject from a clinical standpoint. But in the various forms which are known, we deal with a reduction in the number of red blood cells or a reduction in the amount of hemoglobin. Such a loss immediately affects the amount of oxygen which can combine with hemoglobin. According to Zuelzer, this disease may be regarded as due to either "diminished production of hemoglobin by the marrow or excessive loss of hemoglobin from the circulation, or a combination of both." Krumbhaar believes that anemia is due (1) to disorder of erythrocyte formation; (2) to loss of blood; and (3) to excessive destruction. Both nutritional anemias and pernicious anemia would come under (1). In anemias associated with formation of giant red blood corpuscles (macrocytosis), characteristic of pernicious anemia, the liver extract treatment of Minot and Murphy has proved of great benefit. Where the deficiencies are associated with "an acquired microcytosis, especially if hypochromic," the treatment indicated is one of iron (in the form of one of its many compounds).

Nutritional anemia will be discussed in another chapter (Chap. 18). But the dramatic recoveries in pernicious anemia, resulting from the pioneer researches of Whipple, Minot, Murphy, Castle, etc., make further comment pertinent at this point.

Whipple, as a result of many years of work on blood regeneration, came to the conclusion that pernicious anemia results from improper formation of the stroma of the red corpuscles. In this disease the primitive blood cells crowd the bone marrow. Minot and Murphy showed that feeding large amounts of liver or certain fractions obtained from liver, produced a prompt increase of young blood cells, particularly reticulocytes, in the peripheral blood. The active principle in liver promotes the growth of the primitive cells. The increase in reticulocytes continues for about nine days; then there is a decrease. In the meantime, the red blood cells begin to increase. The two are in inverse ratio. Beyond 3,000,000 red blood cells per cubic millimeter, the reticulocyte response is slight (Fig. 48).

A striking symptom in pernicious anemia is the almost invariable absence of free hydrochloric acid in the gastric juice of the patient. Castle postulated that "the significant defect in the patient with pernicious anemia is an inability to carry out some essential step in the process of gastric digestion. . . ." The daily administration of 200 gm. of beef muscle as such, or after digestion with pepsin-hydrochloric acid, to patients suffering from pernicious anemia led to no improvement. The daily administration of 300 ml. of human gastric juice (secreted by normal fasting subjects in response to histamine injection) proved no better. However, when normal human gastric juice and beef muscle were given together "reticulocyte responses, increases of the red cells and hemoglobin, and clinical improvement promptly appeared."

THE CHEMISTRY OF THE SUBSTANCE INVOLVED IN PERNICIOUS ANEMIA. Cohn prepared active extracts from liver which contained no iron. That folic acid is not the active material is now generally believed, since though it appears to be of some value, the neurological symptoms of the disease are not relieved by its administration.

A discovery by Shorb that *Lactobacillus lactis* (Dorner) requires a growth factor found in liver extracts led to chemical work to isolate the liver factor. This substance, which has been isolated and contains the element cobalt, seems to be the antipernicious anemia factor. It is called "vitamin B_{12}" (see further Chap. 20) and, among other properties, does overcome the neurological symptoms.*

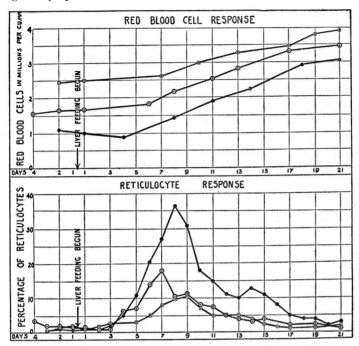

Fig. 48. The effect on the reticulocytes in pernicious anemia of feeding daily 220 gm. of liver pulp to each of three patients with different red blood cell levels. In general, the highest blood cell count is accompanied by the lowest reticulocyte count and vice versa. (Minot, Murphy, and Stetson: Harvey Lectures, Ser. 23, Williams and Wilkins Co.)

WHITE CELLS

Leukocytes, or white cells, of which there are several varieties, are, as a rule, larger in size than erythrocytes, and, unlike the latter, possess a nucleus. They also possess the power of ameboid movement, whereby they can wander into surrounding tissues. They may number 10,000 per cubic millimeter, the proportion of leukocyte to erythrocyte being roughly 1:500.

These leukocytes, being typical cells, are composed of characteristic cellular material—protein, lipid, etc. They act as phagocytes, thereby defending the organism against invading bacteria.

In leukemia, a fatal disease of the blood-forming organs, there is an

* In sickle cell anemia, the erythrocytes of some individuals undergo reversible changes in shape with changes of the partial pressure of oxygen. The lowering of the oxygen pressure changes the cells from the normal, biconcave disk to crescent, holly wreath, etc. This process is known as sickling. This type of anemia is largely confined to the Negro and is hereditary. There is some indication that in this condition there is an altered hemoglobin.

enormous increase in the number of leukocytes (from 600,000 to 800,000 per cubic millimeter). The leukemic process is considered by many to be a form of malignant tumor. Some success has attended its treatment with nitrogen mustard, folic acid antagonists, cortisone, etc.

THROMBOCYTES (platelets)

Blood platelets, or thrombocytes, are believed to be of importance in blood coagulation. They are round oval disks, in diameter about one third that of the erythrocytes, and they may number some 300,000 per cubic millimeter.

BLOOD PLASMA

The plasma is the blood from which the corpuscles have been removed. It is, therefore, devoid of hemoglobin, for example, but otherwise contains much of what is found in whole blood. Of the 9 per cent of solids which are present, some 7 per cent is due to proteins.

Plasma Proteins.   Aside from fibrinogen, which plays a specific role in blood coagulation, the proteins of the blood (and this applies more particularly to the albumin fraction) maintain the water balance between the blood and tissues. While it is quite true that the osmotic pressure of the plasma proteins is almost negligible when compared with the electrolytes present, nevertheless the latter, unlike the proteins, play a less important role in the distribution of water, owing to the fact that the protein is largely confined to the interior of the cell.

That these proteins—and more particularly the albumin, because it has a smaller molecule and is present in larger quantity *—are important in the distribution of water is evident from the fact that patients with a deficient amount of serum albumin suffer from edema (Fig. 49). In *edema* we find abnormal amounts of fluid in intercellular spaces, which results in swelling. An experimental procedure of producing edema points to a similar conclusion. The procedure is known as *plasmapheresis*. This consists in removing blood from the animal and reinjecting the washed corpuscles bathed in Ringer-Locke solution (a solution of inorganic salts comparable in osmotic pressure to that of the blood itself). The amount of plasma proteins removed in this way will depend upon the amount of blood removed. Leiter found by this method that when the plasma proteins reached a level of less than 3 per cent, edema developed.

What is the mechanism by which edema develops? Fluids, foods, and waste rush through the capillaries, and exchanges occur between the blood and the tissues across the capillary membrane. Unlike the blood plasma, which contains some 7 per cent of protein, the tissue fluids surrounding the capillary membrane contain practically no protein. This difference in the concentration of protein develops an osmotic pressure, and water attempts to flow from the tissue into the capillary. (area of greater con H_2O to lesser con of H_2O)

This osmotic pressure is approximately the equivalent of 22 mm. of mercury. However, a counterforce, due to blood pressure, tends to equalize

* About 60 per cent of plasma protein is composed of albumin, "but it is responsible for nearly 80 per cent of the blood's osmotic efficiency" (Cohn).

the osmotic pressure by attempting to move fluid from the capillary to the tissue.

At the arterial end of the capillary, the blood pressure is approximately 35 mm. of mercury, which means that this pressure is greater than the osmotic pressure (22 mm.); and therefore fluid—which includes food material—will pass from the capillary into the tissue, and thence to the cells.

At the venous end of the capillary, the blood pressure is only about 12 mm. of mercury; which is considerably less than the osmotic pressure; and therefore fluid—containing the waste products in the tissue and from

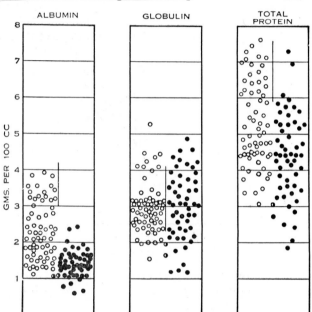

Fig. 49. The relation between plasma protein concentration and edema in dogs. Open circles indicate estimations when no edema was present; black circles refer to determinations when edema was present; vertical lines in the middle of each column indicate the range of normal variation. (Weech: Bull. N. Y. Acad. Med., Feb., 1939, p. 63.)

the cell—will flow back from the tissue into the venous end of the capillary.

Such is the situation under normal conditions. But assume, now, a condition in which the protein of the plasma has been reduced considerably below the normal amount—a result due to loss of protein from the body or due to a decreased intake of protein, etc. The osmotic pressure will drop, and the drop will vary with the drop in protein. Assume that the osmotic pressure instead of 22 mm. is 10 mm. From now on, fluid will flow from the capillary into the tissues not only at the arterial end but at the venous end. The result is an abnormal accumulation of fluid in the tissue, with a development of edema. The blood vessels are squeezed and the blood supply is reduced.

The edema common in nephrosis has been associated with loss of plasma protein, and with a correspondingly lowered osmotic pressure.

Weech has pointed out that edema rarely appears before the albumin is below 2 per cent. Between globulin and edema there is little, if any, correlation (see Fig. 49). Weech defines serum albumin as that fraction of the protein of serum which remains in solution after half saturation with ammonium sulfate; the fraction which is precipitated is the globulin. Chemically, these are not very sharp separations.

Of secondary importance is the buffering power of the albumin and globulin. Van Slyke and his co-workers have shown that, among the proteins of the blood, the hemoglobin is the important buffering agent. Nevertheless, the albumin and globulin do help to some extent. The isoelectric point of albumin is given as pH 4.8, and that of globulin, pH 5.5; and since the blood itself is at a pH of 7.4, these proteins are present as anions.

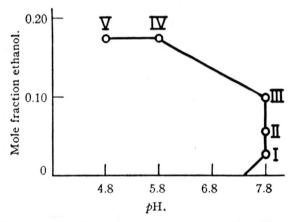

Fig. 50. Ethanol concentration and pH for separation of plasma fractions, method 1. (Cohn, Strong, Hughes, Mulford, Ashworth, Melin, and Taylor: J. Am. Chem. Soc., 68: 459, 1946.)

FRACTIONATION OF PLASMA PROTEINS. Cohn and his group have made a study of the various factors which affect the solubility of proteins. As a result of these studies they have formulated methods which can be used for the separation of protein mixtures such as occur in plasma. The factors which are carefully controlled and which may be varied are: pH, ionic strength, temperature, and alcohol concentration. At relatively high concentrations of protein, alcohol at low temperatures (below zero degrees) will not denature most proteins.

Figure 50 illustrates a method used for the separation of the plasma proteins into a number of fractions. Thus, starting with a pH of 7.4 of the original plasma, the pH is raised to 7.8 and alcohol is added to a definite concentration. A precipitate is formed which is separated by centrifugation and is called fraction I. The diagrams show how the separation is continued.

Table 19 lists the fractions which have been obtained using this technique. Albumin has been prepared in the crystalline state and fibrinogen has been prepared so that it appears homogeneous electrophoretically. The other fractions have revealed themselves as mixtures. The α- and β-globulins contain the various lipoproteins and many enzymes. The γ-globulins contain a mixture of various antibodies to disease organisms and have been used for the passive immunization against these diseases. Thus in mixed plasma samples from an adult population, the γ-globulin fraction will contain antibodies to poliomyelitis, measles, mumps, etc.

ORIGIN OF PLASMA PROTEINS. These proteins originate in the protein (amino acids) of the food, and their synthesis, to a large extent, occurs in the liver. They are in "dynamic equilibrium" with the other proteins of the body; that is to say, the proteins of plasma, liver, and other tissues are in constant exchange. Feeding rats isotopic amino acids, Schoenheimer confirmed this view; the concentration of isotopic nitrogen in the plasma proteins was slightly lower than that in the liver, but somewhat higher than that of the internal organs. "They demonstrate," he writes, "the

Table 19   FRACTIONS OBTAINED BY THE COHN FRACTIONATION PROCEDURE

	Gm. Protein per Liter Plasma	Gm. Protein per Liter of Plasma in Fraction					Protein in Fractions
		I	II + III	IV	V	VI	
Protein	60.3	4.3	16.3	9.7	29.6	0.6	60.5
Albumin	33.2	0.2	0.7	1.0	29.0	0.3	31.2
α-globulin	8.4	0.2	1.8	5.4	0.6	0.3	8.3
β-globulin	7.8	0.8	6.2	3.1			10.1
γ-globulin	6.6	0.5	6.0	0.2			6.7
Fibrinogen	4.3	2.6	1.6				4.2

continuous chemical interactions of serum proteins with body proteins and diet." *

PROTEIN DEFICIENCY. Plasma protein in amounts below normal (5.5 gm. protein per 100 ml. of blood, or below) (hypoproteinemia) is also an indication of loss of body protein.

The hypoproteinemia may be the result of one or more of the following: insufficient intake of protein; poor utilization; excessive loss of blood, and, therefore, of plasma proteins.

In nephritis there is a marked loss of blood albumin, giving rise to albuminuria.

The hypoproteinemia is often accompanied by edema and anemia. The edema results from an increased interstitial fluid volume, because with less protein within the blood vessels, less liquid is drawn into them than would normally be the case.

If the blood volume is sufficiently reduced, what is known as *shock* develops.

SHOCK. Physiological shock is a state which results essentially in the reduction of effective circulating volume and blood pressure. It may be brought about by injury, extensive burns, or by blood loss due to hemorrhage. There are two phases in shock which can be characterized by the ability of the animal to respond to blood transfusion. The early state of

* Incidentally, in contrast to the proteins of the plasma and organs, hemoglobin had a low concentration of isotope.

shock is a reversible one, and blood replacement will bring the circulation of the animal back to normal. After prolonged periods of low blood pressure, due to any of the above states, transfusion of blood is ineffective. During World War II, blood transfusions, especially of plasma, demonstrated the effectiveness of such therapy in the early stages of shock. The need, on a large scale, for "synthetic" blood substitutes, or as they are now termed, plasma "expanders," has led to a study of such materials as gelatin, polyvinyl pyrrolidone (PVP) and dextran (p. 25). The action of such compounds is based on their ability to maintain the osmotic pressure in the circulation at such levels as to prevent the movement of water into the tissues (edema).

The inability of the organism to react favorably to the transfusion of large quantities of blood after an extended period of shock has led several groups to an investigation of the fundamental properties of the circulation during this state. Shorr and his associates have shown that in the plasma of an animal in shock there appears first a compound which originates from the kidney, and, in the early stages, tends to compensate for blood loss by restricting the blood to the larger blood vessels. In the later or irreversible state, there appears in the plasma a substance which originates from the liver and which has a decompensatory action: it opens up the capillaries to the blood in the larger vessels and thus there is an over-all loss in blood flow with an outward filtration of water to the tissues.

Both of these substances are protein in nature, and one of them, the compound formed by the liver, Mazur has shown to be identical with ferritin (see Chap. 18). The ferritin in the normal liver has its cystine sulfur in the form of the disulfide linkage. In shock, the ferritin in the liver is reduced to the sulfhydryl state and now appears in the plasma in low concentrations which inhibit the smooth muscle cells of the small blood vessels from active contraction. In this way the blood escapes to the vast capillary network with a subsequent collapse of the circulation. These two substances have been shown to play a role in other disturbances of the circulation (such as in hypertension).

BLOOD COAGULATION

Much work has been and is being done on the mechanism of the clotting of blood. A variety of theories are to be found in the literature but the following is an attempt to outline the main features of the process.

Coagulant Factors.   FIBRINOGEN.   When whole blood which is shed is allowed to stand, it clots. The clot consists of an insoluble protein called fibrin, and red cells, which are enmeshed in the clot. If, however, the blood is quickly treated with oxalate or citrate, no clot is formed. On the addition of excess Ca^{++}, the blood will clot. The reaction may now be written:

$$\text{Fibrinogen} + Ca^{++} \longrightarrow \text{Fibrin}$$

PROTHROMBIN.   If whole blood is treated so as to remove the calcium and the resulting blood is centrifuged, plasma will be obtained. Now treat this plasma with $BaSO_4$ and filter. The filtrate will not clot if an excess of calcium is added. The missing factor, which is adsorbed by the $BaSO_4$, can be recovered and added to the filtrate, which will now clot in the presence of calcium. This adsorbed factor is called prothrombin. The reaction may now be written:

$$\text{Fibrinogen} + \underline{\text{Prothrombin}} + Ca^{++} \longrightarrow \text{Fibrin}$$

THROMBOPLASTIN. Instead of using plasma or blood one may set up a purified system containing fibrinogen, prothrombin and Ca^{++}. No clot will be formed unless there is added another factor called thromboplastin. This factor is present in tissues, such as lung, but is probably formed from injured platelets in shed blood. We may now write a more complete picture:

$$\text{Fibrinogen} + \text{Prothrombin} + \text{Thromboplastin} + Ca^{++} \longrightarrow \text{Fibrin}$$

It has been shown that thromboplastin acts so as to convert prothrombin to thrombin, which is able now to clot fibrinogen:

$$\text{Prothrombin} \xrightarrow[\text{calcium}]{\text{thromboplastin}} \text{Thrombin}$$

$$\text{Fibrinogen} \xrightarrow{\text{thrombin}} \text{Fibrin}$$

Velocity Factors. ACCELERATORS. In an in vitro system containing prothrombin, calcium, thromboplastin (in excess) and fibrinogen, the velocity of clotting is slower than that obtained with plasma. If to this system one adds plasma from which prothrombin has been removed by adsorption with $BaSO_4$, the velocity of clotting is accelerated. This factor in plasma which is responsible for the acceleration of the clotting process, and which has been partially purified, is called the accelerator globulin or *Ac-globulin*. Its specific function is to accelerate the conversion of prothrombin to thrombin.

INHIBITORS. There is normally present in the plasma, associated with the albumin fraction, a factor called *antithrombin*. It destroys the thrombin as it is formed.

Chemical Nature of the Factors. All of the factors which have been described are protein-like in their behavior. Only fibrinogen has been purified to any extent; the others are still crude products. Thrombin behaves like an enzyme. Further, the conversion of prothrombin to thrombin is probably enzymatic. Trypsin, under certain conditions, can convert prothrombin to a form which possesses thrombin activity. Thus, thromboplastin may be a proteolytic enzyme. Thromboplastin appears to be a lipoprotein.

Fibrinolysin. There is present in the plasma a substance named fibrinolysin which can dissolve (lyse) the fibrin clot. The time for this action varies from a few hours to several weeks. It is present in plasma in an inactive form but can be activated in vitro by shaking the plasma with chloroform. Its action is proteolytic since there is a formation of non-protein nitrogen (p. 149).

Measurements of Clotting. The following are methods used in the measurement of clotting:

A. CLOTTING TIME OF WHOLE SHED BLOOD.

B. PROTHROMBIN TIME. This method measures the time required for enough thrombin to be formed in a given quantity of plasma, in order to clot the fibrinogen in that amount of plasma. This time will be low where the velocity of conversion is low due to (a) a low concentration of prothrombin or (b) a lack of Ac-globulin. The latter compound is labile and disappears from stored blood.

C. THE TWO STAGE METHOD. This method separates the clotting measurement into two stages: (a) fibrinogen to fibrin, and (b) prothrombin to thrombin. Plasma is treated so as to remove the fibrinogen by either adding an excess of thrombin, or by heating to 50° C. The plasma is diluted 50 times and Ac-globulin is added. Thromboplastin and calcium are added and, from time to time, aliquots of this mixture are added to a standard quantity of fibrinogen. The clotting time is measured. There is a direct relationship between the concentration of thrombin and the clotting time.

Anticoagulant Factors.   Many influences can retard or inhibit clotting; such anticoagulant factors include physical agents (cold, dilution, excess salts, protein precipitants, etc.); decalcifying agents (oxalate, citrate, fluoride); lipid solvents; heparin; Dicumarol. These anticoagulants may act either by preventing thrombin formation or by preventing the reaction between thrombin and fibrinogen.

HEPARIN: AN ANTIPROTHROMBIN. A substance first obtained by Howell and MacLean, and to which the name "heparin" was given, prevents blood from coagulating. It is the most potent anticoagulant known. Jorpes found it to be a polysulfuric ester of mucoitin; it contains glucuronic acid, glucosamine, and a large amount of esterified sulfuric acid.

Heparin acts on all the components of the coagulating system: on the prothrombin, the thrombin, and the thromboplastin. Its action involves the exceedingly strong negative electric charge of its polysaccharide. Significant in this connection is that its anticoagulant activity is abolished by protamines, which are strongly basic proteins.

Heparin, found largely in the liver, is produced and stored in a specific kind of cells (the mast cells of Ehrlich), usually located close to the walls of the finest blood vessels.

The evidence points to different heparins in different species. Thus, the heparin from the dog is 2.5 times stronger than that from cattle; and hog heparin is weaker than that of cattle.

Heparin is used for the prevention and treatment of thrombosis and pulmonary embolism.*

---

* *Dicumarol,* the hemorrhagic substance in sweet clover disease, is also an inhibitor of blood coagulation, and interferes with the formation of prothrombin. It may, therefore, also be looked upon as an antiprothrombin type of substance. However, it is not a compound like heparin which is a normal constituent of the body.

Like heparin, its use has been suggested in the prevention of thromboses.

The formula for Dicumarol is:

3,3'-Methylenebis (4-hydroxycumarin)
or Dicumarol

HIRUDIN: AN ANTITHROMBIN. Blood-sucking animals (leeches, ticks, etc.) secrete a substance (hirudin) which prevents coagulation. An extract, when mixed with thrombin, will prevent coagulation with fibrinogen.

Synthetic anticoagulants are also known. Two of these substances are the sodium salt of cellulose disulfuric acid $(C_6H_8O_{11}S_2Na_2)_x$ and the potassium salt of polyvinyl sulfuric acid $(C_2H_3O_4SK)_x$. The sulfuric acid esters of the cerebrosides (Chap. 3) also show anticoagulant activity.

Variations in the Time of Coagulation.   Normally, of course, blood does not coagulate within the body. However, in certain diseases (arterio-

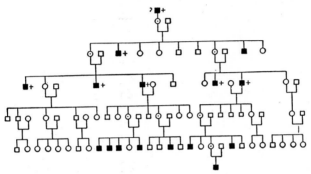

Fig. 51. The family tree of the Hawkins-Cooper family. This family has lived in southern Illinois since before the Civil War. The squares represent males; the black squares, those with hemophilia; the black squares with crosses, those who bled to death; the circles, females; the circles with inner dots, transmitters of hemophilia. The chart shows fifteen patients known to have hemophilia and one whose condition is questionable. All eight persons in this generation who have hemophilia have been seen. (Birch: J. Am. Med. Assoc., *99:* 1566.)

sclerosis, varicose veins, etc.), such a coagulation may occur (thrombosis). On the other hand, whereas blood when shed usually coagulates within five minutes or so, in some rare cases the coagulation time is much prolonged, and in few cases the blood does not clot at all. Here we are dealing with a disease known as *hemophilia.* The disease is carried by the female, who is not the sufferer, and transmitted to the male, who is the sufferer (see Fig. 51).

The delayed clotting time may be restored to normal values by repeated transfusions of blood.

The cause of bleeding in hemophilia is not known. There seems to be no lack of prothrombin or fibrinogen. Just how much thromboplastin is available from thrombocytes and other sources when tissue disruption occurs is not clear. Brinkhaus is of the opinion that there is a deficiency in a plasma factor required for thrombocyte utilization.

Cumarin itself has the following structure:

It has been observed that the addition of whole blood, plasma, or certain plasma fractions to hemophilic blood reduces the clotting time; and it has been suggested that injections of freshly processed, frozen, normal human plasma might be of some benefit.

In the laboratory, coagulation may be hastened by bringing the blood in contact with some outer surface—handkerchief, bandage, etc.; or by gentle heat (using hot cloths). On the other hand, coagulation may be retarded or prevented in a number of ways, some of which have already been indicated; cooling, precipitating the calcium ion (with sodium oxalate) or preventing its ionization (with sodium citrate); addition of large quantities of neutral salts; the addition of hirudin, Dicumarol or heparin; the addition of snake venom; etc.

TESTS FOR BLOOD

Two of the tests depend upon color production, the result of oxidation: the *guaiac test* and the *benzidine test*. The former involves the use of guaiac dissolved in glacial acetic acid, to which are added the blood and hydrogen peroxide; a blue color is formed. The benzidine test involves the use of an acid (glacial acetic) solution of benzidine mixed with blood and hydrogen peroxide. A blue or green color develops.

The best chemical test—a test which definitely indicates the presence of blood, though it does not distinguish human blood from other varieties—is the *hemin test*, to which reference has already been made (p. 152).

The immunological test distinguishes human blood from other varieties. Rabbits are injected with human blood serum over a period of several weeks and in increasing quantities. The rabbit develops antibodies. Blood is withdrawn from the animal and its serum mixed with human serum under examination. A turbidity, gradually changing to a flocculent precipitate, indicates the presence of human blood.

INTERSTITIAL FLUID

Surrounding the intracellular fluid of the cell proper, there is what is called the extracellular fluid (Gamble), which consists of (a) the blood plasma and (b) the *interstitial fluid*. This interstitial fluid includes the lymph (Fig. 52).

The lymph, formed probably from the plasma of the blood and filling tissue spaces, acts as a medium between the blood and cells. In composition it resembles the plasma (Table 20). Lymph capillaries, abounding in the tissue spaces, carry away the lymph into vessels which become larger, and which unite at the thoracic duct, which in turn, empties into the subclavian vein; so that ultimately the products in the lymph find their way into the general circulation.

One of the important functions of the lymph system is a defense against inflammatory processes.

BLOOD ANALYSES

Table 18 (p. 150) gives the composition of the blood. For details with regard to such analyses, more detailed texts must be consulted (see the

Table 20 COMPARISON OF THE CONCENTRATIONS OF SOME OF THE CONSTITUENTS IN PERIPHERAL (CERVICAL) LYMPH AND BLOOD PLASMA OF THE DOG UNDER NORMAL CONDITIONS
(From Heim: Am. J. Physiol., *103*: 553.)

	Protein (Kjeldahl)	NPN	Urea	Uric Acid	Creatinine	Sugar	Amino Acids	Chlorides as NaCl	Phosphorus Total	Phosphorus Inorganic	Calcium
	per cent	mg. per 100 ml.	mg. per 100 ml.	mg. per 100 ml.	mg. per 100 ml.	mg. per 100 ml.	mg. per 100 ml.	mg. per 100 ml.	mg. per 100 ml.	mg. per 100 ml.	mg. per 100 ml.
Plasma:											
Average.........	6.18	32.6	21.7	Trace	1.37	123.0	4.90	678	22.0	5.6	11.70
Range.........	(5.54–7.23)	(21.1–46.0)	(17.9–28.0)	.....	(1.22–1.54)	(112.0–143.0)	...	(649–721)	(18.3–26.1)	(4.4–6.9)	(10.85–12.95)
Lymph:											
Average.........	3.32	34.8	23.5	Trace	1.40	132.2	4.84	711	11.8	5.9	9.84
Range.........	(1.38–4.57)	(19.8–45.4)	(19.8–33.0)	.....	(1.28–1.49)	(107.0–144.0)	...	(690–730)	(10.2–13.7)	(4.7–7.3)	(8.93–10.84)

references at the end of the chapter). However, a few brief remarks at this stage may not be amiss.

The importance of blood analyses as aids in clinical diagnosis has been realized for a long time. To take but a few examples at random: a low iron content in the various anemias, hyperglycemia in diabetes, low phosphorus and increased serum phosphatase in rickets (Chap. 20), decreased plasma prothrombin in obstructive jaundice, increased blood NPN (urea N, creatinine, uric acid, etc.) in renal impairment, etc.

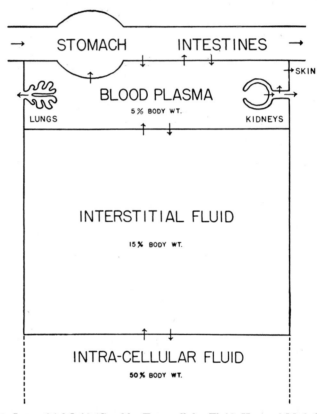

Fig. 52. Interstitial fluid (Gamble: Extracellular Fluid. Harvard Med. School).

For a long time, progress in blood chemistry was more or less at a standstill, due to the fact that the methods were not adapted to small quantities. With the introduction of micro methods, more particularly with the introduction of the colorimeter and the photoelectric colorimeter, blood chemistry became a very important adjunct to clinical diagnosis.

REFERENCES

For a general review, the chapters in *Fulton:* Textbook of Physiology, 1949, are recommended. Clinical factors are stressed in *Bodansky and Bodansky:* Biochemistry of Disease, 1952, and in *Best and Taylor:* The Physiological Basis of Medical Practice, 1943.

For quantitative methods, see *Hawk,*

Oser, and Summerson: Practical Physiological Chemistry, 1947; and *Todd and Sanford:* Clinical Diagnosis, 1948.

Krebs: Ann. Rev. Biochem., *19:* 409, 1950, is the author of an article on the chemical composition of blood plasma and serum.

For some aspects of red cell production and destruction, see Annals N. Y. Acad. Sciences, *48:* 577–704, 1947, by *Ponder, Castle, Charipper, Dameshek, Gordon, Granick, and Robscheit-Robbins;* and *Wintrobe:* Harvey Lectures, 1949–50, p. 87.

Several reviews include the following: *Drabkin:* Ann. Rev. Biochem., *11:* 531, 1942 (animal pigments); *Dobriner and Rhoads:* Physiol. Rev., *20:* 416, 1940 (the porphyrins in health and disease); *Roughton and Kendrew:* Haemoglobin, 1949; *Lemberg and Legge:* Hematin Compounds and Bile Pigments, 1949.

For the amino acid composition of various hemoglobins, see *Schroeder, Kay, and Wells:* J. Biol. Chem., *187:* 221, 1950.

Amyes, Ray, and Brockman: J. Am. Med. Assoc., *142:* 1054, 1950, deal with carbon monoxide poisoning and its treatment. For studies of cyanide poisoning, see *Chen and Rose:* Ibid., *149:* 113, 1952. For reactions of hemes with cyanides, etc., see *Keilin:* Nature, *165:* 151, 1950.

As to the origin of heme and the chemistry of prophyrins, see *Wittenberg and Shemin:* J. Biol. Chem., *178:* 47, 1949; *185:* 103, 1950; *192:* 315, 1951; *Shemin and Kumin:* Ibid., *198:* 827, 1952; *Muir and Neuberger:* Biochem. J., *47:* 97, 1950; *Neuberger and Niven:* J. Physiol., *112:* 292, 1951; *Rimington:* Lancet, Sept. 29, 1951, p. 551; *Lemberg and Legge:* Ann. Rev. Biochem., *19:* 431, 1950; *Drabkin:* Physiol. Rev., *31:* 345, 1951; *Granick:* Harvey Lectures, 1948–49, 220 (structures of heme and chlorophyll compared).

The plasma proteins are dealt with by *Whipple:* Physiol. Rev. 20: 194, 1940, and by *Sahyun* in Proteins and Amino Acids in Nutrition, 1948, p. 265. See also Nutr. Rev., *8:* 267, 1950; *Abdou and Tarver:* J. Biol. Chem., *190:* 769, 781, 1951; *Abou, Reinhardt, and Tarver,* Ibid., *194:* 15, 1952; *Yule, Lampson, Miller, and Whipple,* J. Experimental Medicine, *93:* 539, 1951; *Roberts and White:* J. Biol. Chem., *180:* 505, 1949.

For the physiology of edema, see *Krehl and Winters:* Borden's Rev. Nutritional Research, *13:* No. 7, Oct., 1952.

On the subject of blood coagulation, see *Seegers:* Harvey Lectures, 1951–52, 180; *Campbell and Stefanini:* Proc. Soc. Exp. Biol. Med., *83:* 105, 1953; *Smith and Flynn:* Ann. Rev. Physiol., *10:* 417, 1948; *Ferguson:* Annals N. Y. Acad. Sciences, *49:* 486, 1948 (Review); *Quick:* Proc. Institute of Medicine of Chicago, *16:* No. 3, March 15, 1946 (Review); *Salter:* Textbook of Pharmacology, 1952, p. 448; *Lovelock and Porterfield:* Biochem. J., *50:* 415, 1952 (calcium); *Seegers:* Cincinnati J. Medicine, *31:* 395, 1950 (factors in control of bleeding); *Lorand:* Nature, *166:* 694, 1950 (fibrin clots); *Bailey, Bettelheim, Lorand, and Middlebrook:* Ibid., *167:* 233, 1951 (action of thrombin on fibrinogen); *Seegers:* Circulation, *1:* 2, 1950 (prothrombin and Ac-globulin); *Seegers and Ware:* Am. J. Clinical Pathology, *19:* 41, 1949 (prothrombin); *Milestone:* Yale J. Biology and Medicine, *22:* 675, 1950 (thromboplastin); *Milestone:* J. Gen. Physiol., *35:* 67, 1951; *Shulman, Ferry, and Tinoco:* Arch. Biochem., *42:* 245, 1953 (fibrinogen to fibrin); *Biggs, Douglas, and Macfarlane:* J. Physiol., *119:* 89, 1953 (thromboplastin); *Quick:* Bull. N. Y. Acad. Med., March, 1953, 226.

The relationship of vitamin K to coagulation is discussed by *Thayer:* Annals N. Y. Acad. Sciences, *49:* 518, 1948; and *Davidson and Tagnon:* Ibid., *49:* 647, 1948.

In connection with heparin and anticoagulants in general, *Jorpes:* Heparin, 1946, is the author of a book on the subject. For aspects of its chemistry, see *Prins and Jeanloz:* Ann. Rev. Biochem., *17:* 87, 1948; *Jorpes and Gardell:* J. Biol. Chem., *176:* 267, 1948. Possible clinical applications are discussed by *Jorpes:* Ann. Internal Med., *27:* 361, 1947; *Brown and Douglas:* Glasgow Medical J., *33:* 225, 1952; *Marple:* California Medicine, *73:* 1, 1950; *Jorpes:* Annals Internal Medicine, *27:* 361, 1947 (heparin); *Wolfrom, Montgomery, Karabinos, and Rathgeb:* J. Am. Chem. Soc., *72:* 5796, 1950 (structure of heparin); *Ricketts:* Biochem. J., *51:* 129, 1952 (dextran sulfate, a synthetic analog of heparin).

Link's pioneer work on the anticoagulant from spoiled sweet clover hay (Dicumarol) is described in *Harvey Lectures,* 1943–44, 162. See also *Spies:* Ann. Rev. Biochem., *17:* 460, 1948; *Allen:* J. Am. Med. Assoc., *134:* 323, 1947; *MacMillan:* Science, *108:* 416, 1948.

The important problem of blood transfusion therapy is discussed by *Kolmer and Tuft:* Clinical Immunology, Biotherapy and Chemotherapy, 1942, p. 244. For fractination of blood plasma, see *Cohn, etc.:* J. Am. Chem. Soc., *72:* 465, 1950; Chem. Eng. News, *28:* 3770, 1950; *Ibid., 30:* 2218, 1952.

The nature of shock and the involvement, in part, of ferritin, is discussed by *Mazur and Shorr:* J. Biol. Chem., *176:* 771, 1948; *182:* 607, 1950; Nutr. Rev., *9:* 204, 1951; *Richards:* Merck Report, April, 1952, p. 18; *Page:* Bull. N. Y. Acad. Med., March, 1952, p. 131; *Granick:* Physiol. Rev., *31:* 489, 1951 (ferritin).

For blood "substitutes," see J. Am. Med. Assoc., *147:* 658, 1951; Chem. Eng. News, *29:* 650, 1951; *Pulaski:* Ibid., *30:* 2187, 1952; *Ravdin:* J. Am. Med. Assoc., *150:* 10, 1952.

For anemias in general, see *Todd, Sanford, and Wells:* Clinical Diagnosis, 1953, p. 286; *Zuelzer:* J. Am. Med. Assoc., *134:* 998, 1948; *Sturgis:* Bull. N. Y. Acad. Med., Feb., 1949, p. 84; *Salter:* Textbook of Pharmacology, 1952, p. 412; *Heck:* J. Am. Med. Assoc., *148:* 783, 1952.

The sickle cell variety of anemia is discussed by *Pauling, Itano, Singer, and Wells:* Science, *110:* 543, 1949; *Perutz and Mitchison:* Nature, *166:* 667, 1950; *Gray:* Scientific American, August, 1951, p. 56; *Zaberdinos:* J. Am. Med. Assoc., *148:* 549, 1952; *Itano:* Science, *117:* 89, 1953.

For a discussion of leukemia and its treatment, see Nutr. Rev., *9:* 143, 1951; *10:* 57, 1952; *Silverberg and Dameshek:* J. Am. Med. Assoc., *148:* 1015, 1952; *Sturgis:* Ibid., *150:* 1551, 1952; Ibid., *148:* 746, 1952.

Articles on hemophilia are by *Brinkhaus:* Proc. Soc. Exp. Biol. Med., *66:* 116, 1947; *Alexander and Landwehr:* J. Am. Med. Assoc., *138:* 174, 1948; *Lawrence and Craddock, Jr.:* Science, Nov. 14, 1947, p. 473; *Quick:* J. Am. Med. Assoc., *145:* 4, 1951.

For proteolytic enzyme system (fibrinolysin) in blood, see *Lewis and Ferguson:* Am. J. Physiol., *166:* 594, 1951; *Remmert and Cohen:* J. Biol. Chem., *181:* 431, 1949; *Loomis, Rider, and George, Jr.:* Arch. Biochem., *20:* 444, 1949.

Extended data on the composition and reactions of blood are given by Albritton: Standard Values in Blood, 1952.

Chapter 10   *Chemistry of Respiration*

THE PROCESS of respiration involves the absorption of oxygen through the lungs, the transfer of this oxygen by the blood to the cells, and the uptake of CO_2 by the blood, with its ultimate elimination through the lungs. What causes the oxygen to be taken up by the blood, and in quantity far beyond what can be explained on the grounds of a mere simple solution of the gas? What causes the oxygen to leave the blood and enter the cells? How is the elimination of carbon dioxide brought about? How, with the production of so much acid (not only carbonic but also sulfuric from the oxidation of the sulfur in proteins) is the pH of the blood maintained in the neighborhood of 7.4?

This chapter is an attempt to answer these questions. Closely related problems will be taken up in subsequent chapters. For example, what is the mechanism involving oxidations within the cell (Chap. 11)? What are the energy relations involved in the process (Chap. 17)? What are the intermediate products formed when complex substances are oxidized (Chaps. 12, 13, 14)?

The air we breathe consists, approximately (in volumes per cent), of oxygen, 20.96; carbon dioxide, 0.04; nitrogen, 79. The air we expire may have the composition: oxygen, 16.02; carbon dioxide, 4.38; and nitrogen, 79. The essential reaction involves a consumption of oxygen and an elimination of carbon dioxide. The nitrogen as such is not utilized. It is true that cellular material contains nitrogen; but it is also true that the needs of the body for this element can be supplied only in the form of certain compounds of nitrogen (proteins, amino acids, lipids, etc.).*

The air we breathe is under a pressure of one atmosphere, or 760 mm. of mercury at sea level. Since the atmospheric air contains some 20 per cent of oxygen, then one-fifth of 760 mm., or 152 mm., would be the partial pressure of the oxygen of the air.

According to Henry's law, the amount of a gas dissolved in a liquid varies directly with the pressure of that gas and is independent of other gases mixed with it. Thus it has been found that the volume of each gas, measured at 38° C., which is dissolved in 1 cc. of water when the pressure of the gas is 760 mm. over the liquid is

$$0.0262 \text{ cc. } O_2$$
$$0.013 \text{ cc. } N_2$$
$$0.0528 \text{ cc. } CO_2$$

These values are referred to as *absorption coefficients.*

The composition of inspired, expired and alveolar air is as follows (in volumes per cent, which means cubic centimeters of gas per 100 cc. air):

* Man can continue to exist for weeks without food and for days without water; but without oxygen he dies within a few minutes.

171

	N$_2$	O$_2$	CO$_2$
Inspired air..................	79.02	20.96	0.04
Expired air..................	79.07	16.03	4.4
Alveolar air *...............	80.4	15.0	5.6

We can now calculate how much of each gas can be held in physical solution in 100 cc. of arterial blood in the alveoli of the lungs:

$$N_2 = 100 \times 0.013 \times 0.804 = 1.04 \text{ cc.}$$
$$O_2 = 100 \times 0.0262 \times 0.150 = 0.393 \text{ cc.}$$
$$CO_2 = 100 \times 0.0528 \times 0.056 = 2.96 \text{ cc.}$$

In the blood, the gases are actually present in the following amounts (volumes per cent, or cubic centimeters of gas per 100 cc. blood):

	O$_2$	CO$_2$	N$_2$
Arterial blood...............	19.45	49.68	1.7
Venous blood...............	14.04	54.65	1.7

Thus we must account for the much larger quantity of oxygen and carbon dioxide held in solution by blood other than in the physically dissolved state.

OXYGEN IN THE BLOOD

Some time during the development of the animal species a mechanism had to be devised to carry more oxygen than could be obtained by mere solution. In many of the lower animal forms, pigmented proteins in the plasma appeared which had special affinities for molecular oxygen. For example, hemocyanin, a protein-copper complex, is found in the blood of various arthropods. (Table 21).

Table 21   OXYGEN CAPACITIES OF SOME DIFFERENT BLOODS
(From Baldwin: Comparative Biochemistry, Cambridge Univ. Press, London.)

Pigment	Color	Site	Animal	Cubic centimeters oxygen per 100 cc. blood
Hemoglobin	Red	Corpuscles	Mammals	25
			Birds	18.5
			Reptiles	9
			Amphibia	12
			Fishes	9
		Plasma	Annelids	6.5
			Molluscs	1.5
Hemocyanin	Blue	Plasma	Molluscs:	
			Gastropods	2
			Cephalopods	8
			Crustaceans	3
Chlorocruorin	Green	Plasma	Annelids	9

* A mixture of inspired air plus air present in the trachea, bronchi, and subdivisions of the lungs, spreads to the alveoli and so touches the lung capillaries containing venous blood. This mixture in the alveolar spaces is alveolar air.

It was not until the corpuscle was formed that much larger amounts of oxygen could be carried as a protein-oxygen compound in the form of hemoglobin, without, at the same time, increasing the concentration of the plasma proteins to an extent which would make the blood too viscous for adequate flow.

It is believed that the oxygen-carrying power of hemoglobin can be explained on the basis of an iron-porphyrin-protein linkage. The various hemoglobins have been formulated as follows (dotted lines indicate a covalent bond and solid lines, an ionic bond):

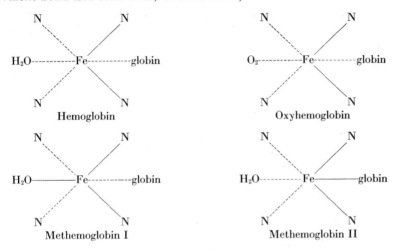

Haurowitz considers these hemoglobins as aqua complexes of iron, with a coordination number of 6. The ferro complexes (hemoglobin and oxyhemoglobin) contain two ionic and four covalent bonds; the ferric (the methemoglobins) contain three ionic and three covalent bonds.

Either by removing hemoglobin from blood and by determining its oxygen-combining capacity, or by determining the amount of oxygen evolved from hemoglobin when the pressure is reduced (in vacuo), it can be shown that by far the larger amount of oxygen in the blood is in combination with hemoglobin.

HOW THE TISSUES GET OXYGEN

The tissues get oxygen as a result of a drop in partial pressure which releases some of the gas from its combination with hemoglobin.

When the partial pressure of oxygen is 150 mm. of Hg (its partial pressure in air), hemoglobin will combine with oxygen to the extent of 20 volumes per cent. This represents the saturation point, because increasing the partial pressure of oxygen causes little further combination of the gas with the pigment. This phenomenon is due to the nature of the oxygen dissociation curve (Fig. 53) which at high partial pressures is asymptotic to the 100 per cent saturation point.

When, however, the pressure is lowered below 150 mm., the oxyhemoglobin begins to dissociate and oxygen is set free. At 80 mm. pressure —which is approximately the pressure in arterial blood—19 cc. of oxygen is dissolved in 100 cc. of blood, and at this stage hemoglobin is saturated with the gas to the extent of 95 per cent (19/20 of 100).

The pressure of oxygen in venous blood is 35 mm. The blood is saturated to the extent of 60 per cent, and it therefore has 12 volumes per cent of oxygen. The lowering of the partial pressure means that oxygen has passed from the blood to the tissues.

In the tissue fluid surrounding the capillaries, the partial pressure of oxygen may be between 20 and 40 mm. It is interesting to note that within this critical range, a lowering of pressure will cause a larger release of oxygen than a corresponding drop at higher pressures. This is due to the S-shape

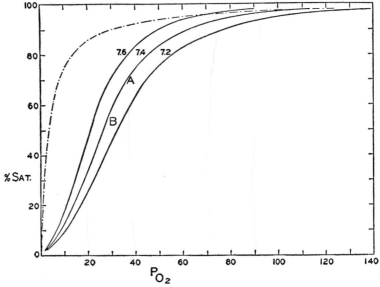

Fig. 53. Normal oxygen dissociation curves of the system hemoglobin, O_2, oxyhemoglobin. Also a representative curve for myoglobin (dashed curve). (Clarke: Topics in Physical Chemistry, 1948, p. 208.)

which the oxygen dissociation curve for hemoglobin assumes at this point. For example, at 40 mm., the blood is 60 per cent saturated; at 20 mm. it is 30 per cent saturated. This means that a lowering of the pressure from 40 to 20 mm. liberates 8 volumes per cent of oxygen (40/100 × 20). On the other hand, at 90 mm. the percentage saturation is 95, and at 70 mm. it has scarcely dropped to 94; liberating, therefore, about 0.5 volumes per cent of oxygen.

Table 22 shows the effect of altitude on the partial pressure of oxygen in the atmosphere and illustrates to what extent the increase in altitude produces a decrease in the partial pressure of oxygen.

Oxygen Carried by Hemoglobin.   The combination of oxygen with hemoglobin may be represented by the equation

$$Hb + O_2 \rightleftarrows HbO_2$$

where Hb represents hemoglobin (reduced hemoglobin), and HbO_2 is oxyhemoglobin. Hb combines with O_2 in the proportion of 16,700 gm. to 32 gm. (one mole). This weight of hemoglobin, strictly speaking, does not represent its molecular weight. The molecular weight of hemoglobin as determined by the ultracentrifuge is roughly four times this figure (68,000).

Since one mole of oxygen at standard temperature and pressure occupies 22.4 liters, it can be calculated that 1 gm. of hemoglobin combines with 1.34 cc. of oxygen.

Since 100 cc. of blood contains 15 gm. of hemoglobin, the hemoglobin in 100 cc. blood can combine with $15 \times 1.34 = 20.1$ cc. of O_2. This represents *full saturation.**

When the pO_2 is high, much of the hemoglobin is combined with oxygen; when the pO_2 is low, relatively little combination takes place.

Table 22   PARTIAL PRESSURE OF OXYGEN IN THE ATMOSPHERE
(From Bureau of Mines Information Circular No. 7575, by Berger and Davenport.)

Altitude	Partial Pressure of Oxygen in the Atmosphere	
(ft.)	(per cent of sea level)	(mm. Hg)
0	100	159
5,000	83	132
10,000	70	111
18,000	50	79.5
33,500	25	39.7
40,000 *	18.4	29.2

* Approximate limit of flying without pressurized equipment.

The *percentage saturation* represents the amount of hemoglobin combined with oxygen, and is expressed as the fraction of total hemoglobin as oxyhemoglobin multiplied by 100.

The dissociation curve (Fig. 54) represents the relation between percentage saturation and pO_2.

The shape of the curve depends upon the temperature and the pH (pCO_2) of the hemoglobin solution.

From the figure it can be seen that with increase in pCO_2 (decrease in pH), the dissociation curve shifts down and more to the right. On the other hand, with a decreased pCO_2 (increased pH), the curve moves up and to the left.

Arterial blood with a pCO_2 of about 40 mm. arrives at the tissues where the pO_2 is low and the pCO_2 is about 46 mm. The low pO_2 causes the equilibrium

$$Hb + O_2 \rightleftarrows HbO_2$$

to be shifted toward the left, with an increase in the amount of free O_2. In other words, oxyhemoglobin loses some of its oxygen. At the same time, the increase in pCO_2 (from 40 to 46 mm.) means that the dissociation curve shifts down and to the right—a further loss of oxygen by hemoglobin, with the oxygen going to the tissues.

* 15 gm. Hb in 100 cc. blood equals 150 gm. in 1 liter; or $150/16,700 = 0.0089$ moles in 1 liter; or 8.9 mM. (millimoles) per liter.

As the blood passes through the lungs, there is a drop in pCO_2; the dissociation curve shifts upward and to the left, and hemoglobin takes up more oxygen.

Myoglobin.   Skeletal muscle contains a protein which resembles hemoglobin in its ability to combine reversibly with oxygen. Its oxygen-carrying ability is also due to the presence of protoporphyrin IX (p. 155) linked to a globin which is different from that of globin in hemoglobin. Its molecular weight is 17,500. Whereas the oxyhemoglobin dissociation curve shows a bulge at lower partial pressures of oxygen, that for oxymyoglobin

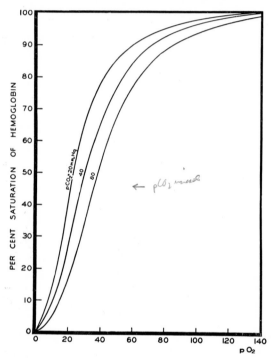

Fig. 54. The dissociation curves of hemoglobin at 38° C. and at partial pressures of carbon dioxide equal to 20, 40, and 80 mm. Hg. (Davenport: The ABC of Acid-Base Chemistry, Univ. of Utah.)

is more rectangular (Fig. 53). Thus, myoglobin can hold a reserve of oxygen when the partial pressure of oxygen is too low for hemoglobin to hold the gas. Further, as the pH of the blood becomes more acid (as in severe exercise), the oxyhemoglobin dissociation curve shifts in the direction of higher partial pressures of oxygen. Thus, when the partial pressure of oxygen is relatively low, and the muscle needs some oxygen, the reserve oxygen of the myoglobin can be unloaded to the tissues.

CARBON DIOXIDE IN THE BLOOD

One hundred cc. of blood contains from 40 to 60 cc. of carbon dioxide—nearer 40 cc. if arterial blood and close to 60 cc. if venous blood. This is determined by withdrawing blood under carefully controlled conditions, treating it with an excess of a weak acid (lactic acid, for example), and measuring the amount of CO_2 evolved. From 2 to 2.5 cc. of the gas is in simple solution. In what state is the rest? And how is the CO_2 eliminated by the lungs?

In the first place the partial pressure of CO_2 in the arterial blood is some 40 mm., and in the tissues it is increased to 50 to 70 mm., owing to its production as a result of metabolic activity. The net result is a tendency for CO_2 to pass from the tissues into the blood.

But the problem involving carbon dioxide is much more complicated. Little is carried by the blood as carbon dioxide itself. Furthermore, the production of carbonic acid might well lead to diminished alkalinity, which, in turn, would produce abnormal results in the body. Yet, as a matter of fact, despite such a possibility, the pH of the blood varies surprisingly little.

The answer to this problem is found in several factors. One of these factors is the buffers of the blood—the proteins and bicarbonate of the plasma, and the proteins, phosphates, and bicarbonates of the cells. Another factor depends upon the acidic properties of oxyhemoglobin and hemoglobin: the former is a stronger acid and prevents the plasma from becoming more alkaline in the lungs and more acid in the tissues. Still another factor is what is known as the *chloride shift*, whereby bicarbonate ion flows from the red cells into the plasma in exchange for chloride ion— a further contribution toward neutrality conditions. The more recent developments deal with still another phase of the carbon dioxide problem— the rapidity with which the gas is removed from the lungs.

These various factors will be discussed in turn.

Forms in Which CO_2 Exists in Blood.   Arterial blood as it travels toward the tissues contains a relatively large amount of oxyhemoglobin and a small amount of carbon dioxide. In the tissues, oxygen is liberated from the oxyhemoglobin and carbon dioxide passes into the blood.

A small amount of carbon dioxide combines with water to form carbonic acid, which ionizes to form bicarbonate ions. Some of the carbon dioxide forms carbamino compounds (p. 153), some passes into the erythrocytes, and some remains in the plasma as dissolved CO_2.

The carbon dioxide which enters the erythrocytes may remain as dissolved CO_2, or form carbamino compounds, or be hydrated in the presence of *carbonic anhydrase* (p. 181), the enzyme. All three reactions take place, but the major reaction is that due to the carbonic anhydrase. Here much of the carbonic acid which is first formed is converted into bicarbonate ions.

As the arterial blood becomes venous and a large amount of bicarbonate appears in the plasma, much of this bicarbonate is drawn to the erythrocytes (where the hemoglobin is a source of temporary combination). What was originally an equilibrium between the bicarbonate of the plasma and that of the cells has now been upset; and to offset this condition, some bicarbonate passes from the cells into the plasma. But this effect upsets electrical neutrality, both in the cells and in the plasma; and the situation can be remedied either by the removal of an equal amount of cation from the cells, or by the substitution of an equal amount of some other anion within the cells. The cells, however, are not permeable to cations, which means that a shift of some suitable anion from the plasma to the cells is the only possibility. The suitable anion in this case is the chloride ion; so that as the bicarbonate ions leave the cells and enter the plasma, an equivalent quantity of chloride ions leave the plasma and enter the cells. This is known as the *chloride shift* (Fig. 55).

The Buffers of the Blood (see appendix). If we remember that the extremes of life range between a *p*H of blood of 7 to 7.8, then the importance

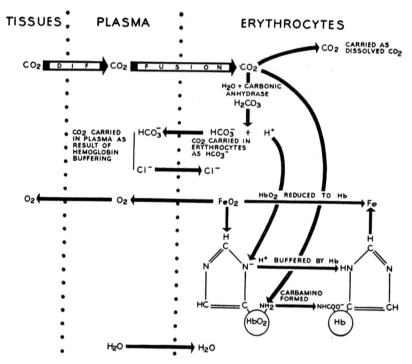

Fig. 55. Processes occurring when CO_2 passes from the tissues into the erythrocytes. (Davenport: The ABC of Acid-Base Chemistry, Univ. of Utah.)

of having an adequate buffering system becomes apparent (Fig. 56).
    The principal buffers of the blood are

$$\frac{H_2CO_3}{BHCO_3}, \quad \frac{BH_2PO_4}{B_2HPO_4}, \quad \frac{HHbO_2}{BHbO_2}, \quad \frac{HHb}{BHb}, \quad \frac{HPr}{BPr}$$

(where $B = Na^+$ or K^+, Hb = hemoglobin and Pr = protein).
    The plasma contains most of the bicarbonate and albumin and globulin, whereas the corpuscles contain the hemoglobin and most of the phosphates. From the appendix it will be seen that in the presence of a buffer system

$$[H^+] = K \frac{[\text{Acid}]}{[\text{Salt}]}$$

To indicate the degree of dissociation of the salt (which in 0.1 to 0.01 molar strength is from 60 to 90 per cent), we shall use the expression λ; so that, more accurately

$$[H^+] = K \frac{[Acid]}{\lambda[Salt]}$$

If we take into account the range of possible concentrations within blood itself, λ remains practically constant; so that we can say that $K/\lambda = K_1$, a new constant; or

$$[H^+] = K_1 \frac{[Acid]}{[Salt]}$$

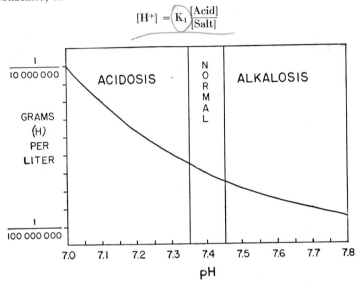

Fig. 56. Possible range of pH in blood. (Gamble: Extracellular Fluid, Harvard Med. School.)

Converting the equation into the pH form, and remembering that pH is the negative logarithm of $[H^+]$

$$pH = -\log K_1 - \log \frac{[Acid]}{[Salt]}$$

or,

$$pH = pK_1 + \log \frac{[Salt]}{[Acid]}$$

where $pK_1 = -\log K_1$.

Where the salts in question are phosphates—where, in other words, the salts are $\dfrac{B_2HPO_4}{BH_2PO_4}$, $pK_1 = 6.8$. Where the salts are the carbonates, $\dfrac{BHCO_3}{H_2CO_3}$, $pK_1 = 6.1$.

It is obvious, then, that knowing the pK_1 and the ratio of salt to acid, the pH can be determined.

It is seen, too, that the hydrogen ion concentration of the buffer solution is proportional to the ratio $\dfrac{[Acid]}{[Salt]}$.

When this ratio = 1, and $[H^+] = K_1$, the pH changes least, giving us maximum buffer effects (Fig. 57). In other words, when we have 50 per cent of the CO_2 as $BHCO_3$, the addition of either acid or alkali causes less change in pH than at any other point on the curve.

With blood at pH 7.4, the $\dfrac{BHCO_3}{H_2CO_3} = \dfrac{20}{1}$. Where $\dfrac{BHCO_3}{H_2CO_3} = 1, p$H = 6.1.*

With the phosphate, when $\dfrac{B_2HPO_4}{BH_2PO_4} = 1, p$H = 6.8.

If, for any reason, the pH of the blood is lowered (as in acidosis), then these buffers become much more efficient.

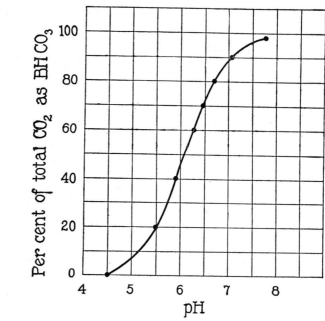

Fig. 57. Action of $NaHCO_3$:H_2CO_3 buffer, showing maximum buffer effect at middle of curve when $NaHCO_3$:H_2CO_3 ratio = 1. (Van Slyke: Physiol. Rev., *1:* 147.)

In so far as the oxyhemoglobin is concerned, its maximum buffering effect is at pH 7.2, which is appreciably nearer to the normal pH of blood.

The Distribution of Buffering Capacities.   That cells are richer in buffering capacity than the plasma has been known for a long time. By determining the CO_2 absorption curves of whole blood and of separated serum, it can be shown that the increase in combined CO_2 in whole blood is more than three times that in serum. The cell buffers are hemoglobin and phosphate, neither of which diffuses into the plasma. Despite this fact, they exert their influence on the plasma.

Hemoglobin-Oxyhemoglobin.   Aside from its buffering properties, the change which hemoglobin undergoes when it is converted into oxyhe-

* The control of carbon dioxide by the respiratory system makes the carbonic acid–bicarbonate buffering in blood much more effective than in vitro. The bicarbonate system is a most important buffer.

moglobin (and vice versa) has an important bearing on the transfer and ultimate elimination of the CO_2. At the lungs hemoglobin combines with oxygen to form oxyhemoglobin. In the tissue capillaries, with a lowered oxygen tension, oxygen passes from the blood into the cells. In the meantime, differences in partial pressure of the CO_2 in blood and tissues cause this gas to leave the tissues and enter the blood.

Oxyhemoglobin is a stronger acid than hemoglobin. pK for the former is 6.62 and for the latter, 8.18. Both these substances are present as salts and as free acids. In the tissues the change from oxyhemoglobin to hemoglobin is also accompanied by a release of base which neutralizes some of the carbon dioxide. In the lungs, with the change of hemoglobin to oxyhemoglobin, the latter acts on the bicarbonate to liberate carbon dioxide.

Carbonic Anhydrase. With the discovery of an enzyme which accelerates the hydration of CO_2 and the decomposition of carbonic acid, a certain modification in point of view became necessary.

In 1928 Henriques showed that the rate of escape of CO_2 from serum was less than that from hemoglobin. This suggested the possibility that the red cells contain a catalyst. Even when diluted 1:20,000, the hemoglobin still retained the accelerating effect in decomposing bicarbonate (in presence of buffers at pH 7.4). Heme itself was devoid of catalytic properties. On the other hand, the globin fraction seemed to act as efficiently as hemoglobin itself. However, the catalyst proved to be neither hemoglobin nor globin, but a substance associated with them.

The enzyme can be separated from the red cells by adding water and alcohol, and then chloroform (to coagulate the hemoglobin). The mixture is centrifuged. The top layer of solution contains the catalyst. By evaporating to dryness in a vacuum desiccator, the impure carbonic anhydrase is obtained in stable form.

The enzyme cannot be dialyzed and is destroyed by heating for thirty minutes at 65° C. It is stable over a wide pH range and has been isolated in crystalline form. It is a protein containing a small amount of zinc. The enzyme is absent in plasma and seems to be entirely concentrated in the red cells.*

Carbamino Compounds. Further work on the rate of evolution of CO_2 suggested to Henriques and to Roughton that some of the CO_2 is combined with protein in the form of a carbamino compound (carbhemoglobin):

$$CO_2 + PrNH_2 \rightleftarrows PrNHCOOH \rightleftarrows PrNHCOO^- + H^+$$

Effect of Carbon Monoxide. The lethal effect of carbon monoxide is due to its ability to combine with hemoglobin to form carboxyhemoglobin, a complex which is 200 times less dissociated than the corresponding complex formed by oxygen with hemoglobin. In this manner carbon monoxide effectively competes with oxygen and removes a portion of the hemoglobin capable of carrying oxygen to the tissues.

* "Without carbonic anhydrase, the release of the amount of CO_2 liberated from the blood during one passage through the lungs would go to within 90 per cent of equilibrium in about 100 seconds. Since erythrocytes spend less than one second in the lung capillaries, enzymic catalysis of the reaction is required." (Davenport)

Importance of Carbonic anhydrase (C.A.)

Effect of Cyanide.   In contrast to the effect of carbon monoxide, cyanide does not affect the oxygen-carrying capacity of hemoglobin. In fact, in cyanide poisoning the venous blood contains enough oxygen so that the arterio-venous difference in oxygen content is lower than normal. The lethal effect of cyanide is due to the inability of the tissue cells to utilize the oxygen. Cyanide has been shown to form a highly undissociable complex with cytochrome oxidase, an enzyme concerned with cellular oxidations (see p. 193). This complex inhibits the activity of the cytochrome oxidase. Normally, compounds are present in the cell which undergo oxidation by the method of a coupled reaction which involves the simultaneous reduction of cytochrome c, as follows:

Compound + Cytochrome c (ox.) $\longrightarrow$ Oxid. Compound + Cytochrome c (red.)

The hydrogen (proton) which is removed can eventually be made to combine with molecular oxygen to form water, if the reduced form of cytochrome c is re-oxidized. This re-oxidation is normally catalyzed by the enzyme, cytochrome oxidase:

$$\text{Cytochrome } c \text{ (red.)} \xrightarrow{\text{cytochrome oxidase}} \text{Cytochrome } c \text{ (oxid.)}$$

$$2H + O \longrightarrow H_2O$$

Since cyanide forms an inactive complex with the enzyme, the utilization of oxygen for this important metabolic reaction is prevented.

Methemoglobin competes with cytochrome oxidase for the cyanide, since the former forms a tighter complex with cyanide (cyanmethemoglobin). This results in the liberation of active cytochrome oxidase. Thus, it is possible to prevent cyanide poisoning if some of the hemoglobin in the circulation is converted to methemoglobin in such quantities as not to interfere with the oxygen-carrying capacity of the blood, since methemoglobin is incapable of combining with oxygen. Some compounds which convert hemoglobin to methemoglobin in vivo are amyl nitrite and p-aminopropiophenone.

DISTURBANCES IN THE ACID-BASE BALANCE

Peters and Van Slyke consider two broad possibilities as causes of acid-base balance disturbance: one, that it is due to a respiratory disturbance, involving the CO_2 content of the blood; and the other, that it is due to a metabolic disturbance—a disturbed relation between acids and alkalis other than carbonic acid. For a summary of possibilities, see Table 23 and Figure 58.

Acidosis, according to Peters and Van Slyke, should be applied to a condition in which the rate of formation or absorption of acids exceeds that of their neutralization or elimination. It may also at times be due to a loss of a considerable amount of base.

From the equation

$$C_H = K \frac{[H_2CO_2]}{[BHCO_3]}$$

it follows that the C_{H^+} is increased when either $[H_2CO_3]$ is increased or when $[BHCO_3]$ is decreased.

Table 23   DISTURBANCES OF ACID-BASE EQUILIBRIUM OF BLOOD
(From Hawk, Oser, and Summerson: Practical Physiological Chemistry, 1947, p. 622, The Blakiston Co.)

Area	Acid-Base Balance	Conditions	Associated Symptoms	Compensatory Mechanisms
1 Uncompensated alkali excess.	[BHCO₃] increased without proportionate rise in [H₂CO₃], therefore pH increased.	Overdosage of NaHCO₃. Excessive vomiting (pyloric obstruction) or gastric lavage (loss of HCl). X-ray or radium treatment.	If marked, tetany.	Diminished respiration (rise in alveolar CO₂) to hold back CO₂. Diuresis and increased NaHCO₃ excretion.
2–3 Uncompensated CO₂ deficit.	[H₂CO₃] decreased without proportionate fall in [BHCO₃], therefore pH increased.	Hyperpnea, voluntary or induced (oxygen want, e.g., at high altitudes). Fever. Hot baths.	If marked, tetany.	Retention of acid metabolites (low NH₃ and titratable acidity of urine). Excretion of Na-HCO₃.
4 Compensated alkali or CO₂ excess.	[BHCO₃] (or [H₂CO₃]) increased but balanced by proportionate rise in [H₂CO₃] (or [BHCO₃]), therefore pH normal.	*Alkali excess.* NaHCO₃ therapy, with slow absorption. *CO₂ excess.* Retarded gas exchange (e.g., emphysema) with CO₂ tension chronically increased.	Cyanosis due to deficient oxygen exchange.	CO₂ retention. BHCO₃ retention.
5 Normal.	[BHCO₃] and [H₂CO₃] normal at ordinary altitudes.			
6 Compensated alkali or CO₂ deficit.	[BHCO₃] (or [H₂CO₃]) decreased but balanced by proportionate fall in [H₂CO₃] (or [BHCO₃]), therefore pH normal.	*Alkali deficit.* Accelerated production (e.g., diabetes) or retarded elimination (e.g., nephritis) of nonvolatile acids. Experimental acid intoxication. Diarrheal acidosis of infancy (marasmus). *CO₂ deficit.* Overventilation at high altitudes (oxygen want).	Hyperpnea.	Increased respiration ("blowing off CO₂"). Accelerated NH₃ formation and acid excretion. Same as in Areas 2 and 3.
7–8 Uncompensated CO₂ excess.	[H₂CO₃] increased without proportionate rise in [BHCO₃], therefore pH decreased.	Retarded respiration as in pneumonia (physical obstruction) or morphine narcosis (deadening of respiratory center). Experimental rebreathing. Cardiac decompensation.	Dyspnea.	Increased respiration. Accelerated NH₃ formation and acid excretion. Probable shift of acid from blood to tissue.
9 Uncompensated alkali deficit.	[BHCO₃] decreased without proportionate fall in [H₂CO₃], therefore pH decreased.	Terminal stages of nephritic acidosis, and diabetic acidosis (compensated by insulin therapy). Deep ether anesthesia. Certain cardiac cases. Eclampsia.	Dyspnea.	Increased respiration. Increased acid excretion and NH₃ formation (except probably in nephritis).

Alkalosis is defined by Cantarow as a state in which either excessive amounts of acid are lost from the body without a comparable loss of alkali, or alkali is formed in or supplied to the body at a rate exceeding that of its neutralization or elimination. This alkalosis may result from a decrease in [H₂CO₃] of the blood, or an increase in [NaHCO₃].

Ketosis is concerned with abnormal amounts of the "acetone bodies"— β-hydroxybutyric acid, acetoacetic acid, and acetone. Acetone is, in reality, a by-product of acetoacetic acid. These substances are involved in the metabolism of fats. The two acids are eliminated in the form of their salts, which means that sodium ion in the body is used for the formation of these salts and is eventually lost. This may give rise to the acidosis seen in diabetes. However, many cases of acidosis are possible without any corresponding ketosis.

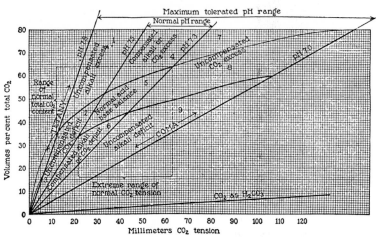

Fig. 58. Normal and abnormal variations of the BHCO₃, H₂CO₃, CO₂ tension and *p*H in oxygenated human whole blood drawn from resting subjects at sea level. (Van Slyke.)

REFERENCES

A fine introduction to the subject will be found in *Davenport:* The ABC of Acid-Base Chemistry, 1947. See also *Johlin:* Introduction to Physical Biochemistry, 1941, Chapters 2, 7, 10, and 11; and *Cantarow and Trumper:* Clinical Biochemistry, 1949, p. 261.

Material pertaining to this chapter will be found in *Gamble:* Extracellular Fluid (Harvard Medical School, 4th Ed.)—a splendid presentation; *Bull:* Physical Biochemistry, 1943; and *West:* Physical Chemistry, 1942.

See also *Roughton and Kendrew:* Haemoglobin, 1949, Chap. 2 (reversible reactions with O₂ and CO) and Chap. 8 (comparative biochemistry and physiology of oxygen carriers).

In connection with carbonic acid and the acid-base balance, see *Peters and Van Slyke:* Quantitative Clinical Chemistry, 1932, vol. 1, p. 868. See also the articles by *Van Slyke:* Physiol. Rev., *1:* 141, 1921;

Pitts and Lotspeich: Am. J. Physiol., *147:* 138, 1946; Merck Manual, 1950, p. 283.

The work on the CO₂ transport by the blood is reviewed in masterly fashion by *Roughton:* Harvey Lectures, 1943–44, p. 96.

A fascinating book by a pioneer in this field is *Henderson:* Blood: A Study in General Physiology, 1928.

Individual papers, to give the reader a "taste" of some of the experimental methods used, are the following: *Conway:* Irish J. Medical Science, Oct.–Nov., 1947 (exchanges of K, Na, and H ions between the cell and its environment); *Peters, Tulin, Danowski, and Hald:* Am. J. Physiol., *148:* 568, 1947 (CO₂ and Cl⁻ between cells and serum); *Lifson, Gordon, Visscher, and Nier:* J. Biol. Chem., *180:* 803, 1949 (fate of utilized molecular oxygen); *Peters:* Bull. N. Y. Acad. Med., Dec., 1949, p. 749 (diagnostic significance of electrolyte disturbances); *Scribner,*

Power, and Rynearson: J. Am. Med. Assoc., *144:* 1167, 1950 (bedside management of problems of fluid balance).

For the work on carbonic anhydrase, see *Meldrum and Roughton:* J. Physiol., *80:* 113, 1933; *Keilin and Mann;* Biochem. J., *34:* 1163, 1940 (zinc is present in the enzyme); *Scott and Mendive:* J. Biol. Chem., *140:* 445, 1941 (the enzyme is a protein); *Scott:* Ibid., *142:* 959, 1942 (a crystalline preparation); *Kiese and Hastings:* Ibid., *132:* 281, 1940 (factors affecting activity); *Krebs and Roughton:* Ibid., *43:* 550, 1948 (enzyme to study reactions involving H_2CO_3, CO_2, and HCO_3^-); *Roughton and Booth:* Ibid., *40:* 319, 1946 (pH and enzyme activity); *Davenport:* Physiol. Rev., *26:* 560, 1946 (enzyme in tissues other than blood); *Tupper, Watts, and Wormall:* Biochem. J., *50:* 429, 1950 (zinc an integral part of the enzyme molecule).

Chapter 11   *Biological Oxidations*

IN THIS chapter we will consider the mechanism by which molecular oxygen brought to the cell is able to oxidize substances in the cell (*metabolites*).

That molecular oxygen by itself is incapable of such oxidations has been proved in many experiments. For example—to take a very simple case—hypoxanthine in contact with an extract of liver is easily oxidized to xanthine in the presence of oxygen; yet in the absence of the enzyme from liver, molecular oxygen has no such effect. In fact, hypoxanthine can be boiled with nitric acid without any appreciable change. The liver contains the enzyme xanthine oxidase, which enables the oxygen to carry out the oxidation.

That tissues contain such oxidases can be readily shown in the very simple experiment of treating a solution of guaiac with an aqueous extract of the potato. The guaiac contains a phenolic derivative which, when oxidized, changes to a blue color (guaiac blue). The blue color is very readily obtained when the tissue extract and the guaiac solution are mixed in the presence of oxygen.*

The mere knowledge that there are enzymes—to which the general name "oxidases" has been given—which catalyze oxidative reactions within the cell brings with it more questions than answers. Are we dealing with one oxidase or with many oxidases? What is their chemical composition? What is the mechanism involved in their reaction with metabolites?

ACTIVATION OF REACTANTS

The Activation of Oxygen. One of the earliest theories dealing with biological oxidation involved a catalyst activating molecular into active, or atomic, oxygen, the latter being then in a position to attack the metabolites within the cell. This theory emphasizes the importance of activating oxygen, but discards the necessity of activating the metabolite.

In 1927, Warburg postulated such an oxygen activation based on his discovery of the *respiratory enzyme* ("atmungsferment"), a heme compound, present in all cells, similar to but not identical with hemoglobin. It was the iron in the enzyme, according to Warburg, which was primarily responsible for the reaction, being first oxidized and then reduced:

$$X.Fe + O_2 \rightleftarrows X.FeO_2$$
(Respiratory
enzyme)

$$X.FeO_2 + 2A \rightleftarrows X.Fe + 2AO$$
(Organic
molecules)

* Catechol (p. 195) is very often used in place of guaiac. With the oxidase the catechol goes through a series of color changes: green, yellow, brown, black.

186

From the work of Keilin and others, it was shown that this respiratory enzyme is identical with an indophenol oxidase, or cytochrome oxidase—as it is now known—which is important in the oxidation of the reduced cytochromes (p. 192). What, for a time, was hailed as the oxidizing agent responsible for all biological oxidations now turns out to be but one of a number of substances.

Indophenol oxidase, present in various animal and some vegetable tissues, gets its name from the fact that when mixed with dimethyl-*p*-phenylenediamine and α-naphthol in the presence of oxygen, an indophenol, a blue substance, is produced; and this reaction is used as a method of identifying the enzyme.

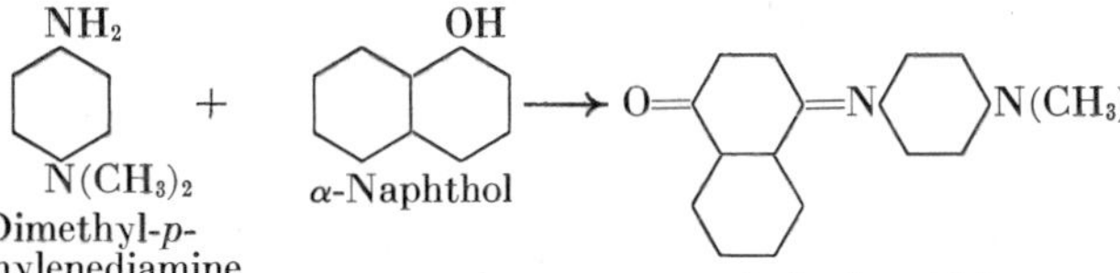

Dimethyl-*p*-
phenylenediamine   α-Naphthol

Indophenol blue

The Activation of Hydrogen.   The next advance we owe to Wieland. His work has played a major role in our understanding of biological oxidations. According to Wieland, in the presence of the suitable enzyme (now commonly called a *dehydrogenase*), certain hydrogen atoms in the metabolite are made active and removed. In order that the reaction may continue, the hydrogen liberated has to be removed continuously. In the simplest examples, the hydrogen acceptor can be oxygen itself. We shall see, however, that between the action of the removal of hydrogen and its eventual combination with oxygen to form water, the hydrogen is passed on to one or more carriers (hydrogen transfer).

Wieland was led to this dehydrogenase theory by experiments involving finely divided platinum or palladium black. He found, for example, that the addition of palladium black to a solution of acetaldehyde converted the latter to acetic acid. What happens, probably, is that the aldehyde first combines with water to form an intermediate hydrate

$$CH_3.CHO \xrightarrow{H_2O} CH_3.\overset{\displaystyle H}{\underset{\displaystyle OH}{C-OH}}$$

and that then two atoms of hydrogen are removed by the palladium:

$$CH_3.\underset{\substack{| \quad | \\ OH \quad OH}}{C-H} \longrightarrow CH_3.COOH$$

In the presence of a hydrogen acceptor, such as quinone, or reducible dyes such as indigo or methylene blue, the hydrogen, temporarily adsorbed by the metal, is transferred to the acceptor (B), and the reaction proceeds to completion. The two reactions are:

$$AH_2 + Pd \longrightarrow A + PdH_2$$
Metabolite

$$PdH_2 + B \longrightarrow Pd + BH_2$$
Quinone

The Activation of Hydrogen and Oxygen.   The discovery of the cytochromes by Keilin (p. 192), which have to do with oxygen activation, led to the view that biological oxidation is possible only if both the hydrogen of the metabolite and the oxygen are activated. This is probably true in many cases. But even here, the more general application of such a theory is possible if we consider that carriers are also essential to the system; in other words, before the hydrogen can be transferred to the oxygen, it must be carried by one or more substances. The most substantial progress has been made in determining the nature of some of these carriers.

HYDROGEN CARRIERS

A hydrogen carrier is a substance present in the cell which can accept hydrogen and so be reduced, and can then be oxidized again (by transferring the hydrogen to another carrier, or by oxidation of the hydrogen by oxygen). The carrier, then, is the hydrogen acceptor; but we must point out that when we talk of carriers, we have in mind substances found in the cell and not palladium black or hydroquinone.

They include pyridine nucleotides, flavoproteins and the cytochromes.

It should be stressed, at this stage, that we are employing the broader concept of oxidation, which deals with the loss of electrons, rather than the narrower concept, which defines oxidation as the mere combination with oxygen. This broader view of oxidation makes it clearer why the intermediate steps—the reactions of the biochemical carriers with hydrogen and the transfer of the hydrogen to other carriers—are as much a part of an oxidation process as is the eventual combination of hydrogen and oxygen to form water.

The need for intermediary carriers may be seen by observing the value for E_0' (the observed potential when an oxidation-reduction system is 50 per cent reduced) of the reaction involving the combination of molecular oxygen with a hydrogen ion (a proton), which is $+0.81$ volts; whereas E_0' for molecular hydrogen is -0.42 volts. Here the difference in potential is great when measured in terms of the energy required to bring about such a change in one step. The advantage of the hydrogen transport system is that it raises the hydrogen to higher levels of potential by short stages, utilizing the energy produced in biochemical reactions, until finally it reaches the stage where it can react with oxygen (see accompanying table).

E_0' (volts)	Stages of Hydrogen Transport
$+0.81$	$\frac{1}{2}O_2 + 2H^+ + 2e \longrightarrow H_2O$
?	Cytochrome oxidase
$+0.29$	Cytochrome a
$+0.27$	Cytochrome c
-0.04	Cytochrome b
-0.08	Flavoproteins
-0.28	Pyridine nucleotides

(-0.42 for H_2 at 1 atmosphere at pH of 7)

Methylene Blue as a Hydrogen Acceptor.   To study hydrogen carriers or "acceptors" in vitro, the dye methylene blue has been introduced; here one can measure the rate of the decolorization of the dye as it is reduced from the blue to the colorless (leuco) form:

$$\underset{\text{(Metabolite)}}{AH_2} \quad + \quad \underset{\substack{\text{(Methylene}\\ \text{blue)}}}{Mb} \longrightarrow \underset{\text{(Leuco dye)}}{A + MbH_2}$$

To prevent re-oxidation of the reduced dye by molecular oxygen, the reaction is carried out in an oxygen-free atmosphere. We owe to Thunberg the invention of such a device whereby the tubes can be evacuated before the enzyme and substrate are mixed. The rate and time of decolorization gives a measure of dehydrogenase activity.

Examples of Carrier Reactions (see Chaps. 12 and 14).

(A) Oxidation of glucose-6-PO$_4$ to 6-phosphogluconic acid:

(1) Glucose-6-PO$_4$ + TPN $\xrightarrow{\text{"zwischenferment"}}$ 6-Phosphogluconic acid + TPNH$_2$

(2) TPNH$_2$ + FMN-protein $\longrightarrow$ TPN + FMNH$_2$-protein

(3) FMNH$_2$-protein + 2 Ferricytochrome c $\longrightarrow$ FMN-protein + 2 Ferrocytochrome c + 2H$^+$

(4) Ferrocytochrome c + 2H$^+$ + $\frac{1}{2}$O$_2$ $\xrightarrow[\text{oxidase}]{\text{cytochrome}}$ Ferricytochrome c + H$_2$O

or

(5) TPNH$_2$ + 2 Ferricytochrome c $\xrightarrow[\text{reductase}]{\text{cytochrome } c}$ TPN + 2 Ferrocytochrome c + 2H$^+$

(6) Ferrocytochrome c + 2H$^+$ + $\frac{1}{2}$O$_2$ $\longrightarrow$ Ferricytochrome c + H$_2$O

(B) D-Amino acid oxidase:

(1) Amino acid + FAD-protein $\longrightarrow$ Keto acid + FADH$_2$-protein

(2) FADH$_2$-protein + O$_2$ $\longrightarrow$ FAD-protein + H$_2$O$_2$

(3) In the presence of the enzyme catalase:

$$2H_2O_2 \xrightarrow{\text{catalase}} 2H_2O + O_2$$

(C) Lactic acid dehydrogenase:

(1) Lactic acid + DPN $\xrightarrow{\text{enzyme}}$ pyruvic acid + DPNH$_2$

(2) DPNH$_2$ + Ferricytochrome c $\longrightarrow$ DPN + Ferrocytochrome c + 2H$^+$

(3) Ferrocytochrome c + 2H$^+$ + $\frac{1}{2}$O$_2$ $\longrightarrow$ Ferricytochrome c + H$_2$O

(Note: TPN = triphosphopyridine nucleotide, DPN = diphosphopyridine nucleotide, FMN = flavin mononucleotide, FAD = flavin adenine dinucleotide. See following pages.)

Dehydrogenases.   Dehydrogenases are made up of two parts: the protein portion is called the apodehydrogenase (apoenzyme), and the non-protein portion is the coenzyme. The removal of the coenzyme from the protein fraction results in a loss of enzymic activity, but such activity is restored when the two fractions are brought together again.

Among the coenzymes are DPN, TPN, FAD and FMN. Each one of these substances contains a vitamin as part of the chemical structure.

Dehydrogenases, according to Sumner, may be divided into three groups: (a) those which require coenzyme I or coenzyme II; (b) those which transfer hydrogen to cytochrome; and (c) the yellow enzymes.

Under (a) may be cited the conversion of lactic acid to pyruvic acid. A specific dehydrogenase (lactic dehydrogenase), found in heart tissue, etc., is needed for this reaction, and the enzyme cooperates with coenzyme I.

Again, in the conversion of glucose to gluconic acid a specific dehydrogenase (glucose dehydrogenase), found in liver and yeast, cooperates with coenzyme II.

Under (b)—dehydrogenases which transfer hydrogen to cytochrome—may be mentioned succinic dehydrogenase as an example. This enzyme, in the presence of the cytochrome system, converts succinic acid to fumaric acid, a reaction which is an important step in carbohydrate metabolism.

Under (c)—the yellow enzymes—are proteins containing groups related to riboflavin.

Pyridine Nucleotides.   These include coenzyme I and coenzyme II.

Coenzyme I has also been called *codehydrogenase I, cozymase, diphosphopyridine nucleotide (DPN)*, and *Co I*. Coenzyme II has also been called *codehydrogenase II, triphosphopyridine nucleotide (TPN)*, and *Co II*.

Both coenzymes are nicotinamide adenine dinucleotides; the one difference being that Co I contains two molecules, and Co II, three molecules of phosphoric acid (p. 88). Nicotinic acid, and its amide, will be discussed under vitamins. The importance of these substances as "building stones" for the respiratory enzymes now becomes clear.

These coenzymes, as has already been stated, combine with and then give up hydrogen. They are oxidation-reduction systems. This combination with and giving up of hydrogen is the property of the nicotinamide part of the molecule and may be represented in simplified form as follows:

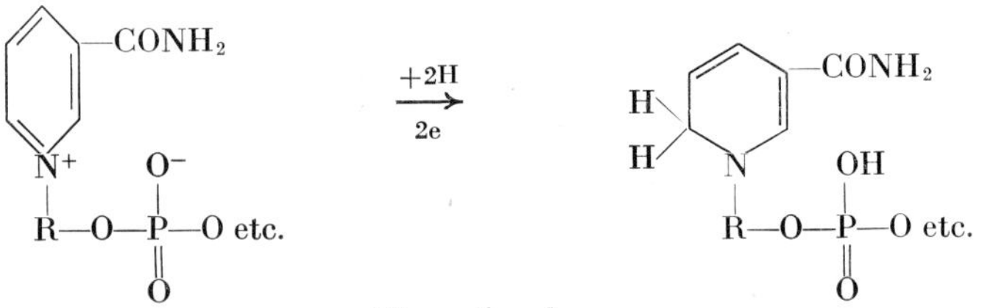

[R = ribose]

The pyridine nucleotides are associated with the vitamin, nicotinic acid (or its amide). It has been shown, for example, that a dog or pig suffering from a deficiency of nicotinic acid exhibits a lowered coenzyme I content of the liver and muscle.

Yellow Enzymes (Flavoproteins).   These enzymes are protein compounds, containing, as prosthetic groups, alloxazine mononucleotide (FMN, flavin mononucleotide), and alloxazine adenine dinucleotide (FAD, flavin adenine dinucleotide).

The structure of these two substances is here given:

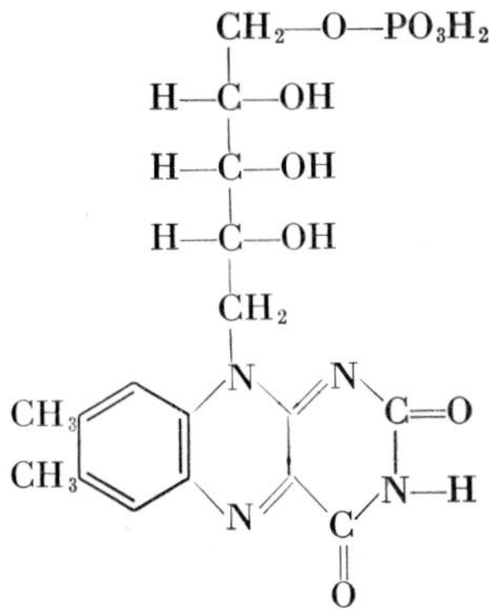

$$CH_2-O-PO_3H_2$$
$$H-C-OH$$
$$H-C-OH$$
$$H-C-OH$$
$$CH_2$$

Riboflavin phosphate [alloxazine mononucleotide (FMN)]

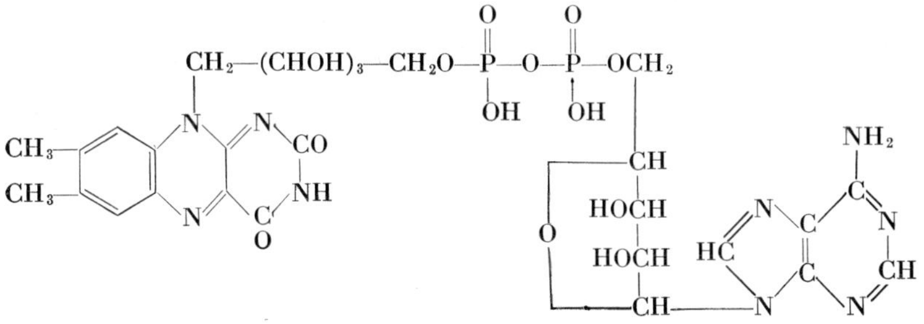

$$CH_2-(CHOH)_3-CH_2O-\overset{O}{\underset{OH}{P}}-O-\overset{O}{\underset{OH}{P}}-OCH_2$$

Flavin adenine dinucleotide (FAD) (Alloxazine adenine dinucleotide)

The alloxazine mononucleotide, together with a protein, has also been called *Warburg's yellow enzyme* and was the first of these yellow enzymes isolated. The newer yellow enzymes belong to the dinucleotide type.

The close connection between the vitamin riboflavin and these yellow enzymes has been shown by creating a riboflavin deficiency in the rat and noting a decrease in the D-amino acid oxidase of the liver and the kidney. The addition of riboflavin to the diet increases the enzyme content of the tissues.

FMN and FAD are interconvertible. In red cells FMN can be converted to FAD. This is also true of rat tissues. In yeast, the reaction mechanism is:

$$\text{FMN} + \text{ATP} * \overset{Mg^{++}}{\underset{}{\rightleftarrows}} \text{FAD} + \text{Pyrophosphate}$$

* See p. 206.

In the potato the reaction is:

$$\text{FAD} + \text{DPN} \xrightarrow{\text{nucleotide pyrophosphatase}} \text{FMN} + \text{Nicotinamide mononucleotide}$$

The yellow enzymes are found in animal tissues and in yeast.

The D-amino acid oxidase which acts on D-amino acids has, as its prosthetic group, alloxazine adenine dinucleotide. This is also true of xanthine oxidase, which acts on xanthine and other purines and of glycine oxidase, which acts on glycine.

In these cases we are dealing with different enzyme proteins (apoenzyme) having the same prosthetic group.

The Cytochromes.   There are present in various cells a group of heme proteins, related in composition to cytochrome oxidase. They are differentiated most easily on the basis of their different light absorption bands and are referred to as a, a_1, a_2, a_3, b, b_1, b_2 and c.

Cytochromes a and a_3 are found in animal tissues. Cytochrome a_3 is autoxidizable and forms a complex with carbon monoxide; it may be identical with cytochrome oxidase. Cytochromes a_1 and a_2 are present in some bacteria. Cytochrome b is found in heart muscle and kidneys; b_1 is found in bacteria, and b_2, in yeast.

Cytochrome c is widely distributed in animal tissues and is the only one which has been isolated and crystallized. Its porphyrin is a derivative of aetioporphyrin III, and so differs from that present in hemoglobin.

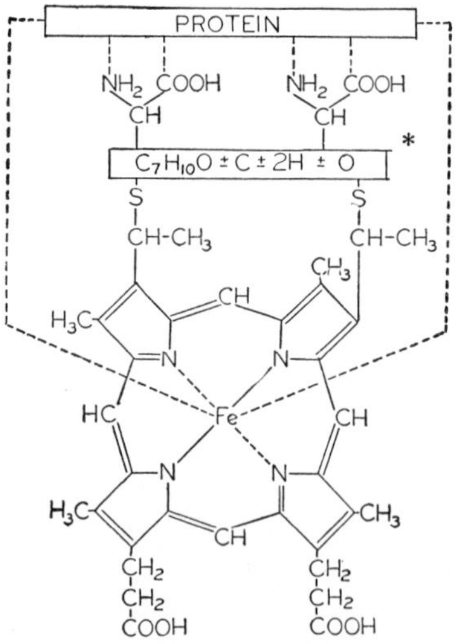

Structure of cytochrome c.

The content of cytochrome c of various tissues is roughly proportional to the oxygen consumption of these tissues, and it is believed that the cytochrome oxidase–cytochrome c system constitutes an essential part of the mechanism of cellular respiration.

* There is uncertainty as to the exact number of C, H, and O atoms.

Cytochrome oxidase (Warburg's "atmungsferment" and Keilin's indophenol oxidase) occurs in the cell in close association with particulate matter (p. 97). It is inhibited by cyanide and carbon monoxide. On the basis of one hemin per molecule, the molecular weight of cytochrome oxidase is calculated to be 75,000.

Death from cyanide is due to the inhibition of cytochrome oxidase, probably by first affecting the enzyme in the brain cells. This makes cyanide a poison of cellular respiration. Carbon monoxide, on the other hand, is a poison because it combines with hemoglobin to form a relatively undissociable compound (p. 181).

Cytochrome c reductase, usually included here, is not a member of the cytochromes at all. It is a yellow enzyme and contains FAD as its prosthetic group. It has been isolated in pure form from hog liver and acts to catalyze the oxidation of $TPNH_2$ to TPN:

$$TPNH_2 + 2\ \text{Ferricytochrome}\ c \xrightarrow[\text{reductase}]{\text{cytochrome}\ c} TPN + 2\ \text{Ferrocytochrome}\ c.$$

The molecular weight of this reductase is about 68,000.

AN APPLICATION OF THE THEORY OF BIOLOGICAL OXIDATION

How does such a theory work in a specific case? How can we, for example, apply it to the metabolism of carbohydrates?

In referring to p. 207, we shall see that hexosediphosphate is changed to lactic acid. During the course of these reactions, glyceraldehyde phosphate is oxidized to phosphoglyceric acid. Here is where our biological system of stepwise oxidations come into play. Table 24, in simplified form, attempts to summarize the facts:

Table 24   OXIDATION OF HEXOSEDIPHOSPHATE TO LACTIC ACID *
(Adapted from Potter: Medicine, *19:* 461.)

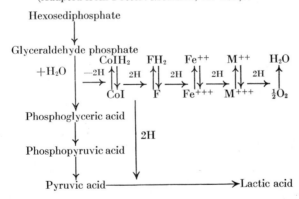

"The whole energy of oxidation," writes Szent-Györgyi, "is liberated in the oxidation of hydrogen. . . . We thus have the whole energy cycle:

* The removal of hydrogen requires a dehydrogenase. CoI = Coenzyme I. $CoIH_2$ = coenzyme I in reduced form. F = flavin compound; FH_2 its reduced form. Fe^{++} and Fe^{+++} = the prosthetic groups of cytochrome. M = group of cytochrome oxidase.

the plant cell, with its chlorophyll, stores the energy of the sun, separating the elements of water, fixing the hydrogen to a solid carbon chain, and sending the oxygen back to the atmosphere. All cells cover the energy need by reversing the process, taking the hydrogen from the organic molecule and uniting it again with the oxygen of the air."

MISCELLANEOUS OXIDASES, GLUTATHIONE AND ASCORBIC ACID

Hydroperoxidases.   This group of iron-porphyrin-protein enzymes is found in both plant and animal tissues and includes *catalase* and *peroxidase*. Both react with the same substrate, but in different ways. These differences may be illustrated as follows:

(*a*) Catalases are a special group of peroxidases which utilize H_2O_2 both as a substrate and as an acceptor:

$$H_2O_2 + \begin{array}{c} HO \\ | \\ HO \end{array} \longrightarrow O_2 + 2H_2O$$

(*b*) With peroxidases the acceptor is an organic compound, such as hydroquinone or catechol:

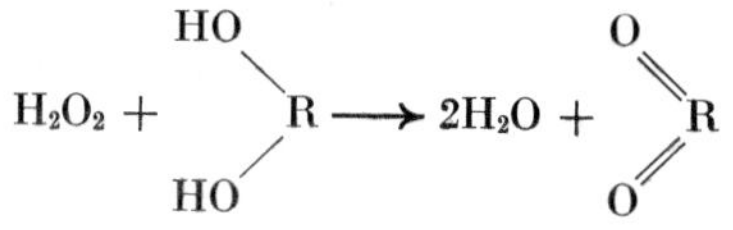

$$H_2O_2 + \begin{array}{c} HO \\ \diagdown \\ \diagup \\ HO \end{array} R \longrightarrow 2H_2O + \begin{array}{c} O \\ \diagdown \\ \diagup \\ O \end{array} R$$

where R is an organic radical, such as C_6H_4—.

Peroxidase is found in horseradish. Several other peroxidases are lactoperoxidase in milk; verdoperoxidase in leukocytes; cytochrome *c* peroxidase in yeast.

Such compounds as tryptophan, ascorbic acid, epinephrine and tyrosine are oxidized by peroxidase.

Catalase is present in liver and red cells. It has been crystallized (Sumner). Keilin and Hartree have suggested the following mechanism for catalase activity involving the iron of the catalase:

$$4\ Fe^{+++} + 2\ H_2O_2 \longrightarrow 4\ Fe^{++} + 4\ H^+ + 2\ O_2$$
$$4\ Fe^{++} + 4\ H^+ + O_2 \longrightarrow 4\ Fe^{+++} + 2\ H_2O$$

These hydroperoxidases were among the first with which direct evidence was obtained for an enzyme-substrate complex as postulated by Michaelis and Menten (p. 108). Stern showed spectroscopically that ethyl hydrogen peroxide and catalase combined, although the complex was found to be enzymatically inactive. Keilin also demonstrated the formation of a complex between H_2O_2 and peroxidase. Chance has since shown that the original Michaelis-Menten formulation must be extended to account for the formation of many complexes, not all of which are active; for example, for catalase:

$$E + S \rightleftharpoons ES_1 \text{ (inactive)}$$
$$ES_1 \rightleftharpoons ES_2 \text{ (active)}$$
$$ES_1 + S \rightleftharpoons E + P$$
$$(E = \text{enzyme}, S = \text{substrate}, P = \text{product})$$

Although H_2O_2 may be shown to occur in isolated enzymes systems outside of the organism, such as the result of the action of D-amino acid oxidase or xanthine oxidase, there is little evidence that it is formed in cells. The absence of H_2O_2 in vivo may be due to the action of the hydroperoxidases; but that these enzymes serve to protect the organism against the toxic action of biologically formed H_2O_2 is still unproven.

Polyphenol Oxidase (potato oxidase).   A variety of polyphenol oxidase is found in the potato, and catalyzes the oxidation of o-diphenols (such as catechol or epinephrine) in the presence of molecular oxygen.

The action on catechol occurs in two stages:

Catechol + cupric enzyme ⟶ o-Quinone + cuprous enzyme

Cuprous enzyme + O_2 ⟶ cupric enzyme

Hydrogen peroxide is not involved in this reaction.*

This enzyme will oxidize monophenols, such as phenol, but very slowly.

How important a constituent the copper is in the makeup of this enzyme is seen by removing the copper from the molecule (by dialysis): the copper-free protein shows no oxidase activity. When copper ions are added the activity is restored. (The copper ions alone also show no activity.) Metals such as iron, cobalt, nickel, manganese, or zinc cannot take the place of the copper.

Laccase.   Another copper-protein enzyme, laccase, is found in the lacquer tree and also catalyzes the oxidation of different polyphenols. But it is different from polyphenol oxidase in the following: laccase is not poisoned by carbon monoxide, whereas polyphenol oxidase (P.O.) is strongly inhibited in its action; laccase readily oxidizes p-phenylenediamine, but its oxidation of catechol is slow; the reverse is true of P.O.

However, there is still some question as to the individuality of laccase.

Tyrosinase (monophenol oxidase).   This is still another copper-protein enzyme which catalyzes the oxidation of monophenols (such as p-cresol, phenol, and tyrosine) in the presence of molecular oxygen. The action is not a clear-cut one. Nelson and others have shown that the ordinary, probably impure, tyrosinase catalyzes two types of reaction: one type introduces a hydroxyl group ortho to the one already present in certain monohydric phenols; and the other type brings about the oxidation of certain o-dihydric phenols to their corresponding o-quinones.

This enzyme converts tryosine into a black pigment (melanin, Chap. 14).

Ascorbic Acid Oxidase.   This enzyme, present in plant tissues which catalyze the oxidation of ascorbic acid to dehydroascorbic acid, is also a copper-protein compound. It has been obtained in a pure state. Its copper content is 0.26 per cent; its molecular weight, 146,000, corresponds to 6 copper atoms per molecule.

It is assumed that, just as the iron in the iron-porphyrin enzymes under-

---

* The brown (or black) color of the potato when exposed to air for a time is due to the combination of the quinone with the proteins of the tissue to form melanin-like (?) pigments.

goes oxidation and reduction during the course of the enzyme's activity, so possibly does the copper in copper-protein enzymes.

Glutathione and Ascorbic Acid.   It is believed that glutathione and ascorbic acid are both concerned with some biological system of oxidation.

Glutathione is a tripeptide of cysteine, glutamic acid, and glycine. It was

$$
\begin{array}{l}
CH_2SH \\
| \\
CHNH\text{———————}CO.CH_2 \\
| \qquad\qquad\qquad\qquad | \\
CONHCH_2COOH \qquad CH_2 \\
\qquad\qquad\qquad\qquad\quad | \\
\qquad\qquad\qquad\qquad\quad CHNH_2 \\
\qquad\qquad\qquad\qquad\quad | \\
\qquad\qquad\qquad\qquad\quad COOH
\end{array}
$$

Glutathione.

isolated from tissues by Hopkins in the form of its cuprous salt. The oxidized form, which may be written as G—S—S—G (where G and G stand for oxidized glutathione minus its two sulfur atoms), is readily reduced by tissues to the sulfhydryl form, G.SH; and the latter, in presence of traces of copper, gives up its hydrogen to molecular oxygen, becoming oxidized in turn.

Barron believes that glutathione maintains enzymes active by keeping their —SH groups (and many possess them) in this (reduced) form.

Ascorbic acid, the antiscorbutic substance (Chap. 20), is a very active reducing agent and may have a role in reactions involving oxidations and reductions in the tissue. It may, in other words, be a carrier; but our information, at present, is meager.

Hopkins believed that ascorbic acid may be a coenzyme for the oxidation of glutathione. He found that the oxidation of ascorbic acid by oxygen and the ascorbic acid oxidase—obtained from cauliflower—is prevented by the addition of glutathione. He believed that the oxidized ascorbic acid reacts with glutathione, forming ascorbic acid and oxidized glutathione, and that this reaction proceeds faster than the oxidation of ascorbic acid.

An enzyme, glutathione reductase, is present in yeast as well as in animal tissues. It catalyzes the reduction of oxidized glutathione by TPN as follows:

$$G\text{—}S\text{—}S\text{—}G + TPNH + H^+ \longrightarrow TPN + 2GSH$$

The enzyme is highly specific and will not act on cystine, nor will it act when DPN is substituted for TPN. Its significance lies in the fact that it may serve as a hydrogen carrier for all enzymes which require TPN as a prosthetic group. Further, reduced glutathione can be oxidized by dehydroascorbic acid, forming ascorbic acid. The latter will undergo oxidation directly by molecular oxygen in the presence of ascorbic acid oxidase, to complete the transfer of hydrogen to molecular oxygen.

REFERENCES

Baldwin: Dynamic Aspects of Biochemistry, 1952. Chaps. 6 and 7 are strongly recommended.

Several volumes on the subject may be mentioned. *Green* is the author of one of these, entitled Mechanisms of Biological Oxidations, 1940. In a volume entitled A Symposium on Respiratory Enzymes, 1942, the following articles should be consulted: Oxidative mechanisms in animal tissues, p. 16 (*Ball*); hydrogen transport, p. 33 (*Potter, Elliott, Ball, Lipmann, Stern, Haas, Stotz*); oxidases, peroxidases, and catalase, p. 74 (*Stern*); nicotinamide nucleotide enzymes, p. 104 (*Schlenk*); flavoproteins, p. 134 (*Hogness*); cytochromes, p. 149 (*Stotz*).

Another volume, *Respiratory Enzymes*, edited by *Elvehjem and Wilson*, with contributions from members of the staff of the Univ. of Wisconsin, covers much the same field. The chapters are the following: historical introduction, p. 1 (*Elvehjem*); dehydrogenases, p. 20 (*Potter*); oxidases, catalase, and peroxidase, p. 38 (*Lipton, Arnold, Berger*); coenzymes, p. 71 (*Baumann, Stare*); cytochrome, p. 93 (*Burris*); flavoproteins, etc., p. 104 (*Stark, Gordon, Christensen*); inhibition of dehydrogenases, p. 137 (*Cohen*); hydrogen transport systems, p. 158 (*Schneider*); oxidation-reduction potentials, p. 168 (*Axelrod, Johnson*); physiochemical theory of enzyme action, p. 203 (*Wilson*).

Sumner and Somers: Chemistry and Methods of Enzymes, 1943, devote several chapters to oxidizing enzymes: chapters 11 (coenzymes I and II); 12 (dehydrogenases); 13 (yellow enzymes); 15 (various oxidases). See also *Sumner and Myrback:* The Enzymes, 1952.

For progress in the field, see Ann. Rev. Biochem., *19:* 1, 1950 (*Potter*); *20:* 1, 1951 (*Wurmster*); *21:* 687, 1952 (*Chance and Smith*); *22:* 17, 1953 (*Slater*).

For a model experimental study of an oxidase system—the oxidation of succinic to fumaric acid—see *Keilin and Hartree:* Biochem. J., *44:* 205, 1949.

For the intermediate catalysts involved in carbohydrate metabolism, see *Ochoa:* Annals N. Y. Acad. Sciences, *47:* 836, 1947.

Several individual articles are the following:

Dehydrogenases. Potter: Medicine, *19:* 441, 1940; J. Biol. Chem., *165:* 311, 1946 (malic dehydrogenase); *Weinmann, Morehouse, and Winzler:* Ibid., *168:* 712, 1947 (succinic dehydrogenase); *Keilin and Hartree:* Biochem. J., *42:* 221, 1948 (glucose oxidase: notatin).

Pyridine nucleotides. A detailed discussion of coenzymes I and II will be found in the article by *Schlenk:* Adv. Enzym., *5:* 207, 1945. See, also, *Sumner, Krishnan, and*

Sisler: Arch. Biochem., *12:* 19, 1947 (preparation of coenzyme I); *Spaulding and Graham:* J. Biol. Chem., *170:* 716, 1947 (degradation of coenzyme I); *Kornberg and Pricer:* Ibid., *186:* 537, 1950 (structure of TPN).

Flavoproteins. For a study of glycine oxidase, a flavoprotein, see *Ratner, Nocito, and Green:* J. Biol. Chem., *152:* 119, 1944. See, also, *Blanchard, Green, Nocito, and Ratner:* J. Biol. Chem., *161:* 583, 1945 (preparation of L-amino acid oxidase); *Dimant, Sanadri, and Huennekens:* J. Am. Chem. Soc., *74:* 5440, 1952 (isolation).

Cytochromes. Keilin and Hartree: Proc. R. S. (London), Series B, *127:* 167, 1939; *Theorell and Akesson;* J. Am. Chem. Soc., *63:* 1804, 1820, 1941; *Haas, Harrer, and Hogness:* J. Biol. Chem., *143:* 341, 1942; *Hogeboom, Claude, and Hotchkiss:* Ibid., *165:* 615, 1946; *Keilin and Hartree:* Biochem. J., *41:* 500, 1947; *Smith and Stotz:* J. Biol. Chem., *179:* 891, 1949; *Wainio, Person, Eichel, and Cooperstein:* J. Biol. Chem., *183:* 89, 1950; *192:* 349, 1951 (cytochrome oxidase); *Horecker:* Ibid., *183:* 593, 1951 (cytochrome c reductase); *Drabkin:* Ibid., *182:* 335, 351, 1950 (cytochrome c).

Catalase. Adams: Biochem. J., *54:* 328, 1953; *Keilin and Hartree:* Biochem. J., *39:* 293, 1945 (function of); *Chance:* Nature, *161:* 914, 1948 (intermediate catalase —H₂O₂ compound); *Herbert:* Biochem. J., *43:* 203, 1948 (crystalline product); *Chance:* J. Biol. Chem., *179:* 1311, 1949; *180:* 947, 1949 (catalase-peroxide complexes).

Peroxidase. Keilin: Proc. Roy. Soc. (London), Series B, *122:* 119, 1936; *Greenstein:* J. Am. Med. Assoc., *148:* 697, 1952 (in cancer). *Agner* is the author of an article on verdoperoxidase in Adv. Enzym., *3:* 137, 1943. See, also, *Chance:* Science, *109:* 204, 1949 (properties); Arch. Biochem., *21:* 416, 1949; *22:* 224, 1949 (enzyme-substrate compounds of peroxidase and peroxides).

Laccase. Tissiéres: Nature, *162:* 340, 1948 (reconstruction of laccase from its protein and copper).

Ascorbic acid oxidase. Powers, Lewis, and Dawson: J. Gen. Physiol., *27:* 167, 1944; *Dunn and Dawson:* J. Biol. Chem., *189:* 485, 1951; *Joselow and Dawson:* Ibid., *191:* 11, 1951 (Cu in the enzyme).

Tyrosinase. Wagreich and Nelson: J. Am. Chem. Soc., *60:* 1545, 1938; *Nelson and Dawson:* Adv. Enzym., *4:* 99, 1944; *Mallette, Lewis, Ames, Nelson, and Dawson:* Arch. Biochem., *16:* 283, 1948 (preparation from mushrooms); *Mallette and Dawson:* Arch. Biochem., *23:* 29, 1949 (purified tyrosinase); *Lerner, Fitzpatrick, Calkins, and Summerson:* J. Biol. Chem., *178:* 185, 1949 (preparation and properties).

Glutathione. Barron, Nelson, and Ardao: J. Gen. Physiol., *32:* 179, 1948 (importance of —SH groups); *Ziegerhagen, Ames, and Elvehjem:* J. Biol. Chem., *167:* 129, 1947 (properties); *Conn and Vennesland:* Nature, *167:* 976, 1951; *Binkley, Fujii, and Kimmel:* J. Biol. Chem., *186:* 159, 1950 (metabolism); *Rall and Lehninger:* Ibid., *194:* 119, 1952 (glutathione reductase); *Racker:* Ibid., *198:* 721, 1952 (glutathione as a prosthetic group in a dehydrogenase).

Chapter 12 · *Metabolism of Carbohydrates*

$\mathbf{M}$UCH of contemporary biochemistry includes studies of the transformation of relatively simple compounds—produced during the digestive process—to a variety of intermediate substances until the final end products are reached. These changes are brought about by enzymes. These studies include the mechanism whereby the energy in the chemical bond, created by photosynthetic activity, is transformed so that it may do the kind of work associated with the living cell. This energy may be associated with heat production, so that enzymic reactions take place at high rates; it may be transformed into mechanical energy, illustrated by muscle contraction; it may be transformed into electrical energy, illustrated by the conduction of nerve impulse; or it may be transformed into light energy, illustrated by the firefly, or the luminescent micro-organisms of the sea.

Studies of this kind include the isolation of many "intermediate" compounds; hence, in the place of "metabolism," we often speak of the "intermediate metabolism" of compounds.

As a result of digestive processes, utilizable carbohydrates are largely in the state of hexoses when absorption begins. Our problem is to discuss what happens to carbohydrate from the point where it is absorbed to the point where it is eliminated in the form of carbon dioxide and water.

The field is a complex one. It deals with the storage of glycogen in liver and in muscle; with the glucose of the blood and the manner in which its amount is controlled; and with the oxidation of carbohydrate, involving a number of enzymes and a number of intermediary products. These topics will be taken up in turn.

SITES OF CARBOHYDRATE STORAGE AND UTILIZATION

The Liver. This organ is so intimately concerned with the mechanism of carbohydrate metabolism (and of fat and protein metabolism too, as we shall see later) that a few preliminary remarks are necessary.

Aside from the secretion of bile and its property of detoxicating substances—to name but two properties of this organ—a third characteristic of the liver is what concerns us particularly in this chapter: its relation to the utilization of food. The liver stores, manufactures, and regulates food materials. Not only are carbohydrates handled—as we shall see in the next section—but so are fats and proteins (in the form of amino acids).

Some vitamins, vitamin A, for example, are stored to an appreciable degree in the liver; and so is the substance effective in pernicious anemia, vitamin B_{12}.

Several syntheses occur in this organ. Heparin, for example, seems to be manufactured here. So are the plasma proteins and fibrinogen and prothrombin—the last with the help of vitamin K.

Various tests have been devised ("liver function tests") to get clinical information. The center of detoxication is considered to be the liver. Here, for example, much of the hippuric acid is synthesized from benzoic acid and glycine. The capacity for such synthesis is considerably reduced in certain liver diseases.

The liver has strong regenerative capacity. As much as 80 per cent of it can be removed without materially disturbing its normal functions. Normal size is regained within six to eight weeks.

GLYCOGEN IN LIVER. Glycogen, stored in the liver in variable quantities, is never absent, even in starvation. In extreme cases, as much as 20 per cent of the weight of the liver may represent this carbohydrate.

Removal of the liver causes a drop in the blood sugar—hypoglycemia— a general breakdown and ultimate death.

Within the liver, processes of glycogenesis and glycogenolysis—synthesis and hydrolysis of glycogen—are forever active. (Where the breakdown of glycogen is more extreme—as in muscle, with the carbohydrate converted to pyruvic or lactic acid—the process is known as glycolysis.) The carbohydrates, absorbed very largely in the form of hexoses, pass into the liver, where some are stored in the form of glycogen and the rest empty into the general circulation. When glycogen is hydrolyzed, glucose alone is obtained, and is normally the one sugar in circulating blood.

Since not only glucose, but fructose and galactose find their way to the liver and are stored as glycogen, and since the hydrolysis of glycogen yields just glucose, there must be a preliminary transformation of fructose and galactose into glucose. Isotopic experiments give some indication of the mechanism of such transformations. For example, when galactose-1-C^{14} * is administered, and the glucose which is obtained from the hydrolysis of glycogen is analyzed, C^{14} is found exclusively in carbon number 1; which leads to the conclusion that the predominant pathway by which galactose is transformed into glucose is by a Walden type of inversion at carbon number 4 (pp. 13, 19). The possible mechanism of this transformation may be as follows:

(a) Galactose + ATP † $\longrightarrow$ ADP † + Galactose-1-PO_4

(b) Galactose-1-PO_4 $\longrightarrow$ Glucose-1-PO_4 (p. 21)

(c) Glucose-1-PO_4 $\longrightarrow$ Glucose-6-PO_4 (p. 21)

(d) Glucose-6-PO_4 $\longrightarrow$ Glucose + $PO_4^=$

The enzyme for reaction (a) is found in yeast as well as in liver and is called *galactokinase;* it resembles *hexokinase* (p. 207). The enzyme for reaction (b) is known as *galactowaldenase* and requires a coenzyme, uridine diphosphate-glucose, found in yeast and in liver. The enzymes for reaction (c)—*phosphoglucomutase*—and reaction (d)—*phosphatase*—are present in animal tissues.

By analogy, it is assumed that not only galactose, but other hexoses are similarly transformed to glucose.

Fructose can be converted to glucose by a series of enzymatic transformations (see p. 207):

* C^{14} is attached to carbon atom 1 in galactose. See pp. 13, 98.
† See p. 206.

$$\text{Fructose} + \text{ATP} \xrightarrow{\text{fructokinase}} \text{ADP} + \text{Fructose-6-phosphate}$$

$$\text{Fructose-6-phosphate} \xrightarrow{\text{isomerase}} \text{Glucose-6-phosphate}$$

$$\text{Glucose-6-phosphate} \xrightarrow{\text{phosphatase}} \text{Glucose} + \text{PO}_4^=$$

We may say at once that one of the important factors controlling the amount of glucose in the blood is the glycogen reserve in the liver. As has been pointed out, if the liver is removed from an animal, there is a marked drop of glucose in the blood (hypoglycemia), even though the muscles retain appreciable quantities of glycogen. In other words, a controlling factor in the amount of glucose in the blood is the conversion of liver glycogen into glucose. The blood sugar is not derived from the glycogen of muscle (except indirectly; see p. 203).

As a matter of fact, not only are the three common monosaccharides stored as glycogen in the liver—the amount stored depending upon the various requirements of the body—but a number of amino acids, and the glycerol portion of the molecule of fat, are also glycogen formers in various degrees, and thereby help to add, if necessary, to the ultimate glucose supply. Among amino acids, mention may be made of glutamic acid, cystine, alanine, proline, serine, and aspartic acid (glycogenic compounds).

It is such experiments dealing with three-carbon compounds that led to views regarding intermediate carbohydrate metabolism. The reasoning was as follows: three-carbon compound A forms glycogen in the liver; the latter, when hydrolyzed, always yields glucose; from which we may, perhaps, conclude that when the tissues oxidize the glucose to carbon dioxide and water, the glucose molecule is first degraded to the three-carbon compound A. In this way, dihydroxyacetone, lactic acid, etc., are featured prominently as "intermediates" in carbohydrate metabolism.

Experiments on isolated livers, perfused with Ringer's solution containing three-carbon compounds, have led to similar results.

As showing how varied may be the source of the glycogen of the liver, we find very appreciable quantities of glycogen on a diet devoid of carbohydrate altogether. As we have already indicated, the glycerol in fat, and a number of amino acids in protein, serve very well as glycogen formers. So true is this that even in starvation, which first depletes the stored carbohydrates, we still find some glycogen in the liver, derived from the breakdown of proteins and fats in the tissues, and also from lactic acid formed in muscle from glycogen (see below).

The Glucose of the Blood.   The glucose of the blood is remarkably constant under normal conditions. It rarely rises (in the normal human) much above 100 mg. per 100 ml. of blood (the range is about 80–120 mg.) The regulatory mechanism consists of a number of factors: the formation of glycogen in the liver and in muscle, and to a lesser extent, in other tissues; the oxidation of carbohydrate; the conversion of carbohydrate into fat; and the excretion of glucose. The hormones of the pancreas and the pituitary play a dominant role.

The Renal Threshold.   In the process of regulating the amount of sugar in the blood, we have discussed a number of factors at work: the amount of liver glycogen transformed to glucose; the amount of glucose itself transformed into muscle glycogen; and, somewhat indirectly, the amount of lactic acid converted into liver glycogen. We have seen that these factors are under the control of hormones. But the amount of glucose in the blood—as has already been indicated—also depends upon how fast the sugar is oxidized: in active muscular exercise, for example, the rapid breakdown of muscle glycogen would demand a rapid transfer of blood sugar to the muscles, and such sugar would then have to be replaced by the further conversion of liver glycogen into glucose. The amount of sugar in the blood also depends upon how much carbohydrate is converted to body fat: the individual who eats much and exercises little will find this process of considerable importance.

There is, however, still another factor which has not yet been discussed; and this one involves the kidney. Normally, the amount of glucose in the urine is negligible. However, when for any reason one or more of the various regulatory mechanisms become impaired and the amount of glucose in the blood increases appreciably above the normal, then the renal threshold is reached and appreciable quantities of glucose begin to appear in the urine.

Normally, the glucose in the blood filters through the glomerular membrane of the kidney and is again reabsorbed in the tubules. But when the sugar in the blood reaches, say, 140 to 160 mg. per 100 ml., and above, the reabsorptive capacity of the tubules may be too highly taxed and sugar may pass into the urine. The renal threshold may, therefore, be defined as "that level of blood glucose beyond which complete tubular reabsorption no longer occurs" (Drabkin).

By using phlorhizin, which prevents the reabsorption of the sugar, glucose readily passes into the urine and experimental glycosuria is established.

Carbohydrate Tolerance.   The ingestion of carbohydrate causes a temporary increase in the amount of sugar in the blood. In a normal individual, after the administration of from 1 to 2 gm. of glucose per kilogram of body weight, the blood sugar will increase in one hour from about 110 mg. per 100 ml. of blood to about 160 mg. At the end of 2 to $2\frac{1}{2}$ hours the amount will be normal again. In a diabetic person, the increase is much more marked, and the return to normal is a slower process. For example, after an ingestion of glucose, the blood sugar of the diabetic person may increase from 200 to 400 mg. in two hours, and at the end of the third hour it is still 300 mg.

The Glycogen in Muscle.   The source of muscle glycogen is the glucose of the blood. As the glycogen of the muscle is used up—during exercise, for example—some of the glycogen in the liver is converted to glucose, which then passes into the blood and serves as source material for the replenishment of the glycogen in muscle.

It can be shown that insulin, the hormone in the pancreas, is involved in the formation of glycogen in muscle. In a depancreatized dog, the injection of glucose alone does little to influence the amount of the polysaccharide in muscle; but when both glucose and insulin are given, the amount increases very perceptibly. Even in normal animals, the injection of insulin increases the glycogen deposit in the muscle. This is not true in so far as the liver is concerned. Only in the animal suffering from diabetes will the injection of insulin cause an increased deposition of glycogen in the liver.

Usually the contraction of muscle forms lactic acid. Some acid finds its way into the blood, thence to the liver, where it is synthesized to glycogen (Cori). The relationship may be outlined thus:

(A) Liver glycogen $\xrightarrow{adrenalin}$ (B) Blood sugar $\xrightarrow{insulin}$ (C) Muscle glycogen $\xrightarrow{adrenalin}$ (D) Blood
lactic acid $\longrightarrow$ (A) Liver glycogen

Epinephrine (Adrenalin), from the adrenal glands, accelerates the conversion of muscle glycogen to blood lactic acid and of liver glycogen to blood sugar; and insulin accelerates the change from blood sugar to muscle glycogen. The former promotes hyperglycemia and the latter, hypoglycemia; and thereby there is a tendency to balance forces. It is possible that, in addition, insulin has a retarding influence on the conversion of liver glycogen to blood sugar, and epinephrine may have a similar retarding influence on the change from blood sugar to muscle glycogen. We shall see that the situation is really more complex; for the pituitary and probably the adrenal cortex are also involved.

HORMONES IN CARBOHYDRATE METABOLISM

Insulin.   This hormone will be discussed elsewhere (Chap. 23). However, since insulin is so intimately involved in carbohydrate metabolism, an account of its influence must be given here. The extirpation of the pancreas in an animal gives rise to diabetes, whereby the sugar of the blood is increased above the normal amount (hyperglycemia) and sugar appears in the urine (glycosuria). Apparently, one important regulatory factor in maintaining the sugar of the blood at a constant level has broken down. This factor is due to a hormone, manufactured by the pancreas, to which the name "insulin" has been given. Banting, Best, Macleod, and Collip were able to extract a fraction from the pancreas which, when injected into a depancreatized animal, lowered the amount of blood sugar. They even showed that the injection of such an extract into a normal animal lowers the blood sugar below the normal amount—so much so, in fact, that the animal may go into convulsions and die. This is a dramatic illustration of the importance of keeping the blood sugar at certain levels.

What, then, is the function of this insulin? The injection of insulin into the depancreatized animal enables more sugar to be utilized and more glycogen to be deposited. There is an actual increase in the amount of glycogen in the liver, and the glycogen in the muscle may also be increased. That oxidation is increased is discovered by determining the respiratory quotient (R. Q.) (see Chap. 17). This is a value obtained by dividing the volume of carbon dioxide eliminated by the volume of oxygen consumed. The rise in the respiratory quotient to a figure usually approaching unity is an indication that carbohydrates, rather than fats or proteins, are being burned in the body. So that we may say that the function of insulin is a double one: it influences directly the oxidation of carbohydrate, and it also regulates the quantity of glycogen deposited in the liver and in the muscle.

In connection with the relationship of insulin to carbohydrate metabolism, it should be mentioned that the injection of insulin causes a decrease in the amount of serum phosphate but an increase in the hexose monophosphate of muscle. As will be seen presently (p. 207), hexose phosphates are formed prior to the further breakdown of carbohydrates, and a source of such phosphate is in the blood (which, therefore, shows a decrease).

Other Hormones Involved in Carbohydrate Metabolism.   The effect of hormones on carbohydrate metabolism is summarized in Fig. 59.

The removal of the pancreas from a dog is fatal; the animal dies in one to two weeks. The cat usually survives not more than five to six days. If, however, the pituitary is also removed from such a depancreatized animal, the survival period is increased to some twenty-two days in the cat, and the blood sugar is markedly decreased (from some 347 mg. per 100 ml. to

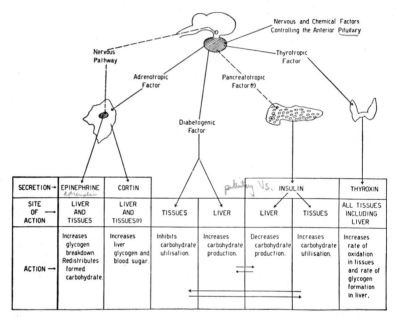

Fig. 59. The endocrine control of carbohydrate metabolism. (Long: Sigma XI Quarterly, *26:* 175.)

190). Somewhat similar results are obtained when the adrenals are removed from a depancreatized animal.

Modification of the diabetic stage by hypophysectomy has been shown by Houssay to be due to the absence, more specifically, of the anterior pituitary. The "antagonistic action" of the hormones—insulin with its tendency to lower blood sugar and the pituitary with its tendency to increase it—is probably not a very exact picture of what actually happens. We know that there is a "diabetogenic hormone" in the anterior pituitary—a hormone which tends to increase the amount of sugar in the blood and which tends to decrease the production of insulin in the pancreas.

By injecting dogs with relatively large quantities of this diabetogenic hormone over a number of days, Young has shown that the diabetes may continue indefinitely after treatment with the extract has ceased.

A relationship somewhat similar to that existing between the pituitary and the pancreas has been postulated for the adrenals and the pancreas.

Here it has been shown that the causative agent is not in the adrenal medulla, containing the epinephrine, but in the cortex. Epinephrine may be of some importance in carbohydrate metabolism, but substances in the cortex appear even more important (see Chap. 23).

OXIDATION OF GLUCOSE

The early work by Pasteur and others on the fermentation of yeast led to a study of reactions whereby glucose is converted to ethyl alcohol and carbon dioxide. Following the discovery by Buchner of enzymes in cell-free extracts of yeast, much work was done on enzymes and substrates (the substances upon which the enzymes act) in the fermentation mixture. In animal tissues, and in some bacteria, the result of fermentation was shown to give rise to lactic acid, rather than to alcohol and carbon dioxide, as in plants. But, nevertheless, certain similarities were observed in reactions involving fermentations in yeast, muscle and liver. (The fermentation reactions occurring in muscle and liver are referred to as "glycolysis.")

It was a study of reactions in connection with muscular activity which led to a more detailed picture of the nature of fermentation.

Carbohydrate Breakdown in Muscle. Fletcher and Hopkins (in 1907) observed that less lactic acid was formed in a muscle which contracted aerobically than in one which contracted anaerobically. During anaerobic *(without O₂)* contraction, lactic acid accumulated until the muscle was fatigued, and then disappeared when the muscle was placed in oxygen, at the same time regaining its ability to contract. Meyerhof showed that the lactic acid had its origin in the glycogen of muscle. There appeared to be a proportionality between the work done, the heat produced, the tension developed and the lactic acid formed. In 1925 Meyerhof succeeded in preparing a cell-free extract from muscle which, in vitro, could convert glycogen to lactic acid. Dialysis of such an extract reduced its activity; but this could be restored by the addition to the dialyzed material of a heated extract of muscle ("kochsaft"). The "kochsaft" contained the activators and coenzymes necessary for full activity.

Phosphocreatine. In 1927 Fiske and Subbarow isolated phosphocreatine from a trichloroacetic acid extract of muscle. Its formula is *

This compound disappeared during muscular activity and was resynthesized when the muscle was at rest. Since the phosphocreatine disappeared more rapidly than did glycogen, it was considered to be the more immediate source of energy for contraction. This idea was strengthened by Lundsgaard's discovery (in 1930) that a muscle poisoned with iodoacetic acid continued to contract before going into rigor, and that during this contraction process no lactic acid was produced. It was shown that in the

* For the formula for creatine, see Chap. 14.

muscle poisoned with iodoacetic acid, the phosphocreatine broke down while work was being done, and in amounts proportional to the amount of energy expended. After the phosphocreatine had been used up, the muscle went into rigor.

Later it will be seen that the action of iodoacetic acid is to poison one of the enzymes involved in glycolysis, and thereby prevent the formation of lactic acid.

Adenosine Triphosphate (ATP).*   In addition to phosphocreatine, phosphate esters of glucose and fructose were shown to be present, and finally ATP itself was discovered. Lohman showed that until some ATP broke down to provide ADP (adenosine diphosphate), there was no decomposition of any phosphocreatine. Apparently, the breakdown of ATP preceded that of phosphocreatine; and the former was, therefore, the more immediate source of the energy needed for contraction.

The breakdown of ATP is catalyzed by an enzyme, adenosine triphosphatase:

$$ATP \longrightarrow ADP + PO_4^=$$

and the Lohman reaction, involving phosphocreatine and ATP, may now be written thus:

$$\text{Phosphocreatine} + ADP \rightleftarrows ATP + \text{Creatine}$$

GLYCOLYSIS

In yeast, glucose is the starting compound for the reactions involving fermentation; in muscle and liver, it is glycogen.† The intermediate compounds formed in such a reaction are not easy to isolate because their existence is fleeting, and they are quickly used for succeeding reactions. This problem is largely overcome by the knowledge that the change of one intermediate compound to another is brought about by an enzyme: for each step, for each link in the chain, a specific enzyme is necessary; and that the reaction may be stopped at certain points by the introduction of an inhibitor specific to some one enzyme in the group involved. In this way the reaction which would normally remove the intermediate compound is brought to a halt, the compound piles up, so to speak, and the isolation and identification can be accomplished all the more readily.

The reactions involved in fermentation have been identified, and many of the enzymes have been both crystallized and their mode of action determined.

In what follows, the conversion of glycogen (or glucose) to lactic acid is divided into three parts: (A) the conversion of glycogen, or glucose, to glucose-6-phosphate; (B) the conversion of glucose-6-phosphate to pyruvic acid; (C) the conversion of pyruvic acid (under anaerobic conditions) to alcohol in yeast and to lactic acid in liver and muscle. (Under aerobic conditions, the pyruvic acid is oxidized via the "tricarboxylic acid

---

* For the chemistry, see p. 88.

† The glucose of the blood does, in fact, enter the reaction sequence via the liver.

cycle," which will be discussed later (p. 212),—a process which prevents the accumulation of lactic acid.)

No O_2 involved — anaerobic

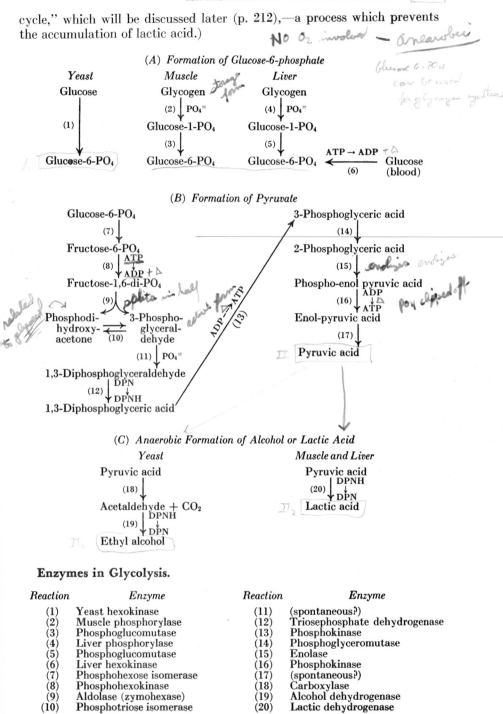

(A) Formation of Glucose-6-phosphate

Yeast	Muscle	Liver
Glucose	Glycogen *storage form*	Glycogen

Glucose 6-PO4 can be used for glycogen synthesis.

(B) *Formation of Pyruvate*

(C) *Anaerobic Formation of Alcohol or Lactic Acid*

Enzymes in Glycolysis.

Reaction	Enzyme	Reaction	Enzyme
(1)	Yeast hexokinase	(11)	(spontaneous?)
(2)	Muscle phosphorylase	(12)	Triosephosphate dehydrogenase
(3)	Phosphoglucomutase	(13)	Phosphokinase
(4)	Liver phosphorylase	(14)	Phosphoglyceromutase
(5)	Phosphoglucomutase	(15)	Enolase
(6)	Liver hexokinase	(16)	Phosphokinase
(7)	Phosphohexose isomerase	(17)	(spontaneous?)
(8)	Phosphohexokinase	(18)	Carboxylase
(9)	Aldolase (zymohexase)	(19)	Alcohol dehydrogenase
(10)	Phosphotriose isomerase	(20)	Lactic dehydrogenase

Structures of Intermediates in Glycolysis.

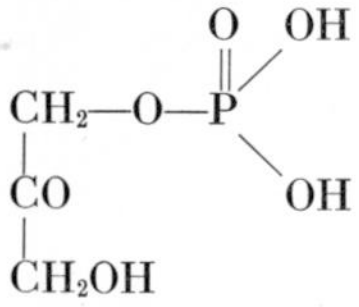

$$
\begin{array}{l}
\text{CH}_2\text{—O—P}\overset{\displaystyle O}{\underset{\displaystyle OH}{\diagup}}\!\!\overset{OH}{}\\
\text{CO}\\
\text{CH}_2\text{OH}
\end{array}
$$

Phosphodihydroxyacetone

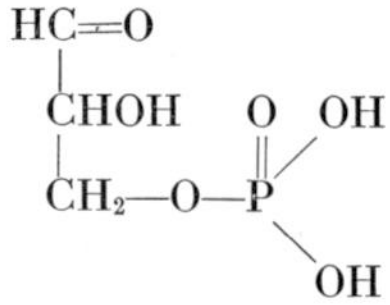

$$
\begin{array}{l}
\text{HC}\!=\!\text{O}\\
\text{CHOH}\quad \text{O}\;\;\text{OH}\\
\text{CH}_2\text{—O—P}\\
\qquad\qquad\text{OH}
\end{array}
$$

3-Phosphoglyceraldehyde

$$
\begin{array}{l}
\text{OH}\quad \text{O}\;\;\text{OH}\\
\text{H—C—O—P}\\
\text{CHOH}\quad\text{OH}\\
\qquad\qquad\text{O}\;\;\text{OH}\\
\text{CH}_2\text{—O—P}\\
\qquad\qquad\text{OH}
\end{array}
$$

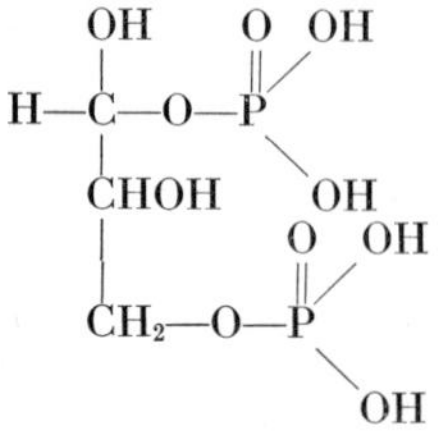

1,3-Diphosphoglyceraldehyde

$$
\begin{array}{l}
\text{O}\quad \text{O}\;\;\text{OH}\\
\text{C—O—P}\\
\text{CHOH}\quad\text{OH}\\
\qquad\qquad\text{O}\;\;\text{OH}\\
\text{CH}_2\text{—O—P}\\
\qquad\qquad\text{OH}
\end{array}
$$

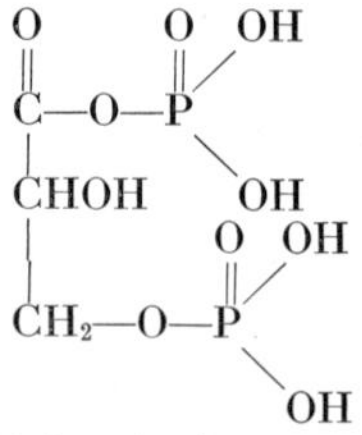

1,3-Diphosphoglyceric acid

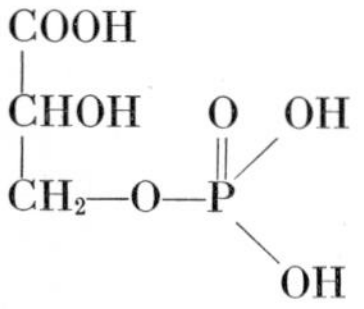

$$
\begin{array}{l}
\text{COOH}\\
\text{CHOH}\quad \text{O}\;\;\text{OH}\\
\text{CH}_2\text{—O—P}\\
\qquad\qquad\text{OH}
\end{array}
$$

3-Phosphoglyceric acid

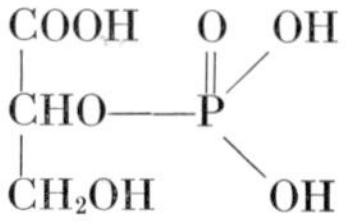

$$
\begin{array}{l}
\text{COOH}\quad \text{O}\;\;\text{OH}\\
\text{CHO——P}\\
\text{CH}_2\text{OH}\qquad\text{OH}
\end{array}
$$

2-Phosphoglyceric acid

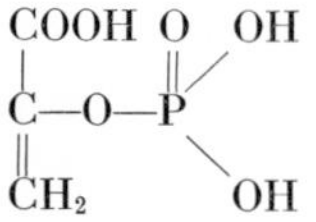

$$
\begin{array}{l}
\text{COOH}\;\;\text{O}\;\;\text{OH}\\
\text{C—O—P}\\
\text{CH}_2\qquad\text{OH}
\end{array}
$$

Phospho-enol pyruvic acid

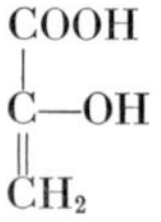

$$
\begin{array}{l}
\text{COOH}\\
\text{C—OH}\\
\text{CH}_2
\end{array}
$$

Enol pyruvic acid

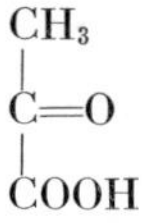

$$
\begin{array}{l}
\text{CH}_3\\
\text{C}\!=\!\text{O}\\
\text{COOH}
\end{array}
$$

Pyruvic acid

$$
\begin{array}{l}
\text{CH}_3\\
\text{CHOH}\\
\text{COOH}
\end{array}
$$

Lactic acid

Examples of Inhibitors. (a) Fluoride inhibits the enzyme enolase (no. 15) by forming a complex with Mg^{++} (which is attached to the enzyme) and with phosphate: a protein-magnesium fluorophosphate.

(b) Iodoacetate inhibits triose phosphate dehydrogenase (no. 12) by combining with the free sulfhydryl groups on the enzyme.

(c) Dialysis inhibits many of these enzymes which require small molecules or ions as activators or coenzymes (e.g., Mg^{++}, DPN).

Examples of Reaction Mechanisms. In a number of instances, the mechanisms for the reactions in the glycolytic scheme have been clarified. Below are several examples:

(a) PHOSPHOGLUCOMUTASE (no. 3). This enzyme converts glucose-1-phosphate to glucose-6-phosphate. Actually, it requires the presence of small quantities of glucose-1,6-diphosphate which acts as a coenzyme and is not used up. The reaction mechanism is indicated below (see p. 110):

Glucose-1,6-diphosphate + *Glucose*-1-phosphate ⇄ Glucose-6-phosphate
+ *Glucose*-1,6-diphosphate

(*b*) Phosphoglyceromutase (no. 14). This enzyme converts 3-phosphoglyceric acid to 2-phosphoglyceric acid. It requires the presence of small quantities of 2,3-diphosphoglyceric acid. It may be written as follows:

3-Phospho*glycerate* + 2,3-Diphosphoglycerate $\rightleftharpoons$ 2-Phosphoglycerate
$\qquad\qquad\qquad\qquad\qquad\qquad\qquad$ + 2,3-Diphospho*glycerate*

(*c*) 3-Phosphoglycerate Kinase (nos. 11, 12 and 13). This enzyme system is responsible for the conversion of 3-phosphoglyceraldehyde to 3-phosphoglyceric acid. It is really a mixture of two enzymes, the reactions for which are:

3-Phosphoglyceraldehyde + DPN + PO_4 $\rightleftharpoons$ 1,3-Diphosphoglycerate + $DPNH_2$

1,3-Diphosphoglycerate + ADP $\rightleftharpoons$ 3-Phosphoglycerate + ATP

Reversibility of Glycolysis and Glycogen Synthesis. Although the reactions on p. 207 have been written with a single arrow, the student should keep in mind that the reactions which are given are, to a large extent, reversible. As an example, the equilibrium mixture which results in the reaction catalyzed by phosphoglucomutase contains 94 per cent glucose-6-phosphate and 6 per cent glucose-1-phosphate. In the next reaction, catalyzed by fructose phosphohexose isomerase, glucose-6-phosphate makes up 70 per cent of the equilibrium mixture, fructose-6-phosphate accounts for 30 per cent. Glucose-6-phosphate can arise from glycogen or glucose and can be used for glycogen synthesis by a reverse series of reactions via glucose-1-phosphate. This appears to be determined largely by the concentration of inorganic phosphate in the cell: in the presence of excess phosphate glycogen is broken down; in the presence of low concentrations of phosphate, glycogen is synthesized. The process of glycogen synthesis is aided by oxidative reactions which result in the incorporation of phosphate into organic phosphate esters. We shall see later (Chap. 23) that insulin and the hormones of the anterior pituitary and adrenal cortex influence glycogen synthesis in several tissues, in vivo. The hypothesis has been suggested, based on some evidence, that the anterior pituitary and adrenal cortex secretions inhibit the hexokinase reaction, whereas insulin can relieve this inhibition. Finally, these reversible reactions which can lead to the synthesis of glycogen explain how so many different types of compounds, when fed, yield added stores of glycogen. Such compounds are sugars and amino acids, which, as will be shown, are metabolically altered to compounds identical with those which take part in the reactions of intermediary carbohydrate metabolism.

Why Phosphorylated Intermediates? Among the high energy phosphate esters in glycolysis are ATP, phospho-enol pyruvate and 1,3-diphosphoglyceraldehyde; the low energy phosphate esters are such compounds as glucose-1- and glucose-6-phosphates, and 2- and 3-phosphoglyceric acids. The average energy associated with the hydrolysis of the low energy bond is about 3,000 cal. per mol, whereas that associated with the high energy bond is from 12,000 to 16,000 cal. per mol. It is believed that one reason for the high potential energy in a compound with a high energy phosphate bond is its ability to form, on hydrolysis, a structure which possesses characteristics of resonance or of tautomerism. An example of how the energy for the formation of $\sim$ph bonds can be obtained is seen in the oxidation reactions which occur in glycolysis (nos. 11, 12, 13, p. 207). Here phosphoglyceraldehyde is oxidized to phosphoglyceric acid, involving the reduction of DPN and the phosphorylation of ADP.

The over-all arithmetic of glycolysis shows that for each molecule of glucose (or a 6-carbon glycogen unit) the following results:

(a) Formation of 2 mols of lactic acid;

(b) reduction of 2 mols of DPN (reaction no. 12) and its subsequent oxidation (reactions no. 19 and 20);

(c) formation of 4 mols of ATP (reactions no. 13 and 16).

Since during glycolysis in liver, 2 mols of ATP are used up (reactions no. 6 and 8) this leads to the over-all yield of 2 mols of ATP or 2 $\sim$ph bonds equivalent to some 30,000 calories. The theoretical energy yield from this reaction, glucose $\longrightarrow$ 2 lactic acid, would be 58,000 calories, so that we observe a 50 per cent efficiency, which is quite good for any energy-producing system. This analysis illustrates how the energy which results from the oxidation of glucose (or glycogen) can be parcelled and transferred by the incorporation of inorganic phosphate into high energy bonds (phosphate esters), the transfer of this bond energy to the adenylic acid system and the utilization of the high energy bond of ATP with the formation of inorganic phosphate. As an example, we can illustrate the conversion of the high energy bond of ATP to the relatively low energy bond in glucose-6-phosphate with the liberation of 9000 calories, making the reaction exergonic: *

$$\text{Glucose} + \text{ATP} \xrightarrow{\text{hexokinase}} \text{Glucose-6-phosphate} + \text{ADP} + 9000 \text{ cal.}$$

MULTIPLE PATHWAYS FOR CARBOHYDRATE OXIDATION†

Besides the reactions described under glycolysis, other pathways for the utilization of glucose are possible. Such pathways exist in animal tissues as well as in lower forms (such as yeasts). For example, the liver contains a glucose oxidase which can convert glucose to gluconic acid (p. 211); the red cell, and yeast, can convert glucose-6-phosphate to 6-phosphogluconic acid and finally to pentose phosphate.

Muscle extracts, free of intact cells, do not respire; here glycolysis can be studied. The intact muscle, however, does respire and is normally supplied with an adequate supply of oxygen (obtained from circulating blood and the oxygen reserve in the form of oxymyoglobin). Under these conditions, lactate does not accumulate—except after strenuous exercise—and the pyruvate, which is formed in the place of lactate, is oxidized to CO_2 and water.

The presence of a variety of metabolic pathways in tissues of the mammal poses a problem which has been well stated by Barron: "Living organisms . . . have developed multiple schemes for a better utilization of the total energy obtained on oxidation of carbohydrate to CO_2 and water. Thus, the multiple pathways of oxidation . . . are the imprint of the biochemical evolution which has been going on from the moment the cell was

---

* An *exergonic* reaction is one which results in the release of free energy, in contradistinction to an *endergonic* reaction, which deals with the absorption of free energy.

† See p. 112.

created. Direct combination with oxygen . . . was replaced because of its wastefulness by stepwise oxidation and decarboxylation of hexoses. There are still a number of organisms (molds, some bacteria) which have retained this primitive pathway and even in some mammalian tissues some of its enzymes can be found (e.g. glucose oxidase in the liver). The introduction of the P group represents a great economy, as many largely exergonic reactions became readily reversible. Direct oxidation was then replaced by the stepwise oxidation of the phosphorylated compounds. There are still many cells which retain this pathway; and many more which utilize it when the more elaborate route—fermentation—has been interrupted. Finally came the fermentation pathway with its obligatory phase of pyruvate formation. . . . Of the two kinds of fermentation, alcoholic fermentation is largely confined to the plant kingdom, while lactic acid fermentation is found in animals and bacteria. . . . Pyruvate is the meeting point of these different pathways."

Aerobic Glycolysis.   Normally, glycolysis—the formation of lactic acid—is restricted to anaerobic conditions, for the presence of oxygen inhibits the formation of lactic acid. This inhibition of glycolysis by oxygen is referred to as the "Pasteur effect." Some believe that a specific enzyme, the "Pasteur enzyme," is responsible for this effect, and that the enzyme regulates the direction of the metabolic reactions in the cell.

Some tissues show a high rate of aerobic glycolysis; they do form lactic acid in the presence of oxygen. This is true of the retina and of cancerous tissue.

A theory to explain the "Pasteur effect" has been proposed by Lynen and Johnson. They suggest that during aerobic cellular metabolism much more esterification of inorganic phosphate takes place than during anaerobic glycolysis. This means that during aerobic conditions, the concentration of inorganic phosphate in the cell will be lowered considerably as compared to the anaerobic cell. The aerobic conditions will therefore favor glycogen synthesis and will tend to depress glycolysis, the formation of lactic acid.

Aerobic Oxidation of Pyruvate.   As has been shown, during glycolytic breakdown, DPN is reduced to $DPNH_2$; at the same time, 1,3-diphosphoglyceraldehyde is oxidized to the corresponding glyceric acid. To conserve this coenzyme, it must be re-oxidized. Under anaerobic conditions, this is done when pyruvic acid is converted to lactic acid. In the presence of oxygen, however, $DPNH_2$ can still be oxidized with the help of the respiratory enzymes (p. 189), reforming DPN; the H is carried by the flavoprotein enzymes and the cytochrome c–cytochrome oxidase system until it reaches molecular oxygen, with which it combines to form water.

In the anaerobic cycle, glycogen is broken down to lactic acid. In the aerobic, or oxidative cycle, which we are about to discuss, the lactic acid or, rather, its oxidation product, pyruvic acid, is oxidized to carbon dioxide and water.

A great deal of work has been done in the study of this mechanism. Szent-Györgyi noticed that the rate of respiration of pigeon breast muscle declines as succinate disappears, and that the respiration is revived when more succinate or fumarate is added. This suggested that the oxidation of carbohydrate was catalyzed by such C_4 acids, and that the path of carbohydrate metabolism would have to include C_4 compounds. Later on, Szent-Györgyi showed that malate and oxaloacetate behaved similarly to succinate and fumarate.

The next step was taken by Krebs. He revealed that citric and α-ketoglutaric acids also act catalytically on minced muscle. This suggested that C_6 and C_5 compounds are also involved. In line with these facts, Krebs suggested that the initial step along the path of oxidation was the combination of pyruvic acid (C_3) and oxaloacetic acid (C_4) to form a compound (C_7) which so far has not been isolated but which is broken down to some citric acid derivative (C_6), and then to α-ketoglutaric (C_5), on to the various C_4 dicarboxylic acids. Actually, Krebs showed that when pyruvate and oxaloacetate are incubated with minced muscle, citric acid can be isolated as one of the products.

The formation of a hypothetical C_7 compound was a stumbling block to the scheme. From the work of Lipmann, there is excellent evidence that pyruvate (C_3) is first converted to acetate (C_2) by oxidative decarboxylation (with the help of coenzyme A, p. 214).

$$\overset{\text{CH}_3}{\underset{\text{COOH}}{\overset{|}{\underset{|}{\text{CO}}}}} \xrightarrow[+\text{O}]{-\text{CO}_2} \text{CH}_3\text{COOH} + \text{CO}_2$$

and that it is this acetate (C_2) which combines with oxaloacetate (C_4) to form a C_6 compound. In other words, the need for postulating a hypothetical C_7 compound disappears.

The "Krebs cycle," the "citric acid cycle," or, more commonly, the "tricarboxylic acid cycle," may be illustrated in the following manner:

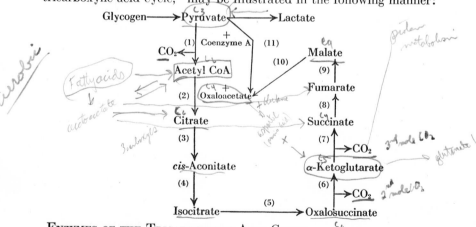

ENZYMES OF THE TRICARBOXYLIC ACID CYCLE.

Reaction	Enzyme
(1)	Pyruvic acid oxidase (requires DPN)
(2)	Condensing enzyme
(3, 4)	Aconitase
(5)	Isocitric dehydrogenase (requires TPN)
(6)	Oxalosuccinic decarboxylase
(7)	Oxidative decarboxylation enzyme (requires DPN)
(8)	Succinic dehydrogenase
(9)	Fumarase
(10)	Malic dehydrogenase (requires DPN)
(11)	β-Carboxylase (requires thiamine pyrophosphate and is present in liver but not in muscle)

EXAMPLES OF INHIBITORS.

(*a*) Arsenite inhibits reaction no. 7.

(*b*) Anaerobiosis inhibits isocitric dehydrogenase (no. 5) since aerobic conditions are necessary in order to re-oxidize the reduced TPNH₂.

(*c*) Fluoracetate inhibits aconitase (nos. 3 and 4) by forming a fluoro-tricarboxylic acid which powerfully inhibits the enzyme.

(*d*) Malonate inhibits succinic dehydrogenase (no. 8) by acting as a competitor of succinic acid for combination with the enzyme.

COMPOUNDS OF THE TRICARBOXYLIC ACID CYCLE.

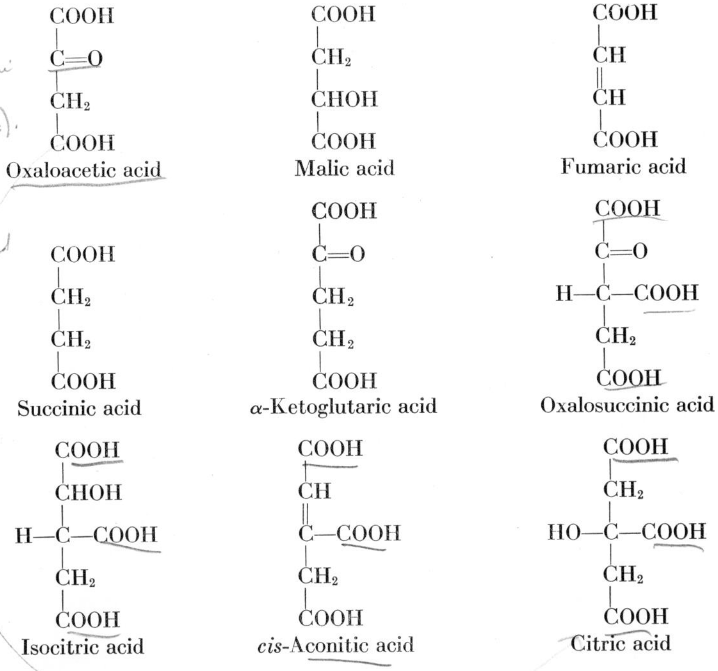

COOH C=O CH₂ COOH Oxaloacetic acid	COOH CH₂ CHOH COOH Malic acid	COOH CH CH COOH Fumaric acid
COOH CH₂ CH₂ COOH Succinic acid	COOH C=O CH₂ CH₂ COOH α-Ketoglutaric acid	COOH C=O H—C—COOH CH₂ COOH Oxalosuccinic acid
COOH CHOH H—C—COOH CH₂ COOH Isocitric acid	COOH CH C—COOH CH₂ COOH *cis*-Aconitic acid	COOH CH₂ HO—C—COOH CH₂ COOH Citric acid

In contrast to the glycolytic cycle, one of the difficulties encountered in the tricarboxylic acid cycle is that here most of the enzymes are present in an insoluble form, associated with a phospholipid-like cement. Some of these enzymes, to be sure, have been brought into solution by suitable means. According to Green, the essential insolubility of these enzymes indicates a need for intercellular organization, and he refers to the entire system of enzymes as the "cyclophorase" system. Essentially, such a system can be obtained by the isolation of the mitochondrial fraction of homogenized cells (p. 100). If suitable co-factors are added to such a system, it can perform all the reactions of the cycle.

COENZYME A. It had been known that acetate as such is not oxidized, and it had been assumed that the acetate is in some "active" form when it condenses with oxaloacetate. Lipmann, working with a bacterial system, showed the presence of acetyl phosphate, and the assumption was made that this substance might serve as the "active" acetate. However, while the acetyl phosphate acted as a phosphate donor to form ATP, it failed as an acetyl donor.

In the meantime, Lipmann had shown that the liver contains an enzyme system which is capable of acetylating sulfanilamide. A co-factor taking part in this reaction can be removed by dialysis, but acetyl phosphate can not replace this co-factor. Nachmansohn, who had discovered the enzyme choline acetylase—an enzyme which brings about the acetylation of choline to form acetylcholine (Chap. 21)—showed that here, too, acetyl phosphate can not serve as the source of acetyl groups.

Lipmann next showed that the coenzyme needed for the acetylating reaction contains pantothenic acid (Chap. 20) together with organically bound sulfur. This substance, known as coenzyme A, not only helps in the acetylation of sulfanilamide and in the acetylation of choline, but seems to be a general, all-around acetylating agent in the body. Ochoa and Stern, for example, have shown that in the citric acid cycle, the condensation of acetate and oxaloacetate to form citric acid is brought about as follows:

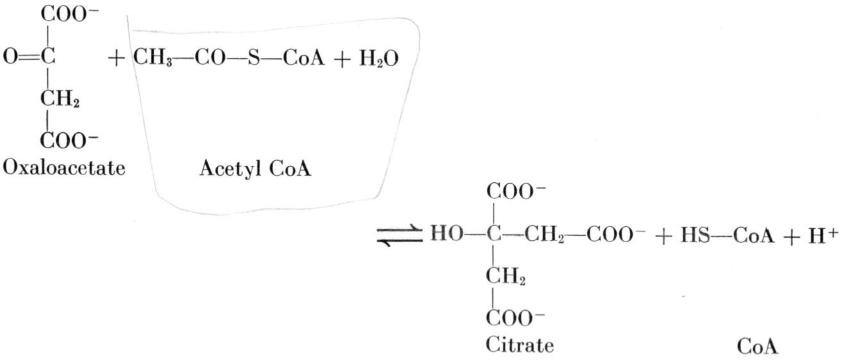

$$
\begin{array}{c}
COO^- \\
| \\
O{=}C \\
| \\
CH_2 \\
| \\
COO^- \\
\text{Oxaloacetate}
\end{array}
+ CH_3{-}CO{-}S{-}CoA + H_2O
$$

Acetyl CoA

$$
\rightleftharpoons HO{-}\underset{\underset{COO^-}{|}}{\overset{\overset{COO^-}{|}}{C}}{-}CH_2{-}COO^- + HS{-}CoA + H^+
$$

$$
\begin{array}{c}
COO^- \\
| \\
HO{-}C{-}CH_2{-}COO^- \\
| \\
CH_2 \\
| \\
COO^- \\
\text{Citrate}
\end{array}
\qquad CoA
$$

a reaction which is catalyzed by a "condensing enzyme" which has been crystallized.

The structure of acetyl CoA is

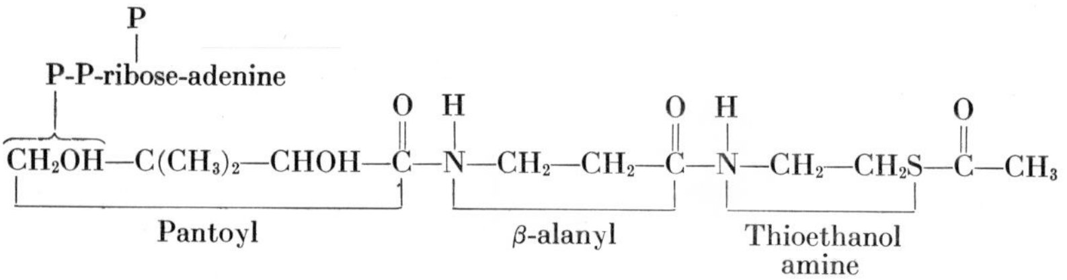

$$
\underset{\text{Pantoyl}}{\underbrace{CH_2OH{-}C(CH_3)_2{-}CHOH{-}\overset{\overset{O}{\|}}{C}}}{-}\underset{\text{β-alanyl}}{\underbrace{\overset{\overset{H}{|}}{N}{-}CH_2{-}CH_2{-}\overset{\overset{O}{\|}}{C}}}{-}\underset{\substack{\text{Thioethanol} \\ \text{amine}}}{\underbrace{\overset{\overset{H}{|}}{N}{-}CH_2{-}CH_2S}}{-}\overset{\overset{O}{\|}}{C}{-}CH_3
$$

with P-P-ribose-adenine attached above (P) the CH_2OH.

(P = phosphoric acid residue) so that CoA would be the above, with the exception that the terminal $-S{-}\overset{\overset{O}{\|}}{C}{-}CH_3$ would be replaced by —SH.

Aerobic Phosphorylation.   The complete oxidation of glucose to CO_2 and water results in the production of 688,000 calories. The conversion of glucose to pyruvic acid furnishes some 60,000 cal. of this total. This, we have seen is accounted for by the over-all synthesis of high energy bonds in the form of ATP. The remainder, some 620,000 cal. must be accounted for by the aerobic oxidation of pyruvic acid to CO_2 and water via the tricarboxylic acid cycle. It can be shown that during this oxidation inorganic phosphate disappears as ATP is synthesized. Thus, oxygen is utilized for the oxidation reactions and high energy phosphate bonds are formed. This coupling of oxygen consumption with phosphorylation yields the P:O ratio. In order that all of the 620,000 cal. be converted to ATP bonds, such a ratio would have to be 3.5; that is, 3.5 high energy bonds formed per atom of oxygen utilized. Ochoa, using purified enzyme systems, has found values approximating 3. It is probable, therefore, that the energy which is stored in the chemical bonds of glycogen is converted to high energy bonds of ATP by the over-all process of carbohydrate oxidation.

It is interesting to note that there are certain compounds which are capable of interfering with the process of phosphorylation without stopping oxygen consumption. Such an action is referred to as an uncoupling of phosphorylation from oxygen consumption. It is observed in the presence of 2,4-dinitrophenol, sodium azide, several dyes such as methylene blue and some drugs such as the antimalarial, Atabrine. Presumably, in the presence of these compounds, although the substrates are oxidized to CO_2 and water, the energy which is liberated is not stored in the form of ATP and is lost to the cell for those reactions which require ATP as a source of energy.

Carbon Dioxide Fixation.   In a general way it may be said that plants can satisfy their nutritional requirements from such simple compounds as carbon dioxide, water, and ammonia (in the presence of light energy), and that by contrast the animal must be provided with amino acids, certain fatty acids, vitamins, etc. The need for carbon in the plant is met by carbon dioxide; in the animal, by various organic substances. Until quite recently, carbon dioxide was regarded as purely an end product of animal metabolism.

In autotrophic unicellular organisms, with no photosynthetic mechanism, carbon dioxide can also serve as the sole source of carbon. Heterotrophic bacteria, it has been shown more recently, can utilize carbon dioxide, but their carbon needs cannot be met by this compound alone. This has also been shown to be true of animals. Carbon dioxide, then, even in animals, can no longer be looked on as a mere end product of metabolism.

The main reaction in animals involving carbon dioxide is a carboxylation, or a fixing of the carbon dioxide as the carboxyl group of a dicarboxylic acid. This is a reaction analogous to the "dark reaction" in photosynthesis (Chap. 16).

All of the reactions of the Krebs cycle are known to be reversible with the possible exception of the conversion of succinate to α-ketoglutarate. This has been determined largely by means of radioactive studies. The feeding of a radioactive member of the cycle is followed by isolation of the liver glycogen and determination of the amount of radioactivity in the various carbon atoms. Wood and Werkman showed that CO_2 can be utilized by propionic acid bacteria with a resulting fixation of its carbon in members of the cycle; Evans and Slotin showed that animal tissues can also incorporate CO_2. The reaction, referred to as the Wood-Werkman reaction (no. 11), is illustrated below:

$$\text{Pyruvic acid} + CO_2 \rightleftharpoons \text{Oxaloacetic acid}$$

This reaction, which requires thiamine pyrophosphate as a coenzyme, makes it possible for pyruvate to enter the main cycle via oxaloacetate and also makes possible the incorporation of CO_2 into glycogen by a reversal of reactions. Hastings and Buchanan showed that when $NaHC^{13}O_3$ is given to an animal, the introduction of C^{13} into the skeletal muscle glycogen as well as into the liver glycogen takes place. The distribution of isotope is qualitatively the same.

After the feeding of a labelled compound, the glycogen of the liver is isolated and glucose prepared from it after hydrolysis. The glucose is subjected to a series of degradation reactions designed to split off each carbon atom in the form of a compound whose radioactivity can be measured. Such a scheme is available. The following scheme, which is simpler, will determine the radioactivity in the three pairs of carbon atoms in glucose:

$$\overset{1}{C}HOH-\overset{2}{C}HOH-\overset{3}{C}HOH-\overset{4}{C}HOH-\overset{5}{C}H-\overset{6}{C}H_2OH \quad \xrightarrow{\text{Lactobacillus casei}}$$

$$\overset{1}{C}H_3-\overset{2}{C}HOH-\overset{3}{C}OOH \quad + \quad HO\overset{4}{O}C-\overset{5}{C}HOH-\overset{6}{C}H_3$$

$$\Big\downarrow +KMnO_4$$

$$\underset{CH_3-CHO}{^{1,6}\quad^{2,5}} \quad + \quad \underset{CO_2}{^{3,4}}$$

$$\Big\downarrow +NaIO_3$$

$$\underset{CHI_3}{^{1,6}} \quad + \quad \underset{HCOOH}{^{2,5}}$$

The Tricarboxylic Acid Cycle and Fat and Protein Metabolism. It has long been suspected that carbohydrate, fat and protein metabolism are closely interrelated. The compounds of the tricarboxylic acid cycle now make it clear how fat and protein metabolism are related to carbohydrate metabolism. In fat metabolism, fatty acids may give rise to "acetyl" or "acetoacetyl" derivatives of CoA (p. 214). In protein metabolism, glutamic acid, aspartic acid and alanine may give rise to α-ketoglutaric acid, oxaloacetic acid and pyruvic acid, respectively (p. 212).

If, therefore, during the course of fat or protein metabolism, a compound is formed which is identical with one found in the tricarboxylic acid cycle, such a compound could contribute towards the production of CO_2 and water, and, if the systems are reversible, to the formation of pyruvate and glycogen.

REFERENCES

Reviews of recent work are to be found in Ann. Rev. Biochem., *19:* 187, 1950 (*Ratner and Racker*); 20: 513, 1951. (*Colowick and Kaplan*); *21:* 547, 1952 (*Ochoa and Stern*); *22:* 179, 1953 (*Leloir and Cardini*). See also *Ochoa:* Harvey Lectures, 1950–51, 153.

Several papers dealing with liver function and liver function tests are *Bruger and Oppenheim:* Bull. N. Y. Acad. Med., Jan., 1949, p. 16; J. Am. Med. Assoc., *142:* 1297, 1950; Seminar (Sharp and Dohme), Feb. and May, 1949. For cirrhosis of the liver, see *Portis and Weinberg:* J. Am. Med. Assoc., *149:* 1265, 1952.

For the influence of amino acids on

glycogen formation, see *Terriere and Butts:* J. Biol. Chem., *190:* 1, 1951.

The fundamental work of Claude Bernard dealing with the glycogen of the liver is described by *Mayer:* J. Nutrition, *45:* 3, 1951.

For the conversion of fructose, galactose, and mannose into glucose, see *Topper and Stetten, Jr.:* J. Biol. Chem., *193:* 149, 1951; *Caputto, Leloir, Cardini, and Paladini:* Ibid., *184:* 333, 1950; *Cori and Stein:* Federation Proceedings, *6:* 245, 1947; *Cook and Lorber:* J. Biol. Chem., *199:* 1, 1952.

The important work of *Cori* is discussed in Biological Symposia, *5:* 131, 1941.

The influence of insulin on glycogenolysis in liver is discussed by *Sutherland and Cori:* J. Biol. Chem., *172:* 737, 1948.

The effect of the adrenals and insulin on the hexokinase reaction is discussed by *Stadie and Haugaard:* J. Biol. Chem., *177:* 311, 1949.

For the effect of cortisone and insulin on the synthesis of fatty acid, see *Balmain, Folley, and Glascock:* Nature, *169:* 447, 1952.

The preparation and properties of crystalline muscle phosphorylase are described by *Green and Cori:* J. Biol. Chem., *151:* 21, 1943; *Cori and Green:* Ibid., *151:* 31, 1943; *Cori, Cori, and Green:* Ibid., *151:* 39, 1943; *Cori and Cori:* Ibid., *151:* 57, 1943.

For the work of Krebs on the citric acid cycle, see *Krebs:* Adv. Enzym., *3:* 191, 1943.

The highly suggestive work of Cori and collaborators on the influence of insulin on hexokinase is discussed in: *Cori:* Harvey Lectures, 1945–46, p. 253.

Studies dealing with the fate of 5-carbon sugars (arabinose, xylose, ribose, desoxyribose) are discussed in the following: *Rice and Roe:* J. Biol. Chem., *188:* 463, 1951; *Gest and Lampen:* Ibid., *194:* 555, 1952; *Cheldelin, Nygaard, Hale, and King:* J. Am. Chem. Soc., *73:* 5003, 1951; *Dickens and Glock:* Biochem. J., *50:* 93, 1951; *McGeown and Malpress:* Nature, *170:* 575, 1952.

For the effect of insulin on carbohydrate metabolism, see *Felts, Chaikoff, and Osborn:* J. Biol. Chem., *191:* 683, 1951; and for the effect of the hormone on fat formation, see J. Am. Med. Assoc., *145:* 566, 1951.

In general, for the effect of the endocrine control of metabolism, see *Engel:* Bull. N. Y. Acad. Med., *29:* 175, 1953.

For a preparation of phosphocreatine, see *Ennor and Stocken:* Biochem., J., *43:* 190, 1948.

For the synthesis of ATP, see *Baddiley, Michelson, and Todd:* Nature, *161:* 761, 1948; for the hydrolysis of ATP, see *Friess:* J. Am. Chem. Soc., *75:* 323, 1952.

On the subject of glycolysis, see *Meyerhof:* Wallerstein Labs., Sept., 1949, p. 225; *Pfeiffer:* Scientific American, Dec., 1948, p. 34; *Ohlmeyer:* J. Biol. Chem., *190:* 21, 1951 (new coenzyme of alcoholic fermentation); *Sutherland, Cohn, Posternak, and Cori:* Ibid., *180:* 1285, 1949 (mechanism of phosphoglucomutase reaction); *Baranowski:* Ibid., *180:* 535, 1949 (crystalline triosephosphate dehydrogenase); *Weil-Malherbe:* Nature, *165:* 155, 1950 (inhibitor of hexokinase); *Oesper and Meyerhof:* Arch. Biochem., *27:* 223, 1950 (determination of phosphotriose isomerase).

For the role of phosphoric esters in biological reactions, see *Avison and Hawkins:* Quart. Rev., London Chem. Soc., *5:* 171, 1951; *Meyerhof:* American Scientist, Oct., 1951, p. 682; *Oesper:* Arch. Biochem., *27:* 255, 1950; *Lipmann:* Currents in Biochemical Research, 1946, p. 137.

The existence of multiple pathways of carbohydrate metabolism is discussed by *Barron:* Trends in Physiology and Biochemistry, 1952, p. 471.

Theories involving the "Pasteur effect" are discussed by *Johnson:* Science, *94:* 200, 1941; and by *LePage:* J. Biol. Chem., *176:* 1009, 1021, 1948.

Various phases of the citric acid cycle, the oxidation of pyruvate, etc., are discussed in the following: *Stern and Ochoa:* J. Biol. Chem., *191:* 161, 1951; *Ochoa, Stern, and Schneider:* Ibid., *193:* 691, 1951; *Stern, Shapiro, Stadtman, and Ochoa:* Ibid., *193:* 703, 1951; *Korkes, Campillo, Gunsalus, and Ochoa:* Ibid., *193:* 721, 1951 (enzymic synthesis of citric acid); *Frohman, Orten, and Smith:* Ibid., *193:* 277, 1951 (chromatographic determination of the acids of the citric acid cycle); *Potter and Heidelberger:* Physiol. Rev., *30:* 487, 1950 (alternate metabolic pathways); *Schweet, Fuld, Cheslock, and Paul:* in McElroy and Glass's Phosphorus Metabolism, vol. 1, p. 246, 1951 (initial stages of pyruvate oxidation); *Gunsalus, Dolin, and*

Struglia: J. Biol. Chem., *194:* 849, 1952; *Gunsalus, Struglia, and O'Kane:* Ibid., *194:* 859, 1952 (pyruvic acid metabolism); *Buchanan and Anfinsen:* Ibid., *180:* 47, 1949 (purification of aconitase): *Pardee, Heidelberger, and Potter:* Ibid., *186:* 625, 1950 (oxidation of acetate).

Articles dealing with coenzyme A are *Lipmann:* Bacteriol. Rev., *17:* 1, 1953; *Ochoa:* Harvey Lectures, 1950–51, 162; *Stern and Ochoa:* J. Biol. Chem., *198:* 313, 1952; *Gregory and Lipmann:* J. Am. Chem. Soc., *74:* 4017, 1952; *Stadtman:* J. Biol. Chem., *196:* 535, 1952; *Chantrenne and Lipmann:* Ibid., *187:* 757, 1950; *Littlefield and Sanadi:* Ibid., *199:* 65, 1952; *Chou and Lipmann:* Ibid., *196:* 89, 1952; *Lynen, Reichert, and Rueff:* Annalen der Chemie, *574:* 1, 1951 (in German); *Lipmann, Novelli, Lynen, Mahler, and Kaufman:* Federation Proceedings, *12:* 673, 1953.

Experiments dealing with the utilization of carbon dioxide are described in the following papers: *Wood:* Physiol. Rev., *26:* 198, 1946; *Moulder, Vennesland, and Evans, Jr.:* J. Biol. Chem., *160:* 305, 1945; *Wood:* Harvey Lectures, 1949–50, p. 127; *Ochoa:* Physiol. Rev., *31:* 56, 1951; Nutr. Rev., *10:* 189, 1952; *Utter:* J. Biol. Chem., *188:* 847, 1951; *Lifson, Lorber, Omachi, Cavert, and Johnson:* Ibid., *188:* 491, 1951; *Korkes, Campillo, and Ochoa:* Ibid., *187:* 891, 1950; *Blanchard, Korkes, Campillo, and Ochoa:* Ibid., *187:* 875, 1950; *Kleiber, Smith, and Black:* Ibid., *195:* 707, 1952; *Crane and Ball:* Ibid., *188:* 819, 1951; *189:* 269, 1951; *Marshall and Friedberg:* J. Biol. Chem., *199:* 783, 1952.

The use of istopic carbon in carbohydrate and general intermediary metabolism is discussed by *Buchanan and Hastings:* Physiol. Rev., *26:* 126, 1946.

Green's "cyclophorase" system is described in J. Biol. Chem., *177:* 655, 1949.

For a review of the interrelationships of carbohydrate and fat metabolism, see *Bloch:* Ann. Rev. Biochem., *21:* 273, 1952.

Chapter 13   *Metabolism of the Lipids*

As HAS already been stated, under the lipids we include true fats, phospholipids, and the sterols. We shall take up each of these in turn.

THE FATS

Energy is stored very largely in the body in the form of its fats. It is not a passive storage, as was at one time supposed; rather the fats are constantly being broken down and restored, the turnover being accomplished in several days.

We will also see that certain unsaturated acids are essential food constituents. Just why they are essential is not known. Are they of the character of vitamins which supply needed groups for the building of biologically important enzymes?

It seems fairly clear that an important part of the fat molecule, the fatty acid, is transported towards its ultimate destination in the form of a phospholipid molecule (as, for example, some of the fatty acids in lecithin). The fatty acids, mainly in the form of phospholipids, constitute one-half of the dry substance of the brain and are found in abundance in liver, lungs, adrenals, and kidneys. In at least one of these organs, the liver, the functions of these fats, or rather phospholipids, are becoming clearer.

We have already seen that the fats are hydrolyzed in the small intestine, resynthesized in the walls of the intestine, and absorbed via the lacteals into the lymph. The fat finds its way into the blood stream through the thoracic duct. The absorption of some 60 per cent, or more, of the fat can be accounted for in this way. It is assumed that the rest must be absorbed directly into the portal circulation, in a manner similar to the carbohydrates and amino acids.

There is some evidence to indicate that a certain amount of fat, finely emulsified, is directly absorbed as such via the lymphatics. Whatever fat is first hydrolyzed is resynthesized into neutral fat in the intestinal mucosa and is sent directly to the liver via the portal vein.

These views, due to Frazer, are based upon the following experiments, among others: after oral administration of olive oil, particles of free fat, visible in blood under dark illumination, appear and multiply in the systemic, but not in the portal blood. On the other hand, when oleic acid and glycerol are administered, particles appear and multiply in the portal and systemic blood. The lacteals are milky after the feeding of olive oil, but not when the acid is fed.

In any case, after a meal rich in fat there is a substantial increase of fat in the blood. Such an increase becomes noticeable in one to three hours after a meal, and the increase may continue up to six or seven hours, when a decrease sets in, and this continues until the normal level is reached again.

219

What happens to the fat after it has reached the blood? Some of it, for a short time at least, is deposited in adipose tissue, liver, etc.; some of it undergoes oxidation in the tissue cells. But how is such an oxidation accomplished? And through what intermediate compounds does the fat pass before it is ultimately eliminated from the body as carbon dioxide and water?

We shall discuss these topics presently. But brief reference must be made here to two theories which, until quite recently, have had an important place in discussions dealing with the metabolism of fat. One theory we owe largely to Bloor, who, as a result of the analyses of the phosphatides of blood during fat absorption, came to the conclusion that the fats (or rather, the fatty acids) before being oxidized, are first converted to phosphatides; for the increase in the latter more or less paralleled the increase in fat.

The other theory dealing with the metabolism of fat we owe to Leathes. Leathes pointed to the relatively high content of unsaturated acids in the liver, and emphasized the fact that unsaturated acids are more readily oxidized—at least in vitro—than saturated ones. He drew the conclusion that desaturation was a preliminary process in the oxidation of fat, and that such desaturation occurred in the liver.

Neither Bloor's nor Leathes' views have gone unchallenged. Chaikoff, for example, claims that the action of choline on the liver is not due to increasing fat transport via plasma phospholipids, but rather to stimulating the utilization of fats within the liver itself.

As for Leathes' opinion, the general evidence points to the view that the degradation of fatty acid is not accomplished by first splitting the double bond. There are, it is true, certain enzymes, lipoxidases, which attack unsaturated fatty acids. While such enzymes are found in plants, it is doubtful whether they occur in animal tissue.

Chaikoff, and others, have introduced the use of "tagged" compounds for the purpose of studying absorption. Long-chain fatty acids—palmitic, for example—were absorbed mainly by the lymphatic pathway. As much as 80 to 90 per cent was recovered from the lymph, a figure decidedly higher than the older 60 per cent. With shorter-chain fatty acids, the recovery from the lymph was less: lauric acid (12 carbons), 15 to 55 per cent; decanoic acid (10 carbons), 5 to 19 per cent. The conclusion was drawn that shorter-chain acids pass directly into the blood stream.

The Storage of Fat.   The body stores fat very largely in three places: subcutaneous connective tissue, abdominal cavity, and intermuscular connective tissue. An analysis of such fat reveals that it is mainly composed of the glycerides of stearic, palmitic, and oleic acids; although smaller quantities of other acids (lauric, myristic) may also be present. The stored fat may have its origin in any one of the three common foodstuffs, carbohydrate, protein, and fat; or it may be derived from a mixture of them.

The tendency is for a production of fat characteristic of the animal. The body fat, in other words, shows differences from the fat of the food. However, it is possible to change the nature of such stored fat by a radical change in the diet. In one experiment, the melting point of the body fat of a dog on a normal diet was 20° C. By feeding mutton tallow, the melting point was increased to 40° C., and by substituting linseed oil, the melting point was reduced to 0° C.

Aside from change in melting point, another easily available means of detecting chemical changes in the composition of fats is a determination of the iodine number. Feeding soybean oil to rats yielded a body fat with an iodine number of 132, and replacing the soybean oil with cocoanut oil lowered the iodine number to 35 (Anderson and Mendel).*

It had always been supposed that the storage of fat occurred during "surplus" periods: that when the body could not burn its foodstuffs fast enough, the excess, for the time being, was stored away as body fat. With this view in mind, it followed that on an insufficient diet no such storage should take place.

Isotopes in Intermediary Metabolism.   Schoenheimer was one of the earliest investigators to introduce the use of isotopes in the study of intermediary metabolism. In the course of this work, he came to the conclusion that fat was not "stored" in the sense that physiologists had assumed it to be.

Ordinary hydrogen, whether obtained from organic or inorganic sources, is a mixture of isotopes—a mixture of hydrogen (atomic weight 1) and "heavy" hydrogen, or deuterium (atomic weight 2). The latter is present to the extent of 0.02 per cent. By treating oleic acid with hydrogen (in the presence of a suitable catalyst such as nickel) we get stearic acid:

$$CH_3(CH_2)_7CH{=}CH(CH_2)_7COOH \xrightarrow{H_2} CH_3(CH_2)_7 . CH_2CH_2 . (CH_2)_7 . COOH$$

If, however, we treat the oleic acid with deuterium instead of hydrogen, we get

$$CH_3(CH_2)_7 . \underset{D}{CH} . \underset{D}{CH} . (CH_2)_7 . COOH$$

Chemically, this acid cannot be distinguished from stearic acid. Nor is the body able to distinguish it—which is indeed a great advantage, for the body treats it in presumably the same way as the normal acid. However, the presence of deuterium in the molecule makes identification simple. In the position in which deuterium finds itself in the molecule of fat, it is "fixed"; which would hardly be true if the deuterium were to replace the hydrogen of the carboxyl group.

In the experiment dealing with fat storage, Schoenheimer fed mice some linseed oil which had been partially hydrogenated with deuterium. The fat in the diet amounted to 1 per cent, and the total diet offered was insufficient for normal development: the animals lost weight. It was supposed that with such a diet, the animals would burn the fat quite rapidly, and, therefore, show no fat deposits. At the end of a four-day period, the animals were killed, the fat of the fatty tissues isolated, and the deuterium determined.

The animals had consumed 251 mg. of fat ("labeled" with deuterium). From the fat depots an amount of deuterium corresponding to 119 mg.,

---

* Livestock producers are able to "harden" (p. 35) animal body fats by feeding the animals a ration high in carbohydrate or protein and low in oils containing unsaturated fatty acids.

or 47 per cent, was recovered. The rest was burned to carbon dioxide and water. Obviously, then, a large part of the fat, even when given in insufficient amounts, is first deposited in the tissues rather than burned directly.

The popular idea that body fat "stays put" for a long time, provided there is no starvation, must be revised. Using adult mice, it has been found that one-half of their fatty acids is regenerated in five to nine days.

This comparatively rapid process of fat regeneration applies equally well to the phospholipids: in both cases there is a continual breakdown and building up of fats and phospholipids.

Cholesterol and sterols in general are also regenerated, but at a slower rate (from fifteen to twenty-five days).*

The Liver and Fat Metabolism.   A large part of the absorbed fat finds temporary storage in the liver. The liver is a depot not only for excess fat (for the time being) but, as we have seen, for excess carbohydrate (in the form of glycogen). It is believed by many that in this organ much of the fat is changed to phospholipid (lecithin, etc.) before it undergoes further metabolic changes.

It was also believed for a time that the fats—or rather, the fatty acids—prior to their oxidation undergo a preliminary desaturation in the liver, a view based largely on the relatively high iodine number of liver fat (Leathes). The discovery by Burr that certain unsaturated fatty acids are essentials in the diet—at least, so far as the rat is concerned—has led many to question the correctness of this hypothesis. Yet mammals can partly desaturate fatty acids, though whether this occurs more specifically in the liver is not yet clear. Schoenheimer and Rittenberg have shown this to be true by feeding mice a diet containing 10 per cent of deuterostearic acid (that is, in this case, a linoleic acid which had been hydrogenated with deuterium). At the end of some twelve days, the animals were killed, the total fatty acids of the carcass isolated, and these acids were next fractionated into saturated and unsaturated acids. Both fractions contained deuterium in combination. The animal, then, has the ability to convert saturated into certain kinds of unsaturated acids.

But, to complicate the situation, the organism can also accomplish the reverse process: the conversion of certain unsaturated to saturated fatty acids. By feeding an unsaturated fatty acid containing deuterium in its molecule, both saturated and unsaturated deutero-fatty acids were isolated.

However, neither linoleic nor linolenic acid is formed by desaturation; which may explain why such acids, needed by the body, must be supplied with the food.

Stetten points out that the quantity of fat (in the form of fatty acids) in the liver is the result of a number of factors: amount received from the diet (Fig. 60, a, b); amount degraded (c); amount transported from liver to depot storage (d); and amount transferred from depot to liver (e).

Blood Fat and Fatty Acids.   If we consider all lipids—neutral fat, fatty acids, phospholipids, and cholesterol—the figure given for normal adults is about 735 mg. per 100 ml. of plasma. Neutral fat (in plasma) is about 225 mg. The concentration of this neutral fat in blood cells is some-

---

* We speak of a rapid or slow turnover of foods or metabolites.

what lower than in plasma. Fatty acids, varying from 190 to 450 mg. per 100 ml. of blood, are equally divided between cells and plasma.

Following the intake of fat, fat and fatty acid in plasma begin to increase after an hour or two until a maximum is reached in from four to six hours. The intake of large quantities of fat may at first increase the concentration of fatty acids in plasma by 100 per cent; the normal level is reached in from seven to eight hours.

In certain abnormal conditions there are increases in fat, fatty acid, and cholesterol in plasma; the cholesterol is usually determined because better methods are available for this substance. During fasting, or on a meat diet, fat and fatty acids in blood plasma show a substantial increase. Increases are also observed in ether narcosis, alcoholism, obstructive jaundice (at times), and after the intake of chloroform and phosphorus. Decreases are most marked in cases of hyperthyroidism.

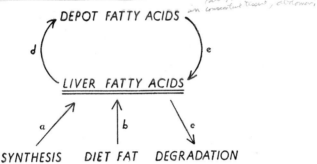

Fig. 60. The sources and fates of liver fatty acids. (Stetten, Jr., and Salcedo: J. Biol. Chem. 156: 27.)

The Oxidation of Glycerol.   The oxidation of fat probably involves, first, the hydrolysis of the molecule into glycerol and fatty acid, and then the oxidation of the two components. There is reason to believe that the intermediate steps in the oxidation of glycerol resemble those in the oxidation of carbohydrates. Glycerol, like glucose, gives rise to glycogen in the liver, though, it is true, not to the same extent. Again, in diabetes produced by means of phlorhizin, glycerol is practically quantitatively converted to glucose. Using glycerol-1-C^{14}, Doerschuk finds that the main metabolic path involves 3-phosphoglyceraldehyde or dihydroxyacetone phosphate, or both; these are then oxidized to CO_2 and water by way of pyruvate and the tricarboxylic acid cycle, or converted to glycogen via the glycolytic phase of carbohydrate metabolism.

The Oxidation of Fatty Acids.   The intermediate stages through which a fatty acid passes as it is changed from, let us say, a C_{18} acid to carbon dioxide and water, are known imperfectly. "Acetone bodies" are produced in the liver and these have been traced to the breaking down of fatty acid. These "acetone bodies" are β-hydroxybutyric acid, $CH_3 . CHOH . CH_2 . COOH$, acetoacetic acid, CH_3COCH_2COOH, and acetone, CH_3COCH_3. The first two are undoubtedly partial oxidation products of butyric acid, and the acetone may be regarded as derived from the acetoacetic acid by the loss of carbon dioxide.

The interconvertibility of acetoacetic acid and β-hydroxybutyric acid can be accomplished by the use of a suitable dehydrogenase and coenzyme:

$$CH_3.CH(OH).CH_2.COOH \underset{\text{Co I + dehydrogenase}}{\rightleftharpoons} Co\ I.2H + CH_3.CO.CH_2.COOH$$

The first important contribution to the problem of the metabolism of fatty acids was made by Knoop.

KNOOP'S β-OXIDATION THEORY. In order to study the mechanism of fatty acid oxidation, Knoop took advantage of the fact that while aliphatic straight chain compounds are readily oxidized in the body, this is not true for compounds containing the aromatic nucleus. Knoop combined various fatty acids with the phenyl group, fed the resulting phenylated compounds, and investigated the products eliminated in the urine. Benzoic acid yielded hippuric acid; which meant that the benzoic acid combined first with the glycine supplied by the body:

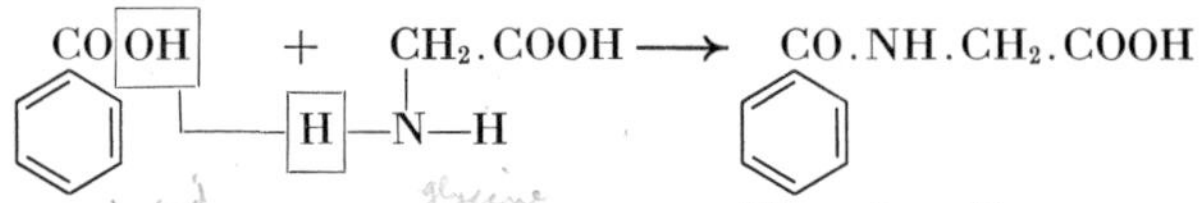

(1)

Hippuric acid

Phenylacetic acid produced phenylaceturic acid:

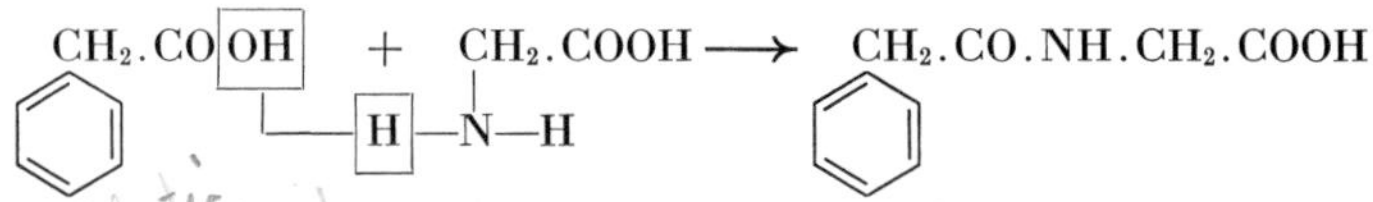

(2)

Phenylaceturic acid

With higher fatty acids, the products isolated were either hippuric acid (1) or phenylaceturic acid (2). For example,

$C_6H_5.CH_2.CH_2.COOH$ yields (1)
$C_6H_5.CH_2.CH_2.CH_2.COOH$ yields (2)
$C_6H_5.CH_2.CH_2.CH_2.CH_2.COOH$ yields (1)
$C_6H_5.CH_2.CH_2.CH_2.CH_2.CH_2.COOH$ yields (2); etc.

We could complicate the procedure by pointing out that the yield is very far from 100 per cent, or that a considerable quantity of such phenylated compounds combine with glucuronic acid, as well as with glycine. However, we will merely state the conclusions drawn by Knoop from these experiments. His results, he argued, indicated that oxidation of fatty acids occurred in such a way that at each stage in the degradation process there was a loss of two carbon atoms, due to oxidation at the β-carbon atom. For example,

$$\overset{\beta}{C_6H_5.CH_2}.\overset{\alpha}{CH_2}.COOH \longrightarrow C_6H_5COOH$$

$$C_6H_5.CH_2.\overset{\beta}{CH_2}.\overset{\alpha}{CH_2}.COOH \longrightarrow C_6H_5CH_2COOH$$

$$C_6H_5.CH_2.CH_2.\overset{\beta}{CH_2}.\overset{\alpha}{CH_2}.COOH$$
$$\downarrow$$
$$C_6H_5.\overset{\beta}{CH_2}.\overset{\alpha}{CH_2}.COOH$$
$$\downarrow$$
$$C_6H_5.COOH$$

Knoop was of the opinion that acetic acid was split off at each stage of the process, though neither he nor others were able to isolate this acid:

$$\ldots\ldots \text{CH}_2.\text{CH}_2.\text{CH}_2.\overset{\beta}{\text{CH}_2}.\overset{\alpha}{\text{CH}_2}.\text{COOH}$$

$$\downarrow$$

$$\ldots\ldots \text{CH}_2.\text{CH}_2.\text{CH}_2.\text{CO} \mid \text{CH}_2.\text{COOH}$$

$$+\text{HO} \mid \text{H}$$

$$\downarrow$$

$$\ldots\ldots \overset{\beta}{\text{CH}_2}.\text{CH}_2.\overset{\alpha}{\text{CH}_2}.\text{COOH} + \text{CH}_3\text{COOH}$$

$$\downarrow$$

$$\ldots\ldots \text{CH}_2.\text{CO}. \mid \text{CH}_2.\text{COOH}$$

$$\text{HO} \mid \text{H}$$

$$\downarrow$$

$$\ldots\ldots \text{CH}_2.\text{COOH} + \text{CH}_3\text{COOH}$$

In other words, no matter what fatty acid derivative we start with, as a result of such β-oxidation, with the resulting loss of two carbon atoms at each stage, the final products must be either benzoic acid or phenylacetic acid; and such acids, by combination with glycine, will be eliminated as hippuric and phenylaceturic acids, respectively.

All these views apply equally well to the naturally occurring fatty acids.

While the natural fats are even-carbon compounds, it does not necessarily follow that odd-carbon fats are not utilized by the body. As a matter of fact, rats have been shown to utilize such odd-carbon fats (made synthetically) for growth and depot fat formation.

A striking confirmation of the two-carbon oxidation comes from the work of Schoenheimer and Rittenberg. These authors have shown that deuteropalmitic acid (C_{16}) can be isolated from mice fed with deuterostearic acid (C_{18}). These mice were fed for five days with deuterostearic acid, and the palmitic acid isolated from their carcasses contained appreciable quantities of deuterium.

As further evidence for the validity of the theory of β-oxidation, a mixture of valeric acids—one labelled with C^{13} in the carboxyl group and the other with C^{14} in the gamma carbon—was fed. Such a mixture is equivalent to the administration of valeric acid containing two labels, each one of which can be determined independently: $CH_3.C^{14}H_2.CH_2.CH_2.C^{13}OOH$. The liver glycogen was isolated, and the glucose prepared from it was degraded for the isotopic analysis of the various carbon atoms.

The glycogen contained three times as much C^{14} as C^{13}, whereas the respiratory CO_2 contained twice as much C^{13} as C^{14}—an indication that the two carbon atoms follow different metabolic paths.

The degradation of the glucose revealed that C^{13} was found only on carbon 3 and carbon 4, whereas the C^{14} was found on carbons 1, 6, 2 and 5. "Since the distribution of C^{13} in liver glycogen is similar to that observed in feeding carboxyl-labelled acetate, and the distribution of C^{14} corresponds to patterns observed following the administration of alpha-labelled propionate, the present results with the doubly labelled valerate are in accord with an *in vivo* metabolic pathway involving β-oxidation to acetate and propionate" (Siegel and Lorber).

The results may be summarized thus:

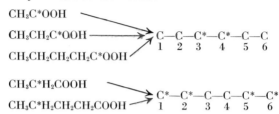

KETONE OR ACETONE BODIES. The plasma of normal individuals contains "ketone" bodies (β-hydroxybutyric acid, acetoacetic acid, and acetone) in small amounts: 0.2 to 0.7 mg. per 100 ml. blood (total "ketone" bodies calculated as acetone). Under abnormal conditions—in fasting and in diabetes—these figures increase. It was supposed for a time that the presence of such compounds reflected an abnormal behavior of the liver, whereby fatty acid oxidation was impaired at the stage of acetoacetic acid, preventing further decomposition beyond the C_4 stage. Later on it became apparent that acetoacetate is a normal intermediate of fatty acid metabolism in the liver, and that extrahepatic tissues—kidney, muscle, etc.—can further oxidize it to CO_2 and H_2O at a rate greater than liver.

Under normal conditions, with available carbohydrate, little acetoacetate accumulates in the blood, for it is oxidized as rapidly as it is formed. However, when the oxidation of carbohydrate is impaired, as in diabetes, or when the amount of liver glycogen has been depleted, as in fasting, fatty acid oxidation to acetoacetate is used as a source of energy.

In addition to fatty acids, acetoacetate is also formed from the oxidative metabolism of a number of amino acids. Thus, the feeding of some compounds tends to increase ketone bodies and these compounds are termed "ketogenic," whereas others, like carbohydrates, are "anti-ketogenic," since they result in a decreased production of ketone bodies.

The ketone bodies, then, are not abnormal products of metabolism, provided the extrahepatic tissues can dispose of them quickly enough. Their so-called "toxicity" is largely due to their property of removing sodium ions from the blood so that they may be excreted, thereby lowering the pH of the blood, and possibly producing a condition of acidosis.

Weinhouse, using the isotopic technique, has studied the "rate of turnover" for acetoacetate. He found that normal rat liver slices produce acetoacetate at a low rate, and that nearly all of the acetoacetate so produced can be oxidized to CO_2. After fasting, however, acetoacetate production is increased, and its oxidation is decreased. He concluded that under normal conditions there is little ketogenesis, and that only in diseased or abnormal dietary conditions does it become a factor.

There exists, apparently, a difference in the metabolism of short chain fatty acids as compared with the metabolism of longer chains. The shorter ones—up to eight carbons—are largely converted to ketone bodies; but palmitic, etc., are largely converted to CO_2.

methyl group to carboxyl

ω-OXIDATION. It should also be pointed out that aside from the theory of β-oxidation, an omega (ω) theory has established itself to some extent. This newer theory does not do away entirely with the older one; it merely acts in a supplementary manner. Verkade, Flaschenträger, and others, have succeeded in isolating dicarboxylic acids from urine after feeding short chain fatty acids to their animals. It has suggested to them that the terminal methyl group may be first oxidized to the carboxyl group, and that then β-oxidation proceeds from both ends. For example,

$$CH_3.CH_2.CH_2 \ldots \ldots CH_2.CH_2.COOH$$
$$\downarrow$$
$$COOH.CH_2.CH_2 \ldots \ldots CH_2.CH_2.COOH$$
$$\downarrow$$
$$COOH \ldots \ldots COOH$$

Even-numbered, saturated dicarboxylic acids are utilized by the organism; but the utilization is more complete the longer the chain length of the acid. The C_{16} and C_{18} acids are practically completely oxidized.

MULTIPLE OXIDATION. Deuel has shown that butyric acid (C_4) and caproic acid (C_6) yield the same amount of acetoacetic acid in the urine, but that caprylic (C_8) yields twice as much of the acid—an indication of a split into two fragments of C_4. Higher acids (palmitic, oleic, and stearic) gave three of the C_4 fragments.

Quastel offered the theory (of multiple alternate oxidation) which suggests that not only does oxidation occur at the β carbon atom, but, at the same time, oxidations probably occur at each alternate carbon atom in the chain, resulting in the formation of chemically simple two- and four-carbon products.

OXIDATION OF FATTY ACIDS VIA THE TRICARBOXYLIC ACID CYCLE. *page 213* Our knowledge of fatty acid oxidation has been greatly aided by the advent of radioactive carbon and the use of tissue slices, homogenates and purified enzymes. These have made it possible for the chemist to study intermediates which could not otherwise have been identified. Early studies had suggested that the oxidative metabolism of the ketone bodies was related to the 4-carbon dicarboxylic acids. Later it was shown that, under certain conditions, acetoacetate led to the formation of citrate if oxaloacetate was present. More recent work has confirmed the fact that the carbon atoms of fatty acids and of acetoacetate appear in the acids of the tricarboxylic acid cycle.

A most significant advance was made when Lehninger found that washed rat liver suspensions could oxidize octanoic acid to form two molecules of acetoacetate, provided the homogenate was fortified with Mg^{++} and ATP. In the absence of oxaloacetate, all of the carbon of the fatty acid was recovered as acetoacetate; in the presence of oxaloacetate, the yield of acetoacetate was diminished and extra citrate accumulated, indicating a diversion to the tricarboxylic acid cycle. Since acetoacetate itself does not form a di- or tricarboxylic acid under these conditions, it is probable that a precursor of acetoacetate—a 2-carbon unit removed from the fatty acid chain—condenses with oxaloacetate to form a tricarboxylic acid. Kennedy and Lehninger have also shown that the fatty acid oxidase of rat liver is associated with the mitochondrial particles in the cell (see p. 100). This mitochondrial system will oxidize fatty acids from butyric to stearic acids.

The mechanism of acetoacetate breakdown has been clarified by experiments using labelled acetoacetate and identifying the isotope in the resulting acids of the tricarboxylic acid cycle.

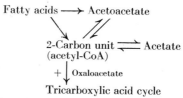

$$
\begin{array}{l}
COOH \\
| \\
C(OH)CH_2C^{13}OOH \\
| \\
CH_2 \\
| \\
C^{13}OOH
\end{array}
\qquad \text{Citric acid}
$$

$$
\begin{array}{l}
CH_3 \\
| \\
C^{13}O \\
| \\
CH_2 \\
| \\
C^{13}OOH
\end{array}
\qquad \text{Acetoacetic acid}
$$

$$
\begin{array}{l}
C^{13}OOH \\
| \\
CH_2 \\
| \\
CH_2 \\
| \\
COOH
\end{array}
\qquad \text{Succinic acid}
$$

$$
\begin{array}{l}
C^{13}OOH \\
| \\
CH \\
|| \\
CH \\
| \\
COOH
\end{array}
\qquad \text{Fumaric acid}
$$

It has also been shown that acetate is not an intermediate in the conversion of acetoacetate to the tricarboxylic acids. The importance of acetate as an intermediate in the formation of tricarboxylic acids lies rather in the formation of some "active" form of acetate. It is believed that this compound is acetyl-CoA (p. 214). A scheme to illustrate these relationships is given by Lipmann:

$$
\text{Fatty acids} \longrightarrow \text{Acetoacetate}
$$

$$
\underset{\text{(acetyl-CoA)}}{\text{2-Carbon unit}} \rightleftharpoons \text{Acetate}
$$

$$
+ \downarrow \text{Oxaloacetate}
$$

$$
\text{Tricarboxylic acid cycle}
$$

As can be seen, the fatty acids can either form acetoacetate (ketone bodies) or they can be degraded by a β-oxidation to 2-carbon fragments, which are eventually oxidized via the tricarboxylic acid cycle.

The individual steps required for the complete oxidation of the fatty acids have not been entirely proven, but enough is known to enable us to present a pattern of reactions which repeats itself until the long chain fatty acid is reduced to the 4-carbon acetoacetate and/or the 2-carbon acetate. Just as "acetate" is now known to exist in combination with coenzyme A as acetyl-CoA, so there is also proof that CoA is linked to the fatty acid chain during its oxidation. The reaction sequence may be summarized in the following manner, on the basis of the purification of the individual enzymes from liver by Green and his group:

(1) $R.CH_2.CH_2.CH_2.\underline{C}OOH + CoA.SH \xrightarrow[\text{enzyme}]{\text{activation}} R.CH_2.CH_2.CH_2.\underline{CO}—SCoA$

$(ATP \longrightarrow AMP + \text{Pyrophosphate})$

(2) $R.CH_2.CH_2.CH_2.CO—S.CoA \xrightarrow[\text{enzyme}]{\text{FAD}^*} R.CH_2.\underline{CH}{=}\underline{CH}.CO—S.CoA$

(3) $R.CH_2.CH{=}CH.CO—S.CoA \xrightarrow[\text{(H}_2\text{O)}]{\text{hydrase}} R.CH_2.\underline{CHOH}.CH_2.CO—S.CoA$

(4) $R.CH_2.CHOH.CH_2.CO—S.CoA \xrightarrow[\text{oxidase}]{\text{fatty acid}} R.CH_2.\underline{CO}.CH_2.CO—S.CoA$

$(DPN + 2H \longrightarrow DPNH_2)$

(5) $R.CH_2.CO.CH_2.CO—S.CoA \xrightarrow[\substack{\text{enzyme} \\ +CoA.SH}]{\text{cleavage}} R.CH_2.CO—S.CoA + CH_3.CO—S.CoA$

$acetyl—S.CoA$

(6) $R.CH_2.CO—S.CoA \xrightarrow[\text{of the sequence}]{\text{repetition}} CH_3.CO.CH_2.CO—S.CoA$

(6a) $CH_3.CO.CH_2.\underline{CO}—S.CoA \longrightarrow CH_3.CO.CH_2.\underline{C}OOH + CoA.SH$

(6b) $2\, CH_3.CO.CH_2.CO—S.CoA \longrightarrow 2\, CH_3.CO—S.CoA$

Biosynthesis of Fatty Acids.   As in many other fields of intermediary metabolism, clues to this mechanism were first obtained by work with micro-organisms. Barker, in experiments with *Clostridium kluyveri*, was able to demonstrate the presence of enzymes which could oxidize fatty acids as well as those which could bring about their synthesis by means of a multiple condensation of 2-carbon units. It has been shown that the method of oxidation of fatty acids is the same in *C. kluyveri* as in mammalian tissues. In *C. kluyveri* the synthesis of fatty acids appears to be a reversal of the oxidative steps; this has not been proven for mammalian tissues.

Rittenberg and Bloch showed that the fatty acids isolated from rats given labelled acetate contained tagged carbon at alternate positions along the entire fatty acid chain. It was also shown that a similar distribution occurs in short chain fatty acids. This could be explained by the formation of "active acetate" with subsequent condensation. It must be remembered that other intermediates can also serve as a source of carbon atoms for fatty acid synthesis. Anker fed equimolar quantities of $1\text{-}C^{13}$ acetate and $2\text{-}C^{14}$ pyruvate and found that the fraction of newly synthesized fatty acids derived from acetate was about twice that derived from pyruvate. The same results can be obtained with tissue slices.

Acetoacetate itself is not an intermediate in the synthesis of fatty acids in animal tissues. The general pattern of synthesis appears to be an elongation of the fatty acid chain at the carboxyl end by the addition of two carbon units, but not at the omega end.

Conversion of Carbohydrate into Fat.   Such a conversion has been common knowledge for a long time. The fattening of animals on a diet with little fat but much carbohydrate, and the experience of men and women on such a diet, make the conclusion inevitable. Adult, fasted rats, fed high carbohydrate (or high protein) diets, synthesize large quantities of fat.

* Flavine-adenine-dinucleotide, p. 191.

Schoenheimer has shown that on a diet of bread, and practically devoid of fat, with heavy water as a source of deuterium, mice not only convert carbohydrate (and presumably some protein) into fat, but, almost as rapidly, break down such fats, to be replaced by a fresh supply.

Using mice, the deuterium content of the fatty acids of the body rose rapidly for a short period and then remained stationary. The animals did not change in weight, which means that the total amount of fat remained constant; and therefore, side by side with the synthesis of fatty acid, there must have taken place a decomposition of a corresponding amount of fatty acid.

These experiments indicate that the conversion takes place on a normal diet, and not necessarily on an excessive diet; and they emphasize the eternal cycle, within the body, of alternate synthesis and destruction of its structural units.

On a fat-free diet, fat is still deposited in the tissues, and it is assumed that such fat is synthesized from carbohydrate. Actually, in the course of an experiment in which uniformly labelled C^{14}-glucose was injested, some 10 to 15 per cent of it could be recovered in the form of fatty acids in the course of 24 hours. Another experiment, in which 2,3-C^{13}-lactate was ingested, using a phlorizinized rat (p. 202), resulted in the discovery that 30 per cent of the labelled lactate was accounted for by the C^{13} content of liver and muscle fat.

Furthermore, pyruvic acid, the central compound in the scheme for the intermediate metabolism of carbohydrate, can be oxidatively decarboxylated to acetic acid, which, as Rittenberg and Bloch have shown, can be used for the synthesis of fatty acid (and, therefore, of fats).

The paths used for the conversion of carbohydrate into fat have already been discussed when dealing with the synthesis of fatty acids (p. 229).

Conversion of Fat into Carbohydrate.   That there may be some conversion of fat into carbohydrate becomes more obvious when we study intermediate products. To begin with, the hydrolysis of fat yields glycerol, and this certainly is a glycogen former, and, therefore, a carbohydrate former. If ω-oxidation is at all prevalent, some succinic acid (among dicarboxylic acids) may well be formed, which, as we already know, is a compound in the cycle of carbohydrate oxidation.

Again using isotopic carbon, a direct conversion of fat into carbohydrate has been shown. Chaikoff and his co-workers have been able to isolate C^{14}-labelled glucose from the urine of diabetic dogs that received either palmitic acid-1-C^{14} or palmitic acid-6-C^{14}.

The Conversion of Protein into Fat.   Using phlorhizinized or diabetic animals, and feeding them protein, an increased excretion of glucose in the urine is obtained. Glutamic acid, arginine, glycine, and the like, are glycogen formers. We know, of course, that carbohydrates can be converted into fats; and now we see that amino acids—obtained from protein —can be converted into carbohydrate. This also means that certain amino acids, in turn, may be converted into fat by first being transformed into carbohydrate.

There are some amino acids which are not glucose formers. Using either leucine, tyrosine, or phenylalanine, and perfusing them through a liver, gives rise to acetoacetic acid—which is also a direct product of fat metabolism. Hence it would appear that some amino acids do not necessarily have to pass through the intermediate carbohydrate stage before being converted into fats.

Longenecker has shown that there can occur a synthesis of fatty acid (and therefore fat) not only from carbohydrate but also from protein. Fasted rats, fed high carbohydrate or high protein diets, synthesize large quantities of fat.

Choline and Fat Metabolism.   Normally, the liver contains from 4 to 5 per cent of fat. Under certain abnormal conditions, this figure may increase to as much as 30 per cent, which may mean that almost one-half of the total weight of the liver is fat.

The amount of fat in the liver of an animal may be very readily increased by placing the animal on a diet rich in fat (low in protein). Another method —and this has also been known for some time—is to include relatively large amounts of cholesterol in the diet offered the animal. In either case, there is produced experimentally a liver abnormally rich in fat—comparable to that which is often observed as a result of pathological changes which affect this organ. Best and Channon proved that the addition of lecithin to the diet prevented this abnormal increase of fat in the experimental animal. A closer investigation revealed the fact that the causative agent is choline, a constituent of the lecithin molecule.

The amount of choline in the liver seems to remain constant under varying conditions. Choline may be supplied in the diet or it may not; fatty liver may be present or it may not: the amount of choline still remains the same.

The answer to this problem is that choline can be synthesized in the body, and in amounts to correspond with the needs of the body, provided, of course, sufficient precursors are available.

The lack of choline also gives rise to an acute renal hemorrhage.

The research connected with choline and its effect on fat metabolism has an interesting historical background. Soon after the discovery of insulin, Allan observed that despite adequate treatment with insulin, depancreatized dogs fed on lean meat, sucrose, and bone ash did not survive beyond a few months. He noticed a disturbed function of the liver, due to a fatty infiltration, and he made the important discovery that this fatty infiltration could be prevented by the addition of raw pancreas to the diet. This suggested to Allan the possibility that the pancreas contained a hormone other than insulin of importance in the normal functioning of the liver.

Somewhat later Hershey discovered that lecithin could replace the raw pancreas in the diet of depancreatized dogs; and then Best showed that, in general, such fatty infiltration of the liver could be cured by the addition of choline. The conclusion drawn from such experiments was that the efficacy of raw pancreas in Allan's original experiments was primarily due to the presence of choline (as part of the lecithin or lipid fraction of the pancreas). Nevertheless, Dragstedt has given reasons for the assumption that in this case we are dealing not with choline, but with a new digestive enzyme or hormone, to which the name *lipocaic* has been given.

Dragstedt finds, in the first place, that the beneficial effect of feeding pancreas is specific, in the sense that other organs, such as the liver and the brain, are quite inert, though they contain more choline than the pancreas. Furthermore, fat-free alcoholic extracts of pancreas have been obtained which contain neither lecithin nor choline and which are active.*

The research on choline in connection with the prevention and cure of fatty livers—the name *lipotropic* has been given to describe this action of choline—was greatly facilitated by the use of isotopes. Chaikoff, using radioactive P as a tracer, found choline to accelerate the rate of formation of phospholipids in the liver (see p. 99).

A scheme for the in vivo synthesis of choline, based on experiments in which N^{15}-labelled compounds were fed to rats, has been proposed by Stetten. When N^{15}-choline and N^{15}-ethanolamine were fed, both were found in the phospholipids. The administration of N^{15}-ethanolamine alone also resulted in the presence of isotopes in ethanolamine and choline. However, when N^{15}-choline was fed, no isotope was found in ethanolamine.

It is known that glycine and serine are precursors of ethanolamine, and Du Vigneaud has shown that the methyl groups of choline are derived from methionine. This has suggested the following scheme:

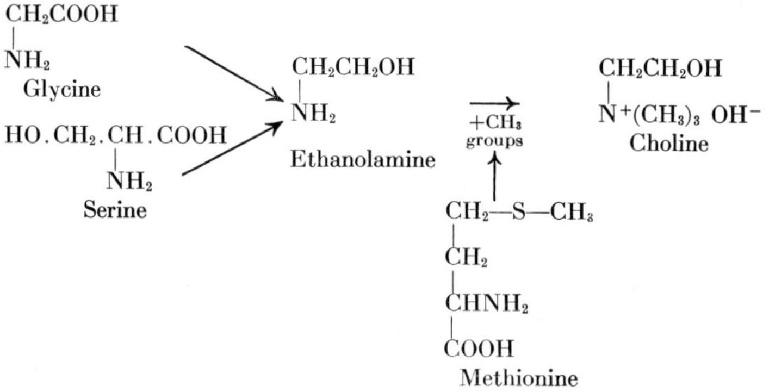

$$CH_2COOH$$
$$|$$
$$NH_2$$
Glycine

$$HO.CH_2.CH.COOH$$
$$|$$
$$NH_2$$
Serine

$$CH_2CH_2OH$$
$$|$$
$$NH_2$$
Ethanolamine

$+CH_3$ groups

$$CH_2CH_2OH$$
$$|$$
$$N^+(CH_3)_3\ OH^-$$
Choline

$$CH_2—S—CH_3$$
$$|$$
$$CH_2$$
$$|$$
$$CHNH_2$$
$$|$$
$$COOH$$
Methionine

Du Vigneaud had previously shown that on a diet devoid of methionine and cystine, rats did not improve when homocystine was added, but became quite normal when offered a mixture of choline and homocystine. This made probable the ability of the body to utilize the methyl group of choline in converting homocystine to methionine.

TRANSMETHYLATION. Such information, added to that obtained from the isotopic studies, emphasized the importance of transmethylation in the body: the ability of the body, for example, to utilize the methyl group of choline in order to transform homocystine to methionine; and to utilize, if necessary, the methyl group of the latter to build up choline from simpler substances such as ethanolamine.

"Labile" methyl groups—groups which can be used for transmethylation purposes—are recognized in one or more of the following ways: lipotropic action, prevention of accumulation of fat in the liver; stimulation of growth when mixed with homocystine, and in the absence of methionine; preven-

* Chaikoff and others maintain that the active fraction in raw pancreas is not lipocaic. See also Wick: Arch. Biochem., *20:* 113, 1949.

tion of renal hemorrhagic degeneration; and prevention of perosis ("slipped tendon disease") in chicks.

An important example of the use of transmethylation by the body is the synthesis of creatine in muscle (Chap. 14).

The chief sources of such labile methyl groups in foodstuffs are lecithin (containing choline) and protein (containing methionine).*

Aside from their methylating properties, choline and methionine exhibit additional important properties. Choline is a constituent of lecithin, sphingomyelin, and acetylcholine (Chap. 21)—all three important cellular compounds. Methionine is one of the essential amino acids.

It is still a question as to whether the pathological symptoms that develop in the absence of choline are due to abnormal transport of fatty acids or to failure of phospholipids (which usually contain choline) to function normally as structural constituents of tissues.

A complication arises from the fact that a substance may be lipotropic without being a methyl donor. For example, this is true of arsenocholine and triethylcholine; both take the place of choline in the lipid molecule. It is also true of inositol; here, too, inositol has been shown to be a constituent of some lecithins.

The theory that lipotropic action of the various substances described (choline, methionine, betaine, inositol, etc.) is due to the fact that they are incorporated into the phospholipid molecule, and in some way facilitate the transport (and metabolism) of fatty acids, is upheld by many.

CIRRHOSIS OF THE LIVER.   When lipotropic substances are available in insufficient quantities, or when the utilization of such substances is poor, or when there is some definite hepatic injury, fatty infiltration may develop and may eventually lead to cirrhosis of the liver (destruction of liver cells). This cirrhosis, then, may be brought about by lowering the resistance of the liver, which may be due not only to deficiencies in lipotropic substances, but to deficiencies in proteins, lipids, etc. But the cirrhosis may also be brought about more directly by producing a necrosis of the functional cells of the liver by means of such substances as chloroform, carbon tetrachloride, phosphorus, lead, and arsenic.

Clinically, some success has been obtained in the use of lipotropic substances in liver disease.

Effect of Vitamins on the Metabolism of Fat.   From the extensive work of McHenry and Gavin, it would seem that protein cannot be converted into fat unless pyridoxine as well as thiamine is present.

It has long been known that thiamine plays an important role in carbohydrate metabolism, primarily in connection with the oxidation of pyruvic acid, a substance which might be utilized for the metabolism of fatty acids.

The importance of pyridoxine in the deposition of fat in the body has again been emphasized by Carter, who has shown that a deficiency of this vitamin prevents the rat from synthesizing fat from carbohydrate.

---

* Betaine, $CH_2.COO^-$, which can be obtained in quantity as a by-product of sugar

$\qquad | $

$\qquad N^+(CH_3)_3$

beet processing, can, to a limited extent, replace choline and methionine.

very fat =

Obesity.   In the vast majority of cases, obesity results from the consumption of too much food (carbohydrate and protein as well as fat), from the consumption of food "above the calorific requirements of the body" (Newburgh). Obesity resulting from endocrine disturbances is rare.

PHOSPHOLIPIDS

Lecithin.   The neutral fats have always been regarded as sources of fuel for the body. Lecithin—and, more broadly speaking, the phospholipids —is an essential structural element of the cell: phospholipids are present in every cell of the body. Their possible function as intermediates in the metabolism of fat has already been referred to. Sinclair fed elaidic acid (the stereoisomer of oleic acid) in the form of its glyceride, elaidin, and found that one-third of the total fatty acids in the phospholipids of the liver (and skeletal muscles) was made up of elaidic acid; from which he concluded that the phospholipid is involved in the intermediary metabolism of fat.

Thannhauser has reasoned that enzymatic hydrolysis of lecithin is probably a stepwise reaction, and it should be possible to isolate intermediate products. By incubating beef pancreas, he has isolated one such product: α-glycerophosphorylcholine,

$$CH_2OH.CHOH.CH_2.O.\overset{\overset{\displaystyle OH}{|}}{\underset{\underset{\displaystyle O}{\|}}{P}}.OCH_2.CH_2.N^+(CH_3)_3$$

King has shown lecithinase to be present in the kidney, liver, and other organs except the small intestine. This would make it appear that, as in the case of neutral fats, lecithin is first hydrolyzed before it is further oxidized. Under such conditions, we get glycerol, fatty acid, phosphoric acid, and choline. The fate of the first two we have already discussed. The phosphoric acid is needed in cell metabolism, in bone formation, etc. The choline, as we have already seen, is of importance in regulating the amount of fat in the liver; and, as we shall see presently (Chap. 21), in the form of acetylcholine, it is of importance in the activity of the nervous system.

The organism has the ability to synthesize phospholipids. The eggs of ducks and hens raised on a diet low in lipid showed more of this substance than was taken in by the food. Rats on synthetic diets, containing fat but devoid of phospholipid, grow quite well. Since lipids are essential cell constituents, we must postulate the synthesis of these constituents within the body.

In the attempt to secure information relative to phospholipid metabolism, Perlman, Ruben, and Chaikoff fed radioactive inorganic phosphate salt to rats, the animals were killed at various intervals, the lipids in the tissues were extracted, and the labeled phosphorus (in the phospholipid) determined by means of a Geiger counter.

Labeled phospholipid appeared in various tissues. Two phases in phospholipid metabolism were observed: formation (or deposition) and utilization (or removal). A sharp increase in labeled phospholipid content was shown by liver and intestine, while carcass, kidney, and brain showed a slower rise. The rate of disappearance of labeled phospholipid from these tissues decreased in the following order: liver, intestine, and kidney. No decline was observed in the carcass (and possibly the brain).

Further studies using radioactive substances have shown that the liver is almost exclusively concerned with the synthesis, the supply, and the removal of plasma phospholipids.

Cephalin.   Of cephalin, the phospholipid closely allied, at least chemically, to lecithin, we know little. According to Chargaff, one important physiological function can be definitely assigned to it: "it is the prosthetic group in the specific protein, the thromboplastic factor, which is the natural activator of blood coagulation."

Sphingomyelin.   In Niemann-Pick disease, characterized by the deposition of phospholipids in the spleen, liver, brain, etc., Klenk showed that the chief lipid in these organs was sphingomyelin. Significantly enough, the amounts of lecithin and cephalin were within normal ranges. This means, in other words, that in this disease there is some disturbance in the metabolism of sphingomyelin.

Phospholipids in Blood.   In blood, the phospholipids are transported in combination with plasma proteins as "lipoproteins." The usual (normal) value given for phospholipids in blood (including not only lecithin but also for sphingomyelin) is 181 mg. per 100 ml. of plasma. In man, practically all of the phospholipids in plasma contain choline. This means that the plasma phospholipids consist almost entirely of lecithins and sphingomyelins.

There is a definite increase in lipid phosphorus in the blood after the ingestion of fat, an increase which continues for some hours.

CEREBROSIDES

These substances are abundant in brain matter, but practically nothing is known of their metabolism. An interesting discovery, however, is that in Gaucher's disease, which is characterized by large lipid deposits in various tissues, the predominant substance present is phrenosin (p. 40), one of the cerebrosides.

CHOLESTEROL

Biosynthesis of Cholesterol.   As early as 1937 Rittenberg and Schoenheimer, using "heavy" water (D_2O), had shown that cholesterol can be synthesized in the animal organism. Later, Bloch and Rittenberg demonstrated that acetate could be incorporated into the cholesterol molecule. The carbons of the acetate were found in the side chain and in the ring of the sterol molecule. Acetoacetate behaved similarly to acetate itself.

More recently, Bloch fed rats labelled acetate of three kinds: 1-C^{14}-acetate, 2-C^{14}-acetate, and doubly labelled 1-C^{13}, 2-C^{14}-acetate, thereby "tagging" the methyl as well as the carboxyl carbon atoms of this compound. The cholesterol was eventually isolated and then degraded, in the attempt to determine the radioactivity of each carbon. Five carbon atoms of the side chain were shown to be derived from the methyl carbon atoms of acetate, and three of the side chain originated with the carboxyl group (Fig. 61).

Two-carbon units, then, can undoubtedly contribute towards the synthesis of a compound as complex as cholesterol, but we know little or nothing as yet as to intermediate compounds. A step in this direction may be possible now that such a synthesis can be demonstrated in vitro by the use of liver slices. In fact, Bloch is of the opinion that squalene may be one such intermediate. Squalene, a hydrocarbon, has been isolated not only from shark liver oil but also from the liver of the rat.

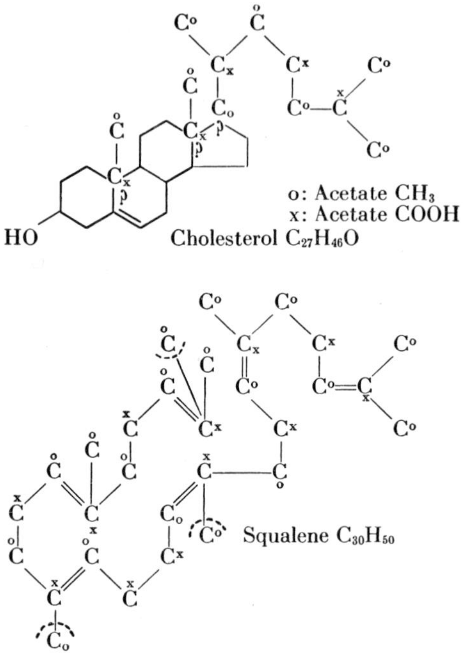

o: Acetate CH₃
x: Acetate COOH
Cholesterol $C_{27}H_{46}O$

HO

Squalene $C_{30}H_{50}$

Fig. 61. Upper drawing, distribution of acetate carbons in cholesterol; lower drawing, postulated distribution of acetate carbons in squalene. (Langdon and Bloch: J. Biol. Chem., *200:* 139, 1953.)

Using rat liver slices and labelled acetate, Bloch has isolated labelled squalene. When this labelled squalene was administered to mice, the cholesterol which was isolated from the animals was found to be labelled—an indication that squalene was converted in vivo into cholesterol.

Metabolism of Cholesterol.   Besides cholesterol, compounds related to it chemically are also found in the animal organism; among them are coprosterol and dihydrocholesterol (Chap. 23), which are found in the colon. These are isomeric reduction products of cholesterol and cannot be absorbed by the body, which suggests that they are probably formed in the large intestine by the action of putrefactive bacteria on cholesterol.

Schoenheimer fed a dog cholestenone containing deuterium and isolated cholesterol and coprosterol, both containing the isotope. He concluded that cholestenone is an intermediary product in the formation of coprosterol from cholesterol. Since coprostanone can be converted to cholesterol, the following scheme was suggested (only the essential part of each formula is shown):

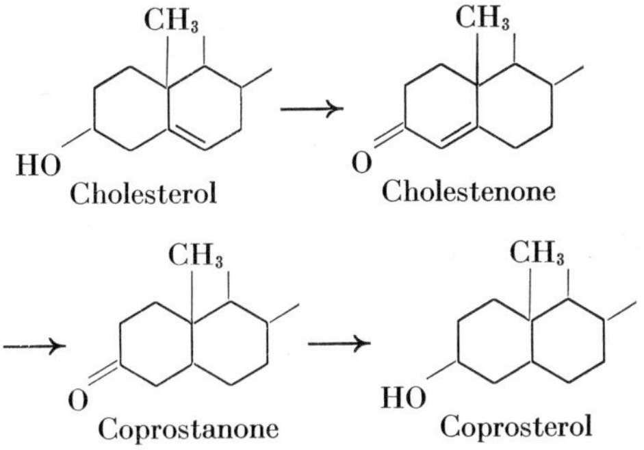

Cholesterol → Cholestenone

→ Coprostanone → Coprosterol

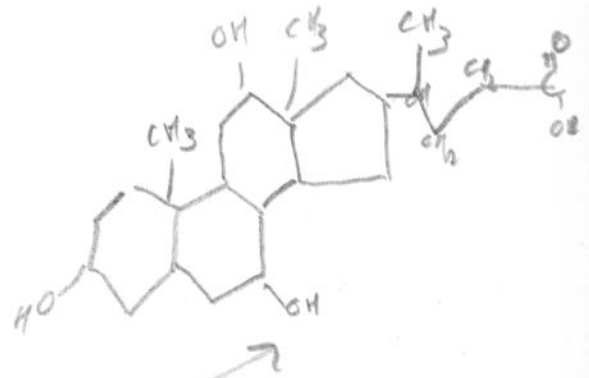

That other steroids in the body, such as the bile acids (p. 132) and the sex hormones (Chap. 23) are related metabolically to cholesterol has been demonstrated experimentally. For example, Bloch and Rittenberg demonstrated the conversion of cholesterol to cholic acid, a constituent of one of the bile salts, using isotopic cholesterol. Further, Bloch fed isotopic cholesterol to a pregnant woman and isolated pregnanediol (Chap. 23) from the urine—a compound which is the excretory product of progesterone (Chap. 23), the hormone of the corpus luteum.

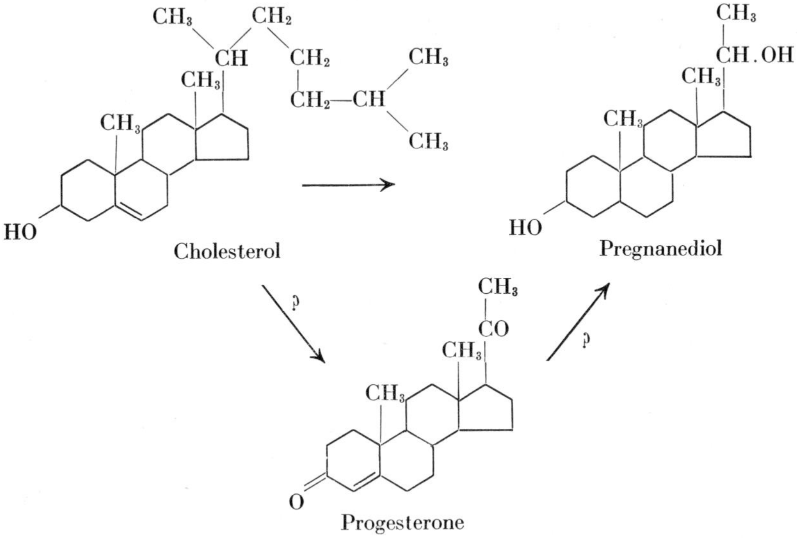

Cholesterol → Pregnanediol

Progesterone

Cholesterol in Blood.   In the erythrocytes most of the cholesterol is in the free state. In the plasma, some 20 to 40 per cent is in the free state and the rest in the form of an ester (cholesterol joined to fatty acid).

Hypercholesterolemia—increased amounts of cholesterol—is found in a number of pathological cases; diabetes is an outstanding one. The plasma cholesterol in this disease runs roughly parallel with the total fatty acids. Rabinowitch goes so far as to claim that the concentration of plasma cholesterol is in some ways even more important than that of blood sugar.

While the total cholesterol may increase several hundred per cent in diabetes, the proportion of free cholesterol to cholesterol ester remains fairly constant.

In diseases of the kidney, hypercholesterolemia is common; values often reach up to 700 mg. per 100 ml.

Still another instance of increase in cholesterol is to be found in jaundice, where there is an obstruction of the bile duct. The increase in the sterol runs hand in hand with the hyperbilirubinemia, such increases disappearing with the removal of the obstruction.

High figures for cholesterol are found in hypothyroidism, such figures being roughly in inverse ratio to the basal metabolic rate (Chap. 17), a low metabolic rate indicating relatively marked hypercholesterolemia.

Sharp decreases in the amount of cholesterol in blood (hypocholesterolemia) often occur in pernicious anemia. In infectious diseases and in hyperthyroidism 50 mg. per 100 ml. is not uncommon. In the last instance, the amount of cholesterol is roughly in inverse ratio to the values found for the basal metabolic rate.

Goffman claims that a relationship exists between the plasma levels of certain lipoproteins and atherosclerosis, a form of arteriosclerosis with fatty degeneration of the connective tissue of the arterial walls. These lipoproteins—lipids attached to proteins—it is believed, are the means by which much of the cholesterol in the blood is transported. It is possible, then, that atherosclerosis should be connected with the levels in blood of these protein complexes rather than with the level of the total plasma cholesterol.

REFERENCES

For a review of progress in the field see Ann. Rev. Biochem., *19:* 215, 1950 (*Medes*); *20:* 179, 1951 (*Gurin and Crandall*); *21:* 129, 1952 (*Samuels and Reich*); *21:* 245, 1952 (*Frazer*); *21:* 273, 1952 (*Bloch*); *22:* 211, 1953 (Artom).

For a review of the work on intermediary metabolism with the aid of isotopes, see *Schoenheimer:* The Dynamic State of Body Constituents, 1942. See also *Kamen:* Radioactive Tracers in Biology, 1951.

For the specificity of action of pancreatic lipase, see *Ravin and Seligman:* Arch. Biochem., *42:* 337, 1953.

Details regarding the absorption of fat may be found in Nutr. Rev., *8:* 300, 1950; *9:* 211, 1951; Ann. Rev. Biochem., *20:* 196, 1951; *Bloom, Chaikoff, and Reinhardt:* Am. J. Physiol., *166:* 491, 1951.

For the further use of isotopes in biology, see *Bergen:* J. Chem. Educ., *29:* 84, 1952; *Brucer:* Merck Report, Jan., 1952, p. 9; *Newell:* Ann. Rev. Medicine, 1950, p. 317; *Wormall:* St. Bartholomew's Hospital Journal, *54:* 3, 1950; *Kelsey:* J. Am. Med. Assoc., *146:* 1131, 1951; *Lawrence:* Bull. N. Y. Acad. Med., *26:* 639, 1950.

In connection with the liver and fat metabolism, see *Zilversmit and DiLuzio:* J. Biol. Chem., *194:* 673, 1952; *Weinhouse, Millington, and Volk:* Ibid., *185:* 191, 1950; *Witter, Newcomb, and Stotz,* Ibid., *185:* 537, 1950; *Goldman, Chaikoff, Reinhardt, Entenman, and Dauben:* Ibid., *184:* 719, 1950; *Volk, Millington, and Weinhouse:* Ibid., *195:* 493, 1952; *Kennedy and Lehninger:* Ibid., *185:* 275, 1950; *Grafflin and Green:* Ibid., *176:* 95, 1948; *Kiyasu, Bloom, and Chaikoff:* Ibid., *199:* 415, 1952.

For choline and fat metabolism, see *Best:* Federation Proceedings, *9:* 506, 1950; *Muntz:* J. Biol. Chem., *182:* 489, 1950; *Arnstein:* Biochem. J., *48:* 27, 1951; *Raman:* Ibid., *52:* 320, 1952; *McArthur and Lucas:* Ibid., *46:* 226, 1950; *Best, Patterson, and Ridout:* Ibid., *48:* 452, 1951; Nutr. Rev., *9:* 329, 1951 (lipotropic action of inositol); *Best, Ridout, Patterson, and Lucas:* Biochem. J., *48:* 448, 1951 (lipotropic action of inositol); *Stetten:* J. Biol. Chem., *142:* 629, 1942.

The subject of methyl groups and transmethylation is discussed in the following: *Woods:* Borden's Review of Nutritional Research, *12:* 11, 24, 1951; *Berg:* J. Biol.

Chem., *190:* 31, 1951; *Cantoni:* J. Am. Chem. Soc., *74:* 2942, 1952; *Toporek, Miller, and Bale:* J. Biol. Chem., *198:* 839, 1952; *Du Vigneaud, Ressler, and Rachele:* Science, *112:* 267, 1950; *Mackenzie:* J. Biol. Chem., *186:* 351, 1950; *Weissbach, Elwyn, and Sprinson:* J. Am. Chem. Soc., *72:* 3316, 1950; *Sakami:* J. Biol. Chem., *187:* 369, 1950; Nutr. Rev., *10:* 21, 1952; Ibid., *8:* 269, 1950; *Williams, Jr., Litwack, and Elvehjem:* J. Biol. Chem., *192:* 73, 1951; J. Am. Med. Assoc., *147:* 1672, 1951; *Du Vigneaud, Verly, Wilson, Rachele, Ressler, and Kinney:* J. Am. Chem. Soc., *73:* 2782, 1951; *Long:* Science Progress, Oct., 1951, p. 678; Nutr. Rev., *9:* 231, 1951; *Brown and Byerrum:* J. Am. Chem. Soc., *74:* 1523, 1952 (transmethylation in plants).

Diet and liver cirrhosis is discussed in Nutr. Rev., *8:* 13, 1950.

For blood fats (lipids), see *Goldman, Chaikoff, Reinhardt, Entelman, and Dauben:* J. Biol. Chem., *184:* 727, 1950.

See *Doerschuk:* J. Biol. Chem., *193:* 39, 1951; *196:* 423, 1952, for the fate of glycerol in the body.

On the subject of β-oxidation, see *Siegel and Lorber:* J. Biol. Chem., *189:* 571, 1951; *Lorber, Lifson, Sakami, and Wood:* Ibid., *183:* 531, 1950.

For acetone bodies, see *Weinhouse and Millington:* J. Biol. Chem., *193:* 1, 1951; *Kennedy and Lehninger:* Ibid., *185:* 275, 1950; *Beatty and West:* Ibid., *190:* 603, 1951.

For the oxidation and biosynthesis of fatty acids, see *Kennedy and Lehninger:* J. Biol. Chem., *185:* 275, 1950; *Lipmann:* Harvey Lectures, 1948–49, p. 99; *Brady and Gurin:* J. Biol. Chem., *199:* 421, 1952; *Barker:* Harvey Lectures, 1949–50, p. 242; *Drysdale and Lardy:* J. Biol. Chem., *202:* 119, 1953; *Anker:* Ibid., *176:* 1337, 1948; *194:* 177, 1952; *Lardy:* Proc. Nat. Acad. Sci. U. S., *38:* 1003, 1952; *Brady and Gurin:* J. Biol. Chem., *189:* 371, 1950; *Zabin and Bloch:* Ibid., *192:* 261, 1951 (butyric acid for the synthesis of fatty acid); *Zabin:* Ibid., *189:* 355, 1951; *Wick and Drury:* Ibid., *199:* 127, 1952; *Stadtman, Doudoroff, and Lipmann:* Ibid., *191:* 377,

1951 (mechanism of acetoacetate synthesis); *Cowie, Duncombe, Folley, French, Glassock, Massart, Peeters, and Popják:* Biochem. J., *49:* 610, 1951; *Stern and Campillo:* J. Am. Chem. Soc., *75:* 2277, 1953; *Weinhouse:* Arch. Biochem., *37:* 239, 1952 (theory of fatty acid catabolism); *Geyer, Cunningham, and Pendergast:* J. Biol. Chem., *185:* 461, 1950 (acetoacetic acid from odd and even numbered fatty acids); *Green, Goldman, and Beinert:* J. Biol. Chem., *202:* 137, 1953.

For the conversion of carbohydrate into fat, see *Masoro, Chaikoff, and Dauben:* J. Biol. Chem., *179:* 1117, 1949; *Gurin, Delluva, and Wilson:* Ibid., *171:* 101, 1947. For the conversion of fat into carbohydrate, see *Strisower, Chaikoff, and Weinman:* J. Biol. Chem., *192:* 453, 1951; *Abraham, Chaikoff, and Hassid:* Ibid., *195:* 567, 1952.

For the effect of vitamins on the metabolism of fat see *Carter and Phizackerley:* Biochem. J., *49:* 227, 1951 (pyridoxine); *Bennett, Joralemon, and Halpern:* J. Biol. Chem., *193:* 285, 1951 (vitamin B_{12}); *Krider and Guerrant:* J. Nutrition, *41:* 115, 1950 (thiamine).

Under synthesis and metabolism of cholesterol, see the following: *Bloch:* Recent Progress in Hormone Research, *6:* 111, 1951 (review); *Wuersh, Huang, and Bloch:* J. Biol. Chem., *195:* 439, 1952 (origin of Isooctyl side chain); *Langdon and Bloch:* J. Am. Chem. Soc., *74:* 1869, 1952 (squalene as a possible intermediary); *Langdon and Bloch:* J. Biol. Chem., *200:* 129, 1953; *Brady, Rabinowitz, Baalen, and Gurin:* J. Biol. Chem., *193:* 137, 1951 (a study of precursors); *Byers, Friedman, and Michaelis:* Ibid., *184:* 71, 1950 (plasma cholesterol); *Hotta and Chaikoff:* Ibid., *198:* 895, 1952 (synthesis in liver).

With regard to cholesterol, lipids and hypertension, see Nutr. Rev., *9:* 70, 1951; *10:* 46, 1952 (dietary treatment); Ibid., *9:* 295, 1951 (experimental arteriosclerosis); *Gofman:* Bull. N. Y. Acad. Med., *28:* 279, 1952 (effect of lipoproteins); *Bruger and Oppenheim:* Ibid., *27:* 539, 1951 (review); *Keys:* J. Am. Med. Assoc., *147:* 1514, 1951 (critical review).

Chapter 14   *Metabolism of Proteins*

THE PROTEINS are first hydrolyzed in the digestive tract to amino acids. Conjugated proteins give rise to amino acids, but, in addition, produce other substances. For example, casein splits off phosphoric acid; nucleoprotein yields nucleic acid, which hydrolyzes further. But the amino acids are certainly the primary constituents of the protein molecule.

These amino acids, of which there are some twenty odd, are absorbed through the lumen of the small intestine, pass into the portal system, and thence to the liver. Some of these amino acids pass on to the tissues to form tissue protein; others are utilized for the formation of specific substances (glutathione, bile salts, enzymes, certain hormones, etc.); others are deaminized. The deamination—the loss of the amino group—takes place largely in the liver and in the kidney.

The main absorption of proteins is undoubtedly in the form of amino acids. Pepsin, trypsin, etc., the proteolytic enzymes of the intestinal tract, are able between them to split proteins to amino acids; and as far back as 1912, Van Slyke and Meyer showed that after a meal rich in proteins the amino acid content of the blood rises. There is, however, some evidence that fragments of proteins larger than amino acids may be absorbed.

As a result of deamination, the amino group, split off as ammonia, contributes to the formation of urea, and the deaminized portion may be oxidized, ultimately to carbon dioxide and water, or it may form glucose, or it may form fatty acid, or it may be resynthesized into the amino acid.

Since the amino acids have, in common, a structure involving the α-amino carboxylic acid, one general reaction for deamination probably serves for all of them. The exceptions are the "basic" amino acids with more than one amino group; it is not yet clear whether, in such a case, deamination affects the second amino group.

However, the oxidation of the deaminized portions of amino acids raises many difficulties. It is, of course, obvious that, having removed the NH_2 groups from the amino acids, we are left with residues which, chemically, resemble one another no more closely than the original substances. These deaminized residues may form glycogen (and therefore glucose) or fatty acid; or they may be oxidized. Since there is good reason to suppose that a partial oxidation at least is necessary in the first two instances, a study of the steps in this oxidation process becomes extremely important. But, unfortunately, the variety of structures among the amino acids is such that few oxidative reactions can be applied to all of them. In almost all cases it is necessary to study the oxidation of each acid.

In the course of the changes which proteins undergo in the body, some 80 per cent of the nitrogen belonging to such proteins is excreted in mam-

240

mals as urea. In the normal adult individual, the nitrogen intake, as represented by the protein intake, is approximately equivalent to the nitrogen output, as represented by the excretion of urea and other nitrogenous substances. The body is said to be in "nitrogen equilibrium."

As a result of these various changes which proteins undergo in the body, not only do we find various end-products of protein catabolism in the urine, but most of these products first appear in the blood. These substances include urea, ammonia, uric acid, creatinine, and amino acids (non-protein nitrogen, NPN).

DYNAMIC STATE OF BODY PROTEINS

Very largely as a result of Folin's work on the output of creatinine—which varies very little despite a varying intake of protein—the idea grew up that the metabolism of protein could be divided into an exogenous and an endogenous variety—the one variable, and not directly concerned with cellular synthesis and breakdown, and the other constant, attributed to cellular wear and tear. The nitrogen excreted by adult animals kept in nitrogen equilibrium (Chap. 19) was looked upon as representing a variable

Table 25   BALANCE OF N^{15} AFTER FEEDING
N^{15}-LEUCINE
(From Schoenheimer, Ratner, and Rittenberg: J. Biol. Chem., *130:* 703.)

Source of Sample	Fraction of N^{15} Administered
	(per cent)
Excreta	
Feces	2.1
Urine	27.6
Animal body	
Non-protein N	7.8
Protein N	57.5

quantity of dietary nitrogen and a fixed quantity of nitrogen derived from the metabolism of the tissues proper.

This view has changed considerably since the work of Schoenheimer with his use of N^{15}-labelled amino acids. The newer concept pictures the body proteins as constantly undergoing a change in individuality by exchanging their nitrogen for nitrogen obtained from a common body "pool," to which dietary amino acids contribute. In his experiments, rats were maintained in "nitrogen equilibrium" by using a satisfactory normal diet, and an amino acid containing N^{15}—in this case leucine—was added. The body proteins and the excreta were analyzed for N^{15}. Table 25 shows the distribution of the isotope.

It can be seen that some 57 per cent of the isotope was found in the body protein and only 30 per cent in the urine and feces. These results were in contradiction with the idea that "excess" dietary proteins would be excreted; rather, the results lent themselves to the view that the nitrogen of the dietary amino acids is constantly being incorporated into the body protein, even at a time when the animal is in nitrogen equilibrium and should not, therefore, demand an extra supply of amino acids for the rebuilding of tissue protein.

Similar results were obtained with other labelled amino acids.

Another experiment involved the N^{15} content of the proteins of the various body tissues (Table 26).

Table 26   DISTRIBUTION IN PROTEINS OF VARIOUS TISSUES OF RATS GIVEN ISOTOPIC LEUCINE

Organ	N^{15} Concentration
	(atom per cent N^{15} excess) *
Plasma	0.108
Red cells	0.019
Liver	0.061
Intestinal wall	0.097
Kidney	0.089
Heart	0.058
Spleen	0.072
Testes	0.050
Skin	0.012
Muscle	0.020
Carcass	0.030

* The phrase "atoms per cent" of isotope has been introduced. Examples will make this clear. Glycine containing 10 atom per cent N^{15} means that the nitrogen of the glycine molecule contains 10 per cent more N^{15} atoms than the normal glycine; or 10.37 per cent of its nitrogen is N^{15}. Valeric acid with 10 atom per cent deuterium means that 10.02 per cent of all of its hydrogen atoms are present as deuterium (D).

Although the muscle shows low activity, it must not be overlooked that it constitutes the largest mass of the animal body, so that it actually represents the highest absolute amount, equivalent to some two-thirds of the total nitrogen deposited (one-third being represented by the internal organs). The skin is the least active of the tissues.

In another experiment the proteins of the various tissues were hydrolyzed, and the individual amino acids were isolated for the analysis of N^{15}. Table 27 makes it clear that the labelled nitrogen in the amino acid which was fed was incorporated by all the amino acids isolated, with the notable exception of lysine.

Glutamic and aspartic acids are notable for their high N^{15} content, indicating a rapid incorporation rate. This is also true when in the place of leucine, other labelled amino acids are given.

The amino acids, then, are continually interchanging nitrogen atoms. Similar results were obtained by feeding other amino acids.

In the attempt to explain this interchange of nitrogen, the "transaminase" reaction (p. 248) may be considered. In this reaction "transaminase" enzymes catalyze the combination of an amino acid and a keto acid whereby an interchange of nitrogen takes place resulting in the formation of a new keto acid and a new amino acid. Another possibility may be sought for in the "deamination" reaction (p. 247) whereby amino acids are transformed into their corresponding keto acids, and the nitrogen is liberated as ammonia. The ammonia would now contain the N^{15} of the

Table 27 N^{15} DISTRIBUTION IN PROTEINS
FROM RATS FED ISOTOPIC LEUCINE

Protein Constituent	Liver	Intestinal Wall
	(atom per cent excess N^{15})	
Total protein	0.061	0.097
Amide nitrogen	0.051	0.081
Glycine	0.048	0.041
Tyrosine	0.033	0.061
Aspartic acid	0.076	0.150
Glutamic acid	0.121	0.194
Arginine	0.058	0.028
Lysine	0.004	0.005
Leucine	0.518	0.480

dietary labelled amino acid and could, conceivably, replace the nitrogen of a protein-bound amino acid. Assuming such a reaction in vivo, ammonia itself, as well as any dietary amino acid, should serve as a source of nitrogen.

In an actual experiment, ammonium citrate, labelled with N^{15}, was fed and the amino acids obtained by hydrolysis of the proteins of tissue were shown to contain the isotope (Table 28).

Table 28 N^{15} DISTRIBUTION IN THE PROTEIN
CONSTITUENTS OF RATS FED N^{15}-
AMMONIUM CITRATE
(From Rittenberg, Schoenheimer, and
Keston: J. Biol. Chem., *128*: 603.)

Protein Constituent	Liver
	(atom per cent N^{15} excess)
Non-protein nitrogen	0.033
Protein nitrogen	0.022
Amide nitrogen	0.022
Arginine	0.026
Glutamic acid	0.046
Aspartic acid	0.031
Glycine	0.019

Even animals on a diet low in protein—where presumably more body protein is broken down than is replaced by the diet—still continue to incorporate nitrogen from the body pool of ammonia (Table 29).

Though the actual mechanism still remains to be discovered, these experiments illustrate the concept of the "dynamic state."

THE FORMATION OF TISSUE PROTEIN

Theoretically, the formation of tissue protein could be the reverse of a hydrolytic process: building up of a protein from the amino acids. We find tissue proteins—proteins actually manufactured in the body—in all the organs; yet we have only the vaguest ideas regarding their method of formation.

Of the various tissue proteins, those which have been most studied are found in blood: hemoglobin, fibrinogen, prothrombin, serum albumin, and serum globulin. In various ways, the liver, the bone marrow, the spleen, and the intestine are involved in the formation of one or more of these proteins; the liver stands out predominantly.*

Plasma proteins, represented by the albumin and globulin fractions, are manufactured in the liver and possibly also in the bone marrow. A marked

Table 29	N^{15} DISTRIBUTION IN PROTEIN CONSTITUENTS OF RATS ON A LOW PROTEIN DIET GIVEN ISOTOPIC AMMONIA (From Foster, Schoenheimer, and Rittenberg: J. Biol. Chem., *127:* 319.)

Protein Constituent	Liver
	(atom per cent N^{15} excess)
Amide N	0.114
Glycine	0.050
Glutamic acid	0.085
Aspartic acid	0.067
Proline	0.037
Histidine	0.012
Lysine	0.003
Arginine	0.033

lowering in the amount of blood protein, hypoproteinemia, is observed in cirrhosis of the liver.

The capacity of the body to regenerate plasma protein has been shown by Whipple, who first caused hypoproteinemia by his method of *plasmapheresis*, wherein the blood plasma is depleted by bleeding the animal and then returning the washed red corpuscles in physiological salt solution (0.9 per cent). When such animals are fed various foods containing protein, a marked increase in plasma protein occurs.

Weech arrived at the same result by inducing hypoproteinemia in his animals with diets low in protein and then adding the test substance rich in protein. Beef serum, egg white, and casein, in decreasing order of efficiency, are prominent "regenerators" of plasma protein.

There is also much evidence that fibrinogen and prothrombin are largely manufactured by the liver. By excision of the liver (hepatectomy), or in the event of damage to the liver, it can be shown that the fibrinogen values are much below normal. There is evidence that prothrombin is formed in the liver with the help of vitamin K (Chap. 20).

* Evidence is accumulating that the liver is to some extent, at least, a storehouse for protein.

There is evidence, too, that the liver plays a role in the manufacture of globin, the protein portion of the hemoglobin molecule. Whipple found liver the most potent among foodstuffs in forming hemoglobin.

We must also bear in mind that in addition to the problem of the syntheses of such tissue proteins and others, the problem of the syntheses in the body of certain hormones which are proteins (insulin, several pituitary hormones) and the various enzymes, all of which are proteins, must also be investigated.

Peptide Bond Synthesis.   Compared with the hydrolysis of proteins, their synthesis in the body presents formidable difficulties. That is to say, the body accomplishes such syntheses easily enough; but to duplicate such experiments in vitro is a difficult task. The difficulty with model systems which can be devised to demonstrate peptide synthesis is that the equilibrium position of such a reaction—assuming the formation of water as a by-product—is far over on the side of hydrolysis rather than synthesis.

To illustrate this point, the hydrolysis of the simple dipeptide, alanylglycine, results in a free energy of hydrolysis of 3170 cal., with an equilibrium constant of 866. At 0.1 M initial substrate concentration, the equilibrium would be 99.99 per cent on the side of hydrolysis. In order to devise conditions which would favor the production of a compound with a peptide bond, Bergmann and his collaborators prepared synthetic amino acid derivatives of such a kind as to form insoluble peptides, thereby driving the equilibrium in the direction of peptide synthesis. When, for example, a solution of carbobenzoxyglycine is incubated with activated papain at 40° C. and pH 4.6 in the presence of aniline, carbobenzoxyglycyl anilide is formed.

$$CH_2.COOH \qquad + H_2NC_6H_5 \longrightarrow CH_2.CO.NHC_6H_5 + H_2O$$
$$| \qquad\qquad\qquad Aniline \qquad\qquad |$$
$$NH.CO.O.CH_2.C_6H_5 \qquad\qquad\qquad NH.CO.O.CH_2.C_6H_5$$

Carbobenzoxyglycine   Carbobenzoxyglycyl
                                                      anilide

Such experiments have yielded some important information. For example, they have emphasized the high degree of specificity of the intracellular enzymes. Peptide bond formation occurred only with the L-, or natural form of the amino acid, and not with the D- form. Bergmann, Fruton, etc., defined the configuration of peptides which would enable proteolytic enzymes to act on them.

From another angle, in viewing the energy requirements for a direct peptide bond synthesis in vivo, such a reaction might be feasible provided it could be coupled with another energy-yielding reaction produced in the course of oxidative metabolism of the cell. This concept has led to such studies as the biological acetylation of aromatic amines; that is to say, to the formation of a peptide-like linkage ($RNH_2 + CH_3COOH \longrightarrow R—NH—CO—CH_3$) requiring the amine, an enzyme, acetate in the form of acetyl-CoA and ATP. Similar studies of peptide formation are the production of hippuric and p-amino hippuric acids, the benzoylation of ornithine, the synthesis of glutamine, and the synthesis of glutathione. All these reactions require ATP as a source of energy.

The biological synthesis of glutathione is of particular interest, because here we deal with a substance present in all cells, and because the enzymes involved in the synthesis of this compound have been separated and studied. A liver homogenate, fortified with Mg^{++} and ATP, will cause glycine, glutamic acid and cysteine to condense to form glutathione. One enzyme produces γ-glutamylcysteine from glutamic acid and cysteine; another couples this dipeptide with glycine.

Another type of enzymic reaction which may throw some light on peptide and protein synthesis is known as "transpeptidation." For example, an enzyme in kidney, γ-glutamyl transpeptidase, catalyzes a reaction between synthetic glutamyl dipeptides and naturally-occurring peptides—such as glutathione—whereby there is a transfer of an amino acid from one peptide linkage to another. Another example of a "transpeptidation" is the reaction between glutathione and arginine, resulting in formation of γ-glutamyl arginine. Fruton and co-workers have shown that chymotrypsin can be used in some "transpeptidation" reactions when suitable synthetic substrates are used. By tagging glycine with N^{15}, an exchange takes place between one glycine and another:

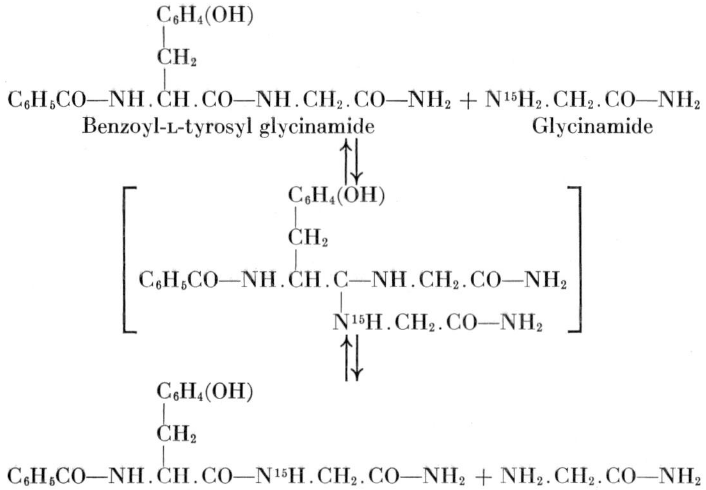

$$C_6H_4(OH)$$
$$|$$
$$CH_2$$
$$|$$
$$C_6H_5CO\text{—}NH.CH.CO\text{—}NH.CH_2.CO\text{—}NH_2 + N^{15}H_2.CH_2.CO\text{—}NH_2$$

Benzoyl-L-tyrosyl glycinamide   Glycinamide

$$\left[\begin{array}{c} C_6H_4(OH) \\ | \\ CH_2 \\ | \\ C_6H_5CO\text{—}NH.CH.C\text{—}NH.CH_2.CO\text{—}NH_2 \\ | \\ N^{15}H.CH_2.CO\text{—}NH_2 \end{array} \right]$$

$$C_6H_4(OH)$$
$$|$$
$$CH_2$$
$$|$$
$$C_6H_5CO\text{—}NH.CH.CO\text{—}N^{15}H.CH_2.CO\text{—}NH_2 + NH_2.CH_2.CO\text{—}NH_2$$

That peptides are synthesized from amino acids in biological systems is brought out in a number of experiments. For instance, Greenberg and Winnick injected glycine, containing C^{14}, into the rat and isolated the dipeptide, leucylglycine, containing the isotope. Also, Bloch incubated glycine, containing N^{15}, with rat liver slices and isolated glutathione, the tripeptide, containing the isotope.

Still other experiments show the incorporation into proteins of amino acids (using liver slices). For example, such incorporation occurred using $C^{14}OOH$-labeled alanine; but, significantly enough, the reaction proceeded only when oxygen was present.

Amino acids can also be incorporated into tissue proteins by incubating them with "particles" prepared from cells. These cytoplasmic particles, obtained by fractional centrifugation, will incorporate a number of amino acids into the protein molecule under aerobic conditions, and in the presence of Mg^{++} and ATP. Although some of the amino acids have been shown to be attached by —S—S—, rather than true peptide (—CO—NH—) bonds, many conform to the latter configuration.

Caspersson has been of the opinion that nucleic acids play a role in the synthesis of protein—an opinion based on the observation that the amount of ribopolynucleotide increases in cells which are laying down protein.

With the notable exception of glutathione, polypeptides as such are not found in cells. If we assume that the synthesis of protein consists in a simple reaction process involving the addition of one amino acid residue at a time, one would expect to find some of these (intermediary) polypeptides. The absence of such intermediates has led some workers to postulate that the synthesis of protein may be the result of a condensation of amino acid units to give rise to a macromolecule, without any intermediate formation of polypeptides.

OXIDATIVE DEAMINATION

Using the Warburg technique, in which tissue slices and the amino acid under examination are mixed in a Warburg apparatus, enabling one to measure the consumption of oxygen and the liberation of ammonia, it can be shown that both the kidney and the liver are effective deaminizing organs according to the scheme:

$$R.CH(NH_2).COOH + \tfrac{1}{2}O_2 \longrightarrow R.CO.COOH + NH_3$$

In a number of cases, the keto acids so formed have been isolated. The enzyme responsible for such an oxidative deamination is known as *amino acid oxidase*.

Two enzymes belonging to the amino acid oxidase class are known: D- and L-amino acid oxidases. The L- form, acting on L-amino acids, is physiologically the more important one, since the amino acids obtained from the proteins in foods belong to the L- series.

D-Amino acid oxidase has been purified from the kidney by Krebs; it contains flavin adenine dinucleotide (FAD) (p. 190) as its prosthetic group. The reaction may be represented thus:

$$RCH(NH_2)COOH + O_2 + H_2O \longrightarrow RCO.COOH + NH_3 + H_2O_2$$

To illustrate the function of FAD, the reaction may be written in two parts:

(a) $RCH(NH_2)COOH \xrightarrow[(-2H)]{\text{oxidase}} RC(=NH)COOH$

$(FAD + 2H \longrightarrow FADH_2)$

(b) $RC(=NH)COOH + H_2O \xrightarrow{\text{(non-enzymic)}} RCO.COOH + NH_3$

$(FADH_2 + O_2 \longrightarrow FAD + H_2O_2)$

Although the biological significance of the D-amino acid oxidase is still in doubt, a number of compounds of physiological importance contain D-amino acids; for example, the ergot alkaloids contain D-proline; the capsular substance of the mesentericus bacteria contains D-glutamic acid; a part of the penicillin molecule is D-cysteine; and a part of the gramicidin molecule is D-leucine.

Green has obtained potent extracts of the L- form (free from the D-variety) from rat kidney and liver, and this one enzyme—presumably just one—catalyzes the oxidation of a number of natural amino acids: leucine, methionine, proline, norleucine, valine, phenylalanine, tryptophan, isoleucine, tyrosine, histidine, cystine, and alanine. In all cases the corresponding keto acids and ammonia are formed. L-Amino acid oxidase contains flavin mononucleotide (FMN) as its prosthetic group.

It should be pointed out, however, that there are a number of amino acids upon which this L-amino acid oxidase has no action: glycine, dicarboxylic amino acids, diamino acids, and β-hydroxyamino acids; which means that in the deamination of these amino acids other amino acid oxidases are required.

TRANSAMINATION

By transamination we mean the reaction between an α-amino acid and an α-keto acid, whereby the amino group of the former is transferred to the latter. This reaction is catalyzed by an enzyme, *transaminase*, present in most tissues, and is reversible:

$$R^1.CHNH_2.COOH + R^2.CO.COOH \rightleftarrows R^1.CO.COOH + R^2.CH(NH_2).COOH$$

This type of reaction, using pigeon breast muscle as the source of enzyme, was extensively studied by Braunstein and Kritzmann, and others, with the following substances:

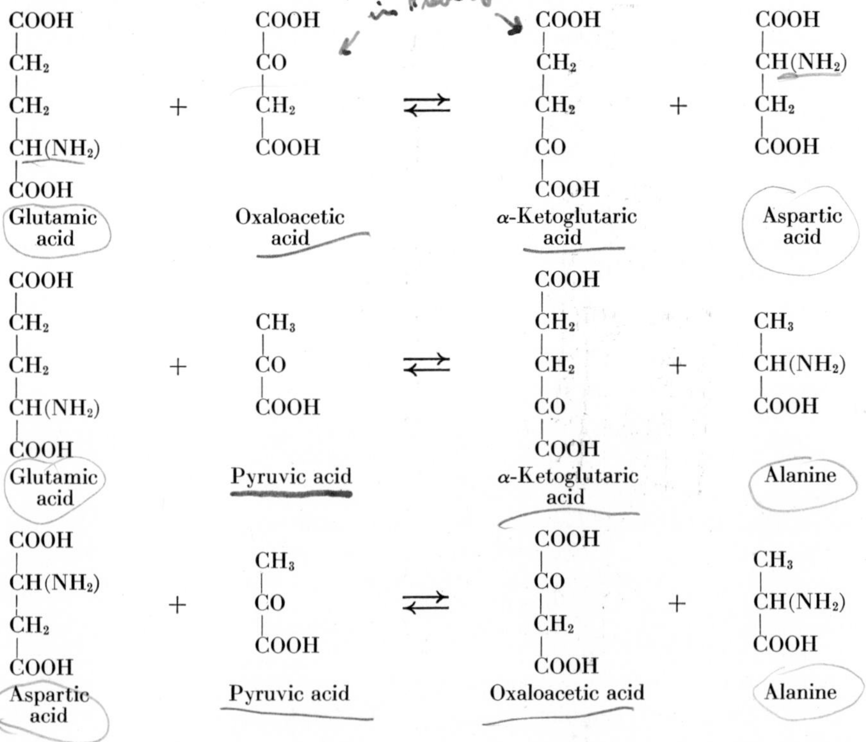

COOH CH₂ CH₂ CH(NH₂) COOH **Glutamic acid**	+	COOH CO CH₂ COOH **Oxaloacetic acid**	⇌	COOH CH₂ CH₂ CO COOH **α-Ketoglutaric acid**	+	COOH CH(NH₂) CH₂ COOH **Aspartic acid**

$$\begin{array}{c} COOH \\ CH_2 \\ CH_2 \\ CH(NH_2) \\ COOH \end{array} + \begin{array}{c} COOH \\ CO \\ CH_2 \\ COOH \end{array} \rightleftarrows \begin{array}{c} COOH \\ CH_2 \\ CH_2 \\ CO \\ COOH \end{array} + \begin{array}{c} COOH \\ CH(NH_2) \\ CH_2 \\ COOH \end{array}$$

Glutamic acid + Oxaloacetic acid ⇌ α-Ketoglutaric acid + Aspartic acid

$$\begin{array}{c} COOH \\ CH_2 \\ CH_2 \\ CH(NH_2) \\ COOH \end{array} + \begin{array}{c} CH_3 \\ CO \\ COOH \end{array} \rightleftarrows \begin{array}{c} COOH \\ CH_2 \\ CH_2 \\ CO \\ COOH \end{array} + \begin{array}{c} CH_3 \\ CH(NH_2) \\ COOH \end{array}$$

Glutamic acid + Pyruvic acid ⇌ α-Ketoglutaric acid + Alanine

$$\begin{array}{c} COOH \\ CH(NH_2) \\ CH_2 \\ COOH \end{array} + \begin{array}{c} CH_3 \\ CO \\ COOH \end{array} \rightleftarrows \begin{array}{c} COOH \\ CO \\ CH_2 \\ COOH \end{array} + \begin{array}{c} CH_3 \\ CH(NH_2) \\ COOH \end{array}$$

Aspartic acid + Pyruvic acid ⇌ Oxaloacetic acid + Alanine

These authors came to the conclusion that the reaction was quite a general one; that any α-amino acid—glycine perhaps excepted—can react with the dicarboxylic acids, α-ketoglutaric, and oxaloacetic acids; and that various α-keto acids, in turn, can react with the dicarboxylic amino acids, glutamic, and aspartic acids.

So far some 22 amino acids, in addition to alanine, aspartic and glutamic acids, have been shown to participate in the transaminase reaction. Each reaction appears to be due to a different transaminase, but all of the reactions are accelerated by the addition of pyridoxal phosphate.

Significant in this connection was the discovery that feeding animals with isotopic amino acids or isotopic ammonia gave rise to a much higher isotopic concentration in the dicarboxylic acids recovered from the tissues than in the other amino acids.

The fact that by transamination an amino acid, in the presence of the enzyme transaminase, is changed to its keto acid, makes this reaction resemble, to some extent, the deamination of an amino acid by the amino acid oxidase. It is probable that of the two, the transamination process is the more limited in scope.

The transaminases are combinations of protein and pyridoxal phosphate. Pyridoxal is a vitamin belonging to the B$_6$ group (p. 365).

It will be noticed, too, that the three ketonic acids, so important in carbohydrate metabolism, α-ketoglutaric, oxaloacetic, and pyruvic (p. 213), become important in protein metabolism because of their property of transamination. On the other hand, the corresponding amino acids, glutamic, aspartic, and alanine, because they can form the ketonic acids, serve in the metabolism of carbohydrates. All this emphasizes connections between protein and carbohydrate metabolism.

FORMATION OF UREA

The average human excretes 30 gm. of urea in 24 hours. This compound has always been regarded as the end product of nitrogen (protein) metabolism. In some species, urea is replaced by uric acid or ammonia (Table 30).

Early explanations for the formation of urea in the body, based on liver perfusion experiments, assumed a reaction involving ammonia (obtained by the deamination of amino acids, p. 247) and carbon dioxide, present in blood:

$$2NH_3 + CO_2 \longrightarrow CO(NH_2)_2 + H_2O$$

Later, Krebs and Henseleit, utilizing the tissue slice technique, also showed that ammonium salts could be converted to urea. Of the many substances tested for their possible stimulating effect in this reaction, ornithine and citrulline showed striking activity. It was discovered that the action of ornithine is a catalytic one: only small quantities were needed, and there was no stoichiometric relation between the quantity of ornithine added and the amount of urea formed.

In an attempt at an explanation, Krebs assumed the formation of an intermediate compound—by the interaction of ornithine, carbon dioxide and ammonia—which then broke down to form urea. This intermediate compound he showed to be arginine, which, in the presence of the enzyme arginase, is broken down to urea.

In this connection, it is of importance to note that there is a correlation between the ability of a tissue to form urea and its content of arginase (Table 30). Where an animal excretes urea, the arginase occurs chiefly in the liver.

Table 30 END PRODUCTS OF PROTEIN AND PURINE METABOLISM IN VARI-
OUS VERTEBRATES, CORRELATED WITH PRESENCE OF LIVER
ARGINASE
(From Baldwin: Comparative Biochemistry.)

	End Product of		
	Protein Metabolism	Purine Metabolism	Liver Arginase
Mammalia	Urea	Allantoin *	+
Birds	Uric acid	Uric acid	−
Reptilia:			
Snakes, lizards	Uric acid	Uric acid	−
Turtles	Urea	Allantoin?	+
Amphibia	Urea	Urea	+
Pisces:			
Elasmobranchii (sharks, dogfish, etc.)	Urea	Urea	+
Teleostei (most bony fish)	Ammonia	Urea	+

* Uric acid in man, higher apes and Dalmatian dogs.

But where does citrulline come into this picture? Here the postulate was made that this compound was doubtless an intermediate in the conversion of ornithine to arginine. This citrulline, originally isolated from the seeds of the watermelon, has since been shown to occur in animals.

The theory by Krebs can now be summarized as follows:

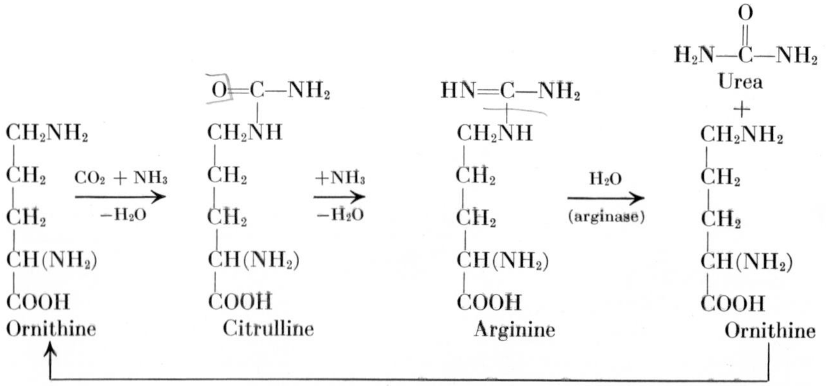

$$
\begin{array}{cccc}
 & O\!\!=\!\!C\text{---}NH_2 & HN\!\!=\!\!C\text{---}NH_2 &
\begin{array}{c}O\\ \|\\ H_2N\text{---}C\text{---}NH_2\\ \text{Urea}\\ +\end{array}\\
CH_2NH_2 & CH_2NH & CH_2NH & CH_2NH_2\\
| & | & | & |\\
CH_2 \quad CO_2+NH_3 & CH_2 \quad +NH_3 & CH_2 \quad H_2O & CH_2\\
| \quad \longrightarrow & | \quad \longrightarrow & | \quad \longrightarrow & |\\
CH_2 \quad -H_2O & CH_2 \quad -H_2O & CH_2 \quad \text{(arginase)} & CH_2\\
| & | & | & |\\
CH(NH_2) & CH(NH_2) & CH(NH_2) & CH(NH_2)\\
| & | & | & |\\
COOH & COOH & COOH & COOH\\
\text{Ornithine} & \text{Citrulline} & \text{Arginine} & \text{Ornithine}
\end{array}
$$

This work of Krebs has been abundantly confirmed since he started this problem (1932). What was needed, in addition, was an explanation of the mechanism of the reaction—the enzymes involved, and the energy needed for the production of urea from ammonia and carbon dioxide (a reaction which involves a change of free energy of 13,000 cal.).

P. P. Cohen first showed that the conversion of ornithine to citrulline involved glutamic acid. Glutamic acid first forms two intermediate compounds, tentatively identified as carbamino-glutamate and carbamyl-glutamate; the latter combines with ornithine to form citrulline, and glutamic acid is regenerated at the same time. For these reactions, Mg^{++} and ATP are also required:

```
COOH              COOH                      COOH
 |                 |                         |
CH₂               CH₂                       CH₂
 |         +CO₂    |       +NH₃ (+ ATP)      |            +ornithine
CH₂      ──────→  CH₂     ───────────────→  CH₂        ──────────────→
 |                 |            −H₂O          |            (ATP, Mg⁺⁺)
CH(NH₂)           CH(NHCOOH)                 CH(NHCONH₂)
 |                 |                          |
COOH              COOH                       COOH
Glutamate         Carbamino-                 Carbamyl-
                  glutamate (?)              glutamate (?)
```

$+CO_2$; $+NH_3$ ($+ATP$); $-H_2O$; $+ornithine$ (ATP, Mg^{++})

```
            O=C.NH₂
             |
            CH₂NH        COOH
             |            |
            CH₂          CH₂
             |            |
            CH₂     +    CH₂
             |            |
            CH(NH₂)      CH(NH₂)
             |            |
            COOH         COOH
            Citrulline   Glutamate
```

Ratner next showed that, in the presence of soluble enzymes extracted from liver tissue, aspartic acid reacts with citrulline to form an intermediate compound, which then breaks down into arginine and fumaric acid:

```
                    COOH
                     |
        HN=C—NH.CH              HN=C—NH₂
              |    |                  |
             CH₂NH CH₂               CH₂NH          COOH
              |     |                 |              |
COOH         CH₂   COOH              CH₂            CH
 |            |                       |             ‖
CH₂          CH₂                     CH₂            CH
 |   +citrulline   |                  |              |
CH(NH₂) ──────→   CH(NH₂)   ──────→  CH(NH₂)  +     COOH
 |   (ATP, Mg⁺⁺)   |                  |
COOH             COOH                COOH
Aspartate        Argininosuccinic    Arginine       Fumarate
                 acid
```

It might be recalled, by reference to the transaminase reaction (p. 248), that aspartic acid may be formed by the interaction of glutamic acid and oxaloacetic acid. Glutamic acid itself may be formed from α-ketoglutaric acid by its reaction with ammonia.

Krebs has summarized the various developments as follows:

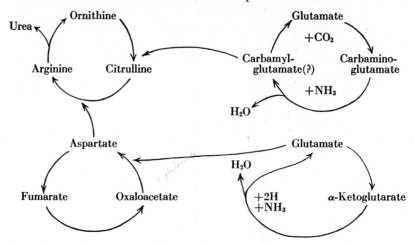

What is not shown in this diagram are reactions involved in the formation of α-ketoglutarate and oxaloacetate. It is important, too, to remember that the major source of energy is ATP.

CONVERSION OF CARBOHYDRATE INTO PROTEIN

The transaminase reaction and the reactions involving oxidative deamination make it plain how, during the intermediary metabolism of amino acids, such compounds as pyruvic, α-ketoglutaric and oxaloacetic acids can be formed. Since these are the intermediates of carbohydrate metabolism, and assuming reversible reactions, carbohydrates can be used to form amino acids and, therefore, protein.

CONVERSION OF PROTEIN INTO CARBOHYDRATE AND FAT

The theoretical possibilities here are more or less obvious. If, for the sake of simplicity, we assume the amino acid (representing the protein) to be alanine, then deamination gives rise to pyruvic acid, $CH_3.CO.COOH$, which, we have already seen, plays its part in the metabolism of carbohydrates.

The actual experimental work has centered itself largely around the use of animals which had been made diabetic by means of pancreatectomy or, more commonly, by the injection of phlorizin. Such animals excrete glucose. They continue to excrete sugar even when starved. Since in this state the reserve supply of carbohydrate has practically disappeared, we may, perhaps, assume that the glucose formed during such starvation is derived from protein (or its corresponding amino acids).

In the phlorizinized dog, and under fasting conditions, there is a fairly constant relationship between the amounts of nitrogen (representing protein) and glucose excreted. The $\dfrac{D}{N}\left(\text{or }\dfrac{\text{dextrose}}{\text{nitrogen}}\right)$ ratio is 3.65, according to Lusk.

If we assume that the percentage of nitrogen in the average protein molecule is 16 then we can say that 16 gm. of nitrogen represents 100 gm. of protein. In terms of the dextrose-nitrogen ratio,

$$\frac{D}{N} = \frac{3.65}{1} = \frac{58}{16}$$

or 100 gm. of tissue protein (16 × 6.25) under the conditions cited, will give rise to 58 gm. of glucose.

When such fasting, diabetic dogs are fed various amino acids, added quantities of glucose are formed. There are obviously amino acids which can be converted to carbohydrates. Some amino acids, however, give rise to acetoacetic acid. Since this acid is usually regarded as a decomposition product of fatty acids, the conversion of amino acids into fatty acids (or proteins into fats) may, possibly, be postulated.

The metabolic interrelationships of carbohydrates, fats, and proteins (in the light of our discussions in the last three chapters) are summarized:

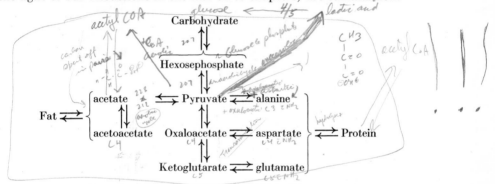

METABOLISM OF INDIVIDUAL AMINO ACIDS

Glycine and Serine. Aside from cellular needs for the synthesis of proteins, glycine is used in the formation of bile acids, glutathione, heme, etc.

Under abnormal conditions, glycine may be used by the body for still other purposes. For example, in the diabetic animal the carbon atoms of glycine contribute to form glucose, and in the fasting animal they contribute towards the formation of glycogen. The amino acid may also be used for detoxicating purposes (Chap. 24); if benzoic acid is administered, hippuric acid is formed (which represents a condensation of benzoic acid and glycine).

This amino acid is a dispensable one in the sense that its absence from a diet otherwise normal does not prevent normal growth in the rat. This view has received very definite confirmation from the more recent work of Rose who, using a mixture of amino acids (but excluding glycine), together with dextrin, sucrose, salt mixture, agar, lard, cod-liver oil, and yeast, obtained excellent growth.

It is known that the organism has the ability to synthesize glycine. It has been shown that rabbits and goats can be fed relatively large quantities of benzoic acid to form hippuric acid, and that the glycine necessary for this condensation is in excess of that which can be derived from the catabolism of the proteins. The amino acid, then, must be synthesized in the body, but we are not certain as to its origin. It is believed that under the abnormal conditions just described—feeding relatively large quantities of benzoic acid—some of the nitrogen which is ordinarily converted into urea and excreted, is diverted from its normal course to build the necessary amino acid.

That glycine is a dispensable amino acid is true so far as the rat and man are concerned. However, Almquist has shown that this amino acid is an indispensable one when dealing with the growth of chicks; and, more specifically, with the synthesis of creatine in muscle; for the feeding of glycine invariably results in an increase of muscle creatine.

Glycine is said to be "glycogenic," in that when fed, added glycogen is deposited. This is not true of fatty acids, even though it has been shown— by the use of isotopically labelled compounds—that some of their carbon atoms may eventually appear in the glycogen molecule.

In this connection, the importance of a 1-carbon intermediate ("formate") * is beginning to rival in importance the 2-carbon intermediate ("acetate," p. 214). For example, C^{13}-carboxyl labelled glycine was fed to rats together with C^{14}-formate. Glucose, isolated from the glycogen of the liver, contained C^{13} almost exclusively in C3 and C4, whereas C^{14} was highest in C1 and C6. These results are in accord with a hypothesis whereby glycine first combines with "formate" to yield serine, followed by the deamination of the latter to yield pyruvic acid, which then is synthesized to C6 compounds and eventually to glycogen by a reverse glycolytic process:

$$2HC^{14}OOH + 2CH_2(NH_2)C^{13}OOH \longrightarrow 2C^{14}H_2(OH).CH(NH_2)C^{13}OOH$$

$$\longrightarrow 2C^{14}H_3.CO.C^{13}OOH + 2NH_3$$

$$\downarrow$$

$$\underset{1}{C^{14}}-\underset{2}{C}-\underset{3}{C^{13}}-\underset{4}{C^{13}}-\underset{5}{C}-\underset{6}{C^{14}}$$

This scheme was further confirmed by the isolation of serine from the liver proteins. The results showed that the C^{14} of formate contributed to the β carbon of serine, whereas the C^{13}-carboxyl carbon of glycine was donated to the carboxyl carbon of serine. This result agrees with findings by other workers that glycine is converted to serine.

Kidney and liver contain an enzyme, glycine oxidase, which forms glyoxylic acid and ammonia from glycine. The enzyme is a flavoprotein and contains flavin adenine dinucleotide (FAD) as a prosthetic group. In an extension of the study of the role of "formate" in glycine metabolism, it has been shown that glycine may also contribute to the formation of "formate" via glyoxylic acid. Glycine, containing C^{14} in its α carbon, was fed and the glucose obtained from the glycogen analyzed as before. The results are in accord with the following scheme:

$$C^{14}H_2(NH_2)COOH \xrightarrow{-NH_3} C^{14}HO.COOH \longrightarrow \text{"}HC^{14}OOH\text{"} + CO_2$$

$$\text{"}HC^{14}OOH\text{"} + C^{14}H_2(NH_2)COOH \longrightarrow C^{14}H_2(OH).C^{14}H(NH_2)COOH$$

$$\longrightarrow C^{14}H_3.C^{14}O.COOH \longrightarrow \text{Glucose}$$

This scheme indicates that glycine contributes directly to the carboxyl and

* The active 1-carbon intermediate does not have to be formate but some derivative.

α position and, indirectly, (via "formate") to the β position of serine. Taken together with the earlier findings that serine can be converted to glycine, the following scheme may be suggested:

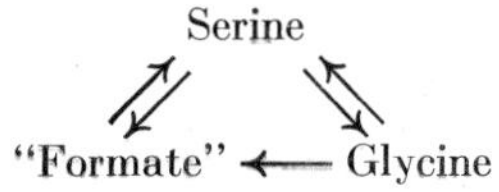

Serine

"Formate" ⟵ Glycine

Shemin has demonstrated the synthesis of the porphyrin of hemin (p. 155) from acetate and glycine. The acetate via the Krebs cycle (p. 212) forms succinate. This succinate, or rather an "active" form (succinyl-CoA?), combines with glycine to form α-amino-β-keto adipic acid, $COOH.-CH_2.CH_2.CO.CH.NH_2.COOH$, a compound which is unstable and probably decarboxylates to form δ-amino levulinic acid, $COOH.CH_2.CH_2.-CO.CH_2.NH_2$, the immediate precursor of the porphyrin molecule.

Threonine.   This is an essential amino acid and can form glycogen and diminish ketonuria in rats. It has been shown that cell-free extracts form α-ketobutyric acid from this amino acid.

Upon feeding N^{15}-leucine to the rat, isolating the proteins from tissues, and hydrolyzing such proteins, little labelled threonine is found. This means that the amino group of threonine does not participate in reversible nitrogen transfer reactions to any appreciable extent; it thereby resembles lysine.

From one-fifth to one-third of the dietary threonine is broken down in the rat to acetate and glycine.

Rat liver homogenates incubated with threonine form aminobutyric acid:

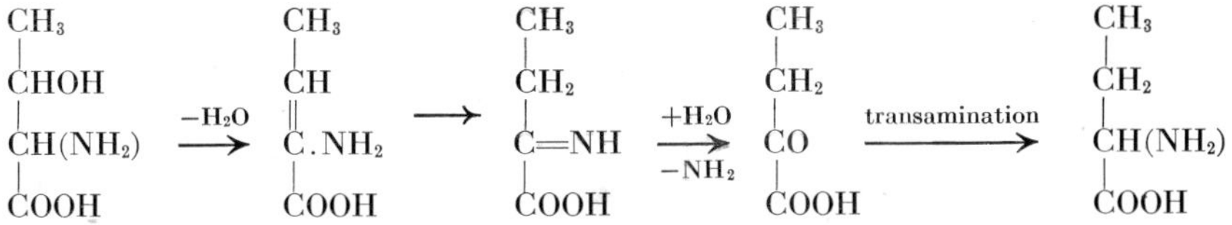

$$
\begin{array}{ccccc}
CH_3 & CH_3 & CH_3 & CH_3 & CH_3 \\
| & | & | & | & | \\
CHOH & CH & CH_2 & CH_2 & CH_2 \\
| & \xrightarrow{-H_2O} \; || & | & \xrightarrow{+H_2O} \; | & \xrightarrow{\text{transamination}} \; | \\
CH(NH_2) & C.NH_2 & C{=}NH & CO & CH(NH_2) \\
| & | & | & {}_{-NH_2} \; | & | \\
COOH & COOH & COOH & COOH & COOH
\end{array}
$$

Leucine and Isoleucine.   Of the three closely related amino acids, leucine, isoleucine, and norleucine, the first two are indispensable for growth, and the last is probably not essential.

Rose has shown that in the place of leucine and isoleucine, the corresponding α-hydroxy and α-keto acids may be used in the diet of rats.

Leucine does not produce glucose in the phlorhizinized dog. Added to a perfusing fluid which passes through a surviving liver, large quantities of acetone bodies are formed. This suggests that leucine may undergo a decomposition somewhat similar to fatty acids.

Studies using isotopic leucine indicate that it forms isovaleric acid. Carbons 1 and 2 form a 2-carbon intermediate which is incorporated into acetoacetate. The 3-carbon fragment, the isopropyl group of isovalerate, is incorporated as a unit into the α, β and γ-positions of acetoacetate. The carboxyl carbon of acetoacetate arises from a fixation of CO_2. The scheme at the top of p. 256 (from Coon: J. Biol. Chem., *187:* 71) illustrates the mechanism of breakdown of leucine to acetoacetate.

Information concerning the metabolism of isoleucine has come also from isotope experiments. 2-Methyl butyrate was identified as a product of

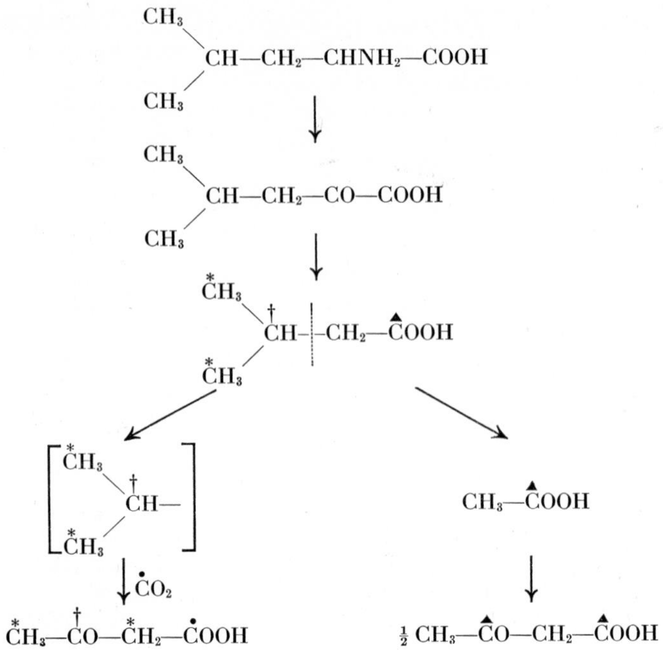

$$CH_3$$
$$\diagdown$$
$$CH-CH_2-CHNH_2-COOH$$
$$\diagup$$
$$CH_3$$

$$\downarrow$$

$$CH_3$$
$$\diagdown$$
$$CH-CH_2-CO-COOH$$
$$\diagup$$
$$CH_3$$

$$\downarrow$$

$$\overset{*}{C}H_3$$
$$\diagdown \overset{\dagger}{}$$
$$CH-|-CH_2-\overset{\blacktriangle}{C}OOH$$
$$\diagup$$
$$\overset{*}{C}H_3$$

$$\swarrow \qquad\qquad\qquad \searrow$$

$$\left[\begin{array}{c}\overset{*}{C}H_3 \\ \diagdown \overset{\dagger}{} \\ CH- \\ \diagup \\ \overset{*}{C}H_3\end{array}\right]$$
$$\downarrow \overset{\bullet}{C}O_2$$
$$\overset{*}{C}H_3-\overset{\dagger}{C}O-\overset{*}{C}H_2-\overset{\bullet}{C}OOH$$

$$CH_3-\overset{\blacktriangle}{C}OOH$$
$$\downarrow$$
$$\tfrac{1}{2}\,CH_3-\overset{\blacktriangle}{C}O-CH_2-\overset{\blacktriangle}{C}OOH$$

isoleucine metabolism. When 2-methyl-C^{14}-butyric acid was used, evidence was obtained for a β-oxidation on the longer carbon chain to produce "acetate" and propionate:

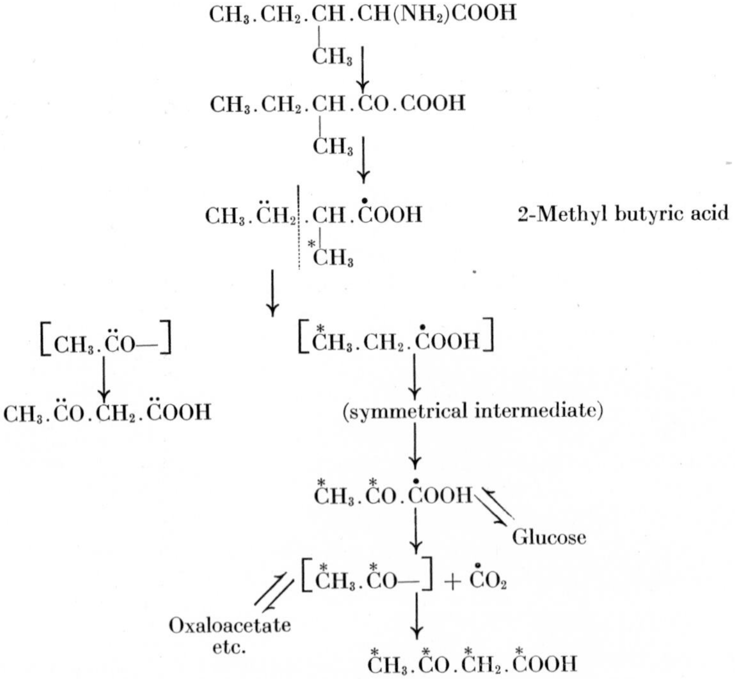

$$CH_3.CH_2.CH.CH(NH_2)COOH$$
$$\overset{|}{C}H_3\,\big\downarrow$$

$$CH_3.CH_2.CH.\overset{\bullet}{C}O.COOH$$
$$\overset{|}{C}H_3\,\big\downarrow$$

$$CH_3.\overset{\cdot\cdot}{C}H_2|.CH.\overset{\bullet}{C}OOH \qquad\qquad \text{2-Methyl butyric acid}$$
$$\overset{*}{|}$$
$$\overset{*}{C}H_3$$

$$\downarrow$$

$$\left[CH_3.\overset{\cdot\cdot}{C}O-\right] \qquad\qquad \left[\overset{*}{C}H_3.CH_2.\overset{\bullet}{C}OOH\right]$$
$$\downarrow \qquad\qquad\qquad\qquad \downarrow$$
$$CH_3.\overset{\cdot\cdot}{C}O.CH_2.\overset{\cdot\cdot}{C}OOH \qquad\qquad \text{(symmetrical intermediate)}$$

$$\downarrow$$

$$\overset{*}{C}H_3.\overset{*}{C}O.\overset{\bullet}{C}OOH\diagdown\!\diagdown$$
$$\downarrow \qquad\qquad\qquad \diagdown\!\diagdown\,\text{Glucose}$$

$$\diagup\!\!\diagup \left[\overset{*}{C}H_3.\overset{*}{C}O-\right] + \overset{\bullet}{C}O_2$$
$$\text{Oxaloacetate}$$
$$\text{etc.} \qquad\qquad\qquad\qquad \downarrow$$
$$\overset{*}{C}H_3.\overset{*}{C}O.\overset{*}{C}H_2.\overset{*}{C}OOH$$

Phenylalanine and Tyrosine.   The experiments of Rose suggest that phenylalanine is an indispensable, and tyrosine a dispensable, amino acid. What such experiments probably mean is that, under certain conditions, the former can be transformed into the latter, whereas the reverse process does not take place.

The feeding of phenylalanine containing deuterium results in a deuterium-containing tyrosine, isolated from the liver proteins. Liver slices can also convert phenylalanine to tyrosine provided oxygen and DPN (p. 88) are present.

Chemically, the two are so similar that one is tempted to treat them alike. In the rare disease known as "alcaptonuria," the urine blackens on standing. This is due to the oxidation of homogentisic acid:

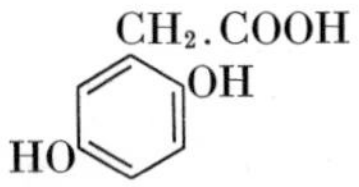

$$CH_2.COOH$$

Homogentisic acid
(2,5-Dihydroxyphenylacetic acid)

The administration of tyrosine or phenylalanine to a patient suffering from alcaptonuria increases the quantity of homogentisic acid excreted. This has led to the view that the latter is possibly an intermediate compound formed during the course of the oxidation of either one of the two amino acids.

That the degradation in the body of the D- and L- series of amino acids may take place in different ways is suggested by experiments in which the claim is made that both L-phenylalanine and L-tyrosine are quantitatively converted into homogentisic acid in the alcaptonuric, whereas only 40–45 per cent of D-phenylalanine, 43 per cent of D-tyrosine and 68 per cent of DL-tyrosine are so transformed.

Liver slices from scorbutic guinea pigs fail to oxidize tyrosine, whereas the administration of vitamin C—either in vivo or in vitro—restores the ability to oxidize. It is, of course, possible that here vitamin C acts as a part of a necessary enzyme system, just as other vitamins have been shown to act.

Both tyrosine and phenylalanine yield acetoacetic acid in perfusion experiments with liver; so that this four-carbon compound is believed to be formed during the oxidation of tyrosine or phenylalanine. Furthermore, p-hydroxyphenylpyruvic acid and homogentisic acid also yield acetoacetic acid in the liver. By the use of tagged compounds, the following series of relationships has been shown:

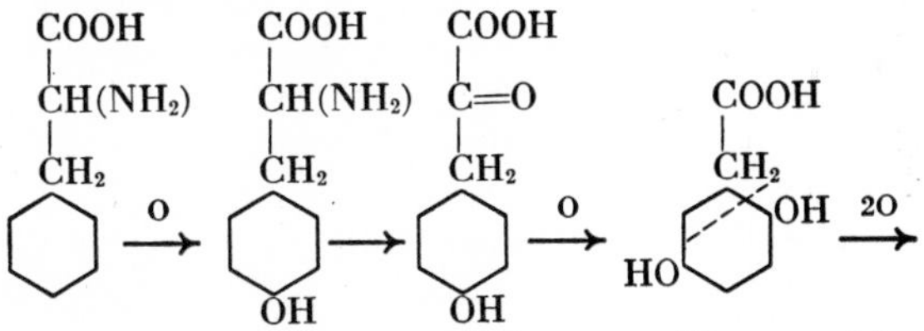

Phenylalanine   Tyrosine   p-Hydroxyphenyl pyruvic acid   Homogentisic acid

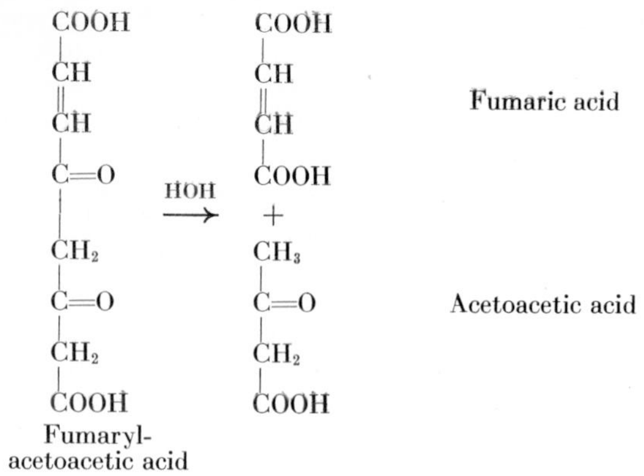

$$
\begin{array}{ll}
\text{COOH} & \text{COOH} \\
| & | \\
\text{CH} & \text{CH} \\
\| & \| \\
\text{CH} & \text{CH} \qquad\qquad \text{Fumaric acid}\\
| & | \\
\text{C=O} \quad\xrightarrow{\text{HOH}} & \text{COOH} \\
| & + \\
\text{CH}_2 & \text{CH}_3 \\
| & | \\
\text{C=O} & \text{C=O} \qquad\quad \text{Acetoacetic acid}\\
| & | \\
\text{CH}_2 & \text{CH}_2 \\
| & | \\
\text{COOH} & \text{COOH} \\
\text{Fumaryl-} \\
\text{acetoacetic acid}
\end{array}
$$

We have already stated that phenylalanine yields acetoacetic acid in the liver. However, phenylpyruvic acid does not yield acetoacetic acid in the liver, but we do get acetoacetic acid if kidney slices are substituted. This suggests two alternate paths of oxidation of phenylalanine: via phenylpyruvic acid in the kidney, and via tyrosine in the liver. That the latter is also probable appears from the work of Medes in connection with a unique case of "tyrosinosis"; here the administration of phenylalanine to the patient produced tyrosine as well as p-hydroxyphenylpyruvic acid.

$$
\underset{\text{Phenylalanine}}{\boxed{}\,\overset{\text{CH}_2.\text{CH.COOH}}{\underset{\text{NH}_2}{}}} \xrightarrow{\text{Kidney}} \underset{\substack{\text{Phenylpyruvic} \\ \text{acid}}}{\boxed{}\,\overset{\text{CH}_2.\text{CO.COOH}}{}} \longrightarrow \underset{\substack{\text{Carbon dioxide} \\ \text{and water}}}{\text{Acetoacetic acid}}
$$

Phenylalanine $\downarrow$ Liver

Tyrosine $\longrightarrow$ p-Hydroxyphenylpyruvic acid $\longrightarrow$ etc.

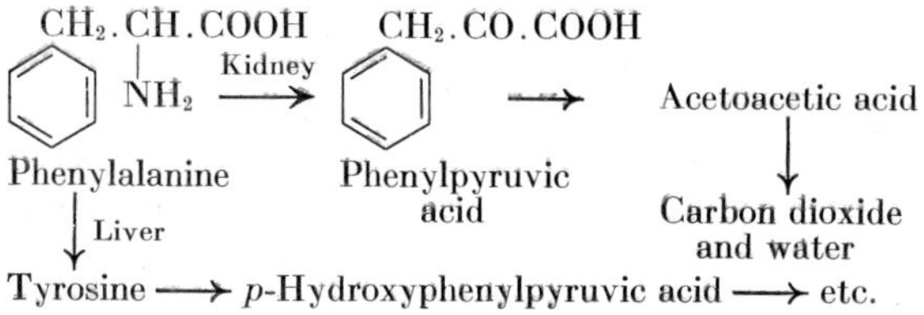

Several workers have described a metabolic abnormality in certain mentally defective patients which is characterized by the excretion of phenylpyruvic acid (phenylketonuria). This mental condition has been given the name of *phenylpyruvic oligophrenia* (imbecility) and is apparently connected with a disturbance in the metabolism of phenylalanine. In an experiment by Jervis, various amino acids (including tyrosine) were fed to a patient with phenylpyruvic oligophrenia, and the results showed that phenylalanine alone increased the output of phenylpyruvic acid.

Beadle points out that in alcaptonuria a mendelian trait can be interpreted in terms of specific chemical reactions. "In individuals homozygous for the mutant gene responsible for this character, homogentisic acid is excreted in the urine instead of being broken down to CO_2 and H_2O, as it is in persons receiving the normal form of alcaptonuric gene from one or both parents."

It is believed that people with alcaptonuria lack a specific enzyme (found in the blood of normal persons) which catalyzes the breakdown of homogentisic acid.

In alcaptonuria, it would seem, "a particular chemical reaction is controlled by a known gene through the mediation of a specific enzyme."

Alcaptonuria, phenylketonuria, and tyrosinosis represent what Garrod called "inborn errors of metabolism"—a defect in metabolism due to certain missing genes, which, in turn, control the production of enzymes necessary for metabolic transformations. "Inborn metabolic error," writes Rimington, "may be described as a deviation from the metabolism normal to the species . . . and referable to the genetic composition of the individual."

In the following diagram the possible breaks in the chain are shown. If, for example, the gene controlling the change from phenylpyruvic acid to *p*-hydroxyphenylpyruvic acid is missing, the reaction stops at the former, and phenylpyruvic acid is eliminated.

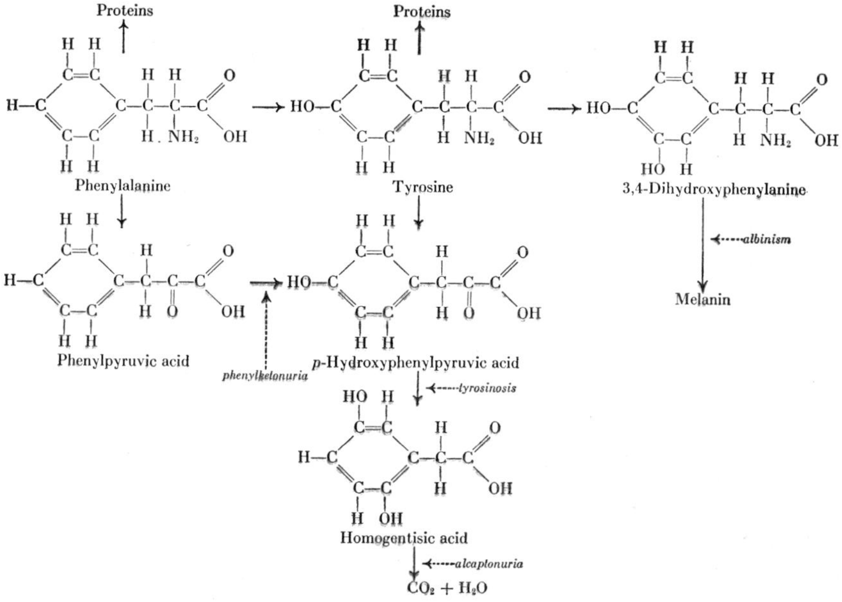

Phenylalanine-tyrosin metabolism in man showing relation of inherited defects to specific chemical reactions. (From Beadle, based on Haldane.)

An enzyme tyrosinase converts tyrosine into *melanin*, a brownish-black pigment present in skin and hair. The mechanism by which this transformation is accomplished is not known. According to Raper and others, a hydroxylation of the benzene nucleus possibly takes place, followed by ring closure, whereby indole derivatives are formed.

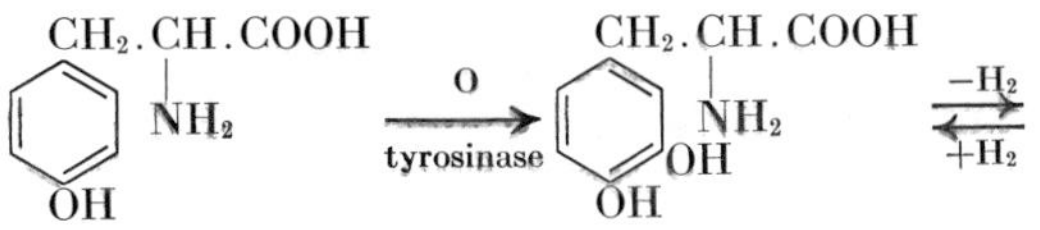

3,4-Dihydroxyphenyl-
alanine ("dopa")

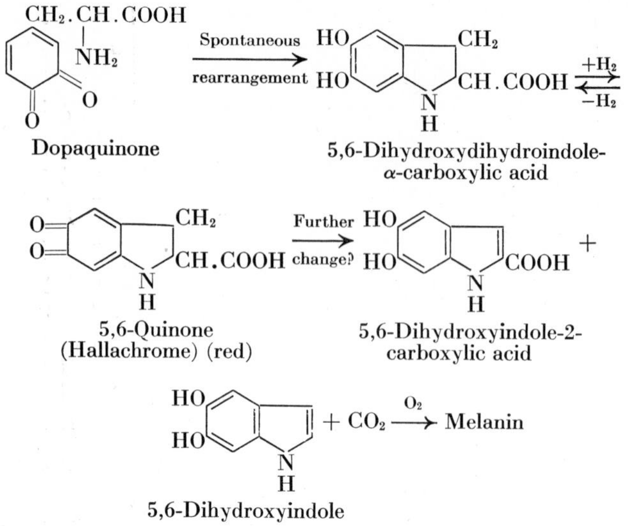

CH₂.CH.COOH

Dopaquinone

Spontaneous → rearrangement

5,6-Dihydroxydihydroindole-α-carboxylic acid

+H₂ ⇄ −H₂

5,6-Quinone (Hallachrome) (red)

Further change?

5,6-Dihydroxyindole-2-carboxylic acid

+

+ CO₂ $\xrightarrow{O_2}$ Melanin

5,6-Dihydroxyindole

Tyrosinase, it should be pointed out, catalyzes the oxidation of a large variety of mono- and polyphenols (see also p. 195), as well as phenolic derivatives such as epinephrine, certain sex hormones, and the poison ivy irritants.

As with tyrosine, so with dopa: ascorbic acid plays a role in the metabolism of the latter, and this means that the vitamin is an important factor in the formation of the melanin pigment. But dopa, unlike tyrosine, is changed by the kidney, whereas tyrosine is changed by the liver. Kidney slices from normal guinea-pigs readily oxidize dopa, but it is not affected when scorbutic kidney slices are used. When the scorbutic animal is cured with ascorbic acid, its kidney again shows the ability to oxidize dopa.

When dopa is oxidized with an oxidase (either mushroom tyrosinase or melanoma dopa oxidase, obtained from mouse tumor material), spectrophotometric evidence can be obtained for the formation of hallachrome.

The formulas for tyrosine, epinephrine, and thyroxine (p. 62) suggest that tyrosine may be the mother substance of these two hormones. Evidence for the conversion of tyrosine into epinephrine has been obtained. Epinephrine, containing C¹⁴ or H³, has been isolated after the administration of labelled phenylalanine.

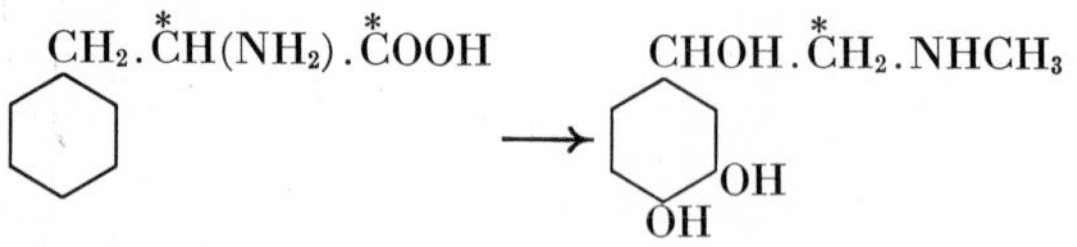

CH₂.ĊH(NH₂).ĊOOH   CHOH.ĊH₂.NHCH₃

An intermediate is 3,4-dihydroxyphenylalanine.

There is definite evidence that diiodotyrosine (p. 61), found in the thyroid, and undoubtedly derived from tyrosine, is transformed into thyroxine.

Cystine and Methionine.   The metabolic interrelationships are shown in the following scheme:

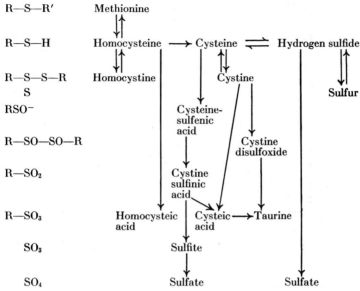

(Fromageot: from Sumner and Myrbäck's The Enzymes, Vol. 2, p. 622, 1951.)

In the rare metabolic disturbance known as "cystinuria," appreciable quantities of cystine as such appear in the urine. A rather remarkable fact is that feeding cystine to such patients does not increase the output of cystine in the urine, but leads to an increased output of sulfates (showing that the amino acid has been oxidized). It has been claimed, however, that feeding proteins rich in sulfur to persons with cystinuria does increase the amount of cystine in the urine; and the suggestion has been made that methionine is involved in this process.

Brand has shown that there is a significant difference in the partition of urinary sulfur when normal and cystinuric types are compared:

	Total sulfate,* per cent	Neutral sulfur,* per cent
Normal	95	5
Cystinuric	55	45

* See forms of sulfur in urine (Chap. 22).

In one of his many experiments dealing with sulfur metabolism, Du Vigneaud has shown that D-cystine cannot support growth in any way comparable to L-cystine. This is not true for all amino acids. For example, both D-tryptophan and D-methionine can replace the corresponding L- forms. If, as a preliminary step to the oxidation of an amino acid, oxidative deamination takes place, whereby the corresponding keto acid is formed, then an explanation for the physiological potency of some D- forms might be offered. For it might be assumed that the D- form of the amino acid is first transformed to the keto acid and the latter asymmetrically converted into the corresponding L-amino acid. In fact, the efficacy of the D- form might be brought forward as an argument in favor of the theory of oxidative de-amination.

It might be pointed out that feeding D-leucine (using isotopic "tracers") enables one to recover L-leucine from the proteins of the tissue.

The inability of D-cystine to replace L-cystine is shown to be due, in part at least, to the much slower oxidation of the former. The feeding of L-cystine leads to the conversion of 82 per cent of its sulfur to sulfate (which appears in the urine), whereas only 42 per cent of the D-cystine is similarly converted.

Cystine (—S—S—) and cysteine (—SH) represent a reversible oxidation-reduction system, also present in glutathione.

The —S—S— linkage plays a role in the mechanical properties of the hair fiber (tensile strength, etc.). Hair is rich in its content of cystine (some 9 to 17 per cent).

Several enzymes are active only so long as the —SH groups in their molecules are free. Mild oxidation will convert the —SH (sulfhydryl) into —S—S— (disulfide), and at the same time inactivate the enzyme. On the other hand, the protein hormone, insulin, is active only in the —S—S— state, and reduction to the —SH form results in inactivation.

The —SH groups of proteins may be blocked by reaction with such reagents as iodoacetic acid, iodoacetamide, p-chloromercuribenzoate, or o-iodosobenzoate. Reactivation is sometimes possible by treatment with an excess of a reducing agent, such as glutathione or cysteine.

Until the discovery of methionine, it had always been assumed that cystine was an indispensable amino acid. It now appears, however, that whereas methionine can replace cystine in a diet deficient in the latter, the reverse is not true: cystine cannot replace methionine. By using methionine containing S^{35}, it could be shown that the S of methionine is a precursor of the S of cystine. In one of his many experiments, Du Vigneaud fed methionine containing both S^{35} and C^{13}; the cystine which was recovered showed S^{35} but no C^{13}, which pointed to the fact that in the conversion of methionine to cystine, the carbon chain of methionine is not used.

Further developments did show that the methyl group of methionine and the carbon atoms of glycine are utilized by the rat for the synthesis of cystine. Since glycine is convertible to serine (p. 255), the pathway to cystine production is probably via serine.

Liver homogenates can convert serine and homocysteine to cysteine. Here an intermediate compound is formed, cystathionine:

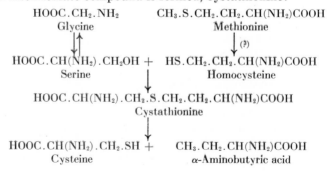

A co-factor in the enzyme systems involved is pyridoxal phosphate.

It may be pointed out, in this connection, that when large amounts of methionine are fed, α-aminobutyric acid can be detected in the urine.

The methyl group required to convert homocystine to methionine can be supplied by choline (p. 232) and, to a somewhat less extent, by betaine (p. 54). Du Vigneaud found, for example, that on a diet free of methionine, but containing homocystine, the rat failed to grow; but growth was resumed upon the addition of choline or betaine.

The direct proof of such interrelationships was obtained by the use of compounds containing isotopes. Rats were fed deuterium-containing methionine (with deuterium in the methyl group) on a diet free from methionine and choline. The choline isolated from the tissues contained the isotope. Even the creatine, isolated from muscle tissue, contained deuterium.

The reverse is also true: the feeding of deuterocholine and homocystine results in the isolation from the tissues of methionine containing the deuteromethyl group.

The methyl groups of such compounds as choline and methionine act, therefore, as transmethylating agents.

The idea that an animal cannot make its own methyl groups but must obtain them from some exogenous source has changed. Sakami showed that acetone, in the rat, contributes its methyl carbon atom for the formation of choline. In light of the fact that "formate" is formed from acetone, it was soon demonstrated by Sakami and Welch that the labile methyl groups of methionine and choline could be formed in rat liver slices from C^{14}-formate. Thus the methyl group can be synthesized from one-carbon compounds.

Recent studies by Cantoni have shown that an active form of methionine is synthesized for purposes of transmethylation. Its formation is illustrated as a reaction between methionine and ATP:

$$\text{L-Methionine} + \text{ATP} \xrightarrow[\text{Mg}^{++}]{\text{GSH}} \text{Active methionine} + \text{PO}_4^{=}$$

$$(\text{GSH} = \text{reduced glutathione})$$

The formula for this active methionine is:

$$\begin{array}{c}
\text{N}-\text{C}-\text{NH}_2 \\
\parallel \quad \parallel \\
\text{HC} \quad \text{C}-\text{N} \\
\diagdown \\
\quad \text{CH} \\
\diagup \\
\text{N}-\text{C}-\text{N}-\text{CH}-\text{CHOH}-\text{CHOH}-\text{CH}-\text{CH}_2-\overset{+}{\text{S}}-\text{CH}_2\text{CH}_2.\text{CH(NH}_2)\text{COO}^- \\
\text{O} \qquad\qquad \text{CH}_3
\end{array}$$

The enzyme responsible for its formation has been partially purified and, unlike methionine, active methionine can act as a methyl donor even in the absence of ATP.

Glutathione, the tripeptide of cysteine, glutamic acid, and glycine, can replace cystine in a diet deficient in this amino acid. An enzyme found in the kidney of the rat hydrolyzes glutathione to cysteinylglycine, and another enzyme, of wider distribution, splits this dipeptide, freeing cysteine.

Tryptophan.   This compound is one of the so-called indispensable amino acids. From what has already been said, it is not surprising to find that the corresponding keto acid, indolepyruvic acid, is able to replace tryptophan in a tryptophan-deficient diet.

In dogs and rabbits, tryptophan is partly converted to a quinoline derivative known as *kynurenic acid*. What appears to be an intermediate product, *kynurenine*, has also been isolated from the urine, as well as by the action of liver slices on tryptophan. Using labeled tryptophan (C^{14}), it has been possible to isolate from the urine of rabbits, dogs, and rats, kynurenine and kynurenic acid containing the carbon isotope. The possible pathways of metabolism are here presented (compare with p. 265):

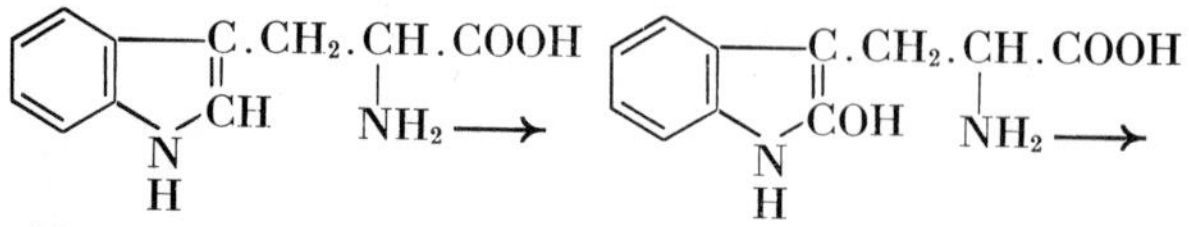

Tryptophan   α-Hydroxytryptophan

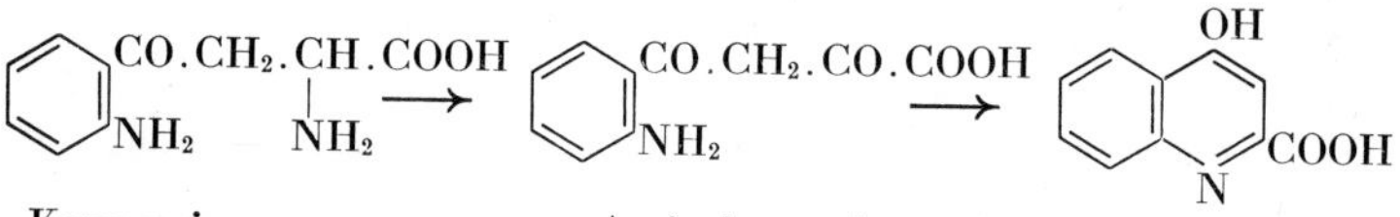

Kynurenine   o-Aminobenzoylpyruvic   Kynurenic acid
                              acid

An important contribution to the metabolism of tryptophan has been made by Lepkovsky, who succeeded in isolating a green pigment from the urine of rats suffering from pyridoxine deficiency. This pigment was identified as xanthurenic acid, a quinoline derivative:

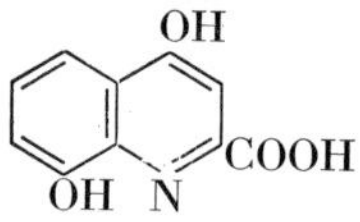

Xanthurenic acid

and the substance disappears from the urine when pyridoxine is added to the diet. (Xanthurenic acid represents a further stage in the oxidation of kynurenic acid, but it does not appear to be formed from kynurenic acid in the body.)

The connection of xanthurenic acid with tryptophan metabolism was suggested by the work of Musajo who found that rabbits and rats excrete xanthurenic acid as well as kynurenic acid on a diet high in protein. He suggested that both these acids had their origin in tryptophan.

This suggestion was confirmed by Lepkovsky, who found that on a tryptophan-deficient diet, xanthurenic acid disappears from the urine of pyridoxine-deficient rats and reappears again when tryptophan is added to the diet of such rats.

As showing a species difference—and incidentally adding to the difficulties of interpretation—pyridoxine-deficient dogs, unlike pyridoxine-deficient rats, excrete very little xanthurenic acid.

Kynurenine itself cannot replace tryptophan in the diet, but it can produce kynurenic acid.

The interrelationship of tryptophan and nicotinic acid (niacin), or rather, the conversion of the former into the latter in the animal organism, is brought out by a number of experiments. For example, tryptophan can replace nicotinic acid in the diet of the rat, dog, pig, and rabbit. The amino acid increases the urinary elimination of nicotinic acid derivatives in man, rat, cotton rat, and horse.

Using the carbon isotope, Heidelberger, Abraham, and Lepkovsky have shown how tryptophan is converted into nicotinic acid in the rat.

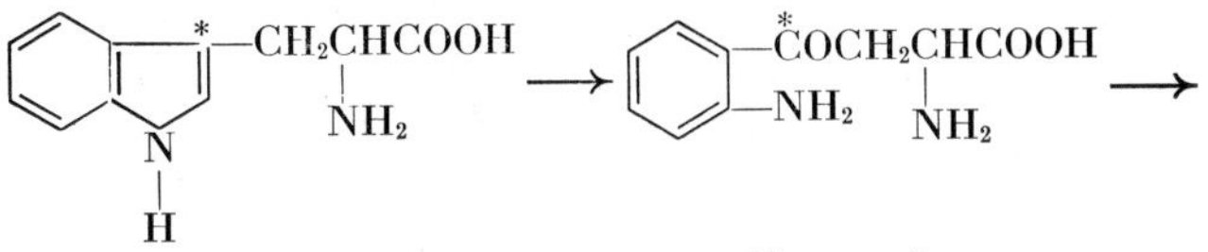

| Tryptophan | Kynurenine |

| 3-Hydroxy-anthranilic acid | Nicotinic acid | Nicotinamide | N-Methyl-nicotinamide |

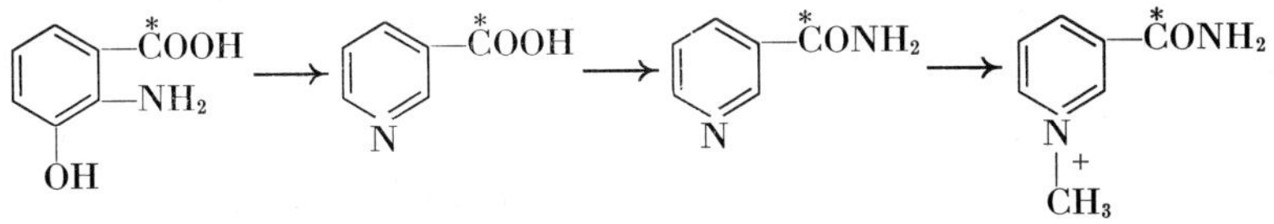

If *Neurospora* is used as a test organism, tryptophan can be substituted for nicotinic acid as a growth stimulant. By the use of mutant strains, one of the intermediates which has been identified is kynurenine. Since 3-hydroxyanthranilic acid was found to be a precursor of nicotinic acid, the conclusion was drawn that kynurenine itself was first changed to this substance.

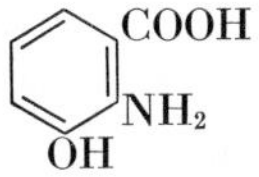

3-Hydroxyanthranilic acid

Further work on *Neurospora* has shown that in this organism tryptophan is synthesized from anthranilic acid (Fig. 62).

The anthranilic acid is converted to indole and the latter condenses with the amino acid serine to form tryptophan. Pyridoxal phosphate may act as a coenzyme in this condensation. The reverse reaction, the conversion of tryptophan to indole, due to *Escherichia coli* (found among intestinal bacteria) has been known for a long time. This reaction has been discussed under intestinal putrefaction.

The fact that diets deficient in tryptophan (using the rat) give reduced plasma protein and hemoglobin values suggests the importance of this amino acid for the syntheses of these proteins.

Proline and Hydroxyproline.   Rose has shown that proline belongs to the group of dispensable amino acids. In the growing rat it can replace, in part, the arginine requirement. Hydroxyproline is also a dispensable amino acid.

The liver is capable of oxidizing these two substances. Proline itself seems to be more rapidly oxidized by the kidney than by the liver. Krebs succeeded in isolating α-ketoglutaric acid and ammonia; which means that glutamic acid (α-aminoglutaric acid) was formed from proline. That

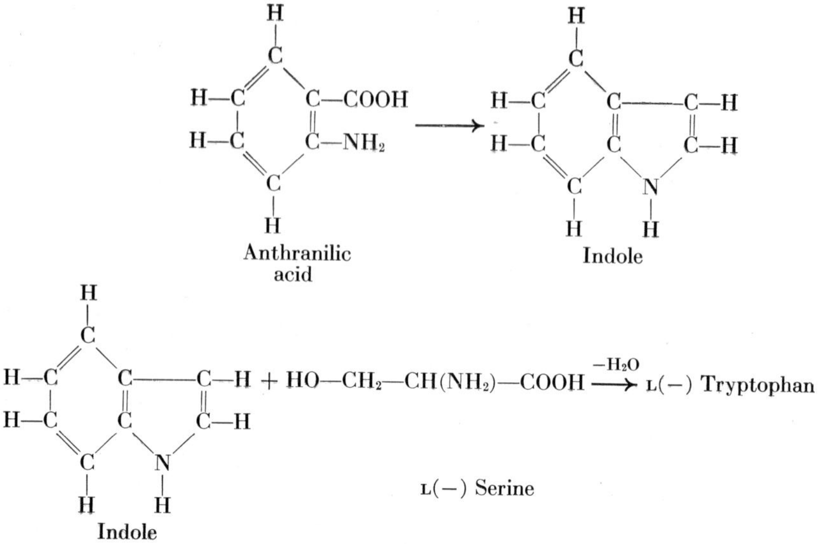

Anthranilic acid

Indole

Indole + HO—CH$_2$—CH(NH$_2$)—COOH $\xrightarrow{-H_2O}$ L(−) Tryptophan

L(−) Serine

Fig. 62. Tryptophan synthesis in *Neurospora*. The numbers designate the genes controlling the various steps. (From Horowitz, Bonner, Mitchell, Tatum, and Beadle: American Naturalist, *79:* 304.)

glutamic acid is, in all probability, an intermediate product was strengthened by the observation that proline and ammonium salts gave rise to glutamine. The scheme proposed, then, is as follows:

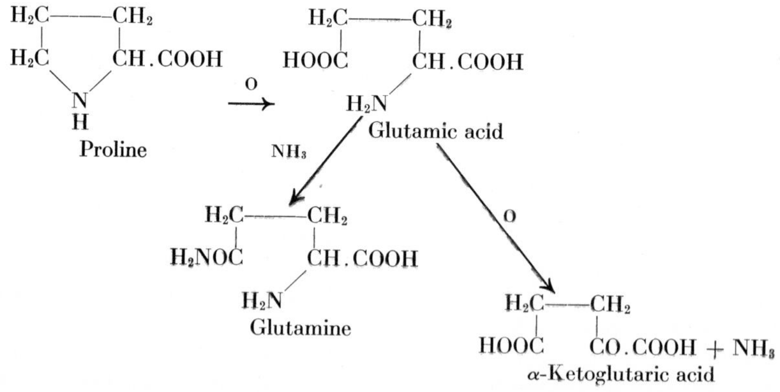

Proline

Glutamic acid

Glutamine

α-Ketoglutaric acid

Schoenheimer fed proline (labelled with deuterium and N^{15}) to rats and isolated various amino acids from the carcass and organ proteins. He found deuterium as well as N^{15} in the glutamic acid isolated. The isolated ornithine contained deuterium and N^{15} in the α- and δ-amino groups. Hydroxyproline also showed an appreciable isotopic concentration.

This—and other experiments—has led to the following possible scheme (Fig. 63):

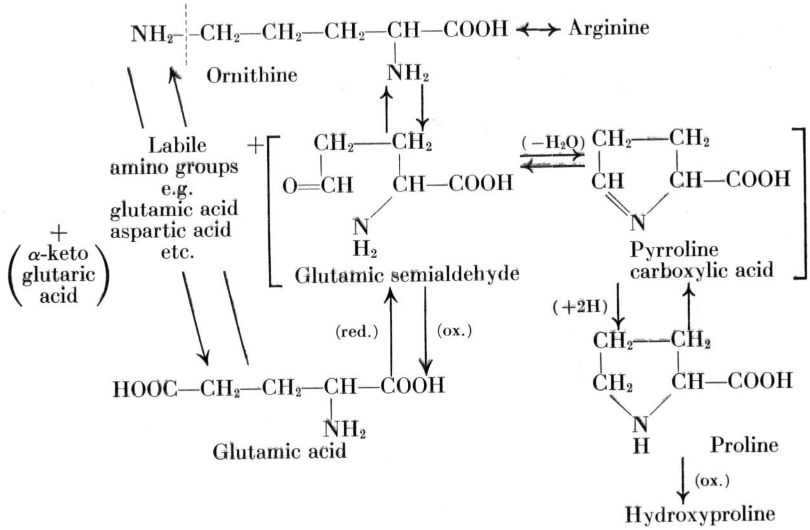

Fig. 63. Metabolic interconversions of 5-carbon amino acids. Hypothetical intermediates are enclosed in brackets. (From Stetten: J. Biol. Chem., *189:* 499, 1951.)

The first step in the breakdown of proline is represented as a dehydrogenation process—similar, in general, to the dehydrogenation of α-amino acids—giving pyrroline carboxylic acid, which yields glutamic semialdehyde upon hydrolysis. The latter substance, under combined reduction and amination, yields ornithine, whereas oxidation of the semialdehyde results in the formation of glutamic acid.

The method of conversion of proline to glutamic acid just described has been confirmed by treating proline with a washed residue of rabbit kidney or liver homogenates, to which ATP, magnesium ions, and inorganic phosphate were added. This homogenate carries the oxidation ultimately to carbon dioxide, water, and ammonia.

Very little is known about the metabolism of hydroxyproline. Lewis finds that whereas the nitrogen of proline is excreted mainly as extra urea nitrogen, only small amounts of extra urea nitrogen are excreted after the administration of hydroxyproline.

Aspartic and Glutamic Acids.   These two dicarboxylic acids can be removed from the hydrolytic products of casein without affecting the growth-promoting properties of the residue. They are probably dispensable amino acids.

Aspartic and glutamic acids have the power of depositing glycogen in the liver, suggesting that the pathway for oxidation is similar to that for carbohydrates. According to Krebs, glutamic acid is of special importance in the metabolism of nervous tissue. Gray cortex and retina utilize ammonia provided glutamic acid is present. Apparently, glutamine is formed. It is claimed that no other amino acid acts in this same way.

By using pigeon liver, it has been discovered that glutamine is also formed from glutamate and ammonia. ATP is required for this. Liberation of inorganic phosphate from ATP parallels the rate of glutamine synthesis.

It is known that α-ketoglutaric acid is readily converted into glutamic acid in vivo. Using radioactive carbon as carbon dioxide, Evans and Slotin have shown that pyruvic acid and carbon dioxide, in the presence of pigeon liver, combine to form α-ketoglutaric acid. Carbon dioxide, then, is used in the synthesis of glutamic acid in the body.

Glutamic acid participates in many biological reactions. It furnishes the carbon skeleton of proline, hydroxyproline, serine, glycine, cysteine, cystine and arginine. It also furnishes the nitrogen for alanine and aspartic acid.

It can now be understood why, in Schoenheimer's experiments, glutamic acid always showed the greatest activity in terms of N^{15} uptake when a labelled amino acid was fed.

Histidine.   This amino acid belongs to the list of essential amino acids, although the corresponding hydroxy and ketonic acids can replace it in the diet (Harrow and Sherwin). Histidine is needed for the growth of young rats and for the maintenance of adult animals (Albanese). The removal of histidine from a diet in which amino acids were the only source of nitrogen caused the rats to lose weight and to show a reduced hemoglobin content and plasma protein production.

As showing how poorly the D(unnatural)-histidine is utilized, it has been found that within nine hours after administration of the DL-amino acid to humans, a total excess of urinary histidine is excreted which practically equals the amount of D- component ingested.

With regard to the oxidation of the imidazole ring itself, it is believed that the enzyme histidase, present in liver, may be involved in such a process. Edlbacher incubated histidine with an aqueous liver extract (from which he later obtained histidase) and isolated ammonia and glutamic acid from the products.

Histamine has already been referred to in connection with putrefaction. There is, however, an enzyme in the kidney and intestines, histidine decarboxylase, which can also change histidine into histamine, the latter being then stored very largely in the lungs. An enzyme, histaminase, may, under certain conditions, destroy histamine.

An insight into the activity of certain groups within the molecule is afforded by the work of Schoenheimer and his associates on isotopic histidine. Histidine containing N^{15} was recovered from the carcass protein of rats fed ammonia containing N^{15}. The isotopic histidine (N^{15}, shown as $\overset{*}{N}$) was converted to its imidazolelactic acid by means of nitrous acid. The derivative so formed contained normal nitrogen; the isotope in the histidine must have resided in the α-amino group:

Three histidine compounds are found in the body: ergothioneine, which is found in the blood; carnosine, a dipeptide of histidine and β-alanine, and anserine, a methyl derivative of carnosine (Chap. 21), are found in muscle. Though chemically related, their metabolic relationships await experimental evidence.

Arginine.   Rose placed arginine among the indispensable amino acids, but with certain reservations: he found that arginine can be synthesized by the animal organism, but not at a sufficiently rapid rate to meet the demands of normal growth. The exclusion of arginine from the diet caused a decrease in the growth rate to about three-fourths of the normal value.

This work by Rose was with rats. Elvehjem, Almquist, and their coworkers, using the chick, found that arginine is necessary for rapid growth. Apparently, the chick is not able to synthesize sufficient arginine to maintain body weight. Neither ornithine nor ornithine plus urea was able to replace arginine in the diet.

The role of arginine in the synthesis of urea has already been described (p. 250).

Lysine.   In the diet, lysine is indispensable. Among the distinctive features of the metabolism of lysine are the following: replacement of the α-amino group by a keto or hydroxyl group or by an acetyl group makes it nonutilizable for growth; it is not involved in reversible deamination-reamination reactions; neither the L- nor the D- form is attacked by the respective amino acid oxidase; and it is not involved in the transaminase reaction.

An important contribution to the metabolism of lysine has been made by Borsook and his associates. Using C^{14} as a tracer, the amino acid was synthesized with the isotope in the ϵ position, and resolved into the L- and D-isomers. They find that guinea-pig liver homogenate converts L-lysine into α-aminoadipic acid (* is the position of the labeled carbon):

$$\overset{*}{C}H_2.CH_2.CH_2.CH_2.CH.COOH \longrightarrow \overset{*}{C}OOH.CH_2.CH_2.CH_2.CH.COOH$$
$$\quad|\qquad\qquad\qquad\qquad|\qquad\qquad\qquad\qquad\qquad\qquad\qquad\qquad|$$
$$\quad NH_2\qquad\qquad\qquad NH_2\qquad\qquad\qquad\qquad\qquad\qquad NH_2$$

This is in line with the hypothesis that before the α-amino group of lysine is acted upon by animal tissue enzymes, the ϵ-amino group must be masked or removed. Furthermore, it explains also why the α-amino group in lysine does not participate in reversible transamination reactions in vivo; it must presumably be first transformed into α-aminoadipic acid before the transfer of the α-amino group becomes possible.

In support of this hypothesis, guinea-pig liver homogenate oxidatively deaminizes α-aminoadipic acid to α-ketoadipic acid:

$$\overset{*}{C}OOH.CH_2.CH_2.CH_2.CO.COOH$$

and the latter is oxidatively decarboxylated to glutaric acid:

$$\overset{*}{C}OOH.CH_2.CH_2.CH_2.\overset{*}{C}OOH$$

Of interest, too, is the finding that α-aminoadipic acid can replace L-lysine in a *Neurospora* mutant requiring lysine for growth.

For the metabolism of creatine and creatinine, see Chap. 21.

REFERENCES

Recent advances are summarized in the Ann. Rev. Biochem., *19:* 235, 1950 (*Swanson and Clark*); *20:* 209, 1951 (*Borsook and Deasy*); *21:* 301, 1952 (*Tarver*); *22:* 233, 1953 (*Christensen*).

In connection with the concept of the dynamic state of body proteins, see *Schoenheimer:* The Dynamic State of Body Constituents, 1942; *Borsook:* Physiol. Rev., *30:* 206, 1950; *San Pietro and Rittenberg:* J. Biol. Chem., *201:* 445, 457, 1953.

The various aspects of the formation of tissue protein and the synthesis of peptide bonds are discussed in the following: *Borsook and Dubnoff:* J. Biol. Chem., *132:* 307, 1940 (free energy); *Cohen and McGilvery:* Ibid., *169:* 119, 1947 (synthesis of hippuric and *p*-amino hippuric acids); *Snoke and Bloch:* Ibid., *199:* 407, 1952 (synthesis of glutathione); *Hanes, Hird, and Isherwood:* Biochem. J., *51:* 25, 1952 ("transpeptidation"); *Kinoshita and Ball:* J. Biol. Chem., *200:* 609, 1953 ("transpeptidation"); *Johnston, Mycek, and Fruton:* Ibid., *187:* 205, 1950 ("transpeptidation"); *Peterson and Greenberg:* Ibid., *194:* 359, 1952; *Kitt and Greenberg:* Ibid., *194:* 377, 1952 (use of cytoplasmic particles); *Canellakis and Tarver:* Arch. Biochem., *42:* 387, 1953.

Several good summaries will be found in the monograph on the biogenesis of proteins (2nd International Congress of Biochemistry, Paris, 1952); these include articles by Fruton, Bloch, Borsook, and Haurowitz.

Still other individual papers are *Campbell and Work:* Biochem. J., *52:* 217, 1952 (uptake of amino acids by mammary gland); *Steinberg and Anfinsen:* J. Biol. Chem., *199:* 25, 1952; *Peters:* Ibid., *200:* 461, 1953 (intermediates in protein synthesis); *Fox and Pettinga:* Arch. Biochem., *25:* 13, 21, 1950 (influence of papain); *Koshland, Jr.:* J. Am. Chem. Soc., *73:* 4103, 1951 (kinetics of peptide bond formation); *Borsook, Deasy, Haagen-Smit, Keighley, and Lowy:* J. Biol. Chem., *196:* 669, 1952 (incorporation of labelled amino acids into proteins); *Hanes, Hird, and Isherwood:* Nature, *166:* 288, 1950 (enzymic reactions involving glutathione); *Black and Gray:* J. Am. Chem. Soc., *75:* 2271, 1953.

Papers dealing with oxidative deamination are *Krebs:* Biochem. J., *29:* 1620, 1935; *Blaschko and Hawkins:* Biochem. J., *52:* 306, 1952 (D-amino acid oxidase);

Green: J. Biol. Chem., *155:* 421, 1944; *161:* 583, 1945; *Thayer and Horowitz:* Ibid., *192:* 755, 1951 (L-amino acid oxidase).

For the "transaminase" reaction, see *Cammarata and Cohen:* J. Biol. Chem., *187:* 439, 1950; *Gunsalus:* Federation Proceedings, *9:* 558, 1950; *Metzler and Snell:* J. Am. Chem. Soc., *74:* 979, 1952; *Holden, Wildman, and Snell:* J. Biol. Chem., *191:* 559, 1951; *Baddiley:* Nature, *170:* 711, 1952; *Rowsell:* Ibid., *168:* 104, 1951; *Meister and Tice:* J. Biol. Chem., *187:* 173, 1950.

In connection with the formation of urea, the original paper by *Krebs and Henseleit* may be found in the German periodical Zeitchschrift. f. Physiol. Chemie, *210:* 33, 1932. Further papers are by *Cohen and Grisolia:* J. Biol. Chem., *198:* 561, 1952; *182:* 747, 1950; *191:* 189, 1951; *Ratner and Petrack:* Ibid., *191:* 693, 1951; *200:* 175, 1953; *Krebs* in Sumner and Myrback's The Enzymes, 1952, Vol. 2. Part 2; *Hirs and Rittenberg:* J. Biol. Chem., *186:* 429, 1950.

Glycine and Serine. Wood: Harvey Lectures, 1949–50, p. 127; *Rittenberg:* Ibid., 1948–49, p. 204; *Sakami:* J. Biol. Chem., *176:* 905, 995, 1948; *179:* 495, 1949; *Winnick, Morning-Claesson, and Greenberg:* Ibid., *175:* 127, 1948; *Sprinson:* Ibid., *178:* 529, 1949; *Kruhoffer:* Biochem. J., *48:* 604, 1951; *Arnstein:* Ibid., *49:* 439, 1951 (metabolism of D- and L-serine); *Siekevitz and Greenberg:* J. Biol. Chem., *186:* 275, 1950 (formation of formates from methyl groups); *Nardi:* Science, *117:* 160, 1953 (glycine to serine).

Threonine. Meltzer and Sprinson: J. Biol. Chem., *197:* 461, 1952; *Lien and Greenberg:* Ibid., *200:* 367, 1953; *Elliot and Neuberger:* Biochem. J., *46:* 207, 1950; *Nakada and Weinhouse:* Arch. Biochem., *42:* 257, 1953.

Leucine and Isoleucine. Zabin and Bloch: J. Biol. Chem., *185:* 139, 1950; *Coon, Abrahamson, and Greene:* Ibid., *195:* 805, 1952; *199:* 75, 1952; *Umbarger and Adelberg:* Ibid., *192:* 883, 1951 (isoleucine); *Meister and White:* Ibid., *191:* 211, 1951.

Phenylalanine (p.) and Tyrosine (t.). Schepartz and Gurin: J. Biol. Chem., *180:* 663, 1949; *193:* 293, 1951 (metabolism of p.); *Ravdin and Crandell:* Ibid., *189:* 137, 1951 (conversion of homogentisic acid); *Lerner:* Ibid., *181:* 281, 1949 (metabolism of p. and t.); *Gurin and Delluva:* Ibid., *170:* 545, 1947 (p. to epinephrine); Nutr. Rev., *10:* 92, 117, 1952 (oxidation of t.); Ibid., *10:* 212, 1952 (p. to t.); *Knox and LeMay-Knox:* Biochem. J., *49:* 686, 1951 (t. to acetoacetate); *La Du and Greenberg:* J. Biol. Chem., *190:* 245, 1951 (t. oxidation system of liver); *Udenfriend and Cooper:* Ibid., *194:* 503, 1952 (p. to t.); *La Du and Greenberg:* Science, *117:* 111, 193 (ascorbic acid and oxidation of t.); *Gilvarg and Bloch:* J. Biol. Chem., *199:* 689, 1952 (glucose and synthesis of p. and t.); *Woods:* Borden's Rev. Nutr. Research, *10:* No. 7, 1949 (vitamin C and aromatic amino acids); *Mauser:* J. Am. Med. Assoc., *146:* 815, 1951 (alkaptonuria); Nutr. Rev., *10:* 263, 1952 (alkaptonuria); *Cowie:* Lancet, Feb. 3, 1951, p. 272 (phenylketonuria); *Prescott, Borek, Brecher, and Waelsch:* J. Biol. Chem., *181:* 273, 1949 (phenylketonuria); *Lerner and Fitzpatrick:* Physiol. Rev., *30:* 91, 1950; *Fitzpatrick, Becker, Lerner, and Montgomery:* Science, *112:* 223, 1950 (tyrosinase); *Mason and Wright:* J. Biol. Chem., *180:* 235, 1949 (chemistry of melanin).

Cystine and Methionine. Du Vigneaud: A Trail of Research in Sulfur Chemistry and Metabolism, 1952; *Stekol, Weiss, and Weiss:* J. Am. Chem. Chem., *185:* 271, 1950; *Rachelle, Reed, Kidway, Ferger, and Du Vigneaud:* Ibid., *185:* 817, 1950 (cystathionine to cysteine); *Cantoni:* J. Biol. Chem., *189:* 745, 1951; J. Am. Chem. Soc., *74:* 2942, 1951; Federation Proc., *11:* 399, 1952; Nutr. Rev., *10:* 113, 1952 (pyridoxal phosphate as co-factor); *Dent and Rose:* Quarterly J. Medicine, July, 1951, p. 205 (cystinuria); *Sakami:* J. Biol. Chem., *187:* 369, 1950: Ibid., *193:* 199, 1951 ("formate"); *Sakami and Welch:* Ibid., *187:* 379, 1950.

Tryptophan (t.). Dalgliesh: Quart. Rev. (London Chem. Soc.), *5:* 227, 1951; Nutr. Rev., *8:* 85, 1950 (t. to niacin); *Partridge, Bonner, and Yanofsky:* J. Biol. Chem., *194:* 269, 1952 (t. and niacin in *Neurospora*); *Sandi and Greenberg:* Arch. Biochem., *25:* 323, 1950 (intermediate metabolism of t.); *Mehler and Knox:* J. Biol. Chem., *187:* 431, 1950 (t. to kynurenine); *Dalgliesh:* Biochem. J., *52:* 3, 1952 (pyridoxin and t. metabolism); *Dalgliesh, Knox, and Neuberger:* Nature, *168:* 20, 1951 (metabolism of t.).

Proline (p.) and Hydroxyproline. Sallach, Koeppe, and Rose: J. Am. Chem. Soc., *73:* 1500, 1951 (glutamic to p.); *Vogel and Davis:* Ibid., *74:* 109, 1952 (intermediates in biosynthesis of p.).

Histidine (h.). Levy and Coon: J. Biol. Chem., *192:* 807, 1951 (role of formate in biosynthesis of h.); *Abraims and Borsook:* Ibid., *198:* 205, 1952 (h. to glutamic acid); *Mann and Leone:* Biochem. J., *53:* 140, 1950 (ergothioneine); *Heath, Rimington and Searle:* Ibid., *50:* 530, 1952 (ergothioneine); *Mehler and Tabor:* J. Biol. Chem., *201:* 775, 1953.

Lysine (l.). Clark and Rittenberg: J. Biol. Chem., *189:* 521, 1951 (l. not involved in transaminase reaction); *Davis:* Nature, *169:* 533, 1952 (diaminopimelic acid and l.).

Some miscellaneous, but significant papers to be added to the list are: *Shemin and Russell:* J. Am. Chem. Soc., *75:* 4873, 1953 (δ-aminolevulinic acid in the biosynthesis of porphyrins); *Ratner, Petrack, and Rochovansky:* J. Biol. Chem., *204:* 95, 1953 (arginosuccinic acid and the biosynthesis of urea); *Meister:* Ibid., *200:* 571, 1953 (transamination-deamidation reactions of glutamine and asparagine); *Awarpa and Wingo:* Ibid., *203:* 189, 1953 (cysteine $\longrightarrow$ taurine); *Snoke, Yanari, and Bloch:* Ibid., *201:* 573, 1953 (synthesis of glutathione from γ-glutamylcysteine).

Chapter 15   *Metabolism of Nucleoproteins*

THE METABOLISM of nucleoproteins is really the metabolism of nucleic acids, for it is assumed, for the time being at least, that the protein portion of the nucleoproteins is metabolized in the usual way (see preceding chapter).

In the digestive tract, nucleic acids are acted upon by nucleases, nucleotidases and nucleosidases—found in pancreatic and intestinal juices—to yield phosphoric acid, sugars and purines and/or pyrimidines. The fate of these substances in the body will be taken up presently.

Partial hydrolysis of nucleic acids yields nucleotides (base–sugar–phosphoric acid) and nucleosides (base-sugar).

The enzymes which degrade nucleic acids are generally called *nucleolytic* enzymes. They are classified as follows:

(*a*) *Nucleodepolymerases* do not liberate free phosphate but hydrolyze the nucleic acid to the mononucleotide stage (e.g., ribonuclease, desoxyribonuclease).

(*b*) *Nucleophosphatases* liberate phosphate (e.g., alkaline phosphatase).

(*c*) *Nucleosidases* liberate a free base (e.g., nucleoside phosphorylase splits a nucleoside into the base and the sugar).

(*d*) *Nucleodeaminases* liberate free ammonia, thereby deaminating the base (e.g., adenylic acid deaminase liberates ammonia when it acts on adenylic acid to form inosinic acid).

It may be well to recall that of the two classes of nucleic acids, pentose and desoxypentose nucleic acids (PNA and DNA), both contain the purines adenine and guanine and the pyrimidine cytosine. The sugar constituent is ribose in PNA and 2-desoxyribose in DNA. The pyrimidine uracil is present only in PNA, and thymine is found only in DNA.

Using radioactive phosphorus, it can be shown that the isotope is rapidly incorporated in nucleic acids. In terms of "renewal" or "turnover" of the phosphorus which has been incorporated, liver and kidney show a low rate of renewal of their DNA, but bone marrow and the thymus gland show a high rate.

PENTOSE METABOLISM

It seems hardly probable, from the knowledge we possess, that appreciable use of any ingested pentoses is made for their incorporation into nucleic acids. More and more evidence is being presented to indicate that the origin of ribose and desoxyribose is to be found in a six-carbon sugar and, more specifically, in glucose itself. Enzymes have been isolated which are able to convert glucose into pentoses. These reactions may also represent an alternate pathway for carbohydrate oxidation in some tissues.

272

Experimental evidence points to the following series of reactions:

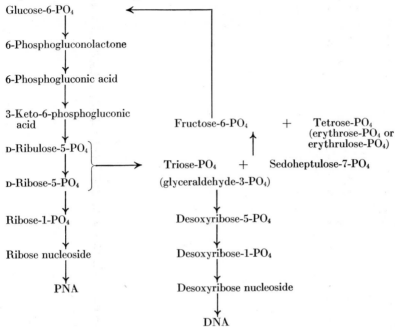

The formulas for several of the compounds which have been referred to are now given:

COOH	COOH	H_2C-OH
H—C—OH	H—C—OH	C=O
HO—C—H	C=O	H—C—OH
H—C—OH	H—C—OH	H—C—OH
H—C—OH	H—C—OH	$H_2C-OPO_3H_2$
$H_2C-OPO_3H_2$	$H_2C-OPO_3H_2$	
6-Phosphogluconic acid	3-Keto-6-phos-phogluconic acid	Ribulose-5-phos-phoric acid

CH_2OH	H—C=O	H—C=O	CH_2OH
C=O	H—C—OH	H—C—OH	C=O
$(CHOH)_4$	H—C—OH	H—C—OH	H—C—OH
$H_2C-OPO_3H_2$	H—C—OH	CH_2OH	CH_2OH
	$H_2C-OPO_3H_2$		
Sedoheptulose-7-phosphoric acid	Ribose-5-phos-phoric acid	Erythrose	Erythrulose

METABOLISM OF NUCLEOTIDES

These include the adenine nucleotides, ATP, ADP and AMP, and the coenzymes DPN and TPN. Little is known about the metabolism of coenzyme A.

A crude preparation of myosin from muscle (Chap. 21) will split ATP to give adenylic acid (AMP) and two mols of inorganic phosphate:

$$\text{ATP} + 2H_2O \longrightarrow \text{AMP} + 2PO_4^{\equiv}$$

However, on further purification, the myosin splits merely the terminal phosphate:

$$\text{ATP} + H_2O \longrightarrow \text{ADP} + PO_4^{\equiv} \qquad \text{(A)}$$

In addition to the enzyme adenosine triphosphatase, responsible for reaction (A), crude extracts also contain another enzyme, myokinase, which is responsible for the formation of adenylic acid and ATP from two molecules of ADP:

$$2\text{ADP} \longrightarrow \text{AMP} + \text{ATP}$$

Some believe that pure myosin is identical with adenosine triphosphatase, ATP-ase, though the question has not yet been settled.

The relationship of ATP to phosphocreatine may be recalled:

$$\text{Phosphocreatine} + \text{ADP} \rightleftarrows \text{Creatine} + \text{ATP}$$

and, also, ATP to phosphoarginine, found in invertebrate muscle:

$$\text{Phosphoarginine} + \text{ADP} \rightleftarrows \text{Arginine} + \text{ATP}$$

ATP may also be a source for DPN, though the enzyme for such a conversion has so far been found only in yeast, and the intermediary, nicotinamide mononucleotide (NMN), has yet to be isolated from natural sources:

$$\text{ATP} + \text{NMN} \longrightarrow \text{DPN} + \text{Pyrophosphate}$$

The liver is capable of forming pyrophosphate, and it is therefore believed that this reaction, as well as the enzyme needed, may be present in this tissue.

Table 31 presents the concentrations of DPN and TPN in various tissues.

Table 31   CONCENTRATION OF DPN AND TPN FROM VARIOUS
SOURCES
(From Schenk in Sumner and Myrback's The Enzymes, 1952, Vol. 2, Part I, p. 255.)

Material	DPN	TPN
	(μg. per gm. fresh weight)	
Brewer's yeast	1000–1500	<10
Baker's yeast	1000–1500	<10
Muscle, striated (rabbit)	>600	
Liver (rat)	600–1200	30
Kidney (rat)	400–1000	40
Muscle (rat)	300–600	80
(human)	400	
Liver (cat)	430	
Thigh (cat)	250	
Oxyntic cells, stomach (cat)	2000	
Retina (cattle)	1700–4100	
Erythrocytes (human)	60–90	
(horse)	100	>12
(rat)	100	40
Lobster (Homarus vulgaris; tail)	450	
Chilomonas paramecium	650	
Pollen (Salix; Populus)	700–1000	

METABOLISM OF NUCLEOSIDES

The following is a scheme for the probable metabolic pathways insofar as enzymes involved are known to exist:

NUCLEOTIDES	NUCLEOSIDES	BASE

```
Adenylic acid  ——→ Adenosine ——→ Adenine
      |               | (A)       (B)   |
      ↓               ↓          ——→     ↓
Inosinic acid  ——→ Inosine     Hypoxanthine
                                         | (C)
                                         ↓        (D)
Xanthylic acid ——→ Xanthosine ——→ Xanthine ——→ Uric acid
      ↑               ↑            ↑   O₂        |
                            (E)    (F)           | (G)
Guanylic acid  ——→ Guanosine ——→ Guanine      Allantoin
```

Several examples of the enzymes involved are: A = adenosine deaminase; B,E = nucleoside phosphorylase; C,D = xanthine oxidase; F = guanase; G = uricase.

Nucleosidases are present in liver, yeast and bacteria. The action of nucleoside phosphorylase is illustrated by:

$$\text{Ribose-1-purine} + PO_4^{=} \longrightarrow \text{Ribose-1-}PO_4 + \text{Purine}$$

Such enzymes are known for hypoxanthine, xanthine, guanine and adenosine nucleosides and for such pyrimidine nucleosides as those of thymine and uracil.

PURINE METABOLISM

In man the end product of purine metabolism is uric acid. Xanthine oxidase, an enzyme found in the liver, is capable of oxidizing hypoxanthine and xanthine to uric acid, which finds its way into the blood stream, and from which it is removed by the kidneys and excreted in the urine. In other species, such as the dog, uric acid is further oxidized to allantoin by the enzyme uricase and is excreted in this form. An exception is the Dalmatian,

```
HN—CO                        H₂N
 |   | H                      |        H
OC   C—N                     OC   OC—N
 |   ‖    CO   uricase         |    |     CO
 |   ‖   /    ——→             |    |    /
HN—C—N                       HN———C—N
     H                            H  H
  Uric acid                    Allantoin
```

which excretes both uric acid as well as allantoin. In birds and reptiles, uric acid is the principal end product of nitrogen metabolism, whereas in man it accounts for less nitrogen than that due to urea, ammonia or creatinine. This may be partly due to the fact that in man uric acid is metabolized to some extent by the liver, although this mechanism is unknown.

Studies with labelled precursors have identified the source of the N and C atoms of uric acid. These may be listed as follows:

C2 and 8 arise from "formate"
C4 arises from the carboxyl group of glycine
C5 arises from the alpha carbon of glycine

C6 arises from carbon dioxide

N1, 3 and 9 arise from the ammonia pool, and therefore via glutamic and aspartic acids

N7 arises from glycine

Since the beta carbon of serine forms "formate," it also is found in C2 and C8 of uric acid. The N of serine is converted to glycine, and so is found in N7 of uric acid.

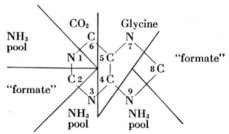

Similar results have been obtained for the various C and N atoms of guanine and hypoxanthine polynucleotides, and guanine and adenine in the chick and rat, suggesting that both nucleic acid purines, as well as uric acid, arise by the same mode of synthesis, and that the pattern of synthesis is the same for the rat, bird and man.

A number of studies have been carried out dealing with the incorporation of purines by nucleic acids. Adenine is incorporated almost entirely by the ribose nucleic acids, but not by DNA. However, where cells are growing rapidly—as in the liver of partially hepatectomized rats—adenine also finds its way into DNA. With cessation of tissue growth, incorporation of the base also stops. Brown is of the belief that DNA is rapidly synthesized during mitosis.

Neither guanine nor the nucleoside, guanosine, is utilized for the production of nucleic acid by the rat. However, it has been found that 2,6-diaminopurine is incorporated into the guanine in nucleic acid, and the suggestion has been made that it may be an intermediate in the reaction 2,6-diaminopurine ⟶ guanine derivative ⟶ nucleic acid.

Another possible intermediate in the biosynthesis of purines is the compound 4-amino-5-imidazole carboxamide

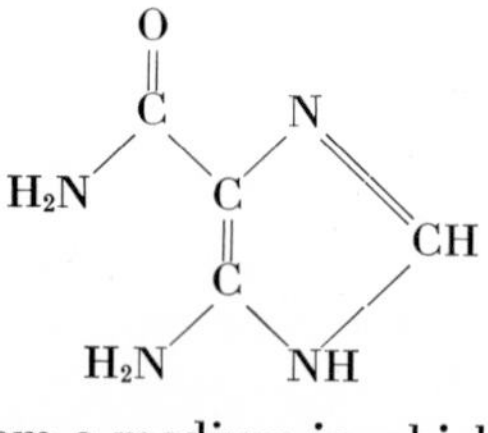

which was first isolated from a medium in which the growth of *E. coli* was inhibited by the presence of sulfanilamides. Pigeon liver homogenates can convert this substance to hypoxanthine, whereas intact pigeon liver metabolizes it to uric acid. Isotopic work has also shown that the C4 of this compound appears in adenine and guanine of nucleic acids, as well as in the allantoin of the urine.

PYRIMIDINE METABOLISM

In contrast to the purines, pyrimidines are not utilized by the rat for purposes of growth. However, when pyrimidine nucleosides are injected, they do appear in the nucleic acid of the body. The pyrimidine ring of the nucleoside cytidine, for example, appears in all the pyrimidines of both types of nucleic acids. This also means that the rat must be capable of converting ribose to desoxyribose when the former is attached to cytosine.

When labelled glycine and serine were fed to rats and the purines and pyrimides were isolated, some 90 per cent of the isotope was found in the methyl group of thymine.

The ureide carbon of uracil, it has been established, is furnished by CO_2; and the beta carbon of serine and the alpha carbon of glycine or formate are sources of the methyl group of thymine. Ammonia and glycine are sources of pyrimidine nitrogen.

A compound has been isolated from milk which appears to be related to pyrimidine metabolism. Its name is orotic acid and it is uracil-4-carboxylic

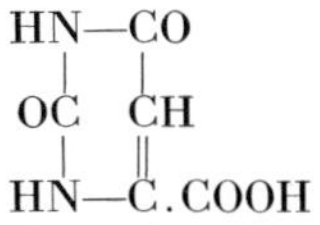

$$HN-CO$$
$$OC \quad CH$$
$$HN-C.COOH$$

Uracil-4-carboxylic acid
(orotic acid)

acid. It was found to stimulate the growth of certain pyrimidine-less mutants of *Neurospora*. In the rat, orotic acid is converted to polynucleotide pyrimidines. This was shown by labelling the orotic acid with N^{15} or with C^{14}. In neither case were any of the purines labelled. It has also been shown that ureidosuccinic acid can replace orotic acid in supporting the growth of certain bacteria. When labelled with C^{14} and injected, the pyrimidine

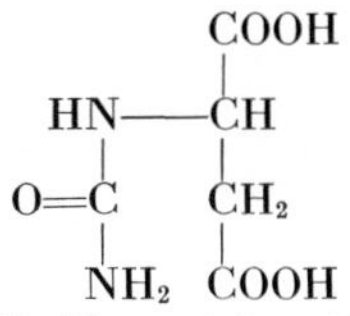

$$COOH$$
$$HN-CH$$
$$O=C \quad CH_2$$
$$NH_2 \quad COOH$$

Ureidosuccinic acid

components of the nucleic acids were found to be labelled. It would appear, then, that orotic acid and ureidosuccinic acid may both be precursors of the pyrimidines.

VITAMINS AND THE BIOSYNTHESIS OF PURINES AND PYRIMIDINES

It will be pointed out (Chap. 25) that the sulfonamide inhibition of bacterial growth can be overcome by *p*-aminobenzoic acid. Methionine can also reverse the inhibition of low concentrations of sulfanilamide. However, at higher concentrations of the inhibitor, purine bases are also needed in order to reverse the inhibition. It has been suggested that *p*-aminobenzoic acid functions in an enzyme system involved in purine metabolism. Some evidence is available to indicate that a formyl derivative of folic acid may be an intermediate in the reaction, whereby *p*-aminobenzoic acid, or a derivative, functions to incorporate a single carbon unit into 4-amino-5-imidazolecarboxamide (p. 276) to form the purine ring. It has also been shown that when the growth of *Lactobacillus casei* is inhibited by a folic acid deficiency, the synthesis of DNA is decreased, whereas that of PNA remains essentially the same.

Vitamin B_{12}, the antipernicious anemia factor of liver (Chap. 20), is also needed for bacterial growth in the presence of folic acid. It can be replaced by substances such as thymidine and the desoxyribosides of adenine, hypoxanthine and cytosine. Since thymine cannot replace thymidine, it is suggested that vitamin B_{12} may function as a coenzyme in the conversion of thymine to its riboside. Jukes has summarized these relationships for some bacteria as follows:

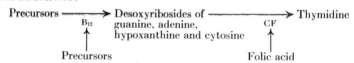

where CF is the citrovorum factor (Chap. 20), a compound with biological activity similar to that of folic acid.

REFERENCES

For reviews of purine and pyrimidine metabolism, see *Christman:* Physiol. Rev., *32:* 303, 1952; *Jordan:* Ann. Rev. Biochem., *21:* 209, 1952; *Brown:* Ibid., *22:* 141, 1953; *Davidson:* The Biochemistry of the Nucleic Acids (1950); *Kalckar:* Harvey Lectures (1949–50), p. 11; *Cohen, Doherty, and Volken* in McElroy and Glass's Phosphorus Metabolism (1952), vol. 2, p. 339; *Brown:* Federation Proceedings, *9:* 517, 1950.

Some individual papers are *Volken and Carter:* J. Am. Chem. Soc., *73:* 1519, 1951 (incorporation of P); *Racker:* J. Biol. Chem., *196:* 347, 1952 (pentose metabolism); *Shemin and Rittenberg:* Ibid., *167:* 875, 1947; *Buchanan, Sonne, and Delluva:* Ibid., *173:* 81, 1948 (biosynthesis of uric acid); *Stetten and Fox:* Ibid., *161:* 333, 1945; *Shive and Eaken:* J. Am. Chem. Soc., *69:* 725, 1947 (intermediate in synthesis of purines); *Hammarsten, Reichard, and Saluste:* J. Biol. Chem., *183:* 105, 1950; *Elwyn and Sprinson:* J. Am. Chem. Soc., *72:* 3317, 1950; *Heinrich and Wilson:* J. Biol. Chem., *186:* 447, 1950 (metabolism of pyrimidines); *Shive and Roberts:* Ibid., *162:* 463, 1946; *Kitay, McNutt, and Snell:* Ibid., *177:* 993, 1949.

Further references are *Bendich, Furst, and Brown:* J. Biol. Chem., *185:* 423, 1950

(role of 2,6-diaminopurine); *Furst and Brown:* Ibid., *191:* 239, 1951 (role of glycine); *Cohen:* Bacteriological Reviews, *15:* 131, 1951 (synthesis of nucleic acid by virus-infected bacteria); *Daly, Allfrey, and Mirsky:* J. Gen. Physiol., *36:* 173, 1952 (uptake of glycine by cell nuclei); *Bentley and Neuberger:* Biochem. J., *52:* 694, 1952 (mechanism of uricase action); *Gutman:* Bull. N. Y. Acad. Med., March, 1951, p. 144 (uric acid metabolism and gout); *Allfrey and Mirsky:* J. Gen. Physiol., *36:* 227, 1952 (desoxyribonuclease).

For enzymatic degradation of nucleic acids, see *Cohen, Doherty, and Volken,* in McElroy and Glass's Phosphorus Metabolism, 1952, vol. 2, p. 339.

Incorporation of P into Nuclei Acids. Volken and Carter: J. Am. Chem. Soc., *73:* 1519, 1951; *Kalckar, Dehlinger, and Mehler:* J. Biol. Chem., *154:* 275, 1944.

Pentose Metabolism. Cohen: J. Biol. Chem., *174:* 281, 1948; *188:* 501, 509, 1951; *189:* 617, 1951; *201:* 71, 1952; *Racker:* Ibid., *196:* 347, 1952; *Horecker, et al.:* Arch. Biochem., *29:* 232, 1950; J. Biol. Chem., *193:* 371, 383, 1951; *194:* 261, 1952; Federation Proceedings, *12:* 219, 1953.

Metabolism of Nucleotides. Kornberg: J. Biol. Chem., *176:* 1475, 1948; *Colowick,*

Kaplan, and Ciotti: Federation Proceedings, *10:* 174, 1951.

Biosynthesis of Purines and Pyrimidines. Kalckar: Harvey Lectures (1949–50), p. 11; *Buchanan and Wilson:* Federation Proceedings, *12:* 646, 1953; *Greenberg:* Ibid., *12:* 651, 1953; *Brown:* J. Biol. Chem., *183:* 251, 1950; *Reichard:* Ibid., *179:* 773, 1949; *Hammarsten and Reichard:* Acta Chem. Scand., *4:* 711, 1950; *Bendich, Furst, and Brown:* J. Biol. Chem., *185:* 423, 1950; *Hammarsten, Reichard, and Saluste:* Ibid., *183:* 105, 1950; *Elwyn and Sprinson:* J. Am. Chem. Soc., *72:* 3317, 1950; *Heinrich and Wilson:* J. Biol. Chem., *186:* 447, 1950; *Totter, Volken, and Carter:* J. Am. Chem. Soc., *73:* 1521, 1951.

4-Amino-5-Imidazole Carboxamide. Stetten and Fox: J. Biol. Chem., *161:* 333, 1945; *Shive and Eakin:* J. Am. Chem. Soc., *69:* 725, 1947; *Schulman, Buchanan, and Miller:* Federation Proceedings, *9:* 225, 1950; *Miller, Gurin, and Wilson:* Science, *112:* 654, 1950.

Effect of Vitamins. Shive: J. Cellular and Comparative Physiology, *38:* 203, 1951; *Shive, et al.:* J. Am. Chem. Soc., *69:* 725, 1947; *70:* 878, 1948; *Prusoff, Tepley, and King:* J. Biol. Chem., *176:* 1309, 1948; *Kitay, McNutt, and Snell:* Ibid., *177:* 993, 1949; *Wright, Skeggs, and Huff:* Ibid., *175:* 475, 1948; *Jukes, Broquist, and Stokstad:* Arch. Biochem., *26:* 157, 1950.

Sonne, Buchanan, and Delluva: J. Biol. Chem., *173:* 69, 81, 1948; *Shemin and Rittenberg:* Ibid., *167:* 875, 1947 (uric acid synthesis); *Gettler, Roll, Tinker, and Brown:* Ibid., *178:* 259, 1949 (metabolism of hypoxanthine and xanthine); Nutr. Rev. *7:* 116, 1949 (biosynthesis); *Brown, Roll, Plentl, and Cavalieri:* J. Biol. Chem., *172:* 469, 1948 (use of adenine for nucleic acid synthesis).

Chapter 16   *Photosynthesis*

THE ULTIMATE source of all energy sustaining life is the radiant energy of the sun. The energy of the sun's rays is captured by the 'green [pigment] of plants, the chlorophyll.' This energy cannot, as such, support life, for if it were essential, life would fail at night. Thus the energy is used to build up carbohydrate molecules from carbon dioxide and water, the oxygen being sent back into the atmosphere as O_2. In essence these carbohydrate molecules represent small parcels of energy, which can be stored and released by the cell according to needs. The 'unpacking' of these parcels is the reverse reaction, in which the carbohydrate molecule is united again with oxygen to form carbon dioxide and water. This process we call oxidation or combustion." (Szent-Györgyi.)

REACTIONS OF PHOTOSYNTHESIS

The fundamental reaction in this synthetic upbuilding is a photochemical one. Primarily it involves the combination of carbon dioxide and water, in the presence of light and the pigments in the chloroplast (chlorophyll *a*, chlorophyll *b*, carotene, and xanthophyll) to yield carbohydrate and oxygen. Closely associated with this reaction is the production of fats and oils and proteins (here inorganic nitrogen compounds are necessary). Still other products, the result of various syntheses within the plant, are given in Table 32.

For the synthesis of starch in the plant, the reactions usually given are

$$6CO_2 + 6H_2O \longrightarrow C_6H_{12}O_6 + 6O_2$$
$$XC_6H_{12}O_6 \longrightarrow (C_6H_{10}O_5)_x + XH_2O$$

That the carbon of carbon dioxide is utilized for starch synthesis can be shown by growing a green leaf in an atmosphere of radioactive $C^{14}O_2$. The starch is extracted from the leaf, hydrolyzed to glucose, and the latter degraded in such a manner that each of its carbon atoms will appear in compounds which can be analyzed for their radioactivity (see p. 216).

In this way it can be shown that all of the six carbon atoms of glucose (obtained from starch) from a leaf grown in $C^{14}O_2$ are derived from the carbon of carbon dioxide.

Using isotopic oxygen (O^{18}) as a tracer, it appears that the oxygen evolved in photosynthesis comes from the water and *not* from the CO_2. The oxygen in the CO_2 remains in the plant material.

Compounds Intermediate between CO_2 and the Sugars. For an understanding of the intermediate chemical reactions which take place during the photosynthetic reaction, use has been made of the fact that the green alga, *Chlorella*, is quite efficient in its ability to convert radiant energy to foodstuffs in the presence of CO_2.

By using radioactive $C^{14}O_2$, and by stopping the reaction at various intervals of time (heating the algal suspension), the compounds in the leaf can be studied with respect to their C^{14} content as they vary with time. The compounds are separated and identified by the use of paper chromatography and then eluted from the paper for an analysis of their C^{14} content.

Some of the results which have been obtained by means of such techniques are the following (Calvin and associates):

(*a*) Very short periods of illumination (5 seconds) result in the appearance of 87 per cent of the C^{14} in phosphoglyceric acid, 10 per cent in phospho-enol pyruvic acid, and 3 per cent in malic acid.

Table 32   SYNTHESIS OF ORGANIC COMPOUNDS IN GREEN PLANTS
(From Conant: Chemistry of Organic Compounds. By permission of The Macmillan Company, Publishers.)

Raw materials	Primary products	*The more important secondary substances*	
		(a) *Molecular weight less than 1000*	(b) *Materials of high molecular weight*
CO_2 H_2O Inorganic nitrogen compounds	Sunlight on chloroplast pigments → Sugars, Amino-acids → ↓↑ Reserve materials → Proteins, fats and oils Polysaccharides (*e.g.*, starch), hemicelluloses	Polyene pigments Aliphatic acids, alcohols Terpenes Sterols Waxes Phosphatides (*e.g.*, lecithin) Inositol Aromatic hydroxy acids Hydroxy compounds as glucosides (phenols, complex alcohols) Volatile aldehydes, alcohols, esters, ethers (in essential oils with terpenes) Alkaloids Pyrrole pigments Anthocyan pigments Nucleic acids	Cellulose Hemicelluloses, gums, pectins Resins Rubber Tannins Lignins

(*b*) Intermediate exposures of 15 to 60 seconds result in the labelling of all three compounds in (*a*), together with aspartic acid, alanine, serine, glycine, glycollic acid, hexosediphosphate, triosephosphates, sucrose and unidentified phosphorus compounds.

(*c*) Longer exposures result in the formation—in addition to those listed above—of succinic acid, fumaric acid, citric acid, glutamic acid, glucose, fructose, and a number of additional amino acids.

(*d*) When the plant is exposed to $C^{14}O_2$ after a period of illumination, 95 per cent of the labelled carbon is found in malic acid, succinic acid, fumaric acid, citric acid, glutamic acid, aspartic acid and alanine.

Taking into consideration that the first photosynthetic compound to appear in quantity is phosphoglyceric acid, and that several other compounds are also formed, though in lesser amounts, and assuming the formation of the phosphoglycerate from some 2-carbon compound by the addition of CO_2, Calvin has suggested the following scheme:

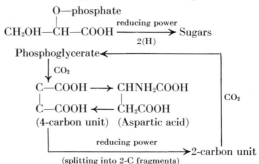

Part of the phosphoglyceric acid is believed to be reduced through the reversible reaction of glycolysis to give rise to triosephosphates, hexose-diphosphates and sucrose ("sugars" in the diagram). Another portion of the phosphoglyceric acid yields phospho-enol pyruvic acid—which then adds CO_2 to yield oxaloacetic acid, malic acid and aspartic acid.

According to this scheme, the photosynthetic reaction must continuously generate the 2-carbon compound, for the latter is necessary to form phosphoglyceric acid.

Heterotropic, nonphotosynthetic bacteria—organisms which cannot form protein and carbohydrate from inorganic nitrogen and carbon—can "fix" carbon dioxide; that is to say, the carbon dioxide can enter directly into a molecule in the course of synthesis.

That such synthetic reactions involve all forms of life, simple and complex, was made probable when it was shown that the synthesis of citric acid from oxaloacetic acid involved utilization of CO_2. Reactions involving radioactive CO_2 have confirmed this view.

CHLOROPHYLL

When seedlings are germinated and grown in the dark, a yellow-green pigment is present to which the name *protochlorophyll* has been given. Upon the illumination of such seedlings, the yellow-green pigment disappears and chlorophyll is formed.

In the chloroplasts we find four pigments in colloidal combination with complex substances; * two of them, chlorophylls *a* and *b* are green, and two, carotene and xanthophyll, are yellow. The chemistry of chlorophyll has engaged the attention of chemists for one hundred years. Berzelius, in 1839, attempted to isolate it from leaves, but his treatment was too drastic, and he obtained decomposition products. We owe to Willstätter primarily our knowledge of the substance. He not only isolated chlorophyll in the pure state, but contributed much toward assigning it its present structure.

Chlorophyll consists of two modifications, an *a* and a *b*. In a mixture of petroleum ether and methyl alcohol, component *a* is found in the former and component *b* in the latter. An analysis of these two substances yields the following:

Chlorophyll *a*, $C_{55}H_{72}N_4O_5Mg$

Chlorophyll *b*, $C_{55}H_{70}N_4O_6Mg$

* The chlorophyll is present in some combination with protein.

Mild hydrolysis produces phytol, $C_{20}H_{39}OH$, an unsaturated alcohol, which constitutes about 30 per cent of the chlorophyll molecule. The *a* component also yields methyl alcohol. The residual molecule is known as chlorophyllin, and chlorophyll *a* itself may be regarded as an ester:

$$C_{32}H_{30}N_4OMg\begin{cases}COOCH_3\\COOC_{20}H_{39}\end{cases}$$

The magnesium can be removed from chlorophyll by means of oxalic acid, yielding pheophytin *a*:

$$C_{32}H_{32}N_4O\begin{cases}COOCH_3\\COOC_{20}H_{39}\end{cases}$$

Chlorophyll when heated with alkali first loses its ester groups, and then carbon dioxide. These various phyllin products lose their magnesium by treatment with oxalic acid, giving phytin products. Some of these relationships (and others) are shown as follows:

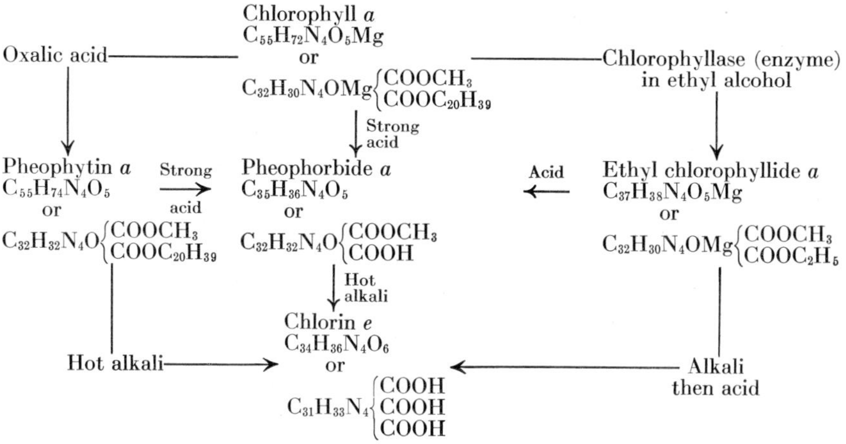

Reduction and oxidation of chlorophyll pigments yield pyrrole compounds (such as hemopyrrole), which suggests the pyrrole nature of chlorophyll itself. Incidentally, a similar series of pyrrole compounds is obtained from hemoglobin.

Drastic alkaline treatment of chlorophyll (and hemoglobin) yields porphyrins, which are red compounds with characteristic absorption spectra, and contain four pyrrole nuclei. Their structure as suggested by Küster is:

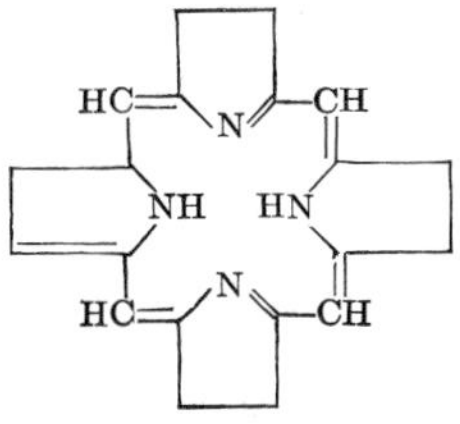

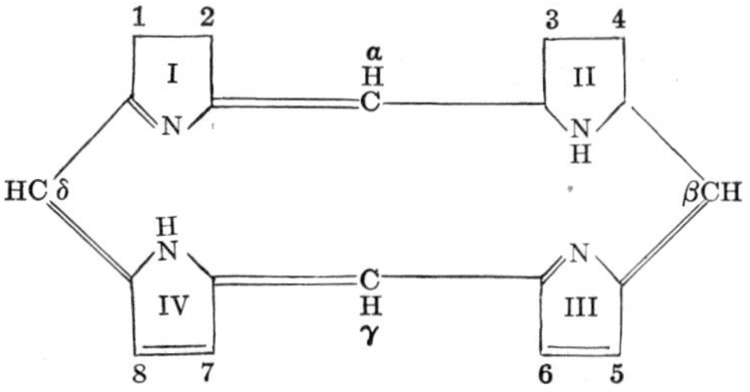

The porphin nucleus

The unsubstituted nucleus is known as *porphin*. The synthesis of a porphyrin, having the characteristic spectrum of the porphyrins, was first accomplished by Hans Fischer in 1926. The structure of chlorophyll *a* and *b* as proposed by Fischer and others, is as follows:

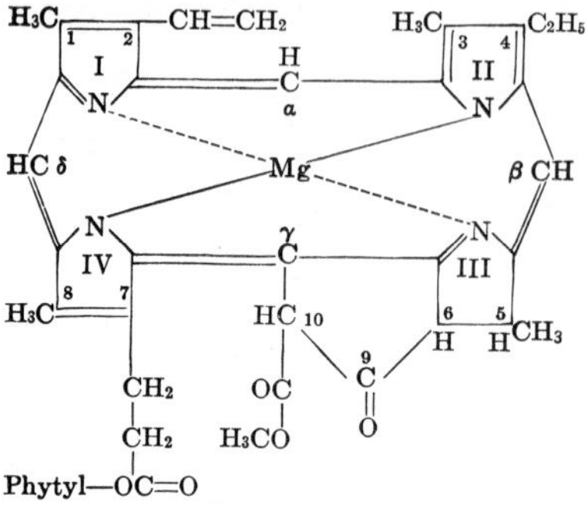

Chlorophyll *a*

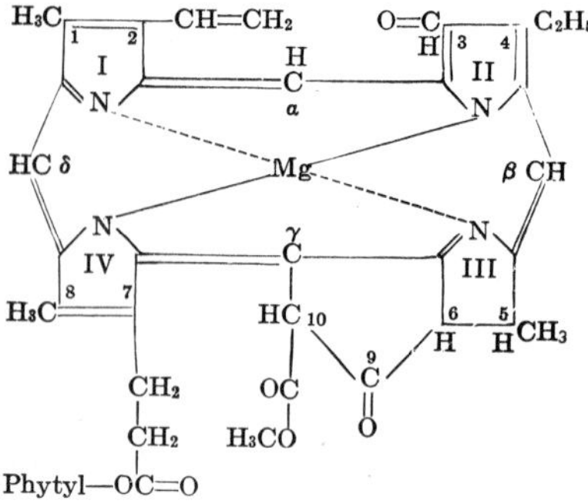

Chlorophyll *b*

CAROTENE AND XANTHOPHYLL

The constant association of these two yellow pigments with chlorophyll has suggested that they also play some part in the photosynthetic or in the respiratory process of plants. Carotenes, $C_{40}H_{56}$, are hydrocarbons whose structure is given on p. 347. They may be looked upon as the mother substances of vitamin A. Xanthophylls, $C_{40}H_{56}O_2$, are dihydroxy derivatives of carotene. It was supposed for a time that carotene and xanthophyll between them have something to do with the transport of oxygen, standing in a relationship comparable to hemoglobin and oxyhemoglobin. But unfortunately for this theory, no simple oxidation converts carotene to xanthophyll, and no simple reduction changes the latter back to the former. Nor is the evidence for their participation in the photosynthetic process any clearer.

THE ASSIMILATION OF NITROGEN BY THE PLANT

During the photosynthetic process, carbon and hydrogen are absorbed and ultimately utilized by the plant. The nitrogen is derived from various nitrogenous products in the soil.

Using isotopic nitrogen (N^{15}) in the form of ammonium chloride, it can be shown that when this is administered to rapidly growing plants, the isotope is present in various parts of the tissues. The nitrogen of the ammonia is rapidly incorporated into nitrogen of amides, amino acids and proteins.

Using isotopic nitrogen, the ability to fix or use molecular nitrogen—attributed from time to time to many biological agents—is in reality limited to a few organisms; among them are *Azotobacter vinelandii;* the blue-green alga, *Nostoc muscorum;* and the anaerobic bacterium, *Clostridium pastorianum.*

Exposing the green alga *Chlorella* to $C^{11}O_2$, and ultimately detecting the amino acids by paper chromatography (p. 26), those so identified correspond to the 3- and 4-carbon amino acids. It is believed that such 3-carbon amino acids as alanine, serine, and β-alanine have their origin in pyruvic acid, and the 4-carbon ones (such as aspartic acid) in oxaloacetic acid.

REFERENCES

For a review of the mechanism of photosynthesis, see *Stiles:* American Scientist, *41:* 66, 1953.

In the Harvey Lectures (1950–51), p. 218, *Calvin* discusses the path of carbon in photosynthesis. See also *Fager, Rosenberg, and Gaffron:* Federation Proceedings, *9:* 535, 1950 (intermediates); *Kamen:* Ibid., *9:* 543, 1950 (hydrogenase activity); *Lipmann, Ochoa, and Wood:* Ibid., *9:* 549, 1950; *Calvin:* Chem. Eng. News, *31:* 1622, 1953; *Brown and Frenkel:* Ann. Rev. Biochem., *22:* 423, 1953.

That the same mechanisms function in the fixation of CO_2 in animal tissues as in photosynthesis is maintained by *Ochoa and Vishniac:* Science, *115:* 297, 1952. See also *Benson and Calvin:* Ann. Rev. Plant Physiol., 1950, p. 25.

For a comparison of photosynthesis and respiration, see *Steward and Thompson;* Nature, *166:* 593, 1950.

For a discussion of the efficiency of photosynthesis, see *Burk, Hendricks, Korzenovsky, Schocken, and Warburg:* Science, *110:* 225, 1949; *Warburg and Burk:* Arch. Biochem., *25:* 410, 1950; *Ryerson:* Chem. Eng. News, *27:* 3560, 1949; *Calvin:* Chem. Eng. News, *31:* 1735, 1953; *Burk:* Federation Proceedings, *12:* 611, 1953.

Articles on the chemistry of chlorophyll are by *Hans Fischer:* Chem. Rev., *20:* 41, 1937; *Steele:* Chem. Rev., *20:* 1, 1937; *Armstrong:* J. Soc. Chem. Industry, Oct. 13, 1933; *Granick:* Chem. Eng. News, *31:* 748, 1953. See also Chap. 30 of *Bonner's* Plant Biochemistry (1950).

Granick: Harvey Lectures (1948–49), p. 220, discusses the structural and functional relationships between heme—part of the hemoglobin of blood—and chlorophyll.

For a commercial chromatographic production of carotene and chlorophyll, see *Shearon and Gee:* Ind. Eng. Chem., *41:* 218, 1949.

For the origin of amino acids in nature, see *Miller:* Science, *117:* 528, 1953.

Chapter 17 *Energy Metabolism*

THE ENERGY required by the living cell must be present in a form which the cell can use. There is energy needed for muscular contraction, for keeping the body warm, for transmission of nerve impulses, etc.; such energy must be convertible to the specific needs of the body.

The complete oxidation of a food to CO_2 and H_2O at the moment when its energy is needed would be a wasteful process. Actually, by a series of intermediary processes, the energy originally incorporated into chemical bonds in foods (chemical compounds) is transferred in a form which can be released when needed.

ATP, for example, stores in its terminal phosphate bond the energy originally present in the chemical bonds of carbohydrates, fats and proteins. When needed for specific cell functions, ATP can transfer its energy to systems which bring about muscular contraction (p. 206), the transmission of nerve impulses (Chap. 21), peptide synthesis, etc.

ATP, it should be emphasized at this point, is widely distributed; and it is constantly being built and rebuilt, largely during aerobic processes.

During the reactions involving metabolism, oxygen is consumed and most of the carbon and hydrogen are excreted as CO_2 and H_2O. Some of the carbon and hydrogen, as well as much of the nitrogen, is excreted as urea, uric acid, creatinine, etc. Elements such as sulfur and phosphorus are excreted in the form of inorganic ions, although some of the former are eliminated as "neutral" sulfur and "ethereal" sulfate (Chap. 22).

In any event, what should be stressed is that, except for nitrogen and sulfur, the elements which have been discussed can be oxidized as completely in the body as outside of it; and one result of such an oxidation is the production of heat—a very necessary result in so far as the activities of living matter are concerned.

It is no small tribute to the genius of Lavoisier that he connected his theory of oxidation with the general process of respiration in man.

THE TEMPERATURE OF THE BODY

The temperature of a normal person (measured by mouth) is in the neighborhood of 37° C. (98.6° F.).* This temperature varies imperceptibly, irrespective of weather. Not only is heat produced, but there must also be some heat-regulating mechanism whereby fluctuations in temperature are prevented.

Mammals and birds, the warm-blooded animals, show such constancy of temperature, irrespective of outside conditions. The reptiles, amphibia, and fishes, the cold-blooded animals, show temperature fluctuations de-

* The normal range of body temperature (measured by mouth) is between 96.7° and 99° F. The rectal temperature is about 97.2 to 99.5° F. Rectal temperature is the more reliable because oral temperature may vary; contact with cold air may lower it; hot drinks may raise it, etc.

pendent upon environmental conditions. Their heat-regulating mechanism is either less efficient, or, for more profound reasons, it may not be needed. Hibernating animals also show a temperature in accord with their surroundings; and during this period, their heat-regulating mechanism seems to function little.

The fact that the temperature of the body is 37° C. and that it remains so indefinitely (for all practical purposes) is a clear indication that heat is being produced. The *quantity* of such heat production can be measured, not by a thermometer, but by a calorimeter.

CALORIMETRY

Calorimeters are of two kinds: one measures the fuel value of coal or food, and the other measures the heat evolved by the body. We shall deal first with the former type.

The "Bomb" Calorimeter.   The principle of the "bomb" calorimeter of Berthelot is easily understood. The fuel (or food) is in a steel cylinder filled with oxygen. The reaction is started by a platinum wire heated by an electric current. The heat evolved in the reaction is communicated to a weighed quantity of water surrounding the cylinder. Without going into details, we can say that knowing the weight of the water and the increase in temperature, the heat evolved by the fuel (or food), measured in calories, can be readily calculated.

Heat is measured in calories. The *calorie* used in physics represents that amount of heat necessary to increase the temperature of 1 gm. of water 1° C. (from 15° to 16° C.). The calorie used in nutritional studies is the large *Calorie* (spelled with a capital *C*)—also written as kg. cal. and kcal.—representing the amount of heat necessary to increase the temperature of 1 kg. of water 1° C. The Calorie, then, is equivalent to 1000 small calories. We shall use the Calorie (C) exclusively.

Returning to our calorimeter, if the quantity of water is represented by 1 kg., and the increase in temperature is 1° C., the heat produced by the burning of the foodstuff would be 1 C(alorie). Similarly,

> 4 kg. of water raised 1° C. corresponds to 4 C.
>
> 1 kg. of water raised 4° C. corresponds to 4 C.
>
> 2 kg. of water raised 2° C. corresponds to 4 C.

The calorific value, then, is obtained by multiplying the weight of the water (in kilograms, in our case) by the increase in temperature (in °C.). In this way we arrive at the following average values:

> 1 gm. of carbohydrate when burned yields 4.1 C.
>
> 1 gm. of fat when burned yields 9.4 C.
>
> 1 gm. of protein when burned yields 5.6 C.

These are the values obtained when such foodstuffs are burned in the calorimeter. Of the three foodstuffs, the absorbed carbohydrates and fats can be burned as completely in the body as in the calorimeter; but this is not true of the protein. Here its nitrogen is not eliminated as such, but in the form of urea and several other nitrogenous products. Making due allowance for such incomplete combustion in the body, the fuel value of 1 gm. of protein, so far as the body is concerned, is nearer 4.1 C. Or, after considering the average degrees of digestibility, the figures are approximately,

> 1 gm. of carbohydrate yields 4 C.
>
> 1 gm. of fat yields 9 C.
>
> 1 gm. of protein yields 4 C.

The Animal Calorimeter.   This apparatus, developed by Atwater, Rosa, and Benedict, is adapted for measuring the heat evolved by an individual (*direct* calorimetry), and for measuring the oxygen intake and carbon dioxide and nitrogen output, from which the amount of protein, carbohydrate, and fat metabolized can be calculated; and these figures also supply data for calculating the heat produced (*indirect* calorimetry).

Several details of the calorimeter—known as a *respiration calorimeter* (see Fig. 64)—include a lighted and furnished room in which the individual (the subject) may remain in comparative comfort, with walls of metal and wood to prevent heat loss. In the room are pipes containing water—with the flow carefully regulated—which take up the heat given off by the body. The amount of heat can be calculated by knowing the temperature of the water as it enters the room, the temperature when it leaves it, and the rate of flow of the water.

Using a closed circuit (see Fig. 65), a measured amount of air is drawn in by a pump, and the eliminated carbon dioxide and water are absorbed and weighed. Measured quantities of oxygen are added when needed. Provision is also made for the collection of urine and feces, with the main object of determining the amount of nitrogen eliminated.

Oxygen.   How and under what conditions the oxygen of the air reaches the cells of the body via the blood have already been discussed (p. 174). Some abnormalities may be stressed at this point.

Anoxia (oxygen deficiency) may develop at times. For example, at high altitudes "mountain sickness" may result, owing to diminished oxygen tension in the air and hence in the alveolar air and blood stream.

A common clinical form of anoxia is observed in diseases of the respiratory tract, as in pneumonia, for example. Here there is an interference with oxygen absorption.

Another common decrease is seen in cases of anemia; owing to a diminished amount of hemoglobin, not so much oxygen can combine with the blood pigment as under normal conditions.

Poisoning due to carbon monoxide interferes with respiration, because of the preferential combining capacity of hemoglobin with carbon monoxide rather than with oxygen.

Certain drugs will cause methemoglobinemia. Such substances oxidize hemoglobin to methemoglobin, which cannot combine with oxygen. The extent of active respiration will depend upon the amount of hemoglobin which has not been changed.

The Respiratory Quotient.   For reasons which will become apparent as we proceed, the value of the respiratory quotient (R. Q.) must be known. By the R. Q. is meant the volume of carbon dioxide evolved divided by the volume of oxygen consumed.

When carbohydrates are oxidized, the reaction may be represented (using glucose as a type):

$$C_6H_{12}O_6 + 6O_2 \longrightarrow 6CO_2 + 6H_2O$$

$$\text{Here the R. Q.} = \frac{6CO_2}{6O_2} = 1$$

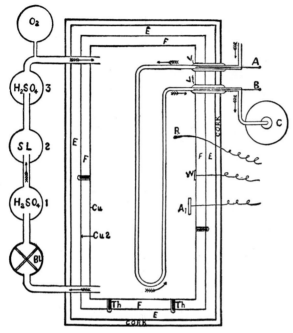

Fig. 64. Schematic diagram of the Atwater-Rosa-Benedict respiration calorimeter. (Lusk: Science of Nutrition.)

Ventilating System:
  O₂, Oxygen introduced as consumed by subject.
  3, H₂SO₄ to catch moisture given off by soda lime.
  2, Soda lime to remove CO₂.
  1, H₂SO₄ to remove moisture given off by patient.
  Bl, Blower to keep air in circulation.
Indirect Calorimetry:
  Increase in weight of H₂SO₄ (1) = water elimination of subject.
  Increase in weight of soda lime (2) + increase in weight of H₂SO₄ (3) = CO₂ elimination.
  Decrease in weight of oxygen tank = oxygen consumption of subject.
Heat-absorbing System:
  A, Thermometer to record temperature of ingoing water.
  B, Thermometer to record temperature of outgoing water.

V, Vacuum jacket.
C, Tank for weighing water which has passed through calorimeter each hour.
W, Thermometer for measuring temperature of wall.
A₁, Thermometer for measuring temperature of the air.
R, Rectal thermometer for measuring temperature of subject.
Direct Calorimetry:
  Average difference of temperatures of A and B × liters of water + (gm. water eliminated × 0.586) ± (change in temperature of wall × hydrothermal equivalent of box) ± (change of temperature of body × hydrothermal equivalent of body) = total calories produced.
Th, thermocouple; Cu, inner copper wall; Cu₂, outer copper wall; E, F, dead air spaces.

Fats contain less oxygen in their molecules than carbohydrates, and need, relatively, more oxygen from the outside for complete combustion:

$$C_{57}H_{104}O_6 + 80O_2 \longrightarrow 57CO_2 + 52H_2O$$
Triolein

$$R. Q. = \frac{57CO_2}{80O_2} = 0.71$$

Since the formula of a protein is unknown, and therefore an equation such as the above cannot be written, the R. Q. must be determined in an indirect way.

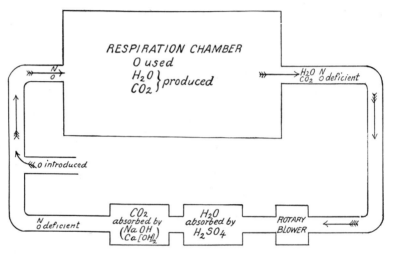

Fig. 65. Diagram of circulation of air through respiration apparatus. (Atwater and Benedict.)

According to Loewy, quoted by Lusk, the analysis of 100 gm. of meat protein gives the following figures (in grams):

	C	H	O	N	S
	52.38	7.27	22.68	16.65	1.02
of which is eliminated in the urine:	9.406	2.663	14.099	16.28	1.02
and in the feces:	1.47	0.212	0.889	0.37	
leaving for the respiratory process:	41.50	4.40	7.69		
deducting intramolecular water:		0.961	7.69		
leaving behind	41.50	3.439			

To oxidize 41.5 gm. of carbon and 3.439 gm. of hydrogen we require 138.18 gm. of oxygen and 152.17 gm. of carbon dioxide are produced.

The *weights* must now be converted into *volumes* in order to get the R. Q. of proteins. One gram of oxygen, at standard conditions, occupies a volume of 0.699 liter; and 1 gm. of carbon dioxide occupies a volume of 0.5087 liter.

For oxygen, then, $138.18 \times 0.699 = 96.63$ liters, and for carbon dioxide, $152.17 \times 0.5087 = 77.39$ liters.

The R. Q. of protein $= \dfrac{77.39}{96.63} = 0.801.$

When 1 gm. of nitrogen (in the form of urea, etc.) is eliminated, it means the following: 1 gm. of urinary nitrogen corresponds to 6.25 gm. of protein, and represents the absorption of 5.92 liters of oxygen, the elimination of 4.75 liters of carbon dioxide, and the production of 26.51 Calories (Lusk).

In severe diabetes, the R. Q., which normally on a mixed diet may be around 0.85, may reach a figure as low as 0.7, indicating that much of the combustion is derived from fats and that less carbohydrate is being metabolized. One of the many striking results of insulin treatment is that the R. Q. increases, showing that carbohydrates (and part of the protein molecule) are being better utilized for energy purposes.

Indirect Calorimetry. By knowing the oxygen consumption and the carbon dioxide output, and the amount of nitrogen (as urea, etc.) eliminated, it is possible to calculate the amount of carbohydrate, fat, and protein consumed, and the amount of heat (in Calories) produced. Here the heat is not measured directly and the apparatus employed is simple.

Bodansky (*Physiological Chemistry*, 1938, p. 517) gives the following instructive example: During a twenty-four-hour period, the subject consumed 400 liters of oxygen, and eliminated 340 liters of carbon dioxide and 12 gm. of nitrogen (as urea, etc.).

The amount of protein represented by 1 gm. of nitrogen (1 × 6.25 gm. protein) requires for oxidation 5.92 liters of oxygen, and 4.75 liters of carbon dioxide are eliminated. Since 12 gm. of nitrogen were eliminated, this would mean 12 × 5.92 = 71 liters of oxygen (approximately), and 12 × 4.75 = 57 liters of carbon dioxide, as being due to protein. The oxygen consumption due to carbohydrate and fat is 400 − 71 = 329 liters; and the production of carbon dioxide due to carbohydrate and fat is 340 − 57 = 283 liters.

The R. Q. of "nonprotein" (carbohydrate + fat) = 283/329 = 0.86.

From Table 33 we gather that when the R. Q. of "nonprotein" is 0.86, 1 liter of oxygen is equivalent to 0.622 gm. of carbohydrate and 0.249 gm. of fat. Therefore, 329 liters of oxygen mean

$$329 \times 0.622 = 204 \text{ gm. of carbohydrate}$$
$$\text{and } 329 \times 0.249 = 82 \text{ gm. of fat}$$
$$\text{and 12 gm. of nitrogen eliminated mean } 12 \times 6.25 = 75 \text{ gm. of protein}$$

In other words, during this twenty-four-hour period, the subject utilized 204 gm. of carbohydrate, 82 gm. of fat, and 75 gm. of protein.

The heat value of these foodstuffs can now be calculated approximately:

$$
\begin{array}{llll}
75 \times 4 = & 300 & \text{Calories from} & \text{protein} \\
82 \times 9 = & 738 & `` \quad `` & \text{fat} \\
204 \times 4 = & \underline{816} & `` \quad `` & \text{carbohydrate} \\
& 1854 & \text{Calories*} &
\end{array}
$$

BASAL METABOLISM

The total energy output is the resultant of two factors. Under normal conditions, one of these factors is a fairly constant one. It represents the energy needed in maintaining the temperature of the body (in warm-

* We can recalculate this in a different and more accurate way. Assume 26.51 Cal./gm. urinary N for protein and 4.875 Cal./liter of oxygen for carbohydrate and fat; then total heat = heat from protein (26.51 × 12 = 318.2 Cal.) + heat from carbohydrate and fat (329 × 4.875 = 1604.2 Cal.) = 1922.2 Cal. This is nearer accurate than 1854 Cal. (Harold Goss).

Table 33   THF SIGNIFICANCE OF THE NONPROTEIN RESPIRA-
TORY QUOTIENT AS REGARDS THE HEAT VALUE OF 1
LITER OF OXYGEN, AND THE RELATIVE QUANTITY IN
CALORIES OF CARBOHYDRATE AND FAT CONSUMED
(Zuntz and Schumberg, Modified by Lusk, Modified by
McClendon.)

One Liter of Oxygen is Equivalent to

Nonprotein respiratory quotient	Grams		Calories
	Carbohydrate	Fat	
0.707	0.000	0.502	4.686
0.71	0.016	0.497	4.690
0.72	0.055	0.482	4.702
0.73	0.094	0.465	4.714
0.74	0.134	0.450	4.727
0.75	0.173	0.433	4.739
0.76	0.213	0.417	4.751
0.77	0.254	0.400	4.764
0.78	0.294	0.384	4.776
0.79	0.334	0.368	4.788
0.80	0.375	0.350	4.801
0.81	0.415	0.334	4.813
0.82	0.456	0.317	4.825
0.83	0.498	0.301	4.838
0.84	0.539	0.284	4.850
0.85	0.580	0.267	4.862
0.86	0.622	0.249	4.875
0.87	0.666	0.232	4.887
0.88	0.708	0.215	4.899
0.89	0.741	0.197	4.911
0.90	0.793	0.180	4.924
0.91	0.836	0.162	4.936
0.92	0.878	0.145	4.948
0.93	0.922	0.127	4.961
0.94	0.966	0.109	4.973
0.95	1.010	0.091	4.985
0.96	1.053	0.073	4.998
0.97	1.098	0.055	5.010
0.98	1.142	0.036	5.022
0.99	1.185	0.018	5.035
1.00	1.232	0.000	5.047

blooded animals), in maintaining the heart beat, etc. The other factor is a widely fluctuating one, depending upon the extent of exercise and upon the amount of food consumed. A subject who has fasted for some twelve hours before the experiment and who is in a state of complete rest during the experiment, will give off an amount of heat which will tend to be constant. The heat output, under these conditions, is called the "basal metabolism," and it is measured in terms of the number of Calories produced per square meter of body surface per hour.

In one form of basal metabolic test, the amount of oxygen consumed is measured. Under the conditions of the experiment, for each liter of oxygen consumed, 4.8 C. of heat is generated.

If, for example, the individual consumes 1 l. of oxygen in four minutes, or 15 l. in one hour, the heat generated would be 15 × 4.8, or 72 C. per hour.

If, depending upon height and weight (Fig. 66), the individual has a surface area of 2 square meters, each square meter will give off 36 C. of heat.

The number "36" represents Calories per square meter of surface per hour.

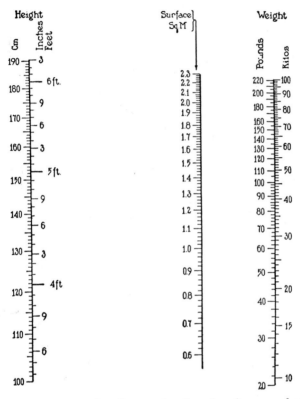

Fig. 66. Nomogram permitting direct estimation of surface area from height and weight by DuBois' formula A = H$^{0.725}$ × W$^{0.425}$ × 71.84. A = surface area in square centimeters, H = height in centimeters, and W = weight in kg. (Sq. cm. = sq. m. × 1/10,000). The surface area is found at the point of intersection of the middle scale with a straight line drawn from the observed height on the left-hand scale to the observed weight on the right-hand scale. (Peters and Van Slyke: Quantitative Clinical Chemistry.)

The importance of surface area was first emphasized by Rubner. The variations obtained by recording metabolic experiments per unit of weight are quite large.

DuBois has developed an empirical formula relating surface area, height and weight.

$$A = W^{0.425} \times H^{0.745} \times 71.84$$

where A = surface area in sq. cm., W = weight in kg., and H = height in centimeters. The nomogram makes the estimation of surface area very simple (Fig. 66).

The average basal metabolic rate for normal adults (between thirty and forty years) is 39.5 C. for males and 36.5 C. for females.

To calculate the basal metabolic rate based on heat production, we shall take an example from Cantarow and Trumper.*

The individual is a male, aged thirty-five, height 67 inches, weight 154 pounds. His surface area is 1.8 square meters.

The actual oxygen consumption is 200 cc. per minute, or 12 l. per hour. For every 1 l. of oxygen consumed, 4.825 Calories of heat are generated. Therefore, the heat expenditure is $12 \times 4.825 = 57.9$ C. per hour.

Since the patient's surface area is 1.8 square meters, the Calories per square meter per hour $= \dfrac{57.9}{1.8} = 32.16$ C.

Table 34   STANDARD VALUES FOR CALORIES PER SQUARE METER PER HOUR

(Boothby, Berkson, and Dunn: Am. J. Physiol., *116:* 468.)

Males		Females	
Age last birthday	Mean	Age last birthday	Mean
Years		Years	
6	53.00	6	50.62
7	52.45	$6\frac{1}{2}$	50.23
8	51.78	7	49.12
$8\frac{1}{2}$	51.20	$7\frac{1}{2}$	47.84
9	50.54	8	47.00
$9\frac{1}{2}$	49.42	$8\frac{1}{2}$	46.50
10	48.50	9–10	45.90
$10\frac{1}{2}$	47.71	11	45.26
11	47.18	$11\frac{1}{2}$	44.80
12	46.75	12	44.28
13–15	46.35	$12\frac{1}{2}$	43.58
16	45.72	13	42.90
$16\frac{1}{2}$	45.30	$13\frac{1}{2}$	42.10
17	44.80	14	41.45
$17\frac{1}{2}$	44.03	$14\frac{1}{2}$	40.74
18	43.25	15	40.10
$18\frac{1}{2}$	42.70	$15\frac{1}{2}$	39.40
19	42.32	16	38.85
$19\frac{1}{2}$	42.00	$16\frac{1}{2}$	38.30
20–21	41.43	17	37.82
22–23	40.82	$17\frac{1}{2}$	37.40
24–27	40.24	18–19	36.74
28–29	39.81	20–24	36.18
30–34	39.34	25–44	35.70
35–39	38.68	45–49	34.94
40–44	38.00	50–54	33.96
45–49	37.37	55–59	33.18
50–54	36.73	60–64	32.61
55–59	36.10	65–69	32.30
60–64	35.48		
65–69	34.80 *		

* Obtained by extrapolation.

* See reference at the end of the chapter.

The normal value, according to DuBois, is 39.5 C. per square meter per hour.

Therefore, the basal metabolic rate =

$$\frac{39.5 - 32.16}{39.5} \times 100 = -18.5 \text{ per cent;}$$

which is 18.5 per cent below normal.

Variations in Basal Metabolism.   Variations due to age are given in Table 34. The most striking variations are observed in thyroid disease. "It must be admitted," write DuBois and Chambers, "that the basal metabolism tests are seldom of great value except in the diagnosis and treatment of the thyroid gland. . . ."

In severe cases of hyperthyroidism, increases of 75 per cent (and more) above normal have been obtained; and in hypothyroidism (myxedema), figures representing 40 per cent below normal are not uncommon.

Table 35   THE INFLUENCE OF DIET AND MECHANICAL WORK UPON THE METABOLISM OF A MAN 61 TO 63 KG. IN WEIGHT

	Heat produced				Heat lost	
Diet and conditions	Twenty-four hours	In-crease	In-crease due to work	Evap. H_2O	Rad. and cond.	Work
	Calories	Per cent	Calories	Calories	Calories	Calories
No food, rest...............	1976	.....	.....	380	1596	
Cane sugar + H_2O, taken during rest.................	2023	+ 2.4	.....	529	1494	
Same + work.............	2868	+45.2	845	907	1727	234
Protein, large amount of meat, rest....................	2515	+27.2	.....	614	1901	
Protein, same diet, + work...	3370	+70.5	855	1235	1901	234

In fevers (pneumonia, typhoid, etc.) the metabolic rate is increased by about 13 per cent for each 1° C.

In prolonged starvation, covering a period of some ten days or more, the metabolic rate is definitely reduced.

Of course, muscular work increases considerably the energy requirements above the basal metabolic level. In Table 35, prepared by Rubner, a comparison is made between the effect on heat production of (a) the addition of carbohydrate and protein, and (b) work. None of the heat production due to work is derived from the specific dynamic action of the foodstuffs.

The effect of certain drugs on the basal metabolic rate has been much investigated. This applies more particularly to phenol derivatives of the type of 2,4-dinitrophenol and 4,6-dinitro-o-cresol. The injection of 3 mg. per kilogram weight of the former substance increases the basal metabolic rate tenfold. In this respect, its effect is comparable to thyroxine. However, in myxedema, such phenols will restore the basal rate without influencing the other symptoms of the disease, which is in striking contrast to the effect of thyroxine.

SPECIFIC DYNAMIC ACTION

When protein equivalent to 100 C. is ingested, heat equivalent to 130 C. is produced. This action of protein in stimulating metabolism Rubner called the "specific dynamic action" (S.D.A.) of protein. Fats and carbohydrates given in equivalent quantities (that is, in amounts to produce 100 C.) produce 113 C. and 105 C., respectively. These are Rubner's figures, but they are considered too high. In any case, the most striking effects are obtained with protein, and here the results are the same whether the protein is taken in as food or whether its constituent amino acids are injected. It is true that the kidney does work in excreting urea and ammonia derived from the protein (or amino acid) ingested; but Borsook asserts that this accounts for less than one-half the observed increase in metabolism. Nor can the result be due to increased gastrointestinal activity, for the feeding of bones and meat extract, which gives rise to much intestinal irritation, has no effect on S.D.A.

The individual amino acids all show powerful S.D.A. effects, although they vary among themselves.

In an experiment dealing with the effect of the ingestion of gelatin, Borsook showed that there was not only an increase in energy metabolism, but also an increase in the excretion of urinary nitrogen, sulfur, and uric acid.

That the liver may be concerned with the process is made probable by Wilhelmj's observation that after hepatectomy, glycine and alanine show no S.D.A.

Borsook expresses S.D.A. as the ratio of the Calories in excess of the basal to urinary nitrogen in excess of the basal. The variation in the S.D.A. of protein, he explains, can be interpreted on the basis of a new theory of specific dynamic action: the S.D.A. is a composite of two factors, the one nearly constant and represented by the increased energy production resulting from the metabolism and excretion of nitrogen (7 to 10 C. per gram of nitrogen); and the other a more variable and, usually, larger fraction, arising from the metabolism of carbon.

The effectiveness of the amino acids (in the form of ingested protein) as an energy producer is made more evident when we consider the relationship of the amino acids to members of the tricarboxylic acid cycle (p. 212).

HEAT REGULATION

Under normal conditions there is, as it were, a balance of forces between the extent of heat produced and the extent of heat lost (Fig. 67). In order that the temperature may remain constant, the equilibrium will shift either to the right or to the left.*

The manner in which heat is lost from the body, as well as its extent, is summarized by Vierordt (quoted by Howell):

---

* "The hypothalamus integrates the reactions responsible for thermal equilibrium. Through its influence on the somatic and visceral motor neurons, the hypothalamus functions as a physiologic thermostat and changes the rate of heat production and heat loss according to the thermal status and requirements of the body." (Wakim)

Through urine and feces..................	1.3 per cent or	48 C.
By expired air: warming of air..............	3.5 " " "	84 C.
Vaporization of water from lungs...........	7.2 " " "	182 C.
Evaporation from skin.....................	14.5 " " "	364 C.
Radiation and conduction from skin........	73.0 " " "	1792 C.

Total daily loss = 2470 C.

While such figures may change with changes in environmental conditions, in general it may be said that loss of heat is due, in the main, to evaporation and radiation. To some extent, such heat loss is controlled by clothing. But the important regulatory mechanism is an automatic reflex control (through sweat nerves and vasomotor nerves).

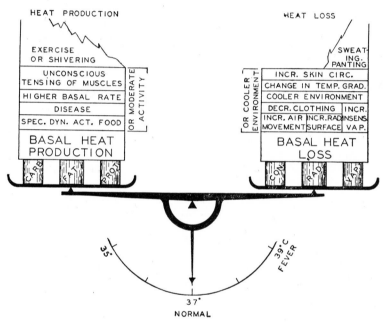

Fig. 67. Balance between factors increasing heat production and heat loss. (DuBois: Harvey Lectures, Ser. 34, p. 88.)

The heat production, on the other hand, is dependent upon the extent of cellular oxidation; and this, in turn, is partly dependent upon the amount of muscular activity and upon the food eaten. But there is also an involuntary control, in the shape of an involuntary reflex on muscular metabolism. For example, as the outside temperature is lowered, the heat production is increased, although the temperature of the body does not change. This is termed "chemical regulation" by Rubner.

ENERGY REQUIREMENTS

Roughly speaking, the energy requirement is the resultant of two factors: a fairly constant factor, as represented by the basal metabolism; and a variable factor, depending upon physical activity. The effect due to S.D.A. must also be taken into account.

An exhaustive study of energy needs has been made by Stiebling and Ward. In preparing "adequate diets," they have constructed a standard table, giving not only the calorific needs at various ages and varying activity, but also the amounts needed of protein, calcium, phosphorus, and iron.

Using this table, we get

$$
\begin{array}{lll}
\text{8 hours of sleep at 65 C. per hour} & = & 520 \text{ C.} \\
\text{2 hours light work at 170 C.} & = & 340 \text{ C.} \\
\text{8 hours carpenter work at 240 C.} & = & 1920 \text{ C.} \\
\text{6 hours sitting at rest at 100 C.} & = & \underline{600 \text{ C.}} \\
& \text{Total daily requirement} & 3380 \text{ C.}
\end{array}
$$

For a moderately active man, with a daily calorific requirement of 3000, the authors suggest 67 gm. of protein. The British Ministry of Health, using the same calorific requirement, is more liberal with its protein. It suggests 80 to 100 gm. per day, "of which not less than one third must be of animal origin."

DuBois and Chambers state that some 1200 of the 2000 to 3000 Calories needed per day should come from "protective foods" to supply the minimum necessary quantities of vitamins, calories and essential amino acids. These 1200 Calories are derived from 1 pint of milk, 1 egg, 1 serving (3–4 ounces) of meat, 3 teaspoons (15 gm.) of butter, 4 servings of whole grain bread or cereal, 2 vegetables, other than potato, one of which is raw, and 2 fruits, one of which is raw.

The energy expenditures (per hour) under different conditions of muscular activity are given by Sherman in Table 36.

OBESITY

The problem of obesity is, in most cases, the problem of overeating. The consequences in terms of life expectancy are serious. Newburgh refers to Dublin's study involving some 200,000 men and concludes that "the penalty of overweight is one-fourth to three-fourth excess in mortality." Fish has reported that 50 pounds overweight impose as much extra mortality as valvular heart disease.

Treatment involves a decrease in total fuel intake without omitting food essentials (such as minerals and vitamins, which are negligible so far as calorific effect is concerned). Protein allowance should remain normal— some 60 to 70 gm. per day. The main restrictions involve fat and certain sources rich in carbohydrates (sugar, breadstuffs). Based on these facts, a balanced diet can be planned to contain not more than 800 to 1000 Calories per day, which diet should be continued until normal weight is reached.

The substitution of drugs for a reduced calorific intake should be discouraged,* because of bad after-effects. For example, while thyroid preparations will cause reduction in weight, they also give rise very frequently to symptoms of hyperthyroidism; and drugs which decrease appetite— such as amphetamine sulfate (Benzedrine)—often cause restlessness, irritability, and insomnia.

* Unless under a doctor's care.

Table 36 ENERGY EXPENDITURE PER HOUR UNDER DIFFERENT CONDITIONS OF MUSCULAR ACTIVITY
(Sherman: Chemistry of Food and Nutrition. By permission of The Macmillan Company, Publishers.)

| | Calories per hour | | |
Form of activity	Per 70 kg. (average man)	Per kg.	Per pound
Sleeping	65	0.93	0.43
Awake lying still	77	1.10	0.50
Sitting at rest	100	1.43	0.65
Reading aloud	105	1.50	0.69
Standing relaxed	105	1.50	0.69
Hand sewing	111	1.59	0.72
Standing at attention	115	1.63	0.74
Knitting (23 stitches per minute on sweater)	116	1.66	0.75
Dressing and undressing	118	1.69	0.77
Singing	122	1.74	0.79
Tailoring	135	1.93	0.88
Typewriting rapidly	140	2.00	0.91
Ironing (with 5-pound iron)	144	2.06	0.93
Dishwashing (plates, bowls, cups, and saucers)	144	2.06	0.93
Sweeping bare floor (38 strokes per minute)	169	2.41	1.09
Bookbinding	170	2.43	1.10
"Light exercise"	170	2.43	1.10
Shoe making	180	2.57	1.17
Walking slowly (2.6 miles per hour)	200	2.86	1.30
Carpentry, metal working, industrial painting	240	3.43	1.56
"Active exercise"	290	4.14	1.88
Walking moderately fast (3.75 miles per hour)	300	4.28	1.95
Walking down stairs	364	5.20	2.36
Stoneworking	400	5.71	2.60
"Severe exercise"	450	6.43	2.92
Sawing wood	480	6.86	3.12
Swimming	500	7.14	3.25
Running (5.3 miles per hour)	570	8.14	3.70
"Very severe exercise"	600	8.57	3.90
Walking very fast (5.3 miles per hour)	650	9.28	4.22
Walking up stairs	1100	15.8	7.18

REFERENCES

One of the early accounts of the "human" calorimeter of Atwater and Rosa is to be found in Bulletin 63, U. S. Dept. of Agriculture, 1899. A later one, by Atwater and Benedict, is described in a publication of the Carnegie Institution, Washington, 1905. See also *Lusk:* The Science of Nutrition, 1928, Chap. 3.

A detailed account of energy metabolism will be found in *Peters and Van Slyke:* Quantitative Clinical Chemistry, volume I, p. 3, 1946.

For a general discussion, with emphasis on clinical values, see the article on "Cal-

ories in Medical Practice" by *DuBois and Chambers* in the Handbook of Nutrition, 1943, p. 55.

Mitchell reviews the subject in Federation Proceedings, *3:* 193, 1944.

Newburgh is the author of an important article on energy metabolism in obesity: Physiol. Rev., *24:* 18, 1944. See, also, his article in the Bull. N. Y. Acad. Med., April, 1948, p. 227.

In connection with the temperature of the body, see *Horvath, Menduke, and Piersol:* J. Am. Med. Assoc., *144:* 1562, 1950 (oral and rectal temperatures);

Buettner: Ibid., *144:* 732, 1950 (effects of extreme heat); *Wakim:* Ibid., *138:* 1091, 1948 (physiological effects of heat).

For nitrogen metabolism, see *Kade, Phillips, and Phillips:* J. Nutrition, *36:* 109, 1948 (nitrogen balance); *Toscani and Wheldon:* Ibid., *45:* 119, 1951 (N loss in feces).

The subject of respiratory quotient is dealt with by *Richardson:* Physiol. Rev., *9:* 61, 1929.

Practical details concerned with basal metabolism are given by *DuBois:* Basal Metabolism, 1936; *Cantarow and Trumper;* Clinical Biochemistry, 1949; and the pamphlet, *Metabolism Testing* (Middlewest Instrument Corp., Chicago).

See also, *Galvão:* Am. J. Physiol., *148:* 478, 1947 (body weight versus body surface); and *Kleiber:* Physiol. Rev., *27:* 511, 1947 (body size and metabolic rate).

The subject of specific dynamic action is reviewed by *Wilhelmj:* Physiol. Rev., *15:* 202, 1935. See, further, *Hawkins:* Science, *116:* 19, 1952; *Glickman, Mitchell, Lambert, and Keeton:* J. Nutrition, *36:* 41,

1948; *Anderson and Nasset:* Ibid., *36:* 703, 1948.

A critical discussion of the heat loss from the human body is to be found in the Bull. N. Y. Acad. Med., March, 1939; and in the *Harvey Lectures,* Ser. 34, 1938–1939, p. 88, by *DuBois.* See, further, *Wakim:* J. Am. Med. Assoc., *138:* 1091, 1948.

The important study by *Stiebling and Ward* dealing with energy requirements is published as U. S. Dept. of Agriculture, Circular 296 (1933). See, further, *Keys:* J. Am. Med. Assoc., *142:* 333, 1950; Federation Proceedings, *8:* 523, 1949; *Taylor and Keys:* Science, *112:* 215, 1950.

Methods of calculating the caloric value of diets are discussed by *Maynard:* J. Nutrition, *28:* 443, 1944.

A suggestive article by *Mills* entitled "Temperature dominance over human life" will be found in Science, *110:* 267, 1949.

For changes during the aging process, see Nutr. Rev., *11:* 100, 1953.

On the subject of obesity, see Nutr. Rev., *11:* 144, 1953.

Chapter 18 *Inorganic Metabolism*

THE MINERAL elements which the body needs in what might be called substantial quantities are calcium, magnesium, sodium, potassium, phosphorus, sulfur, and chlorine. The body also needs, in smaller, or "trace" amounts, iron, copper, iodine, manganese, cobalt, and zinc.

The general biological importance of calcium, phosphorus, iron, sodium, potassium, sulfur, and chlorine has been stressed from time to time in these pages. Their presence in the body has been known for some time, and some of their functions have been discovered. More recent work—in many cases involving spectroscopic examination—has revealed the presence of not less than fifty-five elements in plant or animal tissue. Many of them are present in traces only, and the temptation is strong to dismiss such elements by calling them "impurities." While such a conception may apply to some, it probably does not apply to a number of them. In any case, caution is necessary. We shall see presently how effective traces of copper are in the utilization of iron.

The "trace" elements are also known as "oligo" elements (from the Greek meaning "scanty"). Their concentration is usually in the neighborhood of 1×10^{-6} to less than 1×10^{-12} gm. per gram of wet tissue.

Sherman gives a list of a number of the more important elements (with their percentages), found in the human body (Table 37).

As showing how many more elements in traces there may be, the results of a spectrum analysis of milk ash by Drea may be cited. He has been able to detect the following elements in addition to common ones: aluminum, barium, boron, chromium, fluorine, lead, lithium, molybdenum, silver, rubidium, silicon, strontium, tin, titanium, vanadium, and zinc. In other tissues—in plant as well as animal tissues—we find, in addition, cobalt, nickel, selenium, bromine, bismuth, arsenic, etc.

The functions of some of the mineral elements which have been studied are fairly clear. A number, such as calcium and phosphorus, are constituents of bone and teeth; some, such as iron, sulfur, and phosphorus, are necessary elements in important organic compounds found in the body; still others, such as sodium chloride, serve as electrolytes; and it is possible that some, like copper, play a role as catalysts.

Not only are such elements in themselves important but equally important is their relationship to one another. The relationship of calcium to phosphorus in rickets will be referred to (Chap. 20). But brief mention may be made here of several other elements. When a frog's heart is immersed in solutions containing several salts at various concentrations, it has been found that the heart will beat normally provided the ratio K^+/Ca^{++} is that found in frog's blood. In dealing with the effect of ionic concentrations upon the irritability of tissues, Holmes points out that the irritability depends very largely upon the ratio

$$\frac{Na^+ + K^+ + OH^-}{Ca^{++} + Mg^{++} + H^+}$$

and that when the concentration of the ions in the numerator is increased, there is an increase of irritability; whereas the reverse is true if the ionic concentration in the denominator is increased. Ringer's solution, so often used to retain the activities of tissues and tissue slices, is made up of a

Table 37   APPROXIMATE ELEMENTARY COMPOSITION OF THE BODY

(Sherman and Lanford: Essentials of Nutrition. By permission of The Macmillan Co., Publishers.)

Element	Percentage
Oxygen	65.
Carbon	18.
Hydrogen	10.
Nitrogen	3.
Calcium	2.[a]
Phosphorus	1.1 [b]
Potassium	0.35
Sulfur	0.25
Sodium	0.15
Chlorine	0.15
Magnesium	0.05
Iron	0.004
Manganese	0.00013
Copper	0.00015
Iodine	0.00004
Cobalt	[c]
Zinc	[c]
Others of more doubtful status	

[a] Estimates vary widely.

[b] Percentage varies with that of calcium.

[c] Believed to be essential, but quantitative data are not yet at hand.

solution of chlorides of potassium, sodium, calcium, and magnesium in concentrations comparable to those in blood.

An interesting case of competitive antagonism was noticed by Snell working with certain types of lactic acid bacteria. These bacteria require potassium for growth. When the maximum amount of K ion necessary for growth was present, the addition of Na ion caused inhibition of growth; this inhibition was removed by the addition of K ions. Again, the addition of Na ion caused inhibition.

CALCIUM

This mineral element is present in greater abundance in the body than any other. An adult weighing some 70 kg. contains about 1200 gm. of calcium.

As the chief constituent of bone, calcium is present as a salt resembling minerals of the apatite group; 99 per cent of the total amount of calcium in the body is found in the bones. The element may exist as a double salt of the carbonate and phosphate, $CaCO_3 . nCa_3(PO_4)_2$, where n is not less than 2, nor greater than 3. There is also evidence that the principal inorganic salt in bone may be a hydroxyapatite or a hydrated tricalcium phosphate. Smaller amounts of calcium are found in the teeth (36 per cent in enamel), skin, and blood.

In the blood, calcium is found almost exclusively in the plasma, where it occurs to the extent of about 9 to 11.5 mg. per 100 ml. of serum. The relationship $[Ca] \times [P] = 36$ (where $[Ca]$ and $[P]$ are expressed in milligrams per 100 ml.) holds fairly well. Some 60 per cent of the calcium in the blood is in a diffusible form, and the remainder is quite nondiffusible. The nondiffusible portion is probably attached to the serum albumin.

A concentration of ionic calcium below the normal amount, brought about by a deficiency of the parathyroid hormone, affects the central nervous system and produces an increased irritability of the peripheral nerves. At a later stage, muscle spasms (affecting the face, hands, and feet) and general convulsions make their appearance. We have here an example of tetany which can be cured by an extract of parathyroid glands (Chap. 23).

Hyperactivity of the parathyroids gives rise to an excess of calcium in the blood. At the same time, owing to calcium deposition, there occurs a hardening of various organs (heart, lungs, arteries, etc.). The excess calcium is derived from the bones, which, in turn, become soft and weak.

While the common form of rickets is one in which there is a deficiency of phosphorus, calcium may also be involved (Chap. 20). Vitamin D, possibly by regulating the utilization of calcium from the intestine, influences the extent to which the body uses the element.

It appears that the absorption of calcium is increased by increasing the acidity of the intestinal contents, and it also seems that more calcium is absorbed from concentrated than from dilute solutions.

Apart from the importance of calcium in the structure of bone and teeth and in its influence upon the excitability of the motor system, it also plays a role in blood clotting.

Unlike sodium and potassium, much of the calcium is excreted by the bowel. As a rule, some 65 to 75 per cent of the element is found in the feces, and 25 to 35 per cent in the urine.

Sherman is of the opinion that not less than 0.70 gm. of calcium is the daily need of the adult. From 0.8 to 1.0 gm. represents an optimal rather than a minimal allowance. The National Research Council recommends 1.0 gm.

The ratio of calcium to phosphorus should be 1:1.5 or 2. An excessive amount of phosphorus will form insoluble salts with calcium and so create a deficiency of calcium.

Milk and cheese are particularly rich sources. Milk contains about 1.4 gm. of calcium per liter, and cheese, 5 to 10 gm. per kg.

The mere fact that a food is rich in calcium—or in any other element— does not necessarily mean that eating such a food will cause 100 per cent absorption and assimilation. Various studies have shown that from 20 to

30 per cent of the calcium in milk is utilized by the human organism. In the case of green vegetables and other foods, poor utilization of the element is perhaps due to the presence of oxalic acid, citrates, and phytic acid, which may interfere with the absorption of calcium owing to the insolubility of their salts.

Present-day consumption of large quantities of refined cereals, with much of the original calcium in the whole grain lost, and sugar, which is devoid of minerals, makes the problem of supplying mineral needs difficult.

PHOSPHORUS

This element is present in every cell of the body. Phosphorus is not only present in inorganic combinations (in bones, teeth, blood, etc.), but in many organic combinations. Among the latter may be mentioned phosphatides, nucleic acid, phosphoprotein (as casein), adenylic acid, coenzyme, yellow enzymes, thiamine phosphate, phosphocreatine, hexosephosphates, and triosephosphates. All of these substances have already been discussed in various sections of the book.

It has been estimated that there is some 700 gm. of phosphorus in the body, of which 600 gm. is found in the skeleton, 57 gm. in muscle, 5 gm. in brain, 2 gm. in blood, etc. About 80 per cent of the phosphorus in the body is in combination with calcium in bones and teeth. The daily needs have been calculated by Sherman to be some 1.32 gm. The foods particularly rich in this element are cheese, nuts, eggs, meat, and milk.

The functions of phosphorus are numerous; they involve the chemistry of the blood, acid-base balance of the body, skeletal growth, tooth development, muscle metabolism, intermediary metabolism of carbohydrate, fat, protein, and brain, the activity of enzymes, etc. Fortunately for us, the element is widely distributed in foods.

On a diet containing as little as 0.017 per cent of phosphorus, young rats grow slowly for five to six weeks and then decline and die two weeks later. Metabolic studies reveal a large loss of calcium, excreted mainly through the kidneys. Most of the excreted phosphorus is found in the feces.

The use of isotopes has shown that what is true of the organic constituents is equally true of the inorganic ones: the body constituents are in dynamic equilibrium with each other and with ingested foods. This applies to what were considered as permanent structures, such as bones and teeth; here, too, the constituents exist in a dynamic state, undergoing continuous degradation and synthesis.

The pioneer work using radiophosphorus (P^{32}) was done by Hevesy, who, indeed, was the first to use radioactive tracers in investigating metabolic problems. Hevesy, in his earlier work, showed that an appreciable amount of the phosphorus from food proceeded rapidly to bones, teeth, muscle, etc. Later, Hevesy showed that lecithin could be isolated from the brain of rats, mice, and rabbits which contained the radiophosphorus. Still another experiment on goats showed that the ingestion of sodium phosphate (containing P^{32}) resulted in the deposition of labeled phosphates in milk in from three to four hours. Since the casein in the milk also contained the isotope (P^{32}), the phosphorus used in the synthesis of casein in the mammary gland must have been derived from the inorganic phosphate in blood, which, in turn, was dependent upon the inorganic phosphate of the food.

MAGNESIUM

This element is an essential constituent of the chlorophyll molecule, and therefore is of importance to plant life. That it is also important to animal life has been shown, among others, by McCollum, who found that a diet containing 0.18 mg. of magnesium per 100 gm. of food (but otherwise quite adequate) gives rise, in rats, to vasodilatation and hyperirritability of the nervous system, resembling, in some ways, the tetany due to calcium deficiency. Under these conditions, while, of course, the amount of magnesium in the blood is subnormal, the amount of calcium remains at its normal level. Nor, in a reverse situation, with a low blood calcium, can tetany be prevented by the addition of magnesium. What is called "tetany" due to magnesium deficiency has characteristics which make it different from "tetany" due to calcium deficiency.

About 71 per cent of the total magnesium found in the body is located in the bones (in the form of phosphate and carbonate). In the blood we find 1 to 3 mg. per 100 ml. The serum contains less than half as much magnesium as the cells; in contrast to calcium, which is found almost exclusively in serum.

While the total quantity of magnesium in the body is far less than that of calcium, more of the former is found in muscle than of the latter. On the average, we find about 21 mg. of magnesium per 100 gm. of muscle tissue, as compared to 7 mg. of calcium. The magnesium, according to Lohmann, acts in conjunction with the adenylic acid as a coenzyme in carbohydrate metabolism (and also in yeast fermentation).

Many enzymes require Mg^{++}—in addition to ATP—for their activity.

In general, the metabolism of magnesium is not unlike the metabolism of calcium, which, in turn, must be related to that of phosphorus. From one-fifth to one-half of the magnesium may be excreted via the urine; the rest appears in the feces.

Like the corresponding salts of calcium and strontium, the magnesium salts of mineral acids produce acidosis. This is due to the fact that whereas much of the Mg^{++} is excreted with the feces, the acid ion is absorbed and finally excreted in the urine. Magnesium salts are diuretics and cathartics.

Tables 38, 39, and 40 deal with analyses of calcium, phosphorus, and magnesium.

As to the requirements for magnesium, little is known. The average intake per person (in the U. S.) is 0.27 gm. per day, which is probably sufficient.

SODIUM

Sodium, as sodium chloride, has two important functions: to contribute toward the acid-base balance of the body, and to be responsible, in large measure, for the total osmotic pressure of the extracellular fluids.

Our main source of this element is the salt (sodium chloride) employed in cooking and seasoning, although some, of course, is derived from the foods we eat. The ordinary daily diet contains 10 to 20 gm. of sodium chloride.

Table 38   APPROXIMATE AMOUNTS OF CALCIUM, PHOSPHORUS, AND MAG-
NESIUM IN 100 GM. OF EDIBLE FOOD
(Schmidt and Greenberg: Physiol. Rev., *15:* 300.)

	Calcium	Phosphorus	Magnesium
	Gm.	Gm.	Gm.
Beef (lean)............................	0.007	0.218	0.024
Eggs.................................	0.067	0.180	0.011
Egg yolk..............................	0.137	0.524	0.016
Milk.................................	0.210	0.093	0.012
Cheese...............................	0.931	0.680	0.037
Wheat...............................	0.045	0.423	0.133
Potatoes.............................	0.014	0.058	0.028
Corn meal............................	0.018	0.190	0.084
Oranges..............................	0.045	0.021	0.012
Almonds.............................	0.239	0.465	0.251
Spinach..............................	0.067	0.068	0.037
Beans (dried).........................	0.160	0.470	0.156
Linseed meal.........................	0.413	0.741	0.432
Cotton seed meal......................	0.265	1.193	0.462

Table 39   DISTRIBUTION OF ELEMENTS IN THE BLOOD
OF HUMAN SUBJECTS IN MILLIGRAMS PER
100 ML.
(Schmidt and Greenberg.)

Substance	Normal (mean value)
Total serum calcium..........................	10.3
Diffusible calcium............................	5.4
Nondiffusible calcium.........................	4.9
Inorganic serum phosphorus...................	4.0
Whole blood magnesium.......................	4.6
Red corpuscle magnesium.....................	6.6
Plasma magnesium............................	2.7
Serum magnesium............................	2.5
Diffusible serum magnesium...................	1.9

Table 40   COMPOSITION OF BLOOD IN CERTAIN PATHOLOGICAL CONDITIONS
(Schmidt and Greenberg.)

Disease	Substance	Mg. per 100 ml.
Rickets (human subjects)	Serum calcium	9.0
	Inorganic phosphate	3.0
	Serum magnesium	2.2
Parathyroid tetany (human subjects)	Serum calcium	7.9
	Inorganic phosphate	5.0
	Serum magnesium	2.0
Hyperparathyroidism (human subjects)	Serum calcium	15.9
	Inorganic phosphate	2.2

Sodium (and this is also true of potassium) is very easily absorbed, some 90 to 95 per cent appearing in the urine. It has been claimed by Bunge, and generally accepted, that the addition of an excess of sodium to the diet causes an excessive excretion of potassium, and vice versa. The explanation offered as to why herbivorous animals so often have a craving for salt is that their food is particularly rich in potassium, thereby giving rise to an excessive excretion of sodium. Foods of vegetable origin are richer in potassium than in sodium.

Some 93 per cent of the total cations in blood serum is due to sodium (Table 41). Together with other salts, it maintains the osmotic pressure and equilibrium of the blood.

The extent of the excretion of sodium is dependent upon the amount of intake, and although an animal can maintain itself on surprisingly small quantities—in the rat, as little as 0.1 per cent of sodium chloride in the

Table 41   APPROXIMATE CONCENTRATION OF CATIONS
IN BLOOD AND MUSCLE

	Serum (mEq./liter)	Red Cells (mEq./liter)	Muscle (mEq./kg.)
Na^+	142	0 (?)	31
K^+	5	108	93
Ca^{++}	5	0 (?)	4
Mg^{++}	3	2	19

diet—a minimum amount is probably necessary. Below minimal quantities, there are loss of appetite, retarded growth, disturbance of the reproductive function, and ultimate death.

A relationship between the adrenals and the metabolism of sodium has been established. The removal of the adrenals is followed by a considerable loss of the element from the body (Chap. 23).

Extreme sweating due to high temperature or much exertion may cause so much loss of sodium chloride from the body as to develop leg and abdominal cramps.

Salt (and water) intake may be suggested for the following: prolonged vomiting (chloride loss); diarrhea (sodium loss); adrenal cortex insufficiency (disturbance of salt metabolism); and shock, due to loss of blood volume (in surgery, wounds or severe burns).

A low salt diet has been suggested in the treatment of hypertension.

POTASSIUM

While the ease of absorption and general metabolism resemble those of sodium, each element has very specific functions, since these elements cannot replace one another. It has already been indicated that potassium is found very largely in the cells of the body, whereas sodium is widely distributed in the body fluids (see Table 41).

Using radioactive potassium, it can be shown that the element penetrates rapidly into most of the tissues of the body and only a small quantity is found in the plasma.

The growth of rats is definitely retarded when the daily diet contains less than 15 mg. of potassium. These animals develop lesions of the heart and renal hypertrophy. The retardation of growth applies to chicks too.

In Addison's disease, associated with an adrenal cortex deficiency, the potassium in the blood is definitely increased.

The actual requirement of potassium for the body is not known, but since the element is widely distributed in foods, deficiencies are not apt to occur under normal conditions.

CHLORINE

In the form of sodium chloride, the chloride ion plays a role in osmotic pressure relationships and in maintaining the water content of the body. The loss of salt by the body means loss of water.

The chloride concentration of normal human plasma is equivalent to 5.60 to 6.30 gm. (of Cl as NaCl) per liter. A solution of 9 gm. of sodium chloride per liter is isotonic with serum, which means that the chlorides are responsible for two-thirds of the osmotic pressure of the blood.

The chloride shift is of importance in acid-base equilibria. It will be remembered in this connection that the chloride ion readily passes through the cell membrane, but that the sodium and potassium ions do not.

In tracing the origin of the hydrochloric acid of the stomach, we must ascribe it, to some extent at least, to the sodium chloride of the blood. Changes in gastric acidity involve changes in the composition of the blood and are not influenced by variations in chloride intake.

The metabolism of chlorine cannot be separated from the metabolism of sodium. As has been pointed out, some 10 to 20 gm. of sodium chloride is needed daily. The chlorine (as chloride) is as readily absorbed and metabolized as is the sodium (as sodium chloride); and on a diet deficient in salt, the excretion of chlorine is reduced correspondingly. In one case (cited by Sherman), the excretion dropped from 4.60 gm. per day to 0.17 gm. during the course of thirteen days.

On a chloride-deficient diet, rats showed depression of appetite, increased consumption of water, increased heat production, and diminished body gain of nitrogen and energy.

IODINE

Iodine is obtained largely from the supply of food (other than water), and, to some extent, from salt and water. The amount of iodine found in drinking water is, at times, used to estimate the content of iodine in the soil nearby, as well as its fruits, grains, grasses, and vegetables.

A man weighing 70 kg. probably contains within his body some 25 mg. of iodine, of which some 15 mg. is found in the thyroid.

The concentration of iodine in the thyroid gland is remarkable. Whereas in whole blood the iodine concentration is of the order of one part in 25 million, in the thyroid it is one part in 2500.

Using radioactive iodine, it can be shown that the iodine from the blood stream is rapidly transported to the thyroid, where it quickly becomes incorporated in organic molecules—as 3,5-diiodotyrosine and thyroxine (p. 61).

The blood may show values for iodine ranging from 3 to 20 micrograms per 100 ml. (1 microgram = 0.001 mg.); and about one-fourth of this amount represents thyroxine.

The average excretion of urinary iodine by normal adults (in twenty-four hours) has been estimated at 50 micrograms.

A deficiency of iodine in food (and water) may lead to simple (endemic) goiter. In certain inland regions, such as the Great Lakes district in this country, or the Alpine regions in Europe, the water (and the food grown on the soil) may contain less iodine than is necessary for normal well-being. When that happens, goiter in its various stages makes its appearance. The simplest treatment—and a very effective one—is to incorporate a small quantity of iodine, in the form of sodium iodide, in the common table salt. Usually, one part of sodium iodide in 100,000 parts of sodium chloride ("iodized salt") is sufficient.

It has been estimated that the average person needs from 100 to 200 micrograms per day. Although the concentration of iodine in sea water is low, sea life (algae, fish, oysters) concentrate this element, so that such organisms are a good source of iodine.

BROMINE

That bromine is present in animal tissues is beyond question, but just what its function is, if it has any, is a mystery. The claims made at one time or another, that the metabolism of bromine bears some relation to mental disease, or that there is a bromine-containing hormone in the pituitary, are questionable. It is true that what appear to be significant amounts of bromine have been detected in the brain (hypophysis); and it is also true that the bromine value of blood is markedly lowered in manic-depressive psychoses. Winnek and Smith find that a synthetic diet in which the bromine content is less than 5 parts per 10 million still supports growth in the rat.

It has been estimated that the blood contains from 0.23 to 1.71 mg. per 100 ml. In ordinary salt, for every gram of chlorine there is about 1 mg. of bromine.

FLUORINE

This element is present in various tissues of the body, particularly in bone and teeth. It has been estimated that the normal bone contains from 0.01 to 0.03 per cent of fluorine, and dental enamel, 0.01 to 0.02 per cent.

Since no diet has so far been devised which is free from fluorine, it is difficult to investigate, at present, the function of the element. Mottled enamel, a defect in teeth, endemic in parts of this country and elsewhere, has been attributed to the fluorine in the drinking water. The amount must be in excess of 2 parts per million. Such teeth show chalky white patches, and the enamel is frequently pitted and corroded. Histological examination reveals imperfect calcification. The minimum quantity of fluorine in water to give rise to mottled enamel is believed to be from 1 to 2 mg. per liter. Fluorine (as fluoride), given in relatively large doses, is quite toxic. From 8 to 9 mg. of fluorine per kilo of body weight given to cattle produces loss of appetite, disturbed osseous metabolism, and fatty degeneration. Studies in oxygen uptake suggest interference with cellular metabolism.

Some startling facts have appeared linking dental caries with the lack of fluorine. It would seem that a certain amount of fluorine in the water—somewhere in the neighborhood of 1 part per million, and therefore less than what would give rise to mottled enamel—gives some protection against dental caries. Where the drinking water contains but a trace of the element, caries is more prevalent.

The suggestion has been made that when the enamel contains appreciable quantities of calcium fluoride, it becomes more resistant to attacks by acid.

IRON

A man weighing some 70 kg. contains in his body about 4.3 gm. of iron. About 55 per cent of this amount is found in hemoglobin, and about 10 per cent in muscle myoglobin and heme catalysts (cytochromes, catalase, peroxidase). The remainder—some 30 to 35 per cent—constitutes the storage iron fraction; and the major portion of this fraction—some 0.8 gm.—is found in the liver, spleen, and red bone marrow, largely in the form of ferritin, an iron-protein complex.

Under normal conditions of health and nutrition, the adult absorbs very little iron from the gastrointestinal tract; most of the element taken in with the food is excreted in the feces. This is a remarkable fact, considering that iron is needed for such important compounds as hemoglobin, the cytochromes, etc. To explain this situation, it should be first noticed that the body has a storehouse for iron which it can tap when needed. Further, when hemoglobin is lost, owing to hemorrhage or the destruction of red cells, there is no immediate absorption of iron from the intestine. Instead, ferritin releases its iron for purposes of hemoglobin synthesis. Only after several days, when the liver has been markedly depleted of its store of iron, does its absorption begin. This "brake" by the cells of the intestinal mucosa is referred to by Whipple as the "mucosal block."

Ferritin consists of a protein portion, apoferritin, in combination with colloidal micelles of iron hydroxide–iron phosphate. In contrast to hemoglobin, the content of the iron in ferritin is variable and may reach as high as 25 per cent on a dry weight basis. Ferritin is, in reality, a mixture of different molecules—apoferritin (which contains no iron) together with ferritin molecules which contain variable quantities of iron.

When ferritin is treated with organic reducing agents, such as glutathione or ascorbic acid, the ferric iron is reduced to the ferrous condition.

The fate of the absorbed iron may be followed in Figure 68.

Iron (as ferric iron) in the food enters the gastrointestinal (G.I.) tract and is there reduced to the ferrous state. It is absorbed into the mucosal cells and there appears as ferritin. The ferrous iron in the mucosal cells remains in equilibrium with the ferritin as well as with the plasma iron in the blood stream. Some iron from the ferritin is released and travels to the plasma, where it combines with the iron-binding globulin to form a ferric protein complex.

It is believed that all the iron in the plasma is in combination with this protein. Here again, the iron in the plasma is in equilibrium with the iron of ferritin, stored in the liver, spleen and bone marrow. In the last (the bone marrow) the ferritin iron can be incorporated into hemoglobin for red cell regeneration.

Damaged red cells are destroyed by the phagocytes of the liver, spleen, and marrow. This breakdown still leaves the iron intact, and this iron is again used by the body to build up hemoglobin and its various other iron compounds.

The isolation of ferritin from human placenta affords a reasonable explanation for the mode of transport of iron from the plasma of the mother to that of the fetus, without the necessity of having to assume the passage of an iron-protein complex across the membrane.

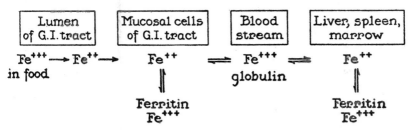

Fig. 68. Scheme representing the role of ferritin in absorption and storage of iron. (Granick: Chem. Rev., *38:* 379. Williams & Wilkins Co.)

It is generally recognized that for the proper utilization of iron, small quantities of copper are needed. Without the copper, the iron is assimilated but not converted into hemoglobin; such a conversion does take place in the presence of copper (Elvehjem).

Table 42 gives the amount of iron in some typical foods.

Anemias due to deficiencies in the amount of iron in the diet are very common. In a survey in Aberdeen, 41 per cent of infants (under two years of age) examined suffered from anemia. In investigations in East Africa on the effect of different diets, it was shown that in a population whose food consisted largely of cereals, 48 per cent of the boys were definitely anemic; whereas in an adjoining district, where the food included relatively large percentages of meat, blood, and milk, the anemic sufferers among a corresponding group numbered less than 12 per cent.

Anemias of this type—the typical nutritional anemia, due to a lack of available iron in the diet—can be treated with gratifying results by incorporating in the diet 25 mg. of iron pyrophosphate and 1 mg. of copper sulfate each day.

It has been estimated that children need 0.6 mg. of iron (available) and 0.1 mg. of copper per kilogram of body weight per day. Sherman is of the opinion that the daily needs for the adult are about 12 mg., and that the diet should also include 2 mg. of copper. During pregnancy, a daily diet including 20 mg. of iron is recommended.*

The iron is conserved and used again and again as it helps to form hemo-

* Whipple suggests that as little as 2–3 mg. suffices for the adult.

globin which, in time, loses its iron (through conversion of the hemoglobin into bile pigments, etc.), paving the way for the freed iron to contribute once again to hemoglobin synthesis (and to the syntheses, in lesser amounts, of other iron-protein compounds such as cytochromes, etc.).

In addition to emphasizing the importance of copper and the importance of supplying available iron, the condition of the subject has to be considered. Prolonged diarrhea often decreases the amount of iron absorbed, perhaps because the chyme does not remain long enough in the intestine.

Table 42　　IRON IN TYPICAL FOOD MATERIALS
(Sherman: Chemistry of Food and Nutrition.
By permission of The Macmillan Company,
Publishers.)

Food	Iron (in mg.) per 100 gm. fresh substance
Beans, dried	10.5
Egg yolk	8.6
Peas, dried	5.7
Wheat, entire grain	5.0
Oatmeal	4.8
Eggs	3.1
Beef	3.0
Prunes	2.8
Spinach	2.5
Beefsteak, medium fat	2.0
Cheese	1.3
Beans, string, fresh	1.1
Potatoes	1.1
White flour	1.0
Rice, polished	0.9
Beets	0.8
Carrots	0.6
Bananas	0.6
Turnips	0.5
Oranges	0.5
Tomatoes	0.4
Apples	0.3
Milk	0.2

Patients suffering from achlorhydria, with deficient quantities of hydrochloric acid in the gastric juice, often suffer from anemia due to lack of utilizable iron.

COPPER*

Copper is present in all living matter, both plant and animal. In plants, it may be associated with the formation of chlorophyll. In animals, its association with hemoglobin formation has been stressed. The mechanism of this reaction is obscure. The largest amounts of the element are found in the liver, spleen, and kidneys.

Among naturally occurring organic substances, several contain copper.

* See also Iron, p. 310.

One of them, hemocyanin, a copper-protein complex, is found in the blood of certain invertebrates (Table 43). In the crab, spider, and snail, for example, the hemocyanin functions as an oxygen carrier similar to hemoglobin in man. Turacin is a pigment found in the feathers of the South African bird, turaco. Certain oxidizing enzymes, such as polyphenoloxidase, laccase, and tyrosinase are copper-protein complexes.

Table 43   COPPER CONTENT OF BLOODS CONTAINING HEMOCYANIN
(Elvehjem: Physiol. Rev., *15:* 472.)

Group	Animal	Copper
		mg. per 100 ml.
Mollusca, Cephalopoda................ {	Octopus vulgaris	23.5
	Sepia officinalis	23.7
Mollusca, Gastropoda.....................Helix pomatia		6.5–7.5
	Astacus fluviatilis	7.0
	Palinurus vulgaris	9.5
Crustacea, Decapoda..................	Homarus vulgaris	10.0
	Cancer pagurus	6.0
	Carcinus maenas	9.0
	Maia squinado	3.5
Crustacea, Stomatopoda.................Squilla mantis		6.1

Other copper compounds were discovered by Keilin and Mann, who isolated a copper-protein compound from the red blood corpuscles of mammals, to which they gave the name *hemocuprein.* They isolated another copper-protein compound, *hepatocuprein,* from the liver. "It is certain," they write, "that some of the copper supplied . . . as food is utilized for building up hemo- and hepatocuprein. The formation of these compounds may therefore represent one of the steps in copper metabolism and may directly or indirectly be responsible for some of the physiological effects which are rightly ascribed to copper."

The copper content of several foods is summarized by Rose (from data by Elvehjem) (Table 44).

Table 44   THE COPPER CONTENT OF FOODS (AVERAGE FIGURES)

Substance (per kg.).	Copper (in mg.)
Liver..	44.1
Nuts..	11.6
Legumes....................................	9.0
Cereals.....................................	4.7
Fruits......................................	4.2
Poultry.....................................	3.0
Fish..	2.5
Green legumes..............................	1.7
Leafy vegetables...........................	1.2

Cow's milk contains from 0.09 to 0.17 mg. of copper per liter. Nelson has isolated a copper-protein compound from milk.

It has been estimated that the daily needs of copper are in the neighborhood of 2 mg. per day. Much of its excretion is via the bowels.

SULFUR

Most of the sulfur is found in the protein molecule and is therefore part of an organic molecule. In fact, the metabolism of sulfur, just like the metabolism of nitrogen, is very intimately associated with the metabolism of protein itself.

The sulfur of the protein is centered in the groups containing cystine and methionine. The essential nature of the latter and the metabolism of both amino acids have already been discussed.

Sulfur is largely oxidized to sulfate in the body and excreted as inorganic and ethereal sulfates, both of which will be discussed under Urine (Chap. 22).

Besides cystine and methionine, organic compounds of sulfur found in the body are glutathione, coenzyme A, insulin, thiamine, ergothionine, taurocholic acid, sulfocyanide, ethereal sulfates (esters of phenols and sulfuric acid), chondroitin sulfuric acid (in cartilage, etc.), and melanins (pigments of the body). Small quantities of inorganic sulfates (mainly sodium and potassium) are found in the blood and various tissues of the body.

The average amount of sulfur in various foods is 1 per cent.

COBALT

Because it is a component of vitamin B_{12}, which is essential for a large variety of animals and even for microorganisms, it is probable that cobalt is essential for man as well as for all animals. However, the amount required is so small that neither in rabbits nor in rats could deficiency symptoms be developed.

A type of nutritional anemia ("pine disease"), occurring in cattle or sheep, has been successfully treated with cobalt.

Using radioactive cobalt, it has been determined that most of the element is quickly eliminated from the body. The element is eliminated almost completely via the kidneys. This is in contrast to manganese, which is excreted almost exclusively in the feces.

Cobalt produces polycythemia (an excess in the number of red corpuscles in the blood) when fed or injected. As little as 0.04 to 0.05 mg. in the entire body (of the rat) is enough to develop polycythemia.

MANGANESE

This element is found in plant and animal tissues and seems to belong to the essential group. When present in deficient amounts there is a marked retardation of growth in the rat. In the female, estrous cycles are irregular, and in the male one finds testicular degeneration and sterility due to absence of spermatozoa.

Elvehjem and Hart, in some extensive experiments on rats, showed that on a synthetic diet which included but 5 γ of manganese per day (γ =

gamma = microgram = 0.001 mg.), the growth of the animals was impaired. The deficient rats had poorer bone formation, and their serum phosphatase was increased two- to three-fold.

The kidney and the liver are the chief storage places for the element in the body. In 100 gm. of tissue, we find 0.17 mg. in the liver and 0.087 mg. in the kidney. The manganese content of blood varies from 0.004 to 0.020 mg. per 100 ml.

It was pointed out under Cobalt that manganese is very largely excreted with the feces. Greenberg, using the radioactive isotope of manganese, makes it clear that the bile plays an important role in the intestinal excretion of the element, for some 50 to 75 per cent of it is carried by the bile.

The amount of manganese in foods varies considerably. In terms of kilogram of dry material, those having from 100 to 200 mg. are beet tops, blueberries, lettuce, pineapple, and wheat bran; those from 35 to 100 mg., beets, blackberries, spinach, whole grain wheat. Fruits, as a rule, have less than 15 mg. per kilogram, and round of beef and the fish so far examined have little or none.

Chicks deficient in manganese reveal reduced levels of blood and bone phosphatase, and a condition of perosis, or "slipped tendon" (an anatomical deformity of the leg bones), may develop.

There is evidence to indicate that the element is involved in activating several enzymes (phosphatases, arginase, cozymase, carboxylase, cholinesterase).

While it has not yet been established that manganese is an essential element for man, the suggestion has been made that from 0.02 to 0.03 gm. of the element per kilogram of body weight, incorporated in the diet (particularly for children), might be of value.

ZINC

The weight of evidence is in favor of the view that zinc is an essential element. Todd, Elvehjem, and Hart kept young rats in monel-metal cages and fed them a highly purified ration which included all of the known vitamins and essential mineral elements, together with 2 ml. of milk. The only probable deficiency of this diet was its low content of zinc—1.6 mg. per kilo of the food offered. These animals were compared with controls which received more zinc; the former were inferior to the latter in rate of growth and maximum weight attained. There is also, on this low zinc diet, some interference with the development of a normal fur coat.

Scott has shown that zinc is a constituent of crystalline insulin, but the full significance of this discovery is not yet apparent. Zinc is also a constituent of the enzyme, carbonic anhydrase.

The zinc content of the pancreas of diabetics is about one-half the normal amount, which suggests that the element may be concerned with the storage and utilization of insulin.

It has been estimated that the average daily diet contains 12 to 20 mg. of the element. Much of the excretion is by the intestinal tract. Radioactive zinc accumulates in the mucosa of the intestine and in the pancreas and the liver.

ENZYMES AND INORGANIC ELEMENTS

Many enzymes require small quantities of inorganic elements for their activity. Smith is of the opinion that the metal acts by forming a bond between the enzyme-protein groups, on the one hand, and the substrate, on the other.

Table 45 presents a list of the metal requirements of several enzymes:

Table 45   ENZYMES AND THEIR METALS
(McElroy and Swanson: Scientific American, Jan., 1953, p. 22.)

Enzyme	Reaction	Metal
Carbonic anhydrase	$CO_2 + H_2O \rightleftharpoons H_2CO_3$	Zn
Inorganic pyrophosphatase	Pyrophosphate $+ H_2O \longrightarrow PO_4$	Mg
Catalase	$2H_2O_2 \longrightarrow 2H_2O + O_2$	Fe
Cytochromes	Electron transport	Fe
Tyrosinase	Tyrosine $+ \frac{1}{2}O_2 \longrightarrow$ Hallochrome	Cu
Laccase	Phenols $\longrightarrow$ Ortho and paraquinones	Cu
Ascorbic acid oxidase	Ascorbic acid $\longrightarrow$ Dehydroascorbic acid	Cu
Prolidase	Glycylproline $\longrightarrow$ Proline	Mn
Carboxypeptidase	Chloroacetyl-tyrosine $\longrightarrow$ Tyrosine	Mg
Glycylglycine dipeptidase	Glycylglycine $\longrightarrow$ Glycine	Zn

The subject of water is treated in Chapter 22.

REFERENCES

For a discussion of "trace" elements, see Nutr. Rev., *10:* 65, 192; *8:* 178, 1950; *McElroy and Swanson:* Scientific American, Jan., 1953, p. 22.

The competitive antagonism between ions—using bacteria—is described in Nutr. Rev., *9:* 135, 1951.

Calcium. Heilbrunn: Scientific American, June, 1951, p. 60; *Sherman:* Nutr. Rev., *10:* 97, 1952; *Stearns:* J. Am. Med. Assoc., *142:* 478, 1950; *Youmans:* Ibid., *143:* 1254, 1950; *Wallace, Shirley, and Davis:* J. Nutrition, *43:* 469, 1951 (excretion into gastrointestinal tract); *Davis:* Nutritional Observatory, *13:* 69, 1952; *Harrison and Harrison:* J. Biol. Chem., *185:* 857, 1950; *188:* 83, 1951 (use of radiocalcium); *Bellin and Laszlo:* Science, *117:* 331, 1953 (metabolism).

Phosphorus. Davis: Nutritional Observatory, *13:* 70, 1952; *Stearns:* J. Am. Med. Assoc., *142:* 480, 1950; *Frost and Sandy:* Proc. Soc. Exp. Biol. Med., *83:* 102, 1953.

Magnesium. Kunkel and Pearson: Arch. Biochem., *18:* 461, 1948 (rat requirements); *Stearns:* J. Am. Med. Assoc., *142:* 481, 1950.

Sodium. Overman: Physiol. Rev., *31:* 285, 1951 (Na, K and Chloride alterations in disease); *Smith:* Nutr. Rev., *11:* 33, 1953 (history and use of salt); Ibid., *9:* 208, 1951 (influence of Na on K requirement); *Stone and Goldzieher:* J. Biol. Chem., *181:* 511, 1949 (determination); *Grunert, Meyer, and Phillips:* J. Nutrition, *42:* 609, 1950 (Na and K requirements of rat); *Dole, Dahl, Cottizias, Dziewiatkowski, and Harris:* J. Clinical Investigation, *30:* 584, 1951 (Na and hypertension).

Potassium. Stephens: Canadian Medical Association J., *66:* 19, 1952 (review); What's New (Abbott Labs.), July–Aug., 1951, p. 8 (review); *Fenn:* Scientific American, Aug., 1949, p. 16 (review); *Muntz and Hurwitz:* Arch. Biochem., *32:* 124, 1951 (effect of K^+ and NH_4^+ upon glycolysis); *Sheppard:* Science, *114:* 85, 1951 (review); *Hoffman:* J. Am. Med. Assoc., *144:* 1157, 1950 (clinical physiology of K); Nutr. Rev., *10:* 163, 1952 (K depletion in man); *Mudge:* Bull. N. Y. Acad. Med., Nov., 1953, p. 846 (K imbalance).

Iodine. Sebrell: Nutr. Rev., *8:* 129, 1950 (review); *Youmans:* J. Am. Med. Assoc., *143:* 1256, 1950 (clinical review).

Fluorine. Nutr. Rev., *9:* 149, 1951 (fluorides and experimental tooth decay): Chem. Eng. News, *29:* 5354, 1951 (fluorides and drinking water); *Melure:* J. Am. Med. Assoc., *139:* 711, 1949 (review).

Iron. Granick: Bull. N. Y. Acad. Med., July, 1949, p. 403; Physiol. Rev., *31:* 489, 1951; *Mazur, Litt, and Shorr:* J. Biol. Chem., *187:* 473, 485, 497, 1950 (iron metabolism); *Darby:* J. Am. Med. Assoc., *142:* 1288, 1950 (review); *McCance and Widdowson:* J. Physiol., *112:* 450, 1951 (metabolism during suckling); *Youmans:* J. Am. Med. Assoc., *143:* 1252, 1950 (review); Nutr. Rev., *8:* 76, 1950 (Fe and the erythrocyte); Ibid., *8:* 7, 1950 (diet and Fe absorption); Ibid., *9:* 293, 1951 (storage); *Hall:* J. Am. Med. Assoc., *151:* 1, 1953 (nutritional anemia); Nutr. Rev., *11:* 73, 1953 (iron storage).

Copper. Darby: J. Am. Med. Assoc., *142:* 1294, 1950 (review); *Glass:* Copper metabolism (Johns Hopkins Univ., 1950) (review); Nutr. Rev., *9:* 180, 1951 (Cu in mother's milk); Ibid., *9:* 121, 1951 (Cu deficiency); *Teague and Carpenter:* J. Nutrition, *43:* 389, 1951 (Cu deficiency); *Keilin:* Biochem. J., *49:* 544, 1951 (turacin); *Chase, Gubler, Cartwright, and Wintrobe:* J. Biol. Chem., *199:* 757, 1952; *Wintrobe, Cartwright, and Gubler:* J. Nutrition, *50:* 395, 1953 (function and metabolism).

Cobalt (see Vitamin B$_{12}$, p. 000). Nutr. Rev., *10:* 238, 1952 (in rats): Ibid., *10:* 177, 1952 (deficiency in lambs); Ibid., *9:* 243, 1951 (Co and red blood corpuscles); *Harp and Scoular:* J. Nutrition, *47:* 67, 1952 (metabolism); *Rosenfeld and Tobias:* J. Biol. Chem., *191:* 339, 1951 (distribution of Co in cytoplasm and nuclei); *Jaffé:* Science, *115:* 265, 1952 (Co and reproduction).

Manganese. Hill, Holtkamp, Buchanan, and Rutledge: J. Nutrition, *41:* 359, 1950 (Mn deficiency); *Bentley and Phillips:* Arch. Biochem., *32:* 338, 1951 (Mn deficiency).

Zinc. Banks, Tupper, and Wormall: Biochem. J., *47:* 466, 1950 (Fate of Zn compounds in body); *Sadasivan:* Ibid., *48:* 527, 1951; *49:* 186, 1951; *52:* 452, 1952 (metabolism).

Chapter 19 Foods

Our FOODS include proteins, fats (lipids), carbohydrates, mineral salts, vitamins, water, and oxygen. A separate chapter is devoted to vitamins; water is discussed in connection with the biochemistry of the kidneys; and under blood and respiration a discussion of the function of oxygen is undertaken. The changes which carbohydrates, fats, proteins, and mineral salts undergo in the body have already been discussed. At this stage we wish to refer to a few pertinent facts involving food and diet in general.

Over a considerable period of time the emphasis was laid on the calorific needs of the body. Calorimetric studies revealed that a normal person weighing 70 kg. expends, on an average, energy equivalent to about 3000 Calories per day.* The variations are considerable, depending upon age and depending upon the amount of physical labor expended. The first column in Table 46 deals with calorific requirements.

For many years, foods have been analyzed for their "energy" content, and those foods high in calorific value have been preferred. While it is well

Table 46 RECOMMENDED DAILY DIETARY ALLOWANCES, REVISED, 1953 (Food and Nutrition Board, National Research Council.)

	Wt.	Ht.	Calories	Protein	Cal-cium	Iron	Vita-min A	Thia-mine	Ribo-flavin	Niacin	Ascorbic acid	Vita-min D
	kg.	cm.		grams	grams	mg.	I.U.	mg.	mg.	mg.	mg.	I.U.
MEN												
25 yrs.	65	170	3200	65	0.8	12	5000	1.6	1.6	16	75	
45 yrs.	65	170	2900	65	0.8	12	5000	1.5	1.6	15	75	
65 yrs.	65	170	2600	65	0.8	12	5000	1.3	1.6	13	75	
WOMEN												
25 yrs.	55	157	2300	55	0.8	12	5000	1.2	1.4	12	70	
45 yrs.	55	157	2100	55	0.8	12	5000	1.1	1.4	11	70	
65 yrs.	55	157	1800	55	0.8	12	5000	1.0	1.4	10	70	
Pregnant (3rd trimester)			Add 400	80	1.5	15	6000	1.5	2.0	15	100	400
Lactating (850 ml. daily)			Add 1000	100	2.0	15	8000	1.5	2.5	15	150	400
INFANTS												
1–3 mos.	6	60	kg.x120	kg.x3.5	0.6	6	1500	0.3	0.4	3	30	400
4–9 mos.	9	70	kg.x110	kg.x3.5	0.8	6	1500	0.4	0.7	4	30	400
10–12 mos.	10	75	kg.x100	kg.x3.5	1.0	6	1500	0.5	0.9	5	30	400
CHILDREN												
1–3 yrs.	12	87	1200	40	1.0	7	2000	0.6	1.0	6	35	400
4–6 yrs.	18	109	1600	50	1.0	8	2500	0.8	1.2	8	50	400
7–9 yrs.	27	129	2000	60	1.0	10	3500	1.0	1.5	10	60	400
BOYS												
10–12 yrs.	35	144	2500	70	1.2	12	4500	1.3	1.8	13	75	400
13–15 yrs.	49	163	3200	85	1.4	15	5000	1.6	2.1	16	90	400
16–20 yrs.	63	175	3800	100	1.4	15	5000	1.9	2.5	19	100	400
GIRLS												
10–12 yrs.	36	144	2300	70	1.2	12	4500	1.2	1.8	12	75	400
13–15 yrs.	49	160	2500	80	1.3	15	5000	1.3	2.0	13	80	400
16–20 yrs.	54	162	2400	75	1.3	15	5000	1.2	1.9	12	80	400

* For the average individual in the white collar class in America, this figure is probably somewhat high. For a definition of the Calorie, see p. 287.

318

recognized that the energy needs of the body must be fulfilled if health is to be maintained, the shift in emphasis has been, first, toward a better distribution within the diet of the three basic foodstuffs (protein, fat, and carbohydrate), and secondly, toward a more careful consideration of the individual components of the diet (and this would also include the mineral salts and vitamins).

THE AMOUNT OF PROTEIN IN THE DIET

This problem has proved a difficult one. More than fifty years ago, Voit made an elaborate study of what the average German laborer consumes in the shape of protein. This led him to the view that the needs of the average

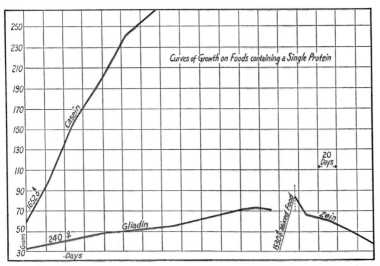

Fig. 69. Showing typical curves of growth of rats maintained on diets containing a single protein. On the casein food (devoid of glycine) satisfactory growth is obtained, on the gliadin food (deficient in lysine) little more than maintenance of body weight is possible, on the zein food (devoid of glycine, lysine, and tryptophan) even maintenance of body weight is impossible. (Osborne and Mendel: Harvey Lectures, Ser. 10, Williams and Wilkins Co.)

man were in the neighborhood of 118 gm. of protein per day. Chittenden, working at Yale twenty years later, maintained nitrogen equilibrium (where the intake and the output of nitrogen are approximately equal) on as little as 45 gm. of protein per day. But the problem assumed an entirely new aspect as a result of the pioneer researches of Kossel and Fischer on the chemical constitution of the protein molecule. It became apparent that the emphasis must be placed on the amino acid content of the protein, rather than on the protein as a whole.

For example, it had been known for some time that gelatin is a "deficient" protein. That is to say, assuming the presence in the diet of optimal amounts of fat, carbohydrate, etc., the use of gelatin as the sole source of protein proved disastrous.* An analysis of gelatin showed that it was de-

* "Cadet de Vaux in Paris during the French Revolution tried to persuade the poor that gelatin soup was a satisfactory and nutritious diet. The poor refused and their attitude has since been amply justified. . . ." *T. F. Dixon:* Nature, March 4, 1944.

ficient in a number of important amino acids. Tryptophan, valine, and tyrosine are entirely missing; cystine is present in small amounts. A number of investigators next showed that growth and development—though probably not *normal* growth and development—are possible by the addition to the diet of the missing amino acids.

Economically, the problem of gelatin is of importance. It is a cheap protein. It is easily obtained from tendon, cartilage, bone, and skin by boiling with water, thereby converting the collagen into gelatin.

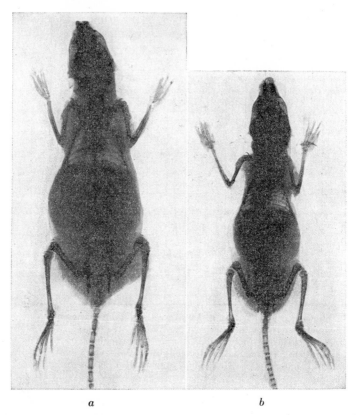

a   *b*

Fig. 70. Radiograph of lysine-deficient animal (*b*) and control (*a*). The animals were littermates, 10 weeks old and had been 6 weeks on their respective diets. (Harris, Neuberger and Sanger: Biochem. J., *37:* 508.)

Osborne and Mendel.   We owe to Osborne and Mendel the fundamental work on the effect in the diet of various proteins viewed in the light of their content of amino acids. Casein, despite its deficiency in glycine, is an excellent protein (Fig. 69). Apparently, glycine is an amino acid which can be synthesized by the body.* Gliadin (a protein in wheat and rye) and zein (in maize) are deficient (Fig. 69).

These experiments—and others later, such as the experiment illustrated in Figure 70—established the indispensability of certain amino acids (such

* This is true for the rat but not necessarily for other animals.

as lysine and tryptophan). It became clear that a diet devoid of such amino acids (or rather, a diet in which the proteins are deficient in such amino acids) is a deficient diet. Apparently, the synthetic abilities of the body are limited.

Rose.   The experimental method adopted by Osborne and Mendel was to feed carefully purified proteins and to supplement "deficient" proteins with the missing amino acids. Another method which has been widely adopted may be illustrated by an example. Casein is first completely

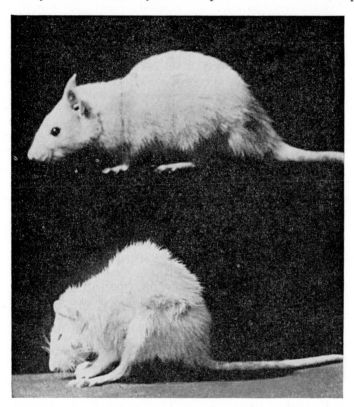

Fig. 71. Lower photograph shows a rat on a histidine-deficient diet. Upper rat received the same diet together with a histidine supplement. (Courtesy Prof. W. C. Rose and Journal of Biological Chemistry.)

hydrolyzed until a mixture of amino acids is obtained. From this mixture histidine is removed as completely as possible. The residue proves deficient. Supplementing the residue with histidine causes recovery. Histidine is, then, an essential, or indispensable, amino acid (Fig. 71) (Rose, and Harrow and Sherwin).

The third method, adopted by Rose, is relatively costly, but it is the most satisfactory method. It consists in feeding a mixture of purified amino acids, comparable in number and in relative amounts to those found in casein (which is a biologically wholesome protein). These highly purified amino acids (nineteen in number), added to a diet of the necessary fat, carbohydrate, mineral salts, and vitamins, were quite inadequate for the normal growth of young rats. This result was in striking contrast to the use of hydrolyzed casein as the source of protein; here growth was obtained. Evidently, some unknown substance or substances essential to growth were present in the hydrolyzed casein and absent in the synthetic mixture of amino acids. The substitution of part of the synthetic amino acid mixture with some native protein, such as casein, improved the condition of the animals. Eventually, from the monoamino-monocarboxylic acid fraction of the hydrolyzed protein, Rose isolated a new amino acid, threonine, or α-amino-β-hydroxybutyric acid (Fig. 72). This acid is found in casein, fibrin, serum albumin, and serum globulin, among others, but hemoglobin contains little, if any.

Even with threonine present, the results are not always beyond question. For instance, Elvehjem and his co-workers, using the chick, find casein as such superior to a synthetic diet (including threonine).

The introduction of protein hydrolysates in clinical medicine has brought out the fact that even hydrolysates may not always be the equal—nutritionally speaking—of unhydrolyzed proteins.

Woolley has shown that some "factor" in casein (and a number of other proteins) stimulates the growth of *Lactobacillus casei;* and that this factor, even though it may be a peptide, is certainly not an amino acid. The unknown substance was called *strepogenin*. It is present in casein, trypsinogen, insulin, and hemoglobin, but not in egg albumin and gelatin.

Mice and rats, fed on hydrolyzed casein—a protein always considered high in the biological series—did not develop normally until strepogenin (in the form of a protein rich in the substance, like casein) was added to the diet.

There is evidence that strepogenin may be a derivative of glutamic acid.

It should be explained that "protein hydrolysates" are hydrolytic products of proteins, brought about by the action of acid or the appropriate enzyme (pepsin or trypsin, for example). The proteins used are casein, lactalbumin, fibrin, etc.

The use of such protein hydrolysates—given parenterally—is of importance in disturbances of digestion and absorption of food, as in severe illness, or after surgical operations involving the digestive tract. The attempt is made to regain nitrogen equilibrium (Chap. 17) and even a positive nitrogen balance.

A list of essential (indispensable) and nonessential (dispensable) amino acids (so far as these have been studied up to the present) is given in Table 47.

Rose defines an indispensable (essential) amino acid as one which cannot be synthesized by the organism out of materials ordinarily available at a speed commensurate with the demands for normal growth.

Another factor which has to be taken into consideration in dealing with these amino acids is their optical activity. Where the synthetic product is used, Rose gives double the theoretical amount to ensure the presence of the active isomer at the desired level.

Rose finds that with the following amino acids, only the *natural* isomers promote growth: valine, leucine, isoleucine, lysine, and threonine; on the

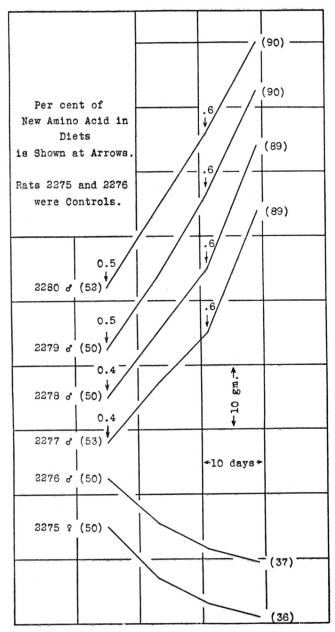

Per cent of
New Amino Acid in
Diets
is Shown at Arrows.

Rats 2275 and 2276
were Controls.

(90)
(90)
(89)
(89)

.6
.6
.6
.6
.6

0.5
2280 ♂ (52)

0.5
2279 ♂ (50)

0.4
2278 ♂ (50)

0.4
2277 ♂ (53)

2276 ♂ (50)

2275 ♀ (50)

←10 gm.→

←10 days→

(37)
(36)

Fig. 72. Rats 2275 and 2276 did not grow on a purified amino acid mixture. The addition of the amino acid threonine caused growth. (McCoy, Meger and Rose: J. Biol. Chem., *112:* 283.)

other hand, in dealing with tryptophan, histidine, phenylalanine, and methionine, it is found that both isomers promote growth.

The experiments of Rose dealing with essential and nonessential amino
acids apply to the rat. He has also used dogs in place of rats and finds that,
in general, the response is similar. These results, however, do not necessarily apply to all other animals. For example, Almquist, using chicks in
the place of rats, showed that glycine and arginine were important.

Table 47   CLASSIFICATION OF AMINO ACIDS
WITH   RESPECT   TO   THEIR
GROWTH EFFECTS IN THE RAT
(Rose, Oesterling, and Womack: J.
Biol. Chem., *172:* 753.)

Essential	Nonessential
Lysine	Glycine
Tryptophan	Alanine
Histidine	Serine
Phenylalanine	Cystine †
Leucine	Tyrosine ‡
Isoleucine	Aspartic acid
Threonine	Glutamic acid §
Valine	Proline §
Arginine *	Hydroxyproline §
Methionine	Citrulline

* Arginine can be synthesized by the rat, but not
at a sufficiently rapid rate to meet the demands of
maximum growth. Its classification, therefore, as
essential or nonessential is purely a matter of definition.

† Cystine can replace about one-sixth of the methionine requirement, but has no growth effect in
the absence of methionine.

‡ Tyrosine can replace about one-half of the
phenylalanine requirement, but has no growth effect in the absence of phenylalanine.

§ Glutamic acid and proline can serve individually as rather effective substitutes for arginine in
the diet. This property is not shared by hydroxyproline.

Rose has extended his studies to man. Arginine, which is necessary for
optimal growth in the rat, is not required for the maintenance of nitrogen
equilibrium (p. 241) in normal human adults. Perhaps the most striking
result is that here histidine is dispensable. This result is a surprising one,
for the amino acid is essential for all species of animals so far tested.

The amino acids which have so far been found essential for man are
given in Table 48.

The clinician is familiar with the results of an inadequate protein diet
over an extended period. One such result is nutritional edema, also known
as war or starvation edema—a condition produced in animals when fed a
low protein diet. In this condition, the plasma protein (the albumin fraction) is considerably below normal in amount (hypoproteinemia).

As showing to what extent these amino acids are the true building stones of the protein in the body, Whipple has restored the plasma protein in dogs which had previously been bled (reducing tissue and plasma protein) by feeding them protein hydrolysates.

It has been suggested that the biological efficiency of a protein may be shown by the regeneration of liver protein after a period of starvation. During starvation, the weight of the liver decreases rapidly, and part of this decrease is due to the absence of protein. Using the rate of regeneration of liver protein as the basis, several authors have shown that casein and lactalbumin bring about such regeneration much more efficiently than, say, gelatin or zein.

Not only are amino acids needed for the building and repair of tissue proteins, but they are needed for the synthesis in the body of enzymes, hormones, and antibodies.

Table 48   MINIMUM AND RECOMMENDED INTAKES FOR NORMAL MAN WHEN DIET FURNISHES SUFFICIENT NITROGEN FOR SYNTHESIS OF NON-ESSENTIAL AMINO ACIDS (STRICTLY TENTATIVE VALUES) (Rose: J. Biol. Chem. *181:* 307, 1949.

Amino acid	Minimum Daily Rqt. (gm.)	Recommended Daily Intake (gm.)
L-Tryptophan	0.25	0.5
L-Phenylalanine	1.10	2.2
L-Lysine	0.80	1.6
L-Threonine	0.50	1.0
L-Valine	0.80	1.6
L-Methionine	1.10	2.2
L-Leucine	1.10	2.2
L-Isoleucine	0.70	1.4

High and Low Protein.   In the light of such work as that of Osborne and Mendel, and of Rose, the danger of incorporating too little protein in the diet becomes apparent. The problem must be attacked, first, from the point of view of including proteins which contain all the essential or indispensable amino acids, and, secondly, from the point of view of including enough of such proteins, so that the essential amino acids may be present in sufficient amounts. Dealing in dietetics for man, with complex natural foodstuffs rather than with artificial mixtures, the answer to the problem is not an easy one. Both Sherman and Rose are of the opinion that an allowance for the adult of 70 to 75 gm. per day of mixed proteins is within the region of safety. This is approximately 1 gm. of protein per kilogram of body weight. The British Ministry of Health advocates 50 gm. of "first class protein," meaning by that protein of animal origin (milk, eggs, cheese, meat, and fish).

It is worth noticing in this connection that meat is by no means the *only* source of animal protein. Nor, if meat it must be, is there evidence that, nutritionally speaking, expensive cuts are necessarily superior to portions less expensive. And some parts of the animal, such as blood, lungs, brain, and heart, richly nutritious, are often spurned.

At this stage a word should be said about the proteins in the soybean, of which *glycinin* is the most abundant. While, from the point of view of essential amino acids, animal proteins are to be preferred to vegetable proteins, the proteins of the soybean take their place somewhere in between—on the whole, better than other vegetable proteins, but probably not quite so good as animal proteins. Cooked soybean meal is superior to the raw variety. Heating seems to remove the effects of a trypsin inhibitor —a substance which interferes with the action of the digestive enzyme.

The proteins in yeast closely approximate, in biological value, those found in the soybean; which means that, on the whole, they are superior to most of the proteins found in the vegetable world.

It may be added, in conclusion, that an abundance of protein in the diet of patients slowly recovering from disease or from wounds is of importance.

THE AMOUNTS OF FAT AND CARBOHYDRATE IN THE DIET

Fats and carbohydrates are essentially energy-yielding foods. The so-called "staple" foods, cereal grains, potatoes and rice often constitute one-half of the calorific intake, and famine is often associated with a decreased supply of these staple foods.

If the protein intake is equivalent to 75 gm., some 300 Calories can be attributed to protein (1 gm. of protein is equivalent to 4 Calories). If the total calorific requirement is about 3000 Calories, more than 2000 Calories must be derived from the burning of fat and carbohydrate in the body. This means that the calorific equivalent of the fat plus the carbohydrate must be between 2000 and 3000 Calories. Just what proportions of fat and carbohydrate should be included is probably not important, within broad limits. This much is definite: in the absence of carbohydrate, and when the fat alone supplies all the energy requirements, acidosis sets in. On the other hand, in the absence of fat from the diet, no matter how much carbohydrate is present, rats develop a deficiency disease (Figs. 73 and 74). This deficiency is due to the absence from the diet of highly unsaturated fatty acids—acids present in various fats. These are known as "essential fatty acids."

Linoleic Acid, $CH_3(CH_2)_3(CH_2CH:CH)_2(CH_2)_7COOH$

Linolenic Acid, $CH_3(CH_2CH:CH)_3(CH_2)_7COOH$

Arachidonic Acid, $CH_3(CH_2)_3(CH_2CH:CH)_4(CH_2)_3COOH$

It should also not be overlooked that many fats are admixed with vitamins.

Fats almost always contain variable quantities of lipids such as lecithin. The choline present in the lecithin molecule prevents the development of fatty liver. Researches by Best, György and others have demonstrated the relationship of nutritional factors to liver injury. Thus, on diets low in protein and moderately or distinctly high in fat, there is produced liver damage in the experimental rat, which is called nutritional cirrhosis. The early stages are characterized by a fatty deposition in the liver, followed by fibrotic changes in this tissue. The fatty infiltration and, to some extent, the fibrosis may be stopped and even reversed by incorporation into the diet of compounds called "lipotropic factors." These are choline, betaine and methionine (or a protein containing adequate amounts of methionine). Inositol, although once claimed as a potent lipotropic substance, seems to be of little value. In contrast to the action of methionine or choline, cystine, either in the form of the free amino acid or of a protein high in cystine and relatively low in methionine, promotes fat infiltration.

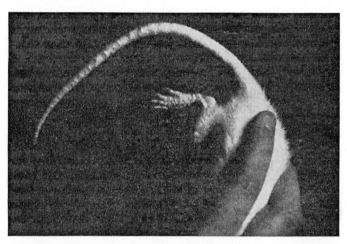

Fig. 73. Scaly skin of hind feet and tail of rat on fat-deficient diet. (Burr, in Visscher: Chemistry and Medicine. University of Minnesota Press.)

Fig. 74. Littermate sisters with and without fat in the diet. (Burr, in Visscher: Chemistry and Medicine. University of Minnesota Press.)

Not only is fat needed in the diet for the various reasons stated, but when used, it should be preferably fresh. A rancid fat is unpalatable and has a destructive action on other foods, particularly vitamins A and E (see next chapter). The fat in this condition may even be somewhat toxic. Sometimes the extent to which a food can be preserved will depend upon the condition of the fat present—the more rancid the fat the more rapid the deterioration of the food mixture.

Apparently, both carbohydrate and fat must be incorporated in the diet. Usually, from 20 to 25 per cent of the total calories represents fat in the diet. Many dietaries contain from four to five times as much carbohydrate as fat (by weight). A typical dietary might be composed of 75 gm. of protein (75 $\times$ 4 = 300 Calories *), 80 gm. of fat (80 $\times$ 9 = 720 Calories), and 400 gm. of carbohydrate (400 $\times$ 4 = 1600 Calories); with a total calorific value of 2620.

INORGANIC ELEMENTS

The common inorganic elements found in animal tissues include calcium, magnesium, sodium, potassium, sulfur, phosphorus, chlorine, iron, and iodine. The spectroscope has revealed traces of many other elements. Some of them, such as copper, seem as essential for the normal development of the animal as do the amino acids themselves. These inorganic elements play various roles: as components of skeletal structures, as cellular constituents, as regulators of body neutrality, etc.

ACID-BASE BALANCE OF FOODS

It may be mentioned that foods metabolized in the body may also influence the acid-base balance. For example, meat and eggs are foods which when oxidized in the body give rise to acids. On the other hand, many fruits and vegetables are potential base-formers. The sulfur and phosphorus of proteins—abundant in meat and eggs—are oxidized to sulfuric and phosphoric acids. On the other hand, the organic acids of fruits are often, though not always, oxidized to carbonates.

The nutritive value of some common foods is given in the Appendix. *Vitamins* are treated in Chap. 20, and *water* is discussed in Chap. 22.

SOME CHARACTERISTICS OF VARIOUS FOODS

Milk.   It is generally agreed that no other natural food compares with milk in its "protective" capacity. No other food so well protects the individual from possible deficiencies in the diet. For the past decade particularly, nutritional experts have been advocating a more liberal consumption of milk; and this applies not altogether to the poorer section of the community, though, of course, the need is most urgent among these people.

Aside from its protein, fat, and carbohydrate supply, milk is rich in calcium, phosphorus, and vitamin A. It also contains appreciable quantities of other vitamins and minerals.

One standard set by a state (New York) insists that milk must contain 11.5 per cent of solids, 3 per cent of fat, and not more than 88.5 per cent of water. As compared with this standard, the actual average composition of milk is as follows (in per cent): casein 3.0, fat 3.7, milk sugar 4.7, albumin 0.4, ash 0.7, other constituents 0.06, and water 87.3. Present in traces, and yet of extreme importance, are a number of the vitamins.

MILK FAT.   The milk fat represents, in the main, a mixture of a number of fats containing, as a rule, saturated fatty acids. Associated with these fats are vitamins A and (to a lesser extent) D. Commercially, the value of

* These are large calories, or Kg. calories.

milk depends upon its fat ("butter-fat") content, for much of cream and butter and cheese represents fat.

The fats in milk and the quantities (in percentages) are as follows: butyrin, $C_3H_5(COOC_3H_7)_3$, 3.8; caproin, $C_3H_5(COOC_5H_{11})_3$, 3.6; caprylin, $C_3H_5(COOC_7H_{15})_3$, 0.5; caprin, $C_3H_5(COOC_9H_{19})_3$, 1.9; laurin, $C_3H_5(COOC_{11}H_{23})_3$, 7.4; myristin, $C_3H_5(COOC_{13}H_{27})_3$, 20.2; palmitin, $C_3H_5(COOC_{15}H_{31})_3$, 25.7; stearin, $C_3H_5(COOC_{17}H_{35})_3$, 1.8; olein, $C_3H_5(COOC_{17}H_{33})_3$, 35.0. If by "fat" we mean "lipids," then small quantities of cholesterol, lecithin, etc., are also present.

THE PROTEINS IN MILK. The known proteins in milk are casein, lactalbumin, and lactoglobulin, the casein constituting 80 per cent of the total protein. Casein is rich in essential amino acids, and the other two proteins are also rich in these substances. Casein is the protein constituent in a synthetic diet for rats which has been used successfully by many investigators in many lands.

Casein is a phosphoprotein; it yields phosphoric acid and amino acids on hydrolysis. The isoelectric point of casein is at pH of about 4.6, but the pH of milk itself is in the neighborhood of 7. This means that casein in milk is in alkaline combination, probably in the form of calcium caseinate.

Casein itself is insoluble in water. The addition of acid to milk precipitates this protein. The same process is accomplished by allowing the milk to stand for some time, when the lactic acid bacteria convert the lactose to lactic acid, which, in turn, precipitates the protein. The casein precipitated under these conditions can be redissolved in alkali and reprecipitated by acids. This is, in fact, one method of purifying the protein.

Milk forms a clot upon the addition of rennin (the rennet of commerce). The composition of this clot has been the subject of much speculation. It is believed that the rennin first changes the casein to another compound, paracasein. Some are of the opinion that this change involves the splitting of one molecule of casein into two molecules of paracasein. At any rate, this changed casein, this paracasein, it is believed, forms the clot by combining with calcium. The calcium paracaseinate, unlike the calcium caseinate, is insoluble in water and insoluble in dilute acids and alkalis. It is quite different from the precipitate obtained by the addition of acid to milk or by the addition of ammonium sulfate to milk. One thing is certain: the clotting of milk does not take place in the absence of calcium.*

Casein, unlike lactalbumin and lactoglobulin, does not coagulate on heating. The skin which forms when milk is boiled is vaguely referred to as a mixture of the protein with the fat.†

LACTOSE. The carbohydrate in milk is lactose, or milk sugar. It is a rich source of energy, similar to cane sugar, and is often of value in aiding lactic acid bacteria to replace the undesirable putrefactive bacteria in the intestine.

THE INORGANIC CONSTITUENTS OF MILK. The inorganic constituents are

---

* Compare the action of calcium in the clotting of milk with the action of the same element in blood coagulation.

† Industrially, casein in solution with certain compounds develops adhesive qualities, and is used in glues, coatings, and the like. With other combinations, it is used in plastics and paints.

many, but only a few are present in any quantity. Among the latter we can include calcium, phosphorus, potassium, sodium, chlorine, and magnesium. Iron is present but in small amounts. The demands for this element by the organism are such that additional iron must be obtained from other foods. Spectroscopic studies have revealed traces of many elements. Copper, for example, is present to the extent of perhaps 0.15 mg. per liter of milk, and yet this trace in conjunction with iron is of importance in preventing anemia. The readiness with which "traces" and "impurities" have been dismissed as of no importance is giving place to a more cautious and critical attitude.

HUMAN VERSUS COW'S MILK.   Human milk contains less protein (1.4 per cent) and more sugar (7.2 per cent) than cow's milk. Even when cow's milk is properly diluted and the correct amount of lactose added, the artificial human milk is not always a complete substitute for the natural milk when feeding the young. Whatever differences there are are obscure.

TYPES OF MILK AND MILK PRODUCTS.   CERTIFIED MILK is raw milk of

Table 49   AVERAGE COMPOSITION OF MILK OF VARIOUS KINDS
(Compiled by Food Composition Section, Bureau of Home Economics.)

Kind of milk	Water	Protein (N × 6.37)	Fat	Lactose (by difference)	Mineral matter (ash)	Fuel value per pound
	Per cent	Per cent	Per cent	Per cent	Per cent	Calories
Human...............	87.5	1.4	3.7	7.2	0.2	307
Cow.................	87.1	3.4	3.9	4.9	.7	310
Goat................	87.0	3.3	4.2	4.8	.7	318
Sheep...............	82.6	5.5	6.5	4.5	.9	447
Reindeer............	63.7	10.3	19.7	4.8	1.5	1078

higher purity. It must not contain more than 10,000 bacteria per cubic centimeter of milk and must not be more than thirty-six hours old when delivered.

GRADE A RAW MILK has an average bacterial count not exceeding 50,000 bacteria per cubic centimeter at the time of delivery to the customer.

PASTEURIZED MILK is "milk that has been subjected to a temperature not lower than 145° F. for not less than thirty minutes."

The composition of milk (from several sources) and of milk products is given in Tables 49, 50, and 51.

CREAM usually contains about 20 per cent of fat, although in the "heavy" cream, fat may reach as high as 40 per cent.

BUTTER, as defined by Federal food laws, is "the clean sound product, made by gathering in any manner the fat of fresh or ripened milk or cream into a mass, which also contains a small portion of other milk constituents, with or without salt, and contains not less than 80 per cent of milk fat."

In the manufacture of butter, cream is usually pasteurized and then ripened. The ripening—an acid fermentation—is accomplished by inoculating with the desired organisms. The next process, that of churning, separates the fat globules, which can be drawn off and thereby separated from the butter milk.

Margarine, or *oleomargarine* as it is sometimes called, is coming into use more and more as a butter substitute. It must contain at least 80 per cent of fat by weight. Its fat content is made up of mixtures of vegetable fats, the basis usually being cottonseed and soybean oils. An agreeable flavor is given to the product by churning these fats and oils in specially cultured skim milk, and the nutritional value is enhanced by incorporating vitamin A.

"When margarine is fortified with vitamin A . . . it can be substituted for butter in the ordinary diet without any nutritional disadvantage" (Council on Food and Nutrition, A.M.A.).

Table 50   AVERAGE COMPOSITION OF MILK AND MILK PRODUCTS
(Compiled by Food Composition Section, Bureau of Home Economics.)

Product	Water	Protein (N × 6.37)	Fat	Lactose, * etc. (by difference)	Mineral matter (ash)	Fuel value per pound
	Per cent	Per cent	Per cent	Per cent	Per cent	Calories
Whole milk..........	87.1	3.4	3.9	4.9	0.7	310
Cream:						
Single.............	72.5	2.9	20.0	4.0	.6	942
Double...........	54.4	2.2	40.0	3.0	.4	1727
Skim milk...........	90.5	3.5	.2	5.0	.8	162
Buttermilk..........	90.7	3.5	.5	4.6	.7	167
Whey..............	93.0	1.0	.3	5.1	.6	123
Evaporated milk, unsweetened.........	73.7	7.0	7.9	9.9	1.5	629
Condensed milk, sweetened.........	27.0	8.1	8.4	54.8 †	1.7	1484
Dried whole milk.....	3.5	25.8	26.7	38.0	6.0	2248
Dried skim milk.....	3.5	35.6	1.0	52.0	7.9	1630
Butter..............	15.5	.6	81.0	.4	2.5	3325
Cheese:						
American cheddar..	34.5	25.6	34.7	1.9	3.3	1916
Swiss.............	34.0	28.6	31.3	1.9	4.2	1831
Cottage (skim milk)	74.0	19.2	.8	4.3	1.7	459
Cream............	42.7	14.5	39.9	1.0	1.9	1910

* Including lactic acid and other undetermined substances. The amount of sugar in some of the cheeses is probably negligible.

† Mainly added sucrose. Average percentage of added sugar is about 42 per cent of the condensed milk.

Vegetable and animal fats, it seems, are absorbed and utilized equally well. The lack of vitamins—particularly vitamin A—in vegetable fats makes the animal fat more desirable; but such a deficiency can be easily overcome, as has just been pointed out.

Mineral oil (liquid petrolatum), sometimes used in the place of other oils and fats, is chemically not a fat at all but largely a mixture of hydrocarbons. It may be objectionable in foods because it may interfere with the absorption of a number of the vitamins, such as vitamins A, D, K, and carotene, the precursor of vitamin A (see the next chapter).

SKIM MILK is milk from which most of the fat has been removed, which

Table 51 NUTRIENT VALUE OF DIFFERENT FORMS OF MILK
[Bowes and Church: Food Values of Portions Commonly Used (Philadelphia Child Health Society)]

Type of milk	Quantity	Energy (calories)	Protein (grams)	Carbohydrate (grams)	Fat (grams)	Calcium (grams)	Phosphorus (grams)	Iron (grams)
Milk, whole..............	6 oz. (1 medium glass)	123	6.1	8.8	7.0	0.212	0.167	0.40
Milk, condensed..............	1 tbsp., or 15 grams (to make 1 glass)	49	1.2	8.2	1.3	0.045	0.035	0.10
Milk, buttermilk..............	6 oz. (1 medium glass)	65	6.3	9.0	0.4	0.189	0.175	0.50
Milk, evaporated..............	1 tbsp., or 16 grams (to make 1 glass)	21	1.1	1.5	1.2	0.040	0.032	0.03
Milk, malted..............	1 tbsp., or 9 grams (to make 1 glass)	38	1.3	6.4	0.8	0.032	0.031	0.20
Milk powder, skim..............	28.35 grams (1 ounce)	102	10.1	14.7	0.3	0.346	0.272	0.90
Milk powder, whole..............	28.35 grams (1 ounce)	141	7.3	10.8	7.6	0.261	0.201	0.40
Milk, skim..............	6 oz. (1 medium glass)	65	6.3	9.0	0.4	0.220	0.173	0.50

means that its fuel value is low, and that its content of vitamin A is very small. From the standpoint of the manufacturer, skim milk is the most important by-product of milk. Casein, skim-milk powder, and condensed, cultured, and chocolate milks are prepared from it. A large amount is fed to farm animals.

BUTTERMILK is comparable to skim milk in composition. It is the product obtained after the removal of the fat of the milk during the course of butter-making.

HOMOGENIZED MILK is produced by forcing milk through minute openings under high pressure. The fat becomes more evenly distributed, and the fat globules are smaller than in milk.

CONDENSED MILK is milk from which a certain amount of water has been removed and to which some sugar has been added. *Evaporated milk* is milk with less than its usual water content, but here no sugar has been added.

In the preparation of condensed milk, some 18 pounds of sugar are used for 100 pounds of milk, and the mixture is evaporated in vacuo at a temperature close to that of pasteurization. In the evaporated, or unsweetened, milk, much of the water from fresh milk is removed (in vacuo), the fat globules are broken up into smaller sizes by means of a "homogenizer," and the product, run into cans and sealed, is sterilized.

DRIED MILK is milk from which practically all the water has been removed. From 100 pounds of milk some 13 pounds of the white powder may be obtained.

In war time, with large food exports from the United States to England and elsewhere, the saving of shipping space by using the dried foodstuffs was of the utmost importance.

DRIED SKIM MILK contains practically none of the fat of whole milk.

FERMENTED MILK, buttermilk and acidophilus milk for example, is a milk which has been acted upon by desirable bacteria, in which the lactic acid bacteria are abundant. Buttermilk is the product left in the churn after the butter has been removed. The cream is usually churned when sour, and the buttermilk is therefore slightly acid.

MILK FORTIFIED WITH VITAMIN D. Few common foods contain vitamin D in any quantity. This is the reason why milk is at times enriched with the vitamin. The addition of other vitamins, or the addition of various minerals, is hardly necessary for an individual whose diet is varied.

CHEESE * is essentially a concentrate of the casein and fat of milk. (Cottage cheese is an exception; it is made from skim milk, rather than from whole milk, and therefore contains very little fat.) After the cheese has been removed, what is left is the "whey," and contains most of the lactose, some protein and some vitamins and mineral salts. What is known as "cream cheese"—made from cream—is richer in fat than cottage cheese. The hard cheeses—Cheddar, Swiss—are usually made from whole milk. The manufacture of cheese is based on the coagulation process resulting from the action of rennin on casein. The variations in cheese depend upon the bacteria, the source of milk, the extent of ripening, the temperature used, etc.

* See U. S. Dept. Agriculture, Bull. No. 608, for varieties of cheese: descriptions and analyses.

ICE CREAM consists of cream or milk fat, sugar, flavoring matter, and binder (such as gelatin). The composition varies widely. The milk fat may range from 10 to 14 per cent, and the total solids, including protein and carbohydrate, from 20 to 30 per cent.

Eggs.   Eggs are valuable in nutrition mainly for their content of protein and lipids. The protein, high in the biological scale, is found largely in egg white (ovalbumin and ovoglobulin) and also in the yolk (ovovitellin, a phosphoprotein). The lipids (fat, lecithin, cholesterol) are largely in the yolk. An approximate composition of the egg as a whole is (in per cent): protein 13.4, fat 10.5, ash 1.0, water 73.7. The egg is rich in a number of vitamins.

Meat.   According to Federal authorities, meat "is the properly dressed flesh derived from cattle, from swine, from sheep, or from goats . . . ;" and flesh is "any clean, sound, edible part of the striated muscle of an animal." Like eggs, meat is of particular value for its content of protein and fat; and like eggs again, it has very little carbohydrate. Lean meat may contain (in per cent): protein 15 to 20, fat 8 to 14, ash 1, and water 65 to 75. The proteins are myogen, a water-soluble substance, and myosin, a globulin and water-insoluble. A small quantity of glycogen (usually less than 1 per cent) is also found in muscle substance. "Extractives," which give rise to the flavor of meat, include creatine and such purine bodies as xanthine and hypoxanthine. The mineral salts are characterized by their relatively high percentage of potassium and phosphorus.

Fish.   As a food, fish is, to a considerable extent, similar to meat or to eggs. In fact, these three foods can largely replace one another in the diet. An approximate composition of fish (in per cent) is: protein 10.9, fat 2.4, ash 0.7 (including, in the case of marine fish and shellfish, appreciable quantities of iodine), water 44.6, refuse 41.6. The fat of mackerel may be as high as 16 per cent. Vitamins are also present.

Cereals.   Cereals are the edible portions (grains) of the grass family, *Gramineae*. The grain, according to Federal authorities, is "the fully matured, clean, sound, air-dry seed of wheat, maize (corn), rice, oats, rye, buckwheat, barley, sorghum, millet, or spelt." For Americans, wheat is the most important cereal, being used very largely in the form of bread. Twenty-five per cent of the average caloric intake in the United States is due to this cereal. Some of the other cereals are used for breakfast foods.

An approximate composition of wheat (in per cent) is: protein 11.9, fat 2.1, carbohydrate 71.9, fiber (cellulose, etc.) 1.8, ash 1.8, moisture 10.5. The two principal proteins are gliadin and glutenin, with smaller quantities of edestin. The "gluten" of flour consists very largely of gliadin and glutenin.

Most wheat flour milled in this country is converted into bread which is made from a mixture of flour and water, fermented with the production of carbon dioxide by an appropriate "leavening" agent, and subsequently baked. The nutritive value of bread depends upon the flour used in preparing it. The milling process has little effect on the protein and carbohydrate, but the fat and ash are reduced in quantity. In the manufacture of white flour, with the consequent removal of the bran and germ, one-half of the calcium is lost, and there are definite losses in phosphorus and iron.

Whole wheat flour is milled to contain 100 per cent of the wheat kernel.

White flour contains that part of the wheat kernel called the "endosperm" (Fig. 75). "Enriched" flour is white flour with various additions such as thiamine, nicotinic acid, iron, etc.

Whole wheat is a very good source of iron, but some four-fifths is lost when white flour is produced. The thiamine, riboflavin, and nicotinic acid present in the whole wheat are also largely lost in the milling process to produce white flour.

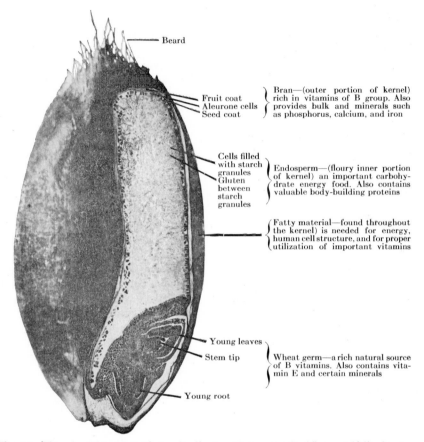

Beard

Fruit coat
Aleurone cells
Seed coat

} Bran—(outer portion of kernel) rich in vitamins of B group. Also provides bulk and minerals such as phosphorus, calcium, and iron

Cells filled
with starch
granules
Gluten
between
starch
granules

} Endosperm—(floury inner portion of kernel) an important carbohydrate energy food. Also contains valuable body-building proteins

{ Fatty material—found throughout the kernel) is needed for energy, human cell structure, and for proper utilization of important vitamins

Young leaves
Stem tip

} Wheat germ—a rich natural source of B vitamins. Also contains vitamin E and certain minerals

Young root

Fig. 75. The wheat kernel (with longitudinal section exposed). (General Mills, Inc.)

In England, during World War II, a flour of 85 per cent extraction of the grain was used in the place of the normal 70 per cent. An 85 per cent extraction means that 15 per cent of the whole grain is not incorporated in the flour. The bread is further enriched with calcium salts—an addition which is sometimes, but not always, made to "enriched" bread in this country.

Wheat flour contains practically none of the vitamins C and D (see next chapter), and very little A, though it does contain an appreciable amount of the water-soluble B vitamins.

In the United States the various cereals contribute about one-third of the calories to the diet; in Europe they very often contribute up to 50 per cent.

Macaroni is defined as the "shaped and dried doughs prepared by adding water to one or more of the following: farina, semolina, wheat flour."

The three main cereals are rice, wheat and corn. One-half of the human race depends upon rice as its main food.

Sugar.   This is practically pure carbohydrate and, therefore, is rich in energy-yielding material. Before World War II, of the 7,000,000 tons used per year, 60 per cent was used by households and restaurants. Other uses were in industries connected with baking, canning, flavoring, soft drinks, dairying, tobacco, etc.

The common food sugars include cane sugar or sucrose, milk sugar or lactose, malt sugar or maltose, glucose or dextrose, and fructose or levulose.

The cane sugar is derived from the sugar cane and the sugar beet. Malt sugar is made from the partial digestion of starch. The malt food for infants contains maltose and dextrins. Glucose is obtained from starch but occurs also as such in nature. The corn syrup of commerce is a mixture of glucose and dextrins. Fructose is found in honey—which also contains glucose— and in many fruits.

Maple sugar and maple syrup represent the sap of the sugar maple. The mother liquor left after the removal of part of the cane sugar from the boiled juice is molasses.

On the whole, much too much sugar (in various forms) is used in this country. The quantities which are consumed lessen the desire for other— and more important—foods.

Fruits and Vegetables.   These contribute relatively little as sources of energy, but they are nevertheless very important for their content of minerals and vitamins. Leafy, green, and yellow vegetables include asparagus, yellow sweet corn, beets, lettuce, parsley, spinach, water cress, etc. They are rich in provitamin A and, as a rule, in iron. Citrus fruits (orange, lemon, grapefruit, etc.) and tomatoes are splendid sources of vitamin C. The presence of moderate amounts of cellulose lends bulk to the food and aids in proper digestion. The average composition of a vegetable such as cabbage is (in per cent): protein 1.4, fat 0.2, carbohydrate (including fiber) 5.6, ash 1.8, water 77.7, refuse 15. The average composition of a number of fruits is (in per cent): protein 1, fat 0.7, carbohydrate (including fiber) 13, ash 0.6, water 63, waste 22.

The potato is a food of high energy value, rich in carbohydrates, relatively poor in protein, and relatively poor in minerals and vitamins. It is a cheap source of iron and vitamin C.*

COOKING

To a greater or less degree, cooking affects more particularly the vitamins and minerals of foods. So variable are the various factors—amount of water, length of cooking, temperature, etc.—that no one statement will cover all the possibilities.†

* Coffee, tea, chocolate, flavoring spices, add to the "spice of life" but are not in themselves necessary foods.

† The following, taken from the Manual of Industrial Nutrition (Government Printing

PROCESSING OF FOODS

Various methods for preserving foods have been developed. These methods received a great impetus during World War II, when urgent demands arose not only for foods which did not deteriorate with time, but also for those which occupied considerably less space than the untreated food (which contains varying quantities of water). The processes employed come under the following headings; drying or dehydration, sterilization (the canning process), low temperature chilling and freezing, pickling, smoking, spicing, fermentation, etc. The products obtained by these means are of the utmost value when fresh foods are unattainable.

The high-vacuum and low-temperature evaporator has made the frozen food industry possible. As to variety, fruits, vegetables, fish, meat, etc., are all obtainable.

Concentration of juices is a spectacular development in recent years. The basis for this achievement, as has been intimated, is the utilization of very high vacua without additional application of heat. Fruit juices—orange juice, particularly—are concentrated to one-fourth their volume. The product, a four-fold concentration, is packed in tin containers and kept in a frozen state.

If properly processed, as much as 98 per cent of the vitamin C (Chap. 20) content of the original orange juice may be retained.

There is, of course, always the danger that foods so prepared have lost some of their nutritional value. This applies more specifically to some minerals and to a number of vitamins of varying stability, such as carotene, vitamin A, thiamine, riboflavin, and ascorbic acid. The extent to which such foods are undamaged depends upon a number of factors: exposure to light; temperature and length of time of heating and of standing; the pH of the solution; the extent of loss of water-soluble material; etc.

It would, of course, be to the advantage of the consumer if complete analyses—including vitamins and minerals—would appear on the labels of cans.

CHEMICALS IN FOODS

Some chemicals are accepted without question. They have undergone adequate investigation, they serve a useful purpose and, so far as rigorous

---

Office, Washington, 1943), are several practical illustrations of things to bear in mind\

Use fresh vegetables and fruits as soon as possible after delivery. Handle very carefully, for bruising causes rapid losses of vitamins. Keep vegetables and fruits crisp and cool until time to cook them. Shred or chop vegetables and fruits just before they are to be served or cooked.

Add vegetables or fruits to rapidly boiling water. Cook quickly and in as little water as possible. Do not add soda to vegetables or fruits to preserve their color because it destroys certain vitamins. Cook until just done with some of the original crispness left. Do not stir or expose to air and light any more than absolutely necessary. Do not let vegetables or fruits stand in water. Standing destroys vitamins. Use vegetable cooking water in gravies, soups, or sauces. Bring precooked canned fruits and vegetables quickly to a boil but do not continue boiling. Add frozen vegetables and fruits directly to boiling water. Do not defrost preliminary to cooking.

With meats, short methods of cooking such as sautéing or broiling are less destructive of vitamins than slower methods. Roasting at a low temperature is less destructive than at a high temperature. As with other foods, meats should be served as soon as possible after cooking. Standing in a warmer or on a steam table is accompanied by vitamin losses.

testing provides evidence, they are not harmful. In this group we may include the addition of potassium iodide to salt to prevent goiter; the use of chlorine in drinking water; the use of baking powder; the addition of vitamins to various foods; the use of certified food colors; etc. However, some chemicals, not adequately tested as to toxicity, may get into foods. For example, foods may become contaminated by substances added to the soil, or by the use of sprays for plants and animals, or by adding chemicals in the course of processing of foods, etc. Here, to prevent possible disaster, the nation's laws relating to nutrition must be made more rigorous.

AN ADEQUATE (NORMAL) DIET

This should include the equivalent of some 2600 to 3000 Calories (for the adult), about 70 gm. of protein, of which 50 gm. should be of animal origin, from 80 to 90 gm. of fat, and from 400 to 500 gm. of carbohydrate. Meat, milk, eggs, and fish supply "first-class proteins," that is, proteins rich in essential amino acids; cereals supply carbohydrates and proteins which are usually not "first-class"; and fruits and vegetables supply minerals and "roughage" (cellulose, etc.). A mixture of such foods contains the more important vitamins. To take care of possible deficiencies in the diet, even on so mixed a fare, it is advisable to consume from one to two glasses of milk a day.

SOCIAL PROBLEMS

Malnutrition.   Bertram * tells us that the world's population increased from 545 million in 1650 to 2057 million in 1933. Of this total, 75 per cent are farmers and their dependents.

It has been estimated that some 75 per cent of Asia's population of over 1000 million live on a subnormal diet. It has been further estimated that even in the two most civilized countries of the world, the United States and Great Britain, from 20 to 30 per cent of the population suffers from malnutrition.

A report by the National Research Council states that in a nationwide canvass in February, 1943, in which one-day diet records were obtained from selective samplings of the population in each of the forty-eight states, the following percentages of persons had none of the following protective foods: citrus fruits, tomatoes, or salad greens, 45; dairy products, 34; leafy and yellow vegetables, 25; other vegetables or fruit, 8; meat, fish or poultry, 12; whole grain or enriched products, 3.

In a carefully controlled study entitled "Food, Health, and Income," by J. B. Orr, the author points out that the consumption of milk, eggs, fruit, vegetables, meat, and fish rises with income. An examination of the composition of the diets shows that the degree of adequacy for health increases as income rises. As income increases, disease and death rate decrease, children grow more quickly, adult stature is greater, and general health and physique improve. Among the poorer children, the improvement of the diet is accompanied by improvement in health and increased rate of growth. This improvement in diet means increased consumption of milk,

* Nature, March 22, 1947.

Table 52 NUTRITIVE VALUE OF A MODERATE-COST DIET
[Family Nutrition. (Philadelphia Child Health Society.)]

Persons	Food energy	Protein	Calcium	Phosphorus	Iron	Vitamin A	Thiamine	Riboflavin	Ascorbic acid
	Calories	Grams	Grams	Grams	Milligrams	International units	Milligrams	Milligrams	Milligrams
Children:									
9–12 months	970	38	1.1	1.0	6	4,400	0.8	1.9	60
1–3 years	1,300	55	1.3	1.3	7	5,700	1.1	2.4	65
4–6 years	1,710	65	1.3	1.4	9	6,200	1.4	2.6	80
7–9 years	2,130	79	1.4	1.6	12	8,000	1.7	3.0	100
10–12 years	2,670	91	1.4	1.8	14	9,200	2.1	3.3	115
Girls:									
13–15 years	2,980	102	1.5	1.9	16	9,700	2.4	3.5	115
16–20 years	2,590	94	1.4	1.8	15	9,800	2.1	3.3	125
Women:									
Moderately active	2,590	86	1.1	1.6	14	9,700	2.1	2.8	120
Very active	3,250	104	1.2	1.8	17	8,800	2.3	3.1	120
Sedentary	2,260	80	1.1	1.5	13	8,800	1.9	2.7	110
Pregnant	2,750	95	1.5	1.8	15	10,500	2.1	3.4	130
Nursing	3,240	114	2.1	2.3	17	12,100	2.6	4.4	170
Boys:									
13–15 years	3,420	112	1.5	2.0	18	9,600	2.6	3.7	130
16–20 years	4,020	122	1.5	2.2	20	10,200	3.0	4.0	140
Men:									
Moderately active	3,250	104	1.2	1.8	17	8,800	2.3	3.1	120
Very active	4,860	139	1.3	2.3	24	10,500	3.5	4.0	140
Sedentary	2,580	85	1.1	1.6	14	9,000	2.0	2.8	115

Table 53 APPROXIMATE FOOD VALUE OF DAILY ALLOWANCE OF MAN, MODERATELY ACTIVE, AND WEIGHING 70 KG.
[Proc. National Nutrition Conference for Defense. (Washington, 1941.)]

Foods	Amount	Approximate measure	Calories	Protein	Calcium	Iron	Vitamin A	Thiamine (B₁)	Riboflavin	Ascorbic acid
	Grams			Grams	Grams	Mg.	I.U.	Gamma *	Gamma *	Mg.
Milk	480	1 pint	336	15.8	0.58	0.15	528	244	1,000	6
Meat	100	¼ pound	150	21.0	.01	3.00	50	120	225	
Potatoes	350	3 medium	300	7.2	.05	3.66	144	432	162	12
Baked beans	200	1 cup	200	13.2	.09	4.00	110	235	130	
Cabbage, raw	100	1 cup	25	1.1	.04	.43	88	70	72	35
Carrots	100	1½ cup	40	1.2	.04	.64	2,100	60	58	
Tomato	200	⅝ cup	50	2.4	.02	.80	2,000	182	122	48
Prunes, stewed	200	⅝ cup	250	1.4	.03	1.88	990	120	132	
Oleomargarine	66	5 tablespoons	500				2,600			
Oatmeal, cooked	300	1¼ cups	200	8.0	.03	2.40		270	60	
Bread, whole wheat or "enriched"	200	6 slices	500	19.0	.10	3.0		480	207	
Gingerbread	75	Large piece	200	3.5	.08	2.0		40	30	
Sugar, jam			250							
Totals			3,001	93.8	1.07	22.0	8,602	2,253 * 2.25 mg.	2,234 * 2.23 mg.	101
Compared with recommended allowances			3,000	70.0	.80	12.0	5,000	1.80 mg.	2.70 mg.	75

* 1 milligram (mg.) equals 1000 micrograms (gamma).

eggs, butter, fruits, vegetables, and meat to the extent of from 12 to 25 per cent.

Where family income is limited, the possibilities of varying the diet in sufficient amounts—so important in the attainment of a "wholesome" diet —become more restricted. The poor spend more on flour and cereals, potatoes and sugar, and less on butter and fats, meat, eggs, milk and fruits and vegetables than do the more prosperous portions of the community.

In a study by Jolliffe, McLester, and Sherman, the conclusion is reached that dietary inadequacies and malnutrition are of frequent occurrence in the United States. They define "dietary inadequacy" as the failure to ingest an essential nutritional factor or factors in amounts sufficient to meet the existing requirement of the body, and "malnutrition" as a bodily condition, detectable by any method of examination, caused by a nutritional inadequacy.

To eat adequately—that is, to have a well-balanced diet—means that one must have a certain sum of money to spend and that one must be familiar with the elements of nutritional science. Assuming both these points, we may quote from an excellent pamphlet by Carpenter and Stiebeling, "Diets to Fit the Family Income."

A liberal diet, as its name implies, provides very generously for all of the food requirements. It contains an abundance of fruits and vegetables, eggs, and lean meat, as well as a generous allowance of milk, along with moderate quantities of cereals, fats, and sugars. This combination of foods allows for better-than-average nutrition, because it provides more than amply for the items necessary for growth, health, and general well-being. At the same time, it offers an assortment pleasing to the eye and the palate, and allows for a great deal of variety from meal to meal.

Table 52 gives the nutritive value of a moderate-cost adequate diet.

It is interesting to compare this table with the one devised by a committee of the National Research Council. This committee first formulated a series of recommendations which is summarized on p. 318. Compare these tables with Table 53, which deals with the approximate food value of the daily allowance of a man moderately active and weighing 70 kilograms. In Table 53 the foods are listed, the approximate measures given, and also the calorific equivalent of each food is listed.

It should not be overlooked that malnutrition may have its origin in factors other than a lack of dietary intake. Poor absorption or poor utilization may also bring about malnutrition. During pregnancy and lactation, in fever, and in cases of hyperthyroidism—to name some examples—the bodily needs are increased, and if such demands are not met, the results may be disastrous.

Obesity.   See p. 298.

REFERENCES

Among the books covering the field of nutrition, we have *McLester and Darby:* Nutrition and Diet in Health and Disease, 1952; *Jolliffe, Tisdall and Cannon:* Clinical Nutrition, 1950.

A review of work in the field of nutrition will be found in the Ann. Rev. Biochem., *19:* 339, 1950, by *Sinclair;* Ibid., *20:* 305, 1951, by *Almquist;* Ibid., *21:* 355, 1952, by *Bigwood;* Ibid., *22:* 299, 1953, by *Hogan.* See also Advances in Food Research, *3,* 1951.

Nutritional Reviews, published monthly by the Nutrition Foundation, reviews advances in nutrition.

Many popular pamphlets on nutrition may be obtained from various Federal and other agencies. For example, Bureau of Home Economics, U. S. Dept. Agriculture; Children's Bureau, U. S. Dept. Labor; Office of Education, and Public Health Service, Federal Security Agency; Dept. Health, N. Y. City; Farmer's Bulletin; U. S. Dept. Agriculture.

A discussion of the findings of the International Commission on Calorie requirements will be found in Nutr. Rev., *9:* 40, 1951.

A stimulating article by *Keys,* dealing with the physiology of the individual as an approach to a more quantitative biology of man, will be found in Federation Proceedings, *8:* 523, 1949.

The pioneer work of *Osborne and Mendel* is described by the latter in an article on nutrition and growth, Harvey Lectures, Ser. 10, p. 1.

For an evaluation of protein hydrolysates, see J. Am. Med. Assoc., *136:* 692, 1948; *Hoffman and McNeil:* J. Nutrition, *44:* 123, 1951; *Robinson:* Food manufacture, *20:* 294, 1945.

Rose's work on amino acids in nutrition is summarized in Chem. Eng. News, *30:* 2385, 1952; Nutritional Observatory (Heinz), July, 1952, p. 52; and Nutr. Rev., *8:* 118, 1950. See further, and in greater detail, *Rose, Johnson, and Haines:* J. Biol. Chem., *182:* 541, 1950 (valine and methionine); *Rose, Haines, Warner, and Johnson:* Ibid., *188:* 49, 1951 (threonine and histidine); *Rose, Haines, and Warner:* Ibid., *193:* 605, 1951 (isoleucine); *Rose, Warner, and Haines:* Ibid., *193:* 613, 1951 (leucine and phenylalanine).

The assay of the nutritive value of a protein by its effect on liver cytoplasm is discussed by *Campbell and Kosterlitz:* Nature, *164:* 1136, 1949.

For a review of the nutritive evaluation of protein, see *Mitchell:* Nutr. Rev., *10:* 33, 1952; and *McLester:* J. Am. Med. Assoc., *139:* 897, 1949.

Animal versus vegetable foods in nutrition is discussed in Nutr. Rev., *10:* 87, 1952; and by *Schultze:* J. Nutrition, *41:* 103, 1950.

For the importance of fat in the diet, see Nutr. Rev., *8:* 232, 1950; and Ibid., *10:* 154, 1952.

For the problem of essential fatty acids, see Borden's Review of Nutrition Research, *9:* No. 4, 1948; Nutr. Rev., *9:* 292, 1951 (in chick); *Ibid., 9:* 200, 1951 (in mice); *Greenberg, Calbert, Deuel, Jr., and Brown:* J. Nutrition, *45:* 521, 1951; *Deuel, Jr., Greenberg, Anisfed, and Melnick:* Ibid., *45:* 535, 1951.

Cuthberton: Chemistry and Industry, 1948, p. 391, discusses trace metals in human nutrition.

Kastens and Baldauski: Ind. Eng. Chem., *44:* 1257, 1952, are the authors of an article on chemicals from milk. The U. S. Dept. Agriculture (Farmer's Bulletin No. 1705) publishes a pamphlet, "Milk for the Family."

Evidence that casein consists of more than one protein is presented by *Gordon, Semmett, Cable, and Morris:* J. Am. Chem. Soc., *71:* 3293, 1949; and *Hipp, Groves, Custer, and McMeekin:* Ibid., *72:* 4928, 1950.

The age-old problem of human milk versus cow's milk is debated by *Jeans:* J. Am. Med. Assoc., *142:* 806, 1950; and by *Aldrich:* Ibid., *135:* 915, 1947; *Morton:* Nature, *171:* 734, 1953 (cow's milk).

For a description of various cheeses, see U. S. Department of Agriculture Bull. No. 608.

The food problem, with its many ramifications, is discussed by *Boyd-Orr:* Scientific American, *183:* 11, 1950; *Phipard and Stiebling:* J. Am. Med. Assoc., *139:* 579, 1949; and *Cowgill:* Ibid., *142:* 721, 1950.

The sterilization (or canning) of food is described by *Jackson and Benjamin:* Ind. Eng. Chem., *40:* 31, 1948.

For frozen orange juice, see J. Am. Med. Assoc., *146:* 35, 1951; and for frozen foods in general, see Nutr. Rev., *9:* 1, 1951; and Chem. Eng. News, *29:* 1009, 1951.

For the problem of chemicals in foods, see J. Am. Med. Assoc., *146:* 731, 1951; Ibid., *148:* 14, 1952; *Fogg:* Chem. Eng. News, *29:* 1933, 1951; Ibid., *30:* 150, 1952; and *Inskeep and Kretlow:* Ind. Eng. Chem., *44:* 12, 1952 (certified food colors).

References to the subject of obesity: Nutr. Rev., *8:* 18, 1950; *Woods:* Borden's Rev. Nutrition Research, *12:* No. 8, 1951; Ibid., *12:* No. 9, 1951; *Armstrong, Dublin, and Wheatley,* J. Am. Med. Assoc., *147:*

1007, 1951; and *Barborka:* Ibid., *147:* 1015, 1951.

On the subject of malnutrition, see Nutr. Rev., *8:* 33, 1950; *Keys:* Science, *112:* 371, 1950; *Spies, Dreizen, Parker, and Silberman:* J. Am. Med. Assoc., *148:* 1376, 1952; *Meiklejohn and Passmore:* Annual Rev. Medicine, *2:* 129, 1951; and *Woods:* Borden's Rev. Nutrition Research, *12:* No. 4, 1951.

Some miscellaneous articles are *Stieglitz:* J. Am. Med. Assoc., *142:* 1070, 1950 (old age and food); *Mann and Stare:* Ibid., *142:* 409, 1950 (nutritional needs in disease); and *Schorr and Swain:* J. Nutrition, *38:* 51, 1949 (food consumption in U. S. army); *Panos and Finerty:* J. Nutrition, *49:* 397, 1953 (effect of fat-free diet); *Sebrell:* J. Am. Med. Assoc., *152:* 42, 1953 (review); *Popjak, Hunter, and French:* Biochem. J., *54:* 238, 1953 (biosynthesis of milk fat).

Chapter 20   *Vitamins*

What Is a Vitamin? A vitamin is an organic substance which belongs to the group of essential foodstuffs. As a rule, the body is unable to synthesize vitamins in sufficient amounts. Ordinarily, these vitamins are found in the various foods which we eat.

As compared to other foods (fats, proteins, carbohydrates, etc.), the amounts of these vitamins which are needed are very small indeed. The explanation is that many, if not all, of these substances act as part of co-enzymes—constituents of essential enzyme systems. For example, thiamine is part of cocarboxylase; riboflavin is part of the yellow enzymes; niacin is part of coenzymes I and II; etc.

History. That disease can result from a food deficiency had been vaguely known for many years. Sailors discovered that scurvy could be prevented by incorporating fresh fruit or fresh vegetables in the diet. In 1882 Takaki eliminated beriberi from the Japanese navy by giving increased quantities of meat, barley, and fruit to his sailors. To be sure, he was wrong in his explanation that a sufficient amount of protein prevented beriberi, but he was right in supposing that a food deficiency was a causal factor in its development. Toward the close of the nineteenth century, a number of physicians began to recognize the value of cod-liver oil in curing rickets.

An impetus for further study was given by Eijkman, a Dutch physician, with his discovery that experimental beriberi could be induced in birds. This occurred in 1897. He found that hens developed the disease when fed with polished rice. Moreover, such hens could be cured by giving them the rice polishings. Still under the influence of Pasteur, Eijkman for a time believed that the rice polishings contained a "something" which neutralized the beriberi "germ" in the polished rice.

An equally important advance we owe to the Norwegians, Holst and Frölich, who, in 1907, caused scurvy in guinea-pigs by feeding them a cereal diet deficient in "greens."

We owe to Funk the first clear evidence of the validity of the vitamin hypothesis. From the very first (1911), Funk regarded the Eijkman factor in beriberi as a definite chemical substance (present in whole rice in relatively small quantities), the absence of which, in polished rice, causes the disease. He boldly attacked the problem of its isolation from rice and from yeast, the latter of which he found to be rich in the antiberiberi factor. He obtained extremely active concentrates, isolating from his fractions nicotinic acid, which is now recognized as one of the vitamins of the B complex. Incidentally, we owe the name "vitamin" to Funk.

Shortly thereafter (in 1912), Hopkins in England published an important paper on the influence of small quantities of milk when added to a synthetic

344

diet. An artificial diet, consisting presumably of all the important constituents found in milk (protein, fat, carbohydrate, mineral salts, and water), proved deficient; but when 2 ml. of milk was added to the diet of each rat each day, the animals recovered (see Fig. 76). Obviously, there was something in milk other than the hitherto recognized components, which was present in minute quantities and which was essential for the normal development of the animal. This "something" is a vitamin.*

The suspicion that there might be more than one vitamin was strengthened by the work of McCollum and Davis in 1915. They showed that the

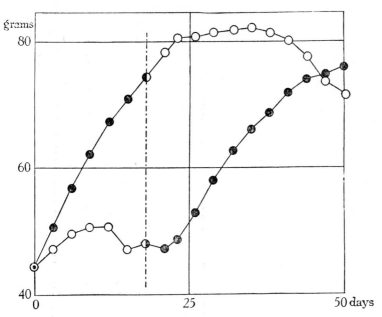

Fig. 76. Growth curves of rats, with and without vitamins (Hopkins). ○ Artificial diet alone. ◐ Artificial diet plus milk.

substitution of lard for egg yolk in a synthetic diet prevented the rats from growing, and that the substitution of highly purified lactose for ordinary lactose prevented growth and also gave rise to polyneuritis. The first factor, associated with fats, was named "fat-soluble A," and the second factor, associated with water-soluble material, was named "water-soluble B." These two substances were later renamed vitamin A and vitamin B, respectively.

The number of vitamins identified has been rapidly multiplying.

The vitamins are usually divided into those which are fat soluble and those which are water soluble. The fat-soluble vitamins are A, D, E and K; the water-soluble vitamins are the B complex (which includes several vitamins) and C.† For the sake of convenience we take them up in alphabetical order.

* With a very pure synthetic diet, 2 ml. of milk is insufficient.
† There are several varieties of vitamins A, D, E, and K.

VITAMIN A

A lack of vitamin A results in loss of weight and decreased resistance in infection. Neither of these symptoms is specific. Wolbach states that characteristic of a deficiency of vitamin A in the animal is the substitution of stratified keratinizing epithelium for normal epithelium in various parts

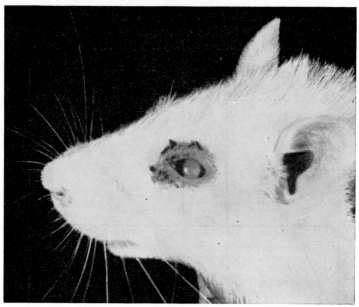

Fig. 77. Xerophthalmia. (Therapeutic Notes, Parke, Davis and Co.)

of the respiratory tract, alimentary tract, eyes, and the genito-urinary tract. What is specific is the development of xerophthalmia, a disease in which the eyes become hemorrhagic, incrusted, and infected (see Figs. 77 and 78). Probably the earliest symptom is hemeralopia, or partial night blindness (that is, loss of visual acuity in dim light).

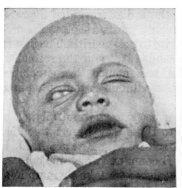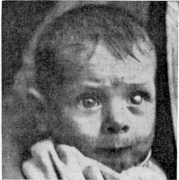

Fig. 78. Xerophthalmia—an eye trouble caused by deficiency of vitamin A. (C. E. Bloch, from Harris: Vitamins in Theory and Practice. Cambridge Univ. Press, Publishers.)

Carotenoids and Vitamin A.   A deficiency in vitamin A can be cured not only by substances containing this vitamin, but by several pigments found in the plant kingdom, particularly carotene (provitamin A), which occurs in three isomeric forms, α, β, and γ. The β-carotene gives the most active response. These plant pigments are converted into vitamin A in the animal body. Earlier work suggested the seat of this conversion to be the liver. Newer evidence seems to point also to the intestinal wall.

Karrer and his associates have established the structures of β-carotene and vitamin A.

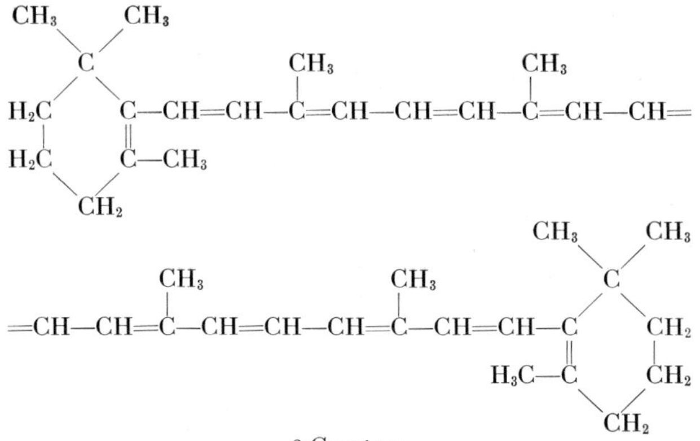

$$CH_3 \quad CH_3$$
$$\underset{\displaystyle H_2C \quad \overset{\displaystyle C}{|} \quad C-CH=CH-\underset{CH_3}{\overset{CH_3}{C}}=CH-CH=CH-\underset{CH_3}{\overset{CH_3}{C}}=CH-CH=}{}$$

β-Carotene

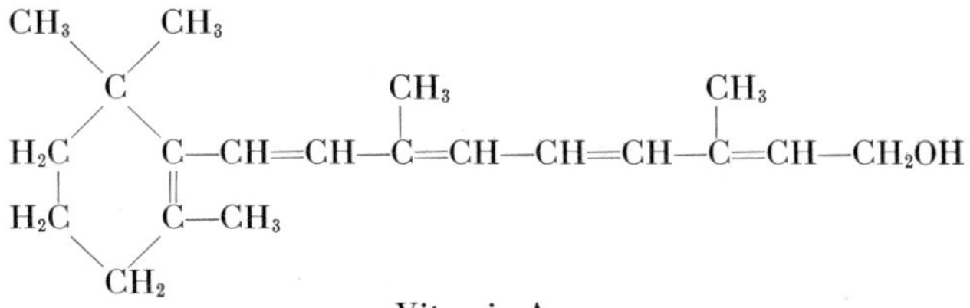

The aliphatic central chain of β-carotene represents four dehydrogenated isoprene residues.

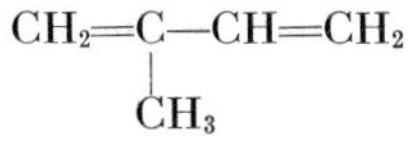

$$CH_2=\underset{\displaystyle CH_3}{\overset{\displaystyle |}{C}}-CH=CH_2$$

Isoprene (2-methyl-1,3,-butadiene)

β-Carotene also contains two β-ionone rings.

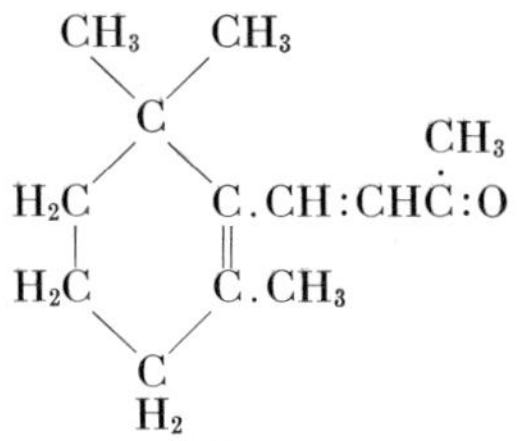

$$CH_3 \quad CH_3$$

β-Ionone

Vitamin A, an alcohol, represents approximately one-half of the molecule of β-carotene. The vitamin has been synthesized, starting with β-ionone.

The conversion of carotene into vitamin A is usually represented thus:

$$C_{40}H_{56} + 2H_2O \longrightarrow 2C_{20}H_{29}OH$$
$$\beta\text{-Carotene} \qquad \text{Vitamin A}$$

The conversion of the hydrocarbon into the alcohol does take place in the body—mainly in the intestinal wall and less in the liver.

It has been suggested that in the body the carotene is split (and oxidized) at the central double bond to form vitamin A aldehyde, which is then subsequently reduced to the alcohol.

There are some thirty carotenoids whose structures are known and several have the β-ionone ring; such as α-carotene, β-carotene, γ-carotene, and

Table 54   A PARTIAL LIST OF CAROTENOIDS, THEIR IMPORTANT SOURCES, AND THEIR RELATION TO VITAMIN A
(Palmer: J. Am. Med. Assoc., *110:* 1748.)

Name	Sources	Molecules of vitamin A possible from one molecule of pigment
α-carotene............	Red palm oil, chestnuts, carrot root, mountain ash berries	1
β-carotene............	Green leaves, carrot root, red palm oil, butter	2
γ-carotene..........	Fruits of Gonocaryum pyriforme (a Dutch East Indies plant), leaves of lily-of-the-valley	1
Cryptoxanthin........	Red calix and fruit of the Chinese lantern plant, yellow corn, egg yolk, green grass	1

cryptoxanthin; these are known collectively as "provitamin A" and are converted (in varying degrees) into vitamin A in the body.

Table 54 gives a list of some of the carotenoids, their sources, and their relation to vitamin A.

Animal fats usually contain the vitamin itself (as the free alcohol, or as the esters of higher fatty acids), while plant fats contain carotene, although mixtures of the vitamin and carotene are known (milk fat, for example).

The oils of the cod liver, the halibut liver, and the shark liver are rich in vitamin A (where it occurs in ester form combined with aliphatic acids such as palmitic). So far, these sources have supplied the needs for medicinal purposes, for enriched poultry feeding—the poultry merchants use large quantities—and for various industrial needs. Industrial methods are available for the extraction of carotene from carrots and alfalfa.

Absorption Bands.   Unlike carotene, vitamin A shows an absorption band at 328 mμ. With antimony trichloride, fractions containing the vitamin yield a blue color the intensity of which, within narrow limits, is roughly proportional to the amount of vitamin present.

The blue compound gives an absorption band at 610 to 630 mμ. Carotene also forms a colored compound with antimony trichloride, but the color is nearer to greenish blue, and the absorption band of this product is at 590 mμ.

Stability. In the absence of air, vitamin A is relatively stable, but it is rapidly destroyed in the presence of oxygen. This is explained by the high degree of unsaturation of the vitamin. McCollum, some years ago, was able to prove the presence of two vitamins in cod-liver oil by heating the latter for twelve hours at 100° C. and aerating it at the same time. Under these conditions, vitamin A is destroyed, whereas vitamin D (the antirachitic factor) is not appreciably affected.

Storage. Animals store relatively large quantities of vitamin A, largely in ester form. The greatest accumulation (about 95 per cent) occurs in the liver (in man), though small quantities are also found in the lungs and kidneys. It has been estimated that in the normal man or rat, the amount of the vitamin in the liver may range from 10 to 20 mg. per 100 gm. of liver tissue. This capacity for the storage of vitamin A is so great that in a few days a rat may accumulate enough of it to supply its needs for several months.

The problem of storage of this vitamin is particularly interesting and somewhat baffling when we consider the livers of fish. Cod-liver oil has long been used as a rich source of vitamin A. But other species of fish, such as the halibut, are richer in vitamin A potency. It has been estimated that about 1 per cent of the weight of halibut livers may be due to this vitamin. As to the origin of this rich supply, the hypothesis has been advanced that phytoplankton, small marine algae (containing carotene), are ingested by small crustacea or small fish, which are eaten by larger fish, and the carotene transmitted in turn to the livers of still larger fish.

Absorption and Utilization of Vitamin A (and Carotene). The absorption of vitamin A through the intestine is improved by the presence of fat. Carotene seems to be absorbed somewhat more slowly than vitamin A. It is probable that the presence of bile facilitates absorption of both these substances, since they are fat-soluble.

Vitamin A is absorbed through the lymphatics and ultimately enters the blood (compare with fat absorption, p. 145), where it is found in the plasma.

As a rule, little if any vitamin A or carotene is excreted by the kidneys; but carotene, and to a less extent vitamin A, may be excreted with the feces.

While, theoretically, one molecule of β-carotene should yield two molecules of vitamin A (see Table 54), it appears from experiments on rats that scarcely more than one molecule of vitamin A is formed from one molecule of carotene. Somewhat the same picture presents itself in man. The greater difficulty in absorbing carotene as compared to vitamin A may be a determining factor.

The presence of mineral oil (in which both carotene and vitamin A are soluble) may interfere with the absorption of these two substances, because the mineral oil itself is not absorbed.

Assay. Colorimetric methods, depending upon the blue color formed with antimony trichloride (p. 348), are used.* However, many careful assays still employ the tedious biological test methods. Here young rats are put on a diet devoid of vitamin A [for example, purified casein, starch, vegetable oil, salt mixture, yeast (vitamin B complex), vitamin D, water], and when they show decline in weight, the tested material is added and compared with a standard sample of the vitamin.

Both these methods can be applied either to vitamin A or to carotene.

A method for vitamin A which is frequently used depends upon the measurement of the absorption of ultraviolet light at the maximum (320 mμ) of the vitamin A absorption band. Still another method is to measure the absorption of light at the maximum (620 mμ) of the absorption band of the blue-colored reaction product formed when vitamin A and antimony trichloride react. Such methods can also be applied to carotene.

Microbiological methods, now so widely applied to vitamins belonging to the B complex (p. 362), are not applicable to vitamin A (or, for that matter, to vitamins C, D, and E). "Broadly speaking," writes Knight, "it is only the basal cellular biochemistry which is common to microorganisms and all higher forms; and in general, microbiological assays are not available for the substances involved in the physiological properties differentiated in higher organisms. Thus the vitamins A, C, D, and E which are concerned in the maintenance of tissue structures characteristic of the more highly organized metazoa are not in general assayed by microbiological methods."

Xerophthalmia. This, the eye disease so characteristic of a deficiency of vitamin A, is rare in this country and in Europe, although during World War I (1914–1918) several cases came to the attention of physicians. One such notable example occurred in Denmark in 1917 (see Figs. 77, 78, p. 346).

Chemical Reactions of the Visual Pigments. We owe to Hecht and Wald much of our information regarding the chemistry and biochemical reactions of the visual pigments. The retina of the eye contains two types of light receptor units, the rods and the cones. The rods are concerned with vision in dim light, the cones with vision in bright light and with color vision. These units contain photosensitive pigments, that is, compounds which undergo chemical alteration on exposure to light. These pigments are rhodopsin and porphyropsin in the rods, and iodopsin (the only one thus far identified) in the cones. These compounds are conjugated proteins consisting of carotenoid pigments linked to proteins. The carotenoids all belong to a group which are isomers of retinene, a compound which is very similar to vitamin A. The retinenes are vitamin A aldehydes; the side chain of vitamin A which ends in an alcohol, —CH$_2$OH, is changed to an aldehyde, —CHO. The general name for the proteins linked to the carotenoids involved in vision is "opsin"; rhodopsin and porphyropsin contain the protein scotopsin; iodopsin contains the protein photopsin.

The sequence of reactions involving rhodopsin is illustrated below:

* The suggestion has been made to use glycerol 1,3-dichlorohydrin treated with antimony trichloride in the place of antimony trichloride alone.

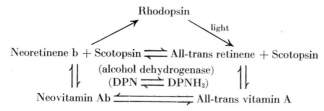

Rhodopsin is photochemically bleached to retinene and the protein scotopsin. The retinene formed is of the all-trans variety. By the action of the enzyme, alcohol dehydrogenase, together with cozymase (DPN), this retinene can be converted to vitamin A. For the synthesis (regeneration) of rhodopsin, not all vitamin A compounds are effective since there are a variety of isomers possible. The all-trans type must first be converted to a specific cis variety, neovitamin Ab. This is probably accomplished in some other part of the body and carried to the retina by the circulation. The neovitamin Ab is then oxidized to the neoretinene b (an aldehyde), which can combine with scotopsin to regenerate rhodopsin. It should be stressed that the vitamin A we are dealing with here is the vitamin A which is present in mammals and is sometimes called vitamin A_1. The regeneration of rhodopsin from retinene and scotopsin takes place spontaneously in the dark.

Porphyropsin is associated with the pigments of the rods of vertebrates which originate in fresh water. In the retinas of mammals, frogs and marine fishes in general, rhodopsin is the pigment. Whereas rhodopsin contains neoretinene b (retinene$_1$), porphyropsin contains cis$_1$-retinene$_2$ (retinene$_2$). Their proteins are the same. The reactions of porphyropsin are similar to those of rhodopsin and are formulated below:

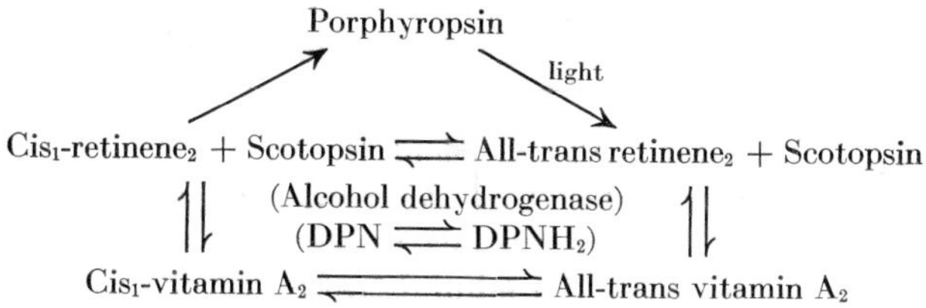

$$\text{Porphyropsin}$$

$$\text{Cis}_1\text{-retinene}_2 + \text{Scotopsin} \rightleftharpoons \text{All-trans retinene}_2 + \text{Scotopsin}$$

$$(\text{Alcohol dehydrogenase})$$
$$(\text{DPN} \rightleftharpoons \text{DPNH}_2)$$

$$\text{Cis}_1\text{-vitamin A}_2 \rightleftharpoons \text{All-trans vitamin A}_2$$

Thus it may be seen that there is another vitamin A called vitamin A_2. The formula for vitamin A_2 is:

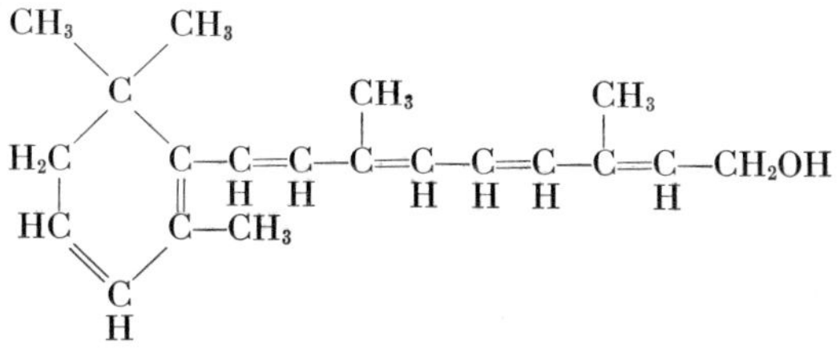

Iodopsin is one of the pigments of cone vision isolated from the chicken retina. Its retinene pigment corresponds to neoretinene b (see Table 55) and is thus similar to that present in rhodopsin. Its protein, however, is different and is called photopsin. The iodopsin system can be formulated as follows:

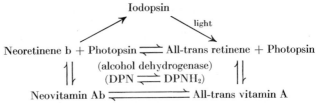

Iodopsin

light

Neoretinene b + Photopsin $\rightleftharpoons$ All-trans retinene + Photopsin

(alcohol dehydrogenase)
(DPN $\rightleftharpoons$ DPNH$_2$)

Neovitamin Ab $\rightleftharpoons$ All-trans vitamin A

Dark Adaptation.   "On coming from a brightly illuminated outdoors into a dimly lighted room," writes Hecht, "one can see hardly anything at first, but, as one stays indoors, objects slowly take shape, and after fifteen or twenty minutes they appear so clear that one recalls the initial visual obscurity with astonishment. The process of achieving this good vision is called 'dark adaptation.' "

The phenomenon of "dark adaptation" can be used to measure vitamin A deficiency. This is due to the fact that the rate of regeneration of rhodopsin depends upon the amount of vitamin A in the body. When there is a deficiency of vitamin A, the process of regeneration is retarded.

Table 55   COMPOSITION OF VISUAL PHOTOPIGMENTS
(Wald: Federation Proceedings, *12:* 606, 1953.)

Pigment	Protein (opsin)	Carotenoid (retinene)	Absorption maxima (mμ)
Rhodopsin	scotopsin	(neoretinene b)	500
Porphyropsin	scotopsin	(cis$_1$-retinene$_2$)	522
Iodopsin	photopsin	(neoretinene b)	562

Infection.   Rats on a diet deficient in vitamin A are very prone to infection. Harris believes that this increased susceptibility is connected with the "drying up" of the mucous membrane, which then ceases to secrete mucus. In any case, the administration of vitamin A to infected animals has no influence in mitigating the severity of the disease. In fact, as Moore has shown, animals can die of an infectious disease and still retain appreciable quantities of vitamin A in the liver (where it is stored).

Vitamin A Values of Foods.   Foods derived from the plant kingdom show a correlation between greenness and the amount of vitamin A or carotene. Green leaves are excellent sources of the provitamin. Such examples are the outer green leaves of lettuce and of cabbage. Other rich sources are green seeds and seed foods (peas, beans, etc.), fleshly vegetables (green peppers, etc.), and green stems (asparagus, broccoli, celery, etc.).

Very often the yellow color of the foodstuff (due to carotene) is a good indication of vitamin A content. Such examples are carrots, sweet potatoes, apricots, yellow peaches, and bananas.

Cereal grains, nuts, and legumes are, as a rule, poor sources of provitamin A. Yellow corn is a notable exception.

Among foods of animal origin, eggs (excellent) and whole milk and milk products (from good to excellent) are sources of vitamin A.

As has already been pointed out, the livers of the cod, halibut, shark, etc., are rich in this vitamin.

Foods stored in the frozen state retain their content of vitamin A—to a very large extent, at least. Dried and dehydrated foods often reveal losses of the vitamin, probably due to the oxidation of the vitamin in the course of drying. Foods which lend themselves to storage for some time in their natural state lose little of their content of the vitamin over a period of from nine to twelve months.

The table on p. 318 gives recommended daily allowances for vitamin A.

THE VITAMIN B COMPLEX

Originally, vitamin B referred to the vitamin the absence of which gives rise to beriberi in man and polyneuritis in birds. The work of Goldberger on pellagra led to the view that vitamin B consisted of at least two factors, the heat-labile antiberiberi factor, and the comparatively heat-stable antipellagra factor. Some called the former the true vitamin B, and others, vitamin B_1; some called the heat-stable factor vitamin G, and others vitamin B_2.

In 1933, Kuhn, P. György, and Wagner-Jauregg isolated what they supposed at the time was vitamin G (B_2) and found it to be a flavin. That this flavin—now known as riboflavin—was not the sole antipellagra factor became apparent when it was shown that the pigment does not cure human pellagra, and that a combination of vitamin B_1 plus riboflavin does not prevent dermatitis in rats. Riboflavin, then, had little, if anything, to do with pellagra; and it became obvious that the so-called vitamin B_2 consisted of more than one factor.

Elvehjem and co-workers next found that after removing the flavin from liver extract (a good source of much of the vitamin B complex) by adsorption on fuller's earth, the residue cured pellagra-like symptoms in chicks and blacktongue in dogs. But Elvehjem's arresting contribution was the discovery that nicotinic acid cures canine blacktongue (the analogue of pellagra in man); and he succeeded in isolating the amide of nicotinic acid from highly active concentrates of liver extract.

But the vitamin B complex, as represented by yeast, rice bran, and liver extracts, contains still other factors. These substances have been discovered by showing that the isolated constituents are still not the equivalent in biological response to the yeast or liver or rice bran from which they were extracted.

The Substances Comprising the Vitamin B Complex.   They are:
(a) *Thiamine* (vitamin B_1, antineuritic factor, aneurine, heat-labile factor)
(b) *Riboflavin* (vitamin B_2, vitamin G), a growth factor
(c) *Niacin* (nicotinic acid or nicotinic acid amide, P-P factor), pellagra preventive factor
(d) *Vitamin B_6* (pyridoxine, etc.), antidermatitis factor
(e) *Pantothenic acid* (filtrate factor), chick antidermatitis factor
(f) *Biotin* (vitamin H, coenzyme R, anti-egg white injury factor), needed for the growth of yeasts, molds and bacteria

(g) *Inositol* (mouse anti-alopecia * factor)

(h) *Choline*, a growth factor. It also prevents perosis † in chicks and is needed for methylating compounds in the body (Chap. 13)

(i) *Para-aminobenzoic acid*

(j) *Folic acid*

(k) *Vitamin B₁₂*, anti-pernicious anemia factor

These vitamins—the vitamin B complex—are not related to one another, either chemically or physiologically. If a relationship does exist, it is that most of them, if not all, are part of enzyme systems which play vital roles in metabolism.

The experimental difficulties in working with these vitamins are enhanced by the fact that a number of them can be synthesized by intestinal microorganisms (this is particularly true of ruminants), so that putting an animal on a diet devoid of pyridoxine, say, does not necessarily mean that some pyridoxine may not be formed within the body. To some extent the problem has been overcome by the use of sulfa compounds which tend to destroy such microorganisms.

Fig. 79. Before and after. The effect of thiamine given to a pigeon with beriberi. (Drummond in Plimmer: Vitamins and Choice of Food. Longmans, Green & Co.)

Thiamine.   A deficiency of thiamine primarily involves the nervous and circulatory system. In the absence of this vitamin a peripheral neuritis sets in, resulting in paralysis. The beriberi of man has its corresponding analogue in the polyneuritis of the bird and the rat (Figs. 79, 80). Not only is there the typical paralysis, but cardiovascular symptoms, edema, and loss of appetite are noticed.

In addition to typical cases of beriberi, comparatively rare in this country, there are several related diseases which are not so uncommon. For example, there are the several polyneuropathies, associated with faulty absorption, restricted food intake, and excessive excretion (diarrhea); infectious polyneuritis, alcoholic polyneuritis, polyneuritis of pregnancy, etc. The Wernicke syndrome, characterized by ophthalmoplegia (paralysis of eye muscles), polyneuropathy, and clouding of consciousness, is partly caused by a thiamine deficiency.

FUNCTION.   Thiamine plays a role in carbohydrate metabolism. In thiamine deficiency there is interference with glycogen storage, hyperglycemia, etc. Peters and others have shown that this vitamin acts as a

* alopecia = baldness.

† perosis = a shortening and thickening of the bones.

coenzyme in facilitating the oxidation of pyruvic acid in the body. This pyruvic acid, $CH_3 . CO . COOH$, is an intermediate product of carbohydrate metabolism. In the absence of thiamine, the oxidation of pyruvic acid is impaired. In acting as coenzyme, the vitamin is joined to phosphoric acid (thiamine pyrophosphate or cocarboxylase).

Aside from its connection with pyruvic acid, the probably broader role of thiamine in metabolism is not known.

Where there is a definite thiamine deficiency, the amounts of pyruvic and lactic acids increase in the tissues—a fact made use of in clinical diagnosis.

Fig. 80. The white animal exhibits typical convulsive movements due to degenerative changes of the inner ear resulting from thiamine starvation. The position of the hind legs of this animal is typical of the so-called "polyneuritis" of rats, due to lack of vitamin B_1. The black animal exhibits uncoordinated movements due to lack of vitamin B_1, but the condition of thiamine starvation has not developed to the stage of the typical convulsive movements. (I. F. Harris.)

DISTRIBUTION. See Table 56 for the thiamine content of some foods.

In foods (and in tissues) the vitamin occurs in the free state and also as the pyrophosphate (cocarboxylase).

CHEMISTRY. The vitamin has not only been isolated in the chemically pure state, but it has also been synthesized. Its structural formula, as elucidated by Williams, Clarke, and their co-workers, is

$$
\begin{array}{cc}
& CH_3 \\
N = C . NH_2 . HCl & C = C - CH_2 . CH_2OH \\
CH_3 . C \quad C - CH_2 - N & \\
N - CH & Cl \quad CH - S \\
\end{array}
$$

Thiamine hydrochloride

which shows it to be made up of a pyrimidine and a thiazole nucleus.

Thiamine is soluble in water and in alcohol up to 70 per cent. It is insoluble in fat solvents. The pure substance is quite stable in acid solutions and can be sterilized for thirty minutes at 120° C. without appreciable loss of activity; but in alkaline and neutral solutions, the vitamin is rapidly destroyed, because here it is hydrolyzed into its two main components; substances containing the pyrimidine and thiazole rings.

ASSAY. The biological test can be based either on curing the polyneuritis (in the pigeon), or causing a resumption of growth (in the rat). When the pigeon is used, it is placed on polished rice until the paralytic symptoms appear; the substance under examination is now given. Where the rat is used, young animals (some twenty-five days in age) are selected and placed on a synthetic diet devoid of thiamine; for example, purified casein, starch, salt mixture, butterfat, cod-liver oil, and autoclaved yeast. The butterfat and the cod-liver oil supply vitamin A, the latter also supplies vitamin D, and the autoclaved yeast is a source of the vitamin B complex other than thiamine. The animals stop growing at the end of two weeks. At this point the material under examination is fed.

The biological methods are time-consuming and costly. Several chemical and microbiological methods have been suggested in their place.

One chemical method is based on the measurement of the fluorescence produced by thiochrome, a compound formed when thiamine is oxidized with potassium ferricyanide in alkaline solution.

Several colorimetric methods are based upon the color produced by the coupling of the vitamin with a diazotized aromatic amine (such as sulfanilic acid).

Microbiological methods are having wide applications in the determination of vitamins (and amino acids). The accelerating effect of thiamine on the rate of alcoholic fermentation is specific. Here baker's yeast is used as the test organism; the medium consists of inorganic salts, glucose, and nicotinic acid, the mixture is incubated for three hours at 30° C., and the gas given off is measured.

Another method, of wide applicability, is to select an organism which needs the particular vitamin (or amino acid) for growth, to supply the organism with everything except the substance under examination, and then to add the latter (as a food extract, etc.) and measure the growth response. For example, thiamine may be assayed by selecting as the test organism, *Saccharomyces cerevisiae*, and using the following medium: casein hydrolysate, sucrose, asparagine, inorganic salts, inositol, biotin, calcium pantothenate, pyridoxine, folic acid, and thiamine-free liver and yeast extracts.

THIAMINE REQUIREMENTS. These are given in Table 46, p. 318.

BIOSYNTHESIS OF THIAMINE. In the rumen of animals microorganisms synthesize vitamins which may then be utilized—a fact which often makes experimental observations difficult. Najjar and Holt have had some such difficulty in studies on man. They found that on a diet low in thiamine, some subjects showed no pronounced deficiency symptoms. It was then discovered that thiamine was being synthesized in the bowel.

Another interesting observation was that when succinylsulfathiazole was administered—a drug which tends to inhibit growth of various microorganisms—synthesis of the vitamin in the bowel was largely curtailed.

Using mutant strains of the fungus *Neurospora*, where each differs from the wild type in a single gene, Tatum has shown that these mutants require thiamine for growth, whereas the wild type does not. In this specific instance, the absence of a gene prevents the normal synthesis of thiamine by the organism.

Since we shall have occasion, from time to time, to refer to this work in *biogenetics*, the general procedure used will be discussed.

Beadle and Tatum, basing their work on (*a*) Muller's observation that the use of x-rays could hasten mutations and (*b*) that vitamins of the B complex, particularly, are part of enzyme systems in the body, selected for their experiments the red mold, *Neurospora*. Normally this mold can synthesize many of the amino acids and the various B vitamins, with the exception of biotin. In what way will such synthesis be impaired by developing mutants?

The fungus was first raised on a minimal diet of agar, inorganic salts, biotin, and a disaccharide (medium A, Fig. 81). Just before the occurrence of spore formation, the fungus was irradiated with x-rays. Spores were isolated, cultured on a complete medium (medium B), including yeast (rich in amino acids and B vitamins), and then tested for their ability to grow on minimal medium (medium A). Those strains which did not grow were given vitamins (see Fig. 81). In this way it could be shown that one strain had lost the ability to synthesize thiamine, and another had lost the ability to synthesize nicotinic acid.

Working with some 60,000 single spore cultures, Beadle and his coworkers have obtained forty different strains of neurospora, each strain deficient in the ability to synthesize some one substance.

Since these mutations brought about by x-rays (and also ultraviolet radiations) affect the genes, the inference can be drawn that a specific gene is involved in the synthesis of a specific vitamin; and that when the gene is absent, the vitamin can no longer be synthesized. Since these vitamins are part of enzyme systems, we can broaden the statement by saying that the genes are involved in the synthesis of enzymes in the body.

It may be added that mutations can be induced not only in fungi, but in bacteria and in yeasts. Furthermore, the "mutagen," the substance producing the mutation, can be brought about by ultraviolet rays and certain chemicals (mustard gas, for example), as well as by x-rays.

ENRICHED BREAD.   White bread, made from flour which has been refined and has therefore lost some of its vitamins and minerals, is now made more nutritious by the addition of thiamine, niacin, riboflavin, and iron. Such a bread is known as "enriched bread." Sometimes, but not always, further additions of vitamin D and calcium are made to the bread.

Government specifications are such that every pound of enriched bread must contain not less than 1 mg. of thiamine, not less than 4 mg. of niacin, and not less than 4 mg. (nor more than 16 mg.) of iron.

Alpha-Lipoic Acid.   For a number of years the literature contained references to a variety of substances which were active in supporting the growth of a number of bacteria and protozoa. The unknown factors were variously called alpha-lipoic acid, pyruvate oxidation factor, protogen, etc.

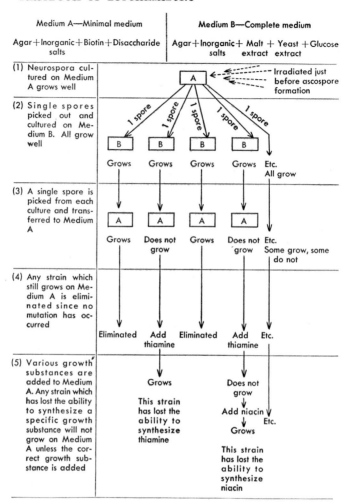

Fig. 81. Diagrammatic explanation of the method used by Beadle and Tatum on *Neurospora*. (Goldstein, P.: Wallerstein Communications.)

Reed et al. isolated a crystalline substance from the insoluble residues of liver which was identical in its activity with all of these factors. It has been identified as a cyclic disulfide derived from 6,8-dimercapto-*n*-caprylic acid, or more simply, 6,8-dithiooctanoic acid:

$$\underset{\underset{S\text{------}S}{|\qquad\quad|}}{\underset{H_2\qquad H_2\ H_2\ H_2\ H_2}{H_2C—C—\overset{\overset{\textstyle H}{|}}{C}—C—C—C—C—COOH}}$$

Its action is that of a catalytic agent for the oxidative decarboxylation of pyruvic acid. The precise enzymatic role of lipoic acid has not yet been determined, although Reed has published suggestive evidence which would place it in the group of B vitamins. He has shown that compounds of lipoic acid with thiamine, or with thiamine pyrophosphate (cocarboxylase), are active in the oxidative decarboxylation of pyruvate, so that the actual oxidation may involve an intermediate complex called by him lipothiamide pyrophosphate. This may then be the actual coenzyme of pyruvate oxidation. It is of interest that this dithiol compound (as well as the thiol, coenzyme A) is involved in acetate formation and may thus be a participant in energy conservation and transfer.

Riboflavin, also called *vitamin B₂*, has the formula

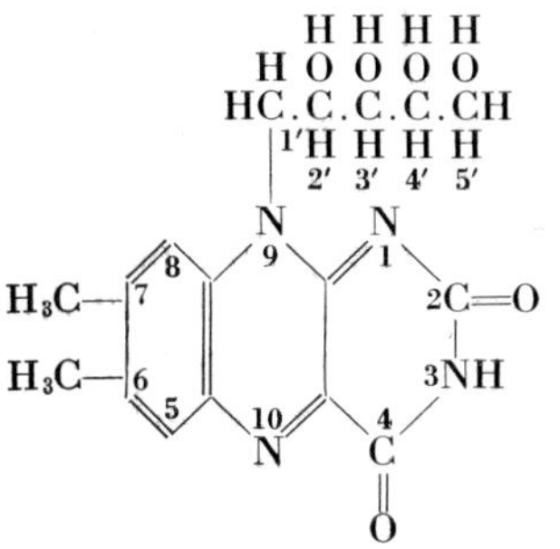

Riboflavin

Riboflavin, derived from isoalloxazine, is 6,7-dimethyl-9-D-1'-ribitylisoalloxazine and has a structure which exhibits several groups: a pyrimidine (1,2,3,4), azine (9,10), benzene (5,6,7,8), and the sugar ribose attached at position 9.

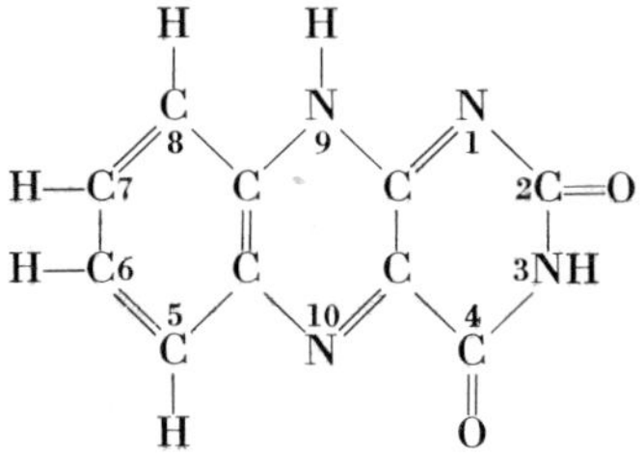

Isoalloxazine

The vitamin properties of the compound are apparently dependent upon these structural components. For instance, by substituting arabinose for ribose, the resulting compound is much less active.

The crystalline, orange-yellow, water-soluble material is fairly heat-stable, and stable to air (and oxygen), but very photolabile, so that solutions are rapidly affected when exposed to light. The solutions are much more stable in acid than in alkaline media.

The solution, greenish-yellow in color, has a greenish-yellow fluorescence. Under ultraviolet rays the fluorescence becomes much more intense, and this is made the basis for an estimation of riboflavin.

Warburg's respiratory yellow enzyme is riboflavin connected to a protein by means of phosphoric acid.

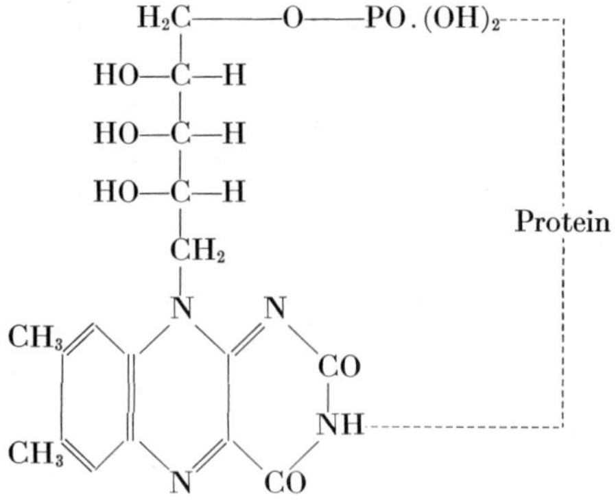

$$H_2C\text{———}O\text{———}PO.(OH)_2$$

HO—C—H

HO—C—H

HO—C—H

CH₂

CH₃

N   N

CO

NH

CH₃

N   CO

Protein

Yellow enzyme (Warburg) *

Even more important than the yellow enzyme are flavin compounds which make up the amino acid oxidase and xanthine oxidase, because these have more obvious functions and are more widely distributed.

As showing how closely related the vitamin is to these enzymes, Elvehjem has found that the enzymes are decreased in activity on a diet deficient in riboflavin. The conclusion is obvious: one important function of the vitamin is to supply the "building stones" for the formation of such enzymes.

In riboflavin deficiency, growth is arrested, but this is not at all characteristic.

The disease due to lack of riboflavin—ariboflavinosis—is characterized by cheilosis, a reddening of the lips, with lesions in the angles of the mouth; glossitis, inflammation of the tongue; seborrheic dermatitis, waxy accumulations in the skin; keratitis, ocular lesions, a burning and roughness of the eyes; and "sharkskin," a roughening of the skin at the mouth and nose.

While it seems definite that riboflavin is a vitamin needed by man, the symptoms of deficiency are usually complicated by other factors.

The effect on rats of riboflavin-deficient diets is shown in Figs. 82 and 83.

ASSAY. One method of estimating riboflavin is to measure its fluorescence under ultraviolet rays.

Another method is a *microbiological* one. The lactic acid group of bacteria are unable to synthesize riboflavin and need it for development. This, therefore, becomes one method of assaying the vitamin. This microbiological method uses *Lactobacillus casei* ε as the test organism. The amount of flavin added to the nutrient solution is proportional to the growth of the organism.

The basal medium for the organism contains all constituents known to be essential for growth, with the exception, of course, of the vitamin to be tested—in this case, riboflavin. Such a diet may include tryptic casein digest, sodium acetate, glucose, KH_2PO_4, K_2HPO_4, $MgSO_4$, $MnSO_4$, $FeSO_4$, cystine, NaCl, uracil, adenine sulfate, guanine hydrochloride, p-aminobenzoic acid, biotin, calcium pantothenate, folic acid, nicotinic acid, pyridoxal hydrochloride, and thiamine chloride.

* This compound, dissociated from the protein, may be regarded as a nucleotide in which the purine group is replaced by isoalloxazine.

This medium is added to a series of tubes, and the vitamin to be assayed is added in graded amounts. The tubes are made up to uniform volume with water, plugged with cotton, inoculated with a suspension of *Lactobacillus casei*, and incubated at 37° C. for sixteen to thirty-two hours. Tubes containing riboflavin will show growth and acid production, but not those lacking the vitamin. Within a certain range, the amount of growth (increased turbidity of solution) or the amount of acid production is proportional to the concentration of the vitamin. Growth is measured by comparing turbidities in a photoelectric colorimeter; or the extent of acid

Fig. 82.

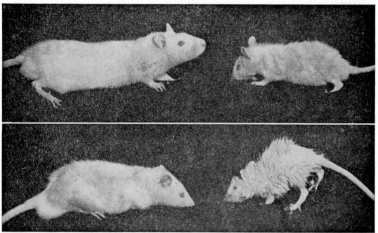

Fig. 83.

Fig. 82. The rat on the right was fed the low riboflavin carbohydrate ration for twelve weeks. The rat on the left received the same ration with intake restricted to that of the former plus 100 micrograms riboflavin per day. (Shaw and Phillips: J. Nutrition, 22: 345.)

Fig. 83. The rat on the right was fed on the high fat ration for eight weeks. The rat on the left received the same ration with intake restricted to that of the former plus 100 micrograms riboflavin per day. (Shaw and Phillips: J. Nutrition, 22: 345.)

production may be measured by titration with standard alkali (Fig. 84).

Because of rapidity, and also because of comparative accuracy, the microbiological and the fluorometric methods are widely used.

HUMAN REQUIREMENTS. Human requirements for riboflavin are stated to be between 2 and 3 mg. per day (see Table 46, p. 318).

It is possible that some riboflavin may be synthesized by microorganisms in the intestines. In ruminants this type of bacterial synthesis (of some vitamins, at least) is so strong that neither a riboflavin nor a thiamine deficiency can be produced by restriction to a deficient diet.

Actual experiments on normal adult males show that the average excretion of riboflavin may be from 800–1200 micrograms * per day.

The question of whether any extra energy may be made available by an

* The microgram is one-thousandth of a milligram.

extra supply of riboflavin—and several other vitamins such as thiamine, nicotinic acid, pyridoxine, and pantothenic acid—has been answered in the negative by Keys as a result of elaborate experiments with United States Army men.

Keys has also studied the effect of restricted intake of some of the vitamins. He finds, for example, that "normal young men suffer no physiological handicap from subsistence for at least five months on a diet providing 0.31 mg. of riboflavin per 1000 Cal. (0.99 mg. per day for 3150 Cal.)." This is considerably less than the amount recommended by the National Research Council.

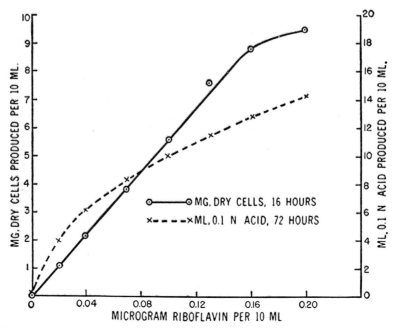

Fig. 84. Growth and acid production of *Lactobacillus casei* as a function of riboflavin concentration. (Snell: Wallerstein Labs., June, 1948.)

However, five months is far from a lifetime; and much can happen of a gradual kind over the course of years.

BIOLOGICAL ANTAGONISM.   The close chemical relationship between sulfanilamide and *p*-aminobenzoic acid, but the striking biological antagonism of these two substances, has led to much work on chemical constitution as related to biological action. Several examples will be given in this chapter, among other places.

By replacing the two methyl groups in riboflavin with chlorine atoms, we get dichlororiboflavin, which acts antagonistically toward the vitamin. Isoriboflavin, a compound in which one of the CH_3 groups is shifted to another position in the benzene ring, also behaves antagonistically towards riboflavin. The growth of rats is arrested by isoriboflavin, and this effect is counteracted by riboflavin.

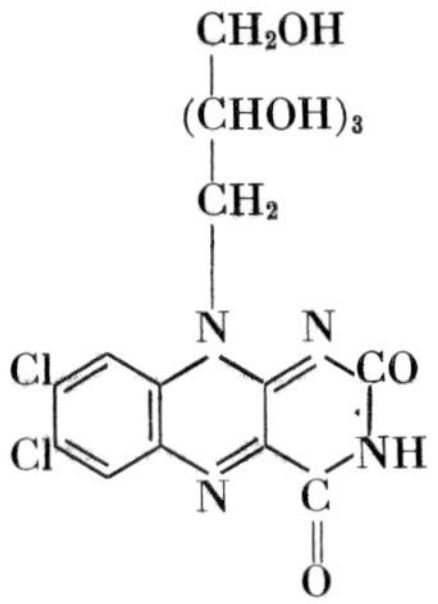

$$CH_2OH$$
$$(CHOH)_3$$
$$CH_2$$

Dichlororiboflavin

Niacin.   This is also called *nicotinic acid, nicotinamide*, and *P-P factor*. It is the curative factor in canine blacktongue (the analogue of pellagra in man) and in human pellagra.

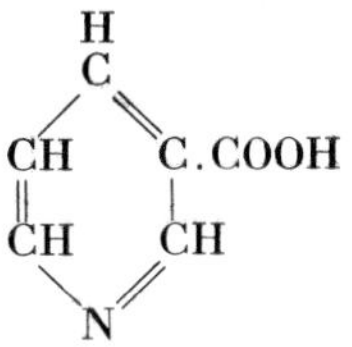

Niacin (Pyridine-3-
carboxylic acid)

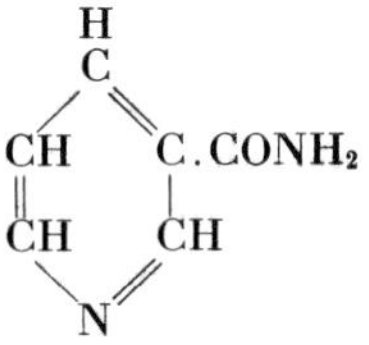

Niacinamide or
nicotinamide

This discovery we owe very largely to Elvehjem and his associates.

It has since been shown that not only can niacin be used to alleviate the deficiency symptoms of this vitamin, but so can the amino acid tryptophan—a result which applies to humans as well as to the rat.

Pellagra is a disease which shows itself by "three d's," as Harris puts it—by dermatitis, diarrhea and dementia. In the southern states, where the disease is still too prevalent, it is brought about by a diet largely of "three m's"—maize meal (corn meal), molasses, and meat (fat pork). Working primarily as a clinician, Goldberger had proved conclusively that pellagrins could be cured by feeding them more fresh meat, eggs, and milk—substances now known to contain nicotinic acid or its derivative.

Pellagra developed among American troops living for three years in Japanese prison camps during World War II. The diet was low in calories, high in carbohydrates, and lacking in animal proteins, fresh fruits, and vegetables.

Niacin, though comparatively new in the vitamin field, has been a well-known substance to chemists since 1867. One method of obtaining it is by the oxidation of nicotine with nitric acid or potassium permanganate.*

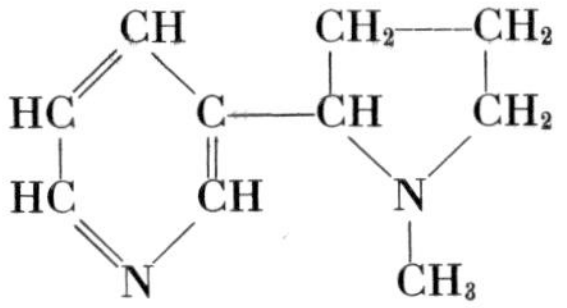

Nicotine

* Unfortunately, smokers cannot convert the nicotine which they inhale into nicotinic acid.

In 1911, long before nicotinic acid was shown to be a cure for pellagra, Funk had actually isolated the substance from rice bran concentrates and had shown that it had no effect in curing polyneuritis in pigeons.

The acid as well as the amide is soluble in water and alcohol.

FUNCTION.   Coenzyme I and coenzyme II (the pyridine nucleotides, p. 88), both of which are involved in carbohydrate metabolism, are derivatives of nicotinamide. The need for the substance now becomes apparent. The administration of niacin to man increases the level of the coenzymes in the red blood cells. In the rat the same result is obtained regardless of whether niacin or tryptophan is offered.

ESTIMATION.   In one biological method, based on curing blacktongue in dogs,* the animal is given a basal ration of yellow corn, purified casein, cottonseed oil, cod-liver oil, calcium phosphate, calcium carbonate, sodium chloride, thiamine, and riboflavin. On this diet blacktongue is regularly produced. The food (or other test object) is then added to test its curative properties.

One satisfactory colorimetric method is based upon the action of cyanogen bromide on the acid—which causes a breakdown of the pyridine nucleus—and coupling the product with aniline, yielding a yellow compound which can be measured colorimetrically.

Several microbiological methods have been suggested. One such method makes use of *Lactobacillus arabinosus* as the test organism. The medium consists of a casein hydrolysate, together with glucose, tryptophan, cystine, sodium acetate, inorganic salts, purine and pyrimidine bases, thiamine, calcium pantothenate, pyridoxine, riboflavin, and biotin. The mixture is incubated for 72 hours at 30° C. The measurement of growth response— after the test object is added—is determined by titrating the acid produced.

FOOD SOURCES OF NIACIN.   See Table 56. For recommended daily allowances, see Table 46, p. 318.

That pellagra may develop on a diet largely of corn meal and patent flour becomes probable when we consider that 100 gm. of these foods contains not more than 1 to 1.5 mg. of niacin, whereas the daily requirements vary from 15 to 23 mg. Furthermore, the chief protein in corn (zein) is deficient in tryptophan, and this amino acid can act, at least to a substantial extent, as a substitute for niacin. Through bacterial synthesis in the digestive tract, the vitamin may also be produced. In the rat the vitamin is important only when the tryptophan content of the diet is low.

Using mutant strains of *Neurospora*, Beadle, Mitchell, and their coworkers suggest that hydroxyanthranilic acid and kynurenine are intermediates in the synthesis of niacin from tryptophan. The steps in this biosynthesis have been formulated as follows:

Tryptophan   Kynurenine

* The rat is not susceptible to niacin deficiencies, unless the amount of tryptophan in the diet is deficient.

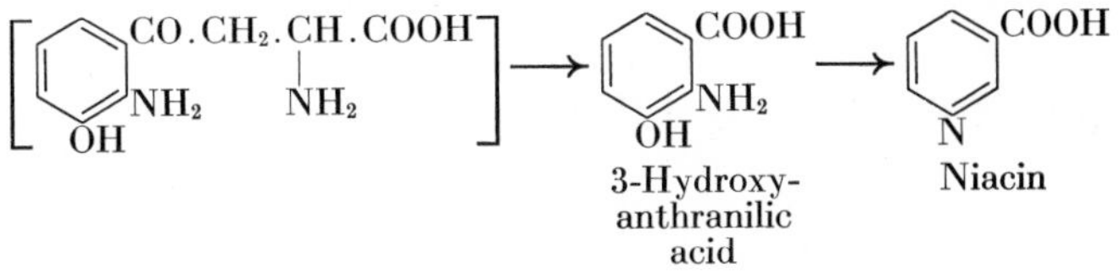

$$\left[\begin{array}{c} \text{CO.CH}_2.\text{CH.COOH} \\ \text{NH}_2 \quad \text{NH}_2 \\ \text{OH} \end{array}\right] \rightarrow \begin{array}{c} \text{COOH} \\ \text{NH}_2 \\ \text{OH} \end{array} \rightarrow \begin{array}{c} \text{COOH} \\ \text{N} \end{array}$$

3-Hydroxy-   Niacin
anthranilic
acid

Quinolinic acid (pyridine-2,3-dicarboxylic acid) is quite probably an intermediate here, preceding niacin.

An excretory product of niacin (or the amide) is N'-methylnicotinamide:

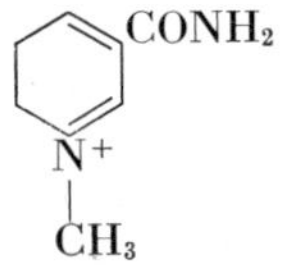

$$\text{CONH}_2$$
$$\text{N}^+$$
$$\text{CH}_3$$

The addition of tryptophan to the diet (in man and in the rat) causes an increased excretion of the methylated compound.

Using radioactive niacin for injection, it has been shown (filter paper chromatography, p. 26) that five other urinary metabolites of niacin can be detected.

Niacin (or its amide) is necessary for the growth of various microorganisms; pyridine-3-sulfonic acid prevents such growth; and growth is re-

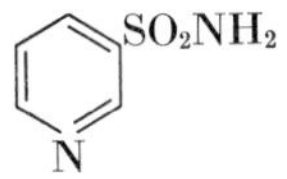

$$\text{SO}_2\text{NH}_2 \qquad \qquad \text{SO}_3\text{H}$$

Pyridine-3-sulfonamide 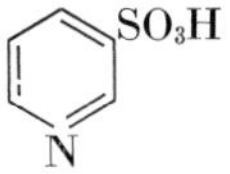   Pyridine-3-sulfonic acid

sumed by the addition of sufficient niacin. Here the relationship of these two substances is not altogether unlike the relationship of p-aminobenzoic acid and sulfanilamide. This fact is even more strikingly brought out by the discovery that pyridine-3-sulfonamide behaves very much the way pyridine-3-sulfonic acid does.

Vitamin B₆ is a general name for three closely related substances: pyridoxine, pyridoxal and pyridoxamine. A deficiency of this vitamin in young rats results in the development of dermatitis, with swelling and edema

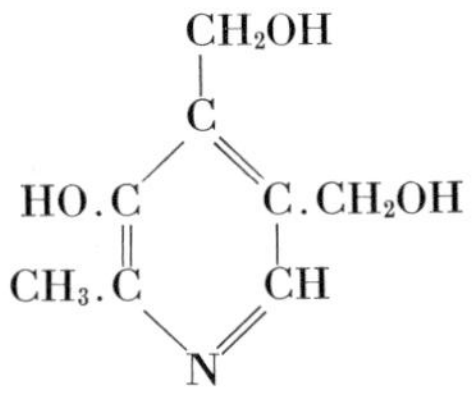

$$\text{CH}_2\text{OH}$$
$$\text{C}$$
$$\text{HO.C} \qquad \text{C.CH}_2\text{OH}$$
$$\text{CH}_3.\text{C} \qquad \text{CH}$$
$$\text{N}$$

Pyridoxine
[2-methyl-3-hydroxy-4,5-di (hydroxymethyl) pyridine]

[especially located in the ears, nose, and digits of the paws (Fig. 85)]. This skin disturbance, at first thought to resemble pellagra, cannot be cured with niacin.

The dermatitis is of a type known as "acrodynia," which is defined as

an eruptive disease, marked by increased sensibilities of the soles and the palms, with pricking sensations in them.

Pyridoxine has been isolated (from rice bran, for example) and synthesized. The hydrochloride, a white, crystalline substance, is soluble in water, less so in alcohol and acetone, and insoluble in ether. The aqueous solutions (pH about 3) are comparatively stable, and sterilization (120° C. for 20 minutes) does not destroy the vitamin.

Fig. 85. Vitamin B_6 deficient rat. (Merck Report, July, 1939.)

Closely allied to pyridoxine are two compounds, pyridoxal and pyridoxamine, also found naturally.

Pyridoxal

Pyridoxamine

Any one of these three compounds can be used to cure a deficiency due to vitamin B_6

ASSAY. For biological tests the rat can be used. A microbiological method has been devised to determine pyridoxine, pyridoxamine, and pyridoxal. When the test organism is *Saccharomyces carlsbergensis*, the total vitamin B_6, or all three, is estimated. However, *Lactobacillus casei* is specific for pyridoxal, and *Streptococcus faecalis* is specific for pyridoxamine and pyridoxal.

REQUIREMENTS. The vitamin is essential for all species of animals so far studied. As to human requirements, little is known. Some 2 mg. per day, comparable in amount to the need for thiamine, is probably sufficient.

OCCURRENCE. Good sources are rice bran, liver, yeast, cereals, legumes and milk.

Source	Pyridoxine: mg. per 100 gm. of food
Whole wheat	0.46
Many meats (fresh basis)	0.4–0.7
Fresh vegetables	0.1
Milk	2 mg. (per quart)

FUNCTION. The metabolism of tryptophan is related to the content of vitamin B_6 in the diet. On a diet containing adequate quantities of pyridoxine, the urine of rabbits, dogs, and rats contains kynurenic acid (Chap.

14). Where rats and dogs are maintained on a diet deficient in pyridoxine, kynurenic acid is replaced by xanthurenic acid, a quinoline derivative.

The phosphate compound of pyridoxal is a coenzyme for enzymes which decarboxylate various amino acids, and is involved in transamination reactions. Various microorganisms require it for the synthesis of such amino acids as tryptophan, phenylalanine, tyrosine, threonine and lysine.

Microorganisms seem to utilize the "unnatural" amino acids—the D series—more efficiently in the presence of pyridoxal phosphate.

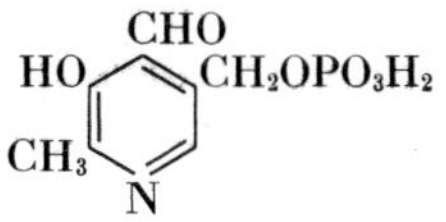

Pyridoxal phosphate
(codecarboxylase)

Desoxypyridoxine possesses potent antipyridoxine activity in the chick. This compound has an inhibition ratio of 2:1, that is to say, 2 moles of "antivitamin" are required to counteract the effect of one mole of vitamin.

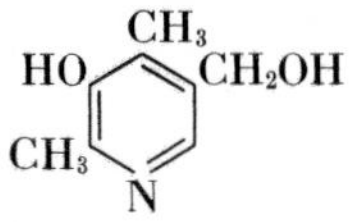

Desoxypyridoxine 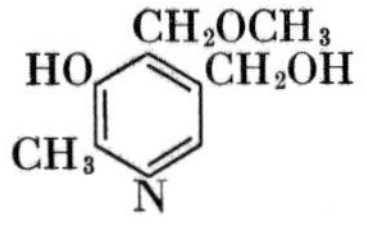   Methoxypyridoxine

Methoxypyridoxine is almost as potent an inhibitor of pyridoxine (in chicks) as is desoxypyridoxine.

Pantothenic Acid.   *Filtrate factor, chick antidermatitis factor,* or pantothenic acid, is represented by formula III. The isolation of pantothenic acid from liver extracts led to a chemical study of the substance. A butyrolactone (I) and β-alanine (II) were obtained from it. The synthesis was accomplished by condensing I and II.

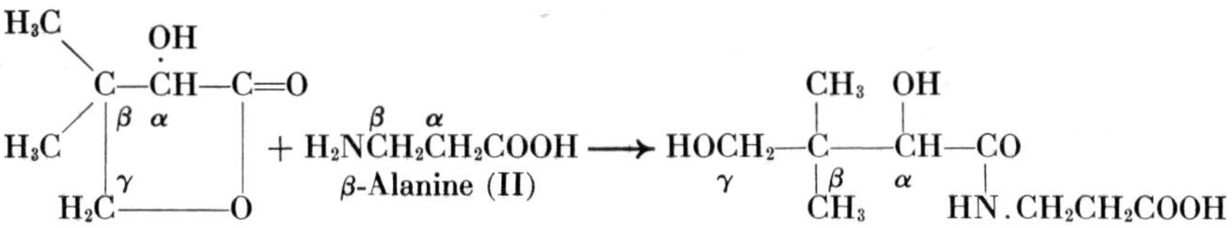

α-Hydroxy-β,β-dimethyl-
γ-butyrolactone (I)

β-Alanine (II)

Pantothenic acid
[N-(α,γ-dihydroxy-β,β-di-
methylbutyryl)-β-aminopropionic acid]
(III)

Working with many types of tissues, R. J. Williams and his co-worker showed that they all contained a "something" which had a stimulating effect on the growth of certain strains of yeast. This "something" was finally isolated and given the name "pantothenic acid" (meaning "from everywhere").

On a diet deficient in pantothenic acid, the rat will exhibit poor growth, dermatitis, and graying of hair.

The acid is most easily isolated in the form of its calcium salt. The dextrorotatory form of the salt is used, for the levo modification shows little biological activity. This calcium salt is a white, crystalline powder, soluble in water, the aqueous solution being alkaline (*p*H 8.5). Autoclaving causes decomposition, and sterile solutions may be obtained by Berkefeld filtration. In animal tissue the acid is found in the bound as well as in the free state. An example of the bound state is coenzyme A (see p. 214).

On a vitamin B complex-free diet, but with daily supplements of thiamine, riboflavin, and pyridoxine and a daily addition of 10 micrograms of pantothenic acid to rat A (Fig. 86), rat B showed signs of graying at the end of three weeks.*

This biological assay is not only time-consuming but not sufficiently quantitative. A more satisfactory procedure is the microbiological method, using *Lactobacillus arabinosus* as the test organism and measuring the in-

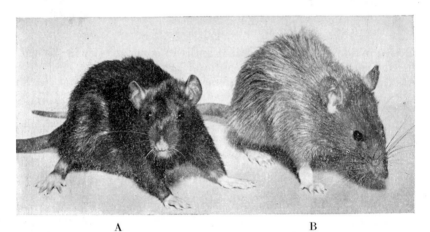

A   B

Fig. 86. Effect of pantothenic acid deficiency. Rat A: Diet includes pantothenic acid. Rat B: Diet is devoid of pantothenic acid. (Research Laboratories, S. M. A. Corporation.)

crease in organic acid production when pantothenic acid (or substances containing it) is added to the medium.

REQUIREMENTS. Little can be said at present as to human requirements of pantothenic acid, assuming that the acid is needed by humans. Excretion studies on man (using *Lactobacillus arabinosus* as the test organism) point to an average daily elimination of 3 to 4 mg., which would indicate that this amount, at least, would have to be replaced in the diet. As high as 5 to 10 mg. have been suggested.

SOURCES. Yeast, kidney and liver are three of the richest sources. Other good sources (in decreasing order of value) are eggs, sweet potatoes, lean beef, whole milk, and tomatoes.

Coenzyme A is an important derivative of pantothenic acid. It was first described by Lipmann who discovered its role in the acetylation of sulfanilamide by enzymes in the liver. In the form of its acetylated compound, acetyl coenzyme A, the coenzyme takes part in many reactions in-

* There are differences of opinion as to whether pantothenic acid is the sole anti-graying factor. Many claim that the anti-graying potency of natural products—rice bran, liver, yeast—is more powerful than the acid. Biotin and para-aminobenzoic acid have been suggested as additional factors.

volving the transfer of acetyl groups, including those of intermediate metabolism (p. 214).

Pantoyltaurine, the sulfonic acid analogue of pantothenic acid, inhibits the growth of microorganisms which need the acid, while the latter causes resumption of growth (Snell).

$$CH_3$$
$$|$$
$$OH.CH_2.C.CH(OH).CO.NH.CH_2.CH_2.SO_3H$$
$$|$$
$$CH_3$$

Pantoyltaurine

A number of organisms—*Saccharomyces cerevisiae*, a strain of yeast, is one—need merely part of the molecule of pantothenic acid for growth; in this case it is the β-alanine portion. Such organisms, grown on a diet which includes β-alanine, cannot be antagonized by pantoyltaurine.

Using a strain of *Streptococcus hemolyticus*, and 10^{-7} M pantothenate, McIlwain showed that pantoyltaurine inhibited growth—an inhibition which was reversed by the addition of pantothenate.

McIlwain has introduced the *antibacterial index*—the minimal value of C_I/C_M, that is, the ratio of the concentration of inhibitor (C_I) just sufficient to prevent the growth of an organism to the concentration of metabolite (C_M) present. The smaller the index, the more effective is the substance as an inhibitor.

Biotin. This is also called *anti-egg white injury factor, vitamin H, coenzyme R*. The word "biotin" is an offshoot of the older word "bios," which was coined by Wildiers more than forty years ago. Wildiers grew yeast on synthetic media and discovered that growth was retarded unless some "x substance" found in beer wort and in *growing* cultures of yeast was present.

One function of biotin became clear after certain studies involving egg white as a source of protein in rat diets. Such a diet gives rise to severe dermatitis. This was traced to the presence in the egg white of a protein known as *avidin*.* It is now believed that in an otherwise wholesome and complete diet, avidin, if present, combines with biotin in the intestinal tract and thereby neutralizes one function of biotin—which is to prevent dermatitis. Of course, if the amount of avidin is limited and there is an abundant supply of biotin, dermatitis is avoided.

A rat suffering from a deficiency of biotin shows symptoms of "spectacle eye," and alopecia (baldness), and at a later stage, spasticity.

Biotin plays a role in the conversion of pyruvic acid to oxaloacetic acid in the presence of carbon dioxide. In fact, in the utilization of carbon dioxide in several other reactions, biotin seems to play a part, probably as a coenzyme.

Normal humans eliminate from 20 to 50 micrograms of biotin per day.

Intestinal bacteria synthesize biotin quite readily, just as they do vitamin K. In fact, because of this, a biotin deficiency is difficult to produce. One

---

* So far the only source of avidin is egg white. Besides avidin, egg white also contains a protein, lysozyme, which lyses or dissolves such microorganisms as *Micrococcus lysodeikticus* by hydrolyzing a mucoid contained in the bacterial membrane.

way is to feed sufficient egg white (or avidin) to neutralize the growth effects of the biotin.

The amount of biotin synthesized by intestinal bacteria may be sufficient so that a source of the vitamin in foods becomes unnecessary.

ASSAY. One method of assay is to test the effect of biotin (or its equivalent in foods) on rats suffering from egg white injury.

More rapid methods are microbiological in character, and depend upon the growth requirements of certain strains of yeast and bacteria.

CHEMISTRY. Kögl isolated the methyl ester of biotin from egg yolk, and du Vigneaud obtained the same substance from a liver concentrate. The hydrolysis of the ester gives the free biotin, with a formula $C_{10}H_{16}O_3N_2S$.

Biotin is a monocarboxylic acid with two fused rings. The acid is valeric acid, $CH_3CH_2CH_2CH_2COOH$. One ring is of the imidazole variety (p. 57) and the other is a thiophene derivative. Its complete structure is

$$
\begin{array}{c}
O \\
\parallel \\
C \\
\diagup \quad \diagdown \\
NH \quad \quad NH \\
| \quad \quad \quad | \\
CH\!-\!-\!-\!CH \\
| \quad \quad \quad | \\
CH_2 \quad CH\!-\!CH_2\!-\!CH_2\!-\!CH_2\!-\!CH_2\!-\!COOH \\
\diagdown \quad \diagup \\
S
\end{array}
$$

and the vitamin has been synthesized.

A complex of biotin, named biocytin, and consisting of the vitamin joined to lysine, is one form of biotin found in tissues. In milk and in vegetables biotin is present largely in the free state, whereas in meat products and in yeast it is present predominantly in the combined form.

SOURCE. Biotin is widely distributed. The chief sources are liver, kidney, yeast, and egg yolk.

According to du Vigneaud, desthiobiotin can be used by an organism for the synthesis of biotin. A closely related substance to desthiobiotin is

$$
\begin{array}{c}
CO \\
\diagup \quad \diagdown \\
HN \quad \quad NH \\
| \quad \quad \quad | \\
H_2C\!-\!-\!-\!CH \\
| \\
CH_2.(CH_2)_4.COOH \\
\text{Imidazoleonecaproic acid}
\end{array}
\qquad
\begin{array}{c}
CO \\
\diagup \quad \diagdown \\
HN \quad \quad NH \\
| \quad \quad \quad | \\
HC\!-\!-\!-\!CH \\
| \quad \quad \quad | \\
CH_3 \quad CH_2.(CH_2)_4.COOH \\
\text{Desthiobiotin}
\end{array}
$$

imidazoleonecaproic acid, which acts antagonistically to it. Presumably imidazoleonecaproic acid competes with desthiobiotin to prevent the latter's conversion to biotin.

Inositol. This is the mouse anti-alopecia factor. We owe to Woolley the addition of inositol to the vitamin B complex. Working with young mice, and using a synthetic diet containing all the known vitamins, Woolley discovered that his mice failed to grow and that their hair was affected. The addition of pantothenic acid—the absence of which may also give rise to hair changes—proved useless. Neither was the addition of biotin or para-aminobenzoic acid any better. Cures were observed by the addition of phytin, obtained from cereal grain, or inositol,* isolated from liver.

Inositol is required by certain yeasts for normal growth. The mouse requires it, as Woolley has shown. Woolley isolated the vitamin from liver. Its formula is

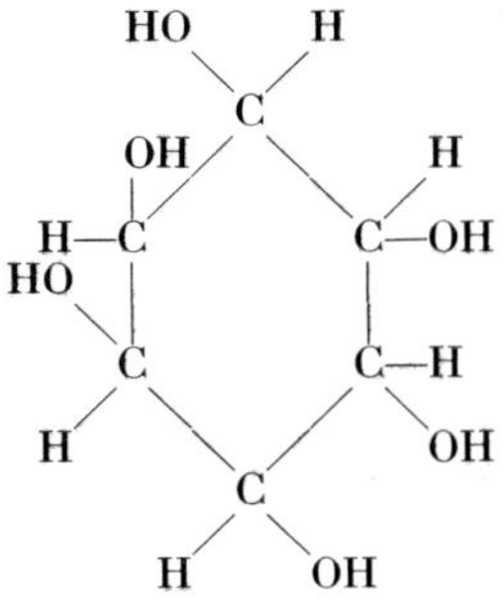

Inositol
(Hexahydroxycyclohexane)

The substance which is biologically active is optically inactive and is also known as *i*-inositol or *meso*-inositol.

It has been claimed that the "spectacle eye" condition in rats can be cured with inositol. This claim has also been made for biotin. Some are of the opinion that an interrelationship exists between inositol and biotin.

The contradictory results occasionally obtained—with mice, for example—have been shown, here again, to be due to the ability of the microorganisms in the intestines to synthesize inositol, sometimes in amounts sufficient to prevent the development of alopecia.

OCCURRENCE. Inositol is found in muscles, liver, kidneys, brain and other animal tissues, and also in various fruits and vegetables.

Inositol has been isolated from the phosphatides of the tubercle bacillus and has been found in the cephalin fraction of the brain and spinal cord. It has also been found in the phosphatide of the soybean; Woolley has given the name "lipsitol" to this phosphatide—a compound containing 16 per cent inositol, besides galactose, fatty acids, phosphoric acid, and ethanolamine.

ASSAY. Inositol stimulates the growth of yeast cells (*Saccharomyces cerevisiae*) in a special medium.

Beadle has described a mutant of *Neurospora* which requires inositol for growth, and which he uses as the basis for a quantitative estimation of the vitamin. Mice showing deficiency symptoms can be cured by feeding 10 mg. of inositol per 100 gm. of food. Whether inositol is needed for human nutrition is not certain.

Since inositol is isomeric with the hexoses, attempts have been made to show whether the vitamin can be converted into glucose in the body. Stetten fed inositol containing an excess of deuterium in the carbon-bound portions to a phlorhizined rat and isolated glucose containing significant concentrations of deuterium from the urine.

* In plants inositol is found in combination with phosphoric acid. Phytin is the calcium-magnesium salt of such a combination.

Choline.   As a constituent of lecithin, choline has already been discussed under the phosphatides.

Its role in nutrition was pointed out by Best, who presented evidence to show that choline prevented the development of fatty livers in depancreatized dogs. On a diet low in choline, many animals develop fatty livers and hemorrhagic renal changes, and if such a diet continues, cirrhosis of the liver appears. In the earlier stages of degeneration, the inclusion of choline in the diet is followed by marked improvement of the condition.

Choline may function in several ways: to stimulate the production of phospholipids, to produce acetylcholine, or to supply labile methyl groups.

Using gene mutations of *Neurospora* which have lost their ability to synthesize choline, Horowitz has shown that this deficiency is due to a lack of such mutants to form a necessary intermediate in the synthesis—N-monomethylaminoethanol. The steps in the synthetic process are suggested as follows:

$$
\begin{array}{ll}
\underset{|}{\text{CH}_2\text{CH}_2\text{OH}} \longrightarrow & \underset{|}{\text{CH}_2\text{CH}_2\text{OH}} \longrightarrow \\
\text{NH}_2 & \text{H—N—CH}_3 \\
\text{Aminoethanol} & \text{N-monomethyl-} \\
& \text{aminoethanol}
\end{array}
$$

$$
\begin{array}{ll}
\underset{|}{\text{CH}_2\text{CH}_2\text{OH}} \longrightarrow & \underset{|}{\text{CH}_2\text{CH}_2\text{OH}} \\
\text{N(CH}_3)_2 & \text{HO—N(CH}_3)_3 \\
\text{Dimethylaminoethanol} & \text{Choline}
\end{array}
$$

Choline may be determined microbiologically by using *Neurospora crassa* (mutant) as a test organism.

OCCURRENCE.   The richest source is egg yolk. Liver and kidney are other good sources. In cereal grains, the choline is found largely in the germ.

Para-aminobenzoic Acid.   Ansbacher noticed that a mouse achromotrichia (lack of pigment in hair) could be cured by feeding rice polishings or by the addition to the diet of para-aminobenzoic acid.

Para-aminobenzoic acid

Ansbacher further claimed that the acid was an essential constituent for the growth of chicks and was needed by rats for the maintenance of a normal fur coat.

RELATION TO SULFANILAMIDE.   Another interesting property of *p*-aminobenzoic acid is its inhibitory effect on the action of sulfanilamide on streptococci. The bacteriostatic properties of the sulfanilamide group towards bacteria are inhibited.

Woods, the discoverer of this antisulfanilamide property of the acid, developed the theory that sulfanilamide competes with *p*-aminobenzoic acid "at the surface of an enzyme which is essential for growth"; and suggested that "normally *p*-aminobenzoic acid is a constituent of this hypothetical enzyme but can be displaced by sulfanilamide," a process which, if it occurs, prevents the enzyme from functioning, and so prevents growth.

Fildes suggested that p-aminobenzoic acid is a necessary food for all organisms which are inhibited by sulfanilamide.

These views, taken in conjunction with the similarity in structure between p-aminobenzoic acid and sulfanilamide, have been a great incentive in furthering the work relating chemical structure to physiological action.

Extracts obtained from yeast have the power of preventing achromotrichia in rats and of inhibiting the action of sulfanilamide on hemolytic streptococci. The conclusion has been drawn that the substance responsible for these effects—present in yeast and part of the vitamin B complex— is para-aminobenzoic acid, a compound which, incidentally, has been familiar to the organic chemist for many years.

p-Aminobenzoic acid has been isolated from yeast. It probably occurs there in the form of a peptide with glutamic acid.

PIGMENTATION.   Para-aminobenzoic acid is one of a number of vitamins which are alleged to function in the process dealing with the pigmentation of the skin. Two other vitamins which have found themselves in this category are pantothenic acid and biotin. It is possible that not merely one of these factors, but all three of them play some part in what appears to be a very complicated problem.

There is, at present at least, no "anti-gray hair vitamin" in the sense that the layman might interpret the phrase: a vitamin which converts gray hair into black hair. In the light of present knowledge, it is possible that diet and gray hair have some causal relationship, but it is highly improbable that diet alone is the sole factor.

It is true that a gray-haired condition has been produced in rats, dogs, guinea-pigs and silver foxes on certain types of deficient diets; but it seems a far cry from this experimental procedure to the process of aging as it occurs in human beings.

ASSAY.   Several microbiological methods have been suggested. One such method makes use of the growth effects of *Acetobacter suboxydans*. Several colorimetric methods have also been suggested, but they are not satisfactory.

Para-aminobenzoic acid (also known as "paba") is a constituent of the molecule of folic acid (see below).

Therapeutically, the acid has been used in the treatment of typhus and Rocky Mountain spotted fever.

Folic Acid and Analogs.   Some lactic acid bacteria require an essential factor which is found in liver extracts. Using *Streptococcus lactis* R. as a test organism, it has been shown that in addition to liver, kidney, mushroom, yeast, and particularly green leaves and grass contain the factor. The name "folic acid" (folium = leaf) has been given to the substance. Folic acid has the formula

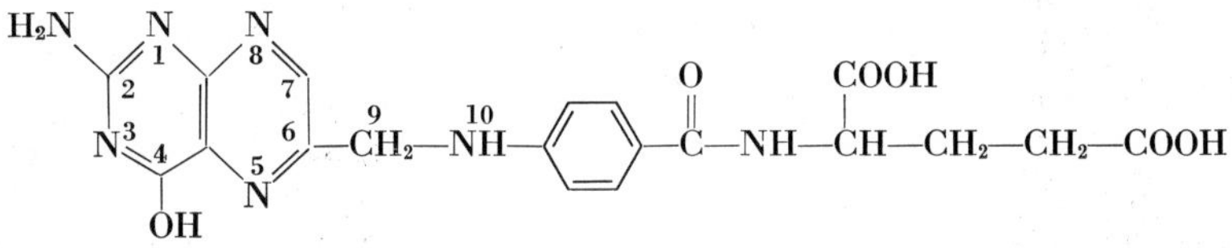

Folic acid

It is a combination of glutamic acid, para-aminobenzoic acid and a pteridine nucleus. This pteridine nucleus together with para-aminobenzoic acid is known as pteroic acid, so that folic acid itself is also called pteroyl glutamic acid (PGA). In nature it is found either as folic acid itself or as compounds with additional glutamic acid—pteroyl triglutamic acid and pteroyl heptaglutamate.

Folic acid has been used with success in some macrocytic anemias,* such as those developed in sprue and the macrocytic anemias of pregnancy. However, the hope held out for a time that it would be of benefit to sufferers with pernicious anemia has not been borne out, because of its failure to cure the neurological lesions in the disease.

It is of interest to note that bacterial organisms which need para-amino-benzoic acid for growth utilize folic acid with almost equal facility.

Folic acid is needed for growth and blood formation by chicks and monkeys, among others. Rats and dogs, as a rule, do not need the vitamin, since sufficient quantities are synthesized by intestinal bacteria. This probably applies to man himself. At any rate, on the basis of analogy, some 0.1 to 0.2 mg. per day should prove ample.

CITROVORUM FACTOR (CF) OR FOLINIC ACID.† For the optimal growth of *Leuconostoc citrovorum*, a non-pathogenic bacterium found in milk and dairy products, a substance other than folic acid and vitamin B_{12} (see below) was found necessary. This has since been isolated and found to be a formyl derivative of folic acid, known as *folinic acid* (also CF):

Folinic acid

which is, therefore, 5-formyl-5,6,7,8-tetrahydro-PGA.

It has been postulated, on the basis of some preliminary experiments, that folic acid, CF and vitamin B_{12} (p. 278) are involved in the synthesis of nucleic acids, which, if true, would be of fundamental importance. An important intermediary in this synthesis is thymidine, a nucleoside of thymine and desoxyribose.

In the formation of CF itself, there is evidence that ascorbic acid is involved. For example, rats and human subjects given PGA with ascorbic acid showed a two- to fourfold increase in urinary excretion of CF; which, incidentally, points to the fact that folic acid can be converted to folinic acid in the body.

The vitamin B content of a few typical foods is given in Table 56.

Vitamin B_{12}. Making use of the observation by Shorb that there is a growth factor for *Lactobacillus lactis* which is present in purified liver ex-

---

* Increase in average size of red corpuscles.

† A substance called *leucovorin* is very closely allied, chemically, with CF, if not identical with it.

tracts, and that the amounts of the growth factor are proportional to the anti-pernicious anemia activity of the extracts, Folkers and associates isolated a factor from liver which is curative in pernicious anemia, according to West, and can be used as a substitute for liver itself. This factor has been given the name "vitamin B_{12}." The vitamin not only induces an increased reticulocyte rise and an increase in the hemoglobin and the red blood cell

Table 56   VITAMIN B CONTENT OF A FEW TYPICAL FOODS

Foods *	Thia-mine †	Ribo-flavin †	Nia-cin †	Panto-thenic Acid † ‡	Vita-min B_6 † ‡	Bi-otin † ‡	Folic Acid † ‡
Apples	0.04	0.02	0.2	0.05	0.03	....	...
Bananas	0.09	0.06	0.6	0.18	0.30	....	0.01
Bread							
White (unfortified)	0.08	0.13	0.8	0.40	0.20	....	...
White (fortified)	0.24	0.15	2.2	0.40	0.20	....	...
Cabbage	0.07	0.06	0.3	0.18	0.29	....	0.01
Carrots	0.07	0.06	0.5	0.24	0.19	0.002	0.01
Cheese	0.04	0.50	0.1	0.35	0.20	0.002	...
Corn meal, degerminated	0.15	0.06	0.9	....	0.25	....	0.02
Eggs, whole fresh	0.12	0.34	0.1	2.70	...	0.025	0.01
Meat							
Beef	0.12	0.15	5.2	1.10	0.40	0.004	0.02
Pork loin	1.04	0.20	4.4	1.50	0.60	0.005	0.01
Poultry, chicken or turkey	0.10	0.18	8.0	0.90	0.20	0.01	...
Liver, pork or beef	0.27	2.80	16.1	5.20	0.80	0.1	0.08
Milk, whole fluid	0.04	0.17	0.1	0.30	0.07	0.005	...
Oatmeal	0.65	0.14	1.1	1.30	0.25	....	0.03
Oranges	0.08	0.03	0.2	0.12	...	....	0.01
Peas, fresh	0.36	0.18	2.1	0.60	0.05	0.002	0.03
Peanuts, roasted	0.30	0.16	16.2	2.5	0.30	....	...
Potatoes	0.11	0.04	1.2	0.40	0.16	....	0.01
Spinach	0.12	0.24	0.7	0.7	0.08	0.002	0.18
Tomatoes	0.06	0.04	0.6	0.37	0.07	0.002	0.01
Turnips	0.06	0.06	0.5	0.25	0.10	0.002	...
Yeast, brewer's dry	9.69	5.45	36.2	20.00	2.90	0.2	0.7
Wheat, whole	0.56	0.12	5.6	1.30	0.40	0.005	0.05

* Edible portion.

† Values are given in milligrams per hundred grams.

‡ Values for pantothenic acid, pyridoxine (vitamin B_6), biotin and folic acid are based on data from only a limited number of samples. Some of the values may be low because of incomplete liberation of the vitamin. (Elvehjem: J. Am. Med. Assoc., 138: 961.)

count but—unlike folic acid—it affects favorably the neurological symptoms.

A convenient source of vitamin B_{12} is the mold, *streptomyces griseus*, which synthesizes the vitamin and which, incidentally, also produces streptomycin.

Curiously enough, the isolated material besides containing phosphorus and nitrogen also contains cobalt—the red color of the substance is due to the presence of cobalt—though the salts of cobalt themselves cannot replace vitamin B_{12}.

Pernicious anemia was first treated successfully in 1926 by Minot and

Murphy. In 1929 Castle suggested that the gastric juice contained a factor ("intrinsic factor") which, together with a factor present in the food ("extrinsic factor"), forms a principle which is responsible for the proper maturation of the erythrocytes. With the isolation of vitamin B_{12} and its dramatic action in pernicious anemia, the extrinsic factor appears to be identified. Vitamin B_{12}, when injected, restores the red cell count to normal and improves the central nervous system effects in pernicious anemia.

Vitamin B_{12} is still not completely characterized but has been assigned an approximate formula of $C_{61-64}H_{86-92}N_{14}O_{13}PCo$. A degradation product of the vitamin has been identified as α-D-ribofuranosido-5,6-dimethylbenzimidazole or, more simply α-ribazole:

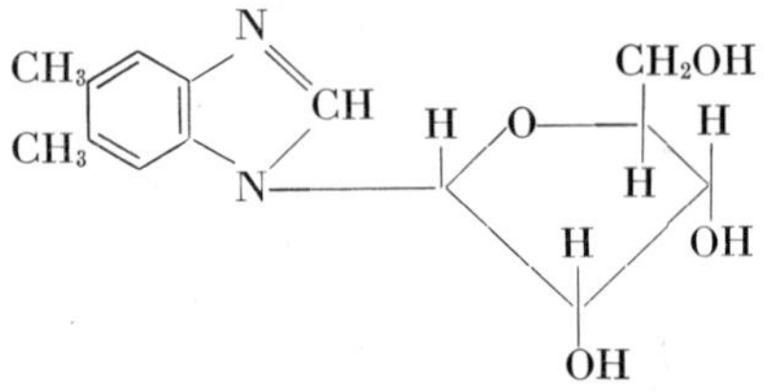

Vitamin B_{12} contains a cyano group bound by a coordinate link to the cobalt, and the vitamin is sometimes referred to as cyanocobalamin. On exposure to air, B_{12} is converted to B_{12a} with a considerably reduced activity. The addition of cyanide ion to B_{12a} leads to the formation of B_{12}.

Vitamin B_{12} apparently plays an important role in transmethylation. Young rats grow well on a diet including homocystine and vitamin B_{12}, despite the absence from the diet of methionine. It would seem that in the presence of this vitamin rats can synthesize methionine, and probably other metabolites with labile methyl groups.

As with folic acid, it is believed that vitamin B_{12} is necessary for the synthesis of nucleic acid.

Animal sources, such as meat, fish, milk, and eggs, contain appreciable quantities of the vitamin. On the other hand, plant sources are comparitively poor in vitamin B_{12}.

Vitamin B_{12} is identical with the "animal protein factor," or "APF." The name is due to the fact that animal protein concentrates, such as fish meal, liver, and milk are much richer in APF than vegetable protein concentrates, such as soybean oil meal.

ASCORBIC ACID

Ascorbic acid, known as *vitamin C*, is the vitamin the absence of which gives rise to scurvy. This disease, so common among sailors at one time, is characterized by a tendency to bleeding, with, among other things, pathological changes in the teeth and gums. In guinea-pigs, in which experimental scurvy can be induced by a diet lacking in "greens," the joints become enlarged and painful.

Source.   It has been known for a long time that fresh fruits and vegetables constitute excellent antiscorbutic sources. Dried cereals and legumes contain practically no vitamin C. Dry seeds, in general, are devoid of the vitamin, but as a result of sprouting (by moistening and warming the seeds) the vitamin appears.

Very good sources of vitamin C are to be found in citrus fruits (orange, grapefruit, lemon), berries, melons, tomatoes, green peppers, raw cabbage, and salad greens. Leafy green vegetables contain appreciable quantities, though losses are incurred in cooking. More particularly among the poor, potatoes are an important source, since relatively large quantities are consumed.

The origin of ascorbic acid in plant tissues is probably glucose.

Chemistry. Ascorbic acid was isolated by Szent-Györgyi and by King, and its chemistry and synthesis we owe primarily to Haworth and Hirst and to Reichstein. The pure substance has the formula $C_6H_8O_6$, and it is soluble in water and alcohol but practically insoluble in fat solvents. It is very easily oxidized. One synthesis, as developed by Haworth and his co-workers, started with xylose:

```
       CHO                          CH:N.NH.C6H5
        |                            |
  HO—C—H                         C=N.NHC6H5
        |                            |
   H—C—OH    Phenylhydrazine     H—C—OH      Hydrolysis
        |        ———————>            |        ———————>
  HO—C—H                         HO—C—H
        |                            |
     CH2OH                        CH2OH
     Xylose                       Xylosazone
```

```
                      CN                    COOH                 CO
                       |                     |                    |
   CHO                CHOH                  CHOH                 COH
    |       HCN        |      Hydrolysis     |        8% HCl      ‖
   CO       ———>      CO       ———>         CO       ———>       COH    O
    |                  |                     |       at 40° C.    |
 H—C—OH             H—C—OH               H—C—OH             H—C———
    |                  |                     |                    |
 HO—C—H             HO—C—H               HO—C—H             HO—C—H
    |                  |                     |                    |
  CH2OH              CH2OH                 CH2OH              CH2OH
 Xylosone          Nitrile of           3-Ketogulonic
                    xylosone               acid
```

A good commercial method starts with glucose. The glucose is reduced to sorbitol and the latter is oxidized (by selective fermentation) to the keto sugar L-sorbose. Oxidation of the sorbose converts it to 2-ketogulonic acid, and in an acid medium the latter lactonizes into ascorbic acid:

```
      COOH
       |
      CO
       |
    HOCH
       |
    HCOH
       |
    HOCH
       |
     CH2OH
  2-Ketogulonic acid
```

Ascorbic acid is an optically active compound, but only the levo form is biologically active.

Assay. There are both chemical and biological methods of determining ascorbic acid. One chemical method is based on the reduction of an indophenol dye, 2,6-dichlorophenolindophenol, in acid solution:

Vitamin C + 2,6-dichlorophenol-indophenol (blue in alkali; red in acid) → Reduced indicator (colorless) + Dehydro-ascorbic acid

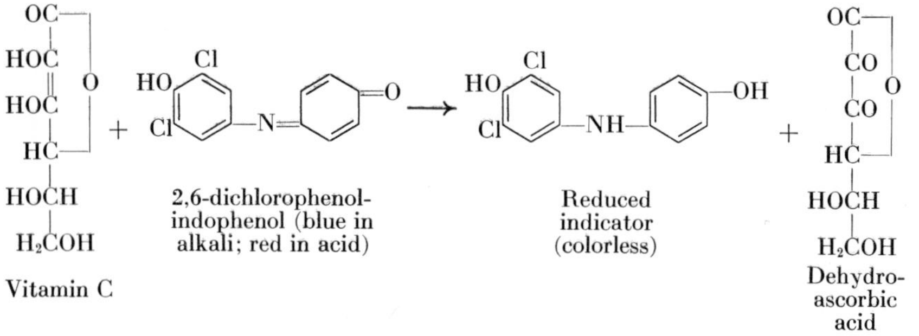

The vitamin is first extracted from the tissue by a mixture of acetic and metaphosphoric acids.

Several micro methods adapted for the determination of ascorbic acid in blood have been suggested. One of these methods, in which no more than 0.2 ml. of blood is used, substitutes methylene blue for the 2,6-dichlorophenolindophenol, since the former has a higher color value.

Another method—applied to blood and urine—measures the color developed upon the addition of 85 per cent sulfuric acid to the 2,4-dinitrophenylhydrazine derivative of dehydroascorbic acid.

In the biological assay, guinea-pigs are used.* The scorbutic diet consists of ground whole oats, heated skim milk powder, butterfat, and table salt; yeast and cod-liver oil are sometimes added. Growth stops in about two weeks, the joints become tender, the paws hemorrhagic, and the animal dies in about four weeks. The addition of an extract containing vitamin C to the animal during the scurvy symptoms will bring recovery. The minimum daily dose necessary for the prevention of scurvy is from 10 to 12 International Units (one such unit being 0.05 mg. of crystalline L-ascorbic acid).

Stability. Exposure to heat and to air causes considerable losses of ascorbic acid. Copper and other metals, even present in traces, hasten destruction. The vitamin is relatively stable in mild acid solutions.

Fresh fruits and vegetables, particularly rich sources for vitamin C, will show wide variations in amounts depending upon such factors as climate, soil, maturity, etc.

Function. It is believed that ascorbic acid plays a role in biological oxidations, due to the ease with which it is oxidized and reduced:

L-Ascorbic acid ⇌ Dehydroascorbic acid

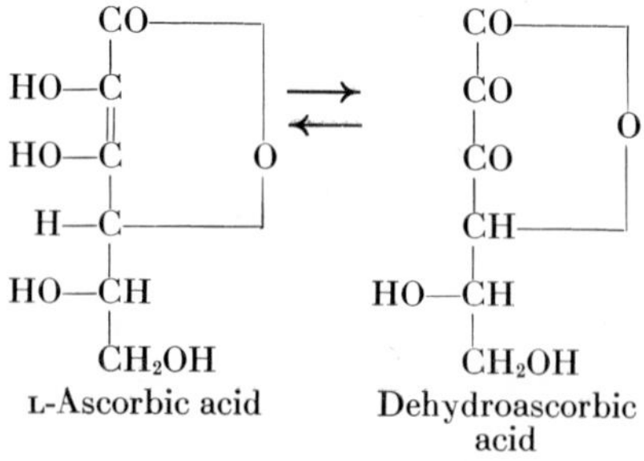

* Plants, and all animals except guinea-pigs, man, and other primates, have the ability to synthesize ascorbic acid. The rat, for example, is apparently resistant to scurvy.

An ascorbic acid oxidase, present in cabbage, cucumbers, adrenal cortex, etc., catalyzes ascorbic acid oxidations. The oxidase isolated from squash is a blue copper-protein compound.

The interesting observation has been made that in conditions arising from a deficiency of ascorbic acid—and this applies to infants as well as guinea pigs—there appears in the urine p-hydroxyphenylpyruvic acid, which suggests a disturbance in the normal metabolism of phenylalanine and tyrosine. In this connection, it may be noted that liver slices from scorbutic guinea-pigs are unable to oxidize tyrosine, whereas slices from normal guinea-pigs can do so. The addition of vitamin C to the slices from scorbutic animals enables the oxidation of tyrosine to take place.

Ascorbic acid seems to be needed for the synthesis of collagen, a property which probably explains its role in the healing of wounds.

REQUIREMENTS. For daily allowances of ascorbic acid, see Table 46, p. 318. While some 75 mg. daily is normally recommended, as little as 10 to 20 mg. will prevent obvious (classic) scurvy; however, this represents a probably dangerous minimum.

VITAMIN D

While several forms of vitamin D are known, only two are important from a practical point of view: vitamin D_2 and vitamin D_3.

Vitamin D_2 (viosterol; calciferol) is prepared when ergosterol (p. 383), a vegetable sterol, is irradiated.

Vitamin D_3 is formed when 7-dehydrocholesterol (p. 384), an animal sterol, is irradiated.

In the absence of this vitamin, or in its presence in insufficient amounts, rickets in varying degree of severity develops. In the child (Fig. 87), the disease is associated with bowlegs, knock knees, enlarged joints, etc. The growing parts of the bone—particularly the ends of the long bones of arms and legs—are affected. An x-ray examination makes diagnosis relatively simple. In experimental animals an analysis of the bone ash is also of diagnostic significance. In rickets the ends of the bones show incomplete calcification; as healing advances the material becomes more dense (Fig. 88). Two other diagnostic tests of value are the decrease of the inorganic phosphorus content of the blood in rickets * (normal amounts are obtained upon healing), and an increase of the enzyme phosphatase in the blood during the disease (with a decrease of the phosphatase upon healing).

* As a rule, it is the inorganic phosphorus, rather than the calcium, which shows low values. The normal phosphorus values for an infant are 4 to 6 mg. per 100 ml. of blood. Values below 3.5 mg. are of diagnostic significance. Sometimes, however, there is a decreased concentration of calcium, and sometimes a decreased concentration of both elements. In any case, we may regard the situation as involving a lowering of the solubility product—a factor which regulates the precipitation of calcium phosphate from the blood into the cartilage and bone.

When the concentrations of calcium and phosphate ions are decreased, and therefore the product of their concentration is decreased below the solubility product of the bone salt, "lime salt deposition in bone and cartilage becomes irregular and, if the value is low enough, deposition stops altogether. The failure in lime salt deposition is responsible for the weakness of the bones. This, in turn, results in the development of the well-known deformities of the disease and at the same time is the cause of almost, if not all, the histological changes. The first demonstrative pathological change in rickets is the failure

Phosphatase can decompose organic phosphorus compounds—hexose phosphate, for example—into inorganic phosphate. There are several phosphatases. The particular one of importance here is known as the "alkaline phosphatase" with an optimum pH action of about 9. This one, in contradistinction to the "acid phosphatase" (about pH 5), is widely distributed in ossifying cartilage, bone, kidneys, intestinal mucosa, liver. It is found, in relatively smaller amounts, in blood serum.

In rickets of infancy and early childhood, the serum alkaline phosphatase may be high.*

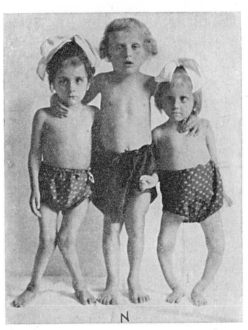

Fig. 87. Children six years of age showing severe rachitic deformities compared with normally grown child (center) of the same age.

That the function of vitamin D may be connected with some enzymic activity is given support by the demonstration that vitamin D activates alkaline phosphatases.

In addition to rickets, vitamin D has been used to treat infantile tetany, characterized by a low calcium content of the blood (in contrast to the usual low phosphorus content in rickets). It is true that the parathyroids play an important role in the metabolism of calcium, but it would seem that both the hormone and vitamin D are involved.

---

of lime salt deposition in the proliferative cartilage of the epiphysis and in newly forming bone" (Park).

A large part of the serum calcium is combined with protein. Out of a total of 10 mg. of calcium in 100 ml. of serum, about 4.5 mg. is ionized.

* The estimation is based upon the amount of phosphorus liberated as PO_4 ions by serum incubated with sodium β-glycerophosphate and buffered at pH 8.6. The "unit" represents the number of milligrams of phosphorus which 100 ml. of the serum can liberate in one hour as phosphate ions.

Treatment with vitamin D has also been used in cases of osteomalacia, an adult disease characterized by the softening of the bones.

Function.   It is believed that the primary function of vitamin D is to regulate the absorption and utilization of calcium and phosphorus. As evidence of this, it is pointed out that in rickets a relatively large quantity of calcium and phosphorus is lost in the feces.

That increased absorption alone is not sufficient to account for the function of the vitamin is brought out by the work of Greenberg. Using radiophosphorus (P^{32}) this author studied the influence of vitamin D on the phosphorus metabolism of rachitic rats. The increase in the absorption of phosphate (administered by stomach tube) was from 10 to 15 per cent. However, the more striking changes occurred in the phosphorus fractions

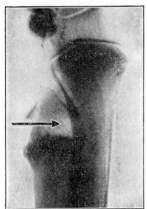 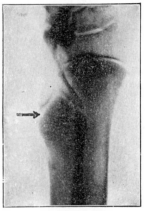

17 weeks: Extremely wide cartilaginous zone; note marked irregularity of end of shaft.   17 weeks: Narrow cartilage and well-defined head of shaft—normal for this age.

Fig. 88. Left, external signs of rickets. Right, normal animal for purposes of comparison. (Fleischmann Laboratories, Standard Brands Incorporated.)

of the bone. The lipoid phosphorus (alcohol-ether–soluble P) was not altered, but the labelled phosphorus of the inorganic fraction increased by 40 per cent.

The absorption of vitamin D, like the absorption of fats and fat-soluble foods in general, is largely dependent upon the presence of bile salts.

The liver is the chief storage place for vitamin D, though smaller amounts are found in other organs (skin, brain, lungs, spleen, and bones).

Vitamin D, suggests Greenberg, may act to aid the conversion of organic to inorganic phosphorus in bone. The vitamin exerts an influence on the process of mineralization in bone.

Assay.   The study of rickets was greatly facilitated by devising diets which readily produced a case of rickets in animals (Fig. 88). Usually, such diets contain relatively large quantities of calcium, little phosphorus, and no vitamin D. For example, the composition of one such diet for the rat is whole yellow corn, 76 per cent; ground gluten, 20 per cent; calcium carbonate, 3 per cent; sodium chloride, 1 per cent. Here the ratio of calcium to phosphorus is nearer to 4.5:1 than to the normal ratio, which is 1.2:1. At the end of some three weeks on this diet, the uncalcified zone in the epiphyseal section of the long bone can be detected by means of x-rays. Furthermore, the phosphorus in the blood drops from a normal of 6 to 8 mg. per 100 ml. to 2 to 3 mg., and the bone ash, from a normal of 50 to 60 per cent to 25 to 35 per cent. As a rule, the calcium content of the blood does not change materially. In fact, the common forms of rickets in children show little change in calcium but a very definite drop in phosphorus.

A spectrophotometric method which has been proposed is based on the reaction between the vitamin and a chloroform solution of antimony trichloride and acetyl chloride, giving rise to a yellowish pink color. The maximum absorption curve of the reaction product is at 500 mμ.

Recovery from Rickets.   Healing may be accomplished in one of several ways. One of the oldest remedies is to feed cod-liver oil, one of the few natural foods rich in vitamin D.* Another is to expose the child or animal to the sun's rays. Here the ultraviolet rays convert the provitamin in the skin (probably 7-dehydrocholesterol, p. 384) into vitamin D, which then exerts its influence on mineral metabolism. The antirachitic region of the spectrum is from 256 mμ to 313 mμ, and the shortest solar radiation is 290 mμ, so that relatively little benefit is obtained except on very clear days and preferably "in the open spaces." This has led to the extensive use of the carbon and mercury arcs, which give off ultraviolet rays, and to the employment of quartz glass in the place of ordinary window glass, because the former, unlike the latter, is not opaque to such rays. The discovery, both by Steenbock and by Hess, that foods devoid of vitamin D can be made antirachitic by exposing them to rays from the carbon or mercury arc has proved important in developing preventive measures against the disease.

Chemistry.   The attempts to isolate the antirachitic vitamins have led to brilliant results. They are found in the unsaponifiable fraction of cod-liver oil. For a time it was supposed that the irradiation of cholesterol itself (found in the unsaponifiable fraction) produced vitamin D, but a rigorous purification of this sterol led to negative results. Windaus finally traced the mother substance of one vitamin D to a closely associated sterol, ergosterol, originally found in ergot (hence its name).

The irradiation of ergosterol produced an antirachitic substance which was finally isolated and named "calciferol" by an English group of investigators and vitamin D$_2$ by Windaus. The name "vitamin D$_2$" has been adopted by the Council of Pharmacy and Chemistry of the American Medical Association. "Viosterol in oil" is another term that has the Council's approval.

Ergosterol is distinguished from cholesterol mainly by having three double bonds:

---

* "When vitamin D is given to rachitic animals . . . the first histological evidence of repair is the presence of degenerated cartilage cells. The effect is visible at the end of twenty-four hours and is accompanied by extensive vascular penetration within forty-eight hours. The penetration of blood vessels permits the deposition of the bone-forming salts. There is thus produced the so-called 'line-test' for healing" (Shohl).

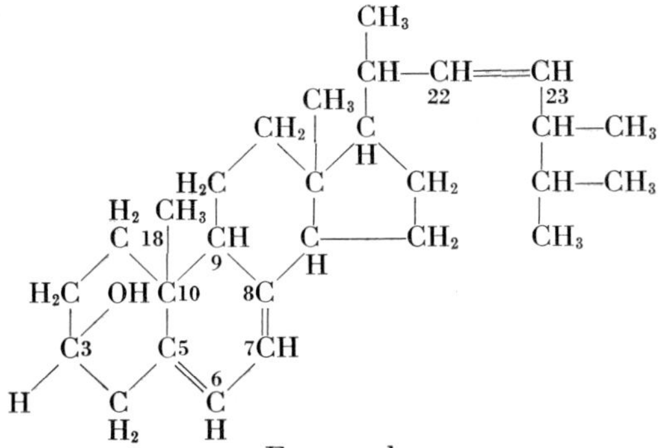

Ergosterol

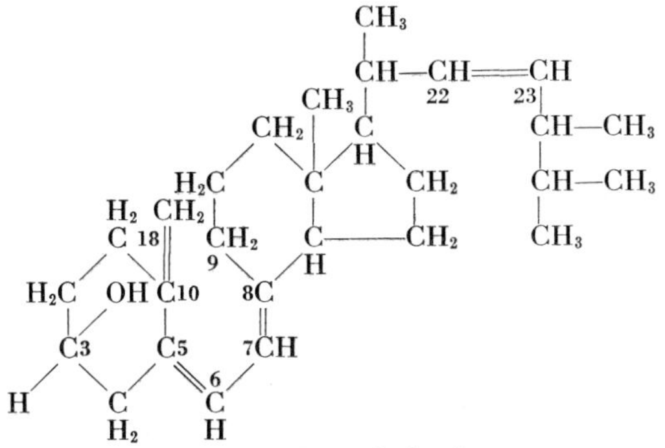

Vitamin D₂ (calciferol)

Its conversion to vitamin D_2 is due to the opening up of the second ring and the introduction of a fourth double bond.

The structures of the antirachitic substances are characterized by the opening of ring B, and the replacement of a methyl group at position 10 by a methylene group, giving rise to three conjugated double bonds.

Actually, the irradiation of ergosterol produces a series of substances only one of which, calciferol, is antirachitic: ergosterol ⟶ lumisterol ⟶ tachysterol ⟶ calciferol ⟶ toxisterol ⟶ suprasterols (I and II). What was originally called vitamin D has proved to be a mixture of lumisterol and calciferol; hence the renaming of calciferol as vitamin D_2.

D Vitamins.   That irradiated ergosterol (vitamin D_2) and the antirachitic vitamin in cod-liver oil are not the same was made probable by the observation that vitamin D_2 was not as effective in curing chicks as an equivalent quantity of vitamin D in cod-liver oil (based on rat assay).

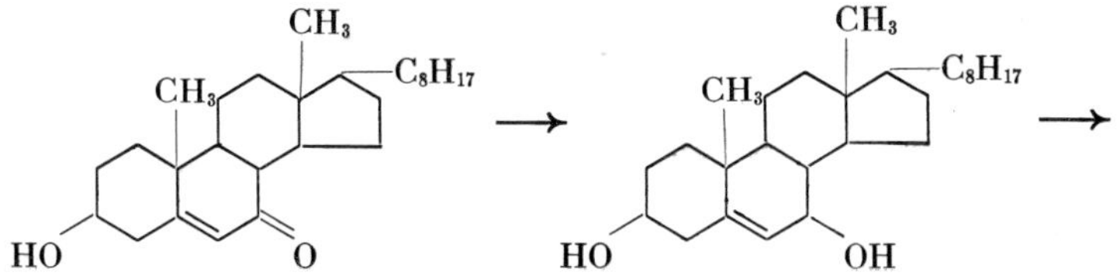

7-Ketocholesterol

7-Hydroxycholesterol

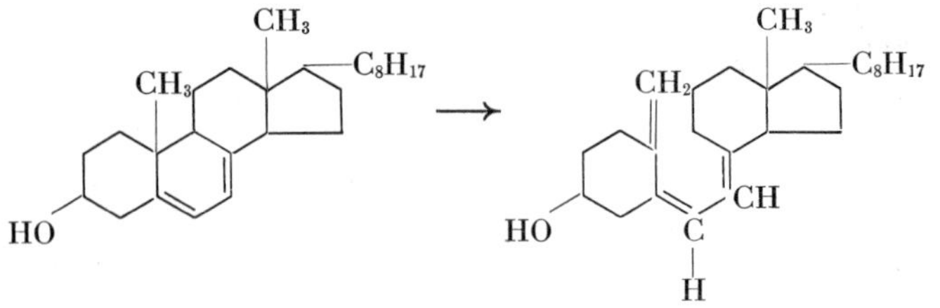

7-Dehydrocholesterol   Vitamin D_3

But the suspicion that there were several provitamins and several vitamins D was considerably strengthened by the brilliant research of Windaus. Starting with 7-ketocholesterol, obtained by oxidizing cholesterol acetate with chromic acid, Windaus reduced it to 7-hydroxycholesterol. The dibenzoate was heated in vacuo at 200° C., whereby a molecule of benzoic acid was split off and another double bond introduced in position 7:8. This substance is 7-dehydrocholesterol, and its double bond arrangement in the second ring corresponds to that of ergosterol. The ultraviolet absorption spectra of the two are similar. The irradiation of 7-dehydrocholesterol gave rise to an antirachitic substance which was isolated and found to be more active than calciferol in tests on chicks. This antirachitic substance is called vitamin D_3.*

7-Dehydrocholesterol, which may be regarded as the naturally occurring provitamin D, has been isolated from fish liver oils.

Wintersteiner has shown that oxidation (by air) of cholesterol gives rise to 7-ketocholesterol. This suggests a possible intermediate in the formation of vitamin D (D_3) in the animal body.

Distribution.   Vitamin D is not very widely distributed. It is found in the flesh of all fat fish; for example, cod-liver oil and the livers of the halibut, tuna, and swordfish. Little of the vitamin is found in natural foods. Some of the vitamin D we need is obtained on exposure to the sun (by irradiation of the provitamin in the skin).

It has been shown that in the ox, the rat, and particularly in the guinea-pig, appreciable quantities of 7-dehydrocholesterol are found in the mucosa of the intestine. The oral administration of cholesterol converts some of it in the intestine into this 7-dehydrocholesterol.

On a comparative scale, next to fish livers, the richest source is egg yolk, followed by butterfat. Milk is quite poor in the antirachitic factor, though it becomes a simple procedure to enrich it with vitamin D. This may be done by the addition of vitamin D concentrates, by irradiation of the milk, or by feeding cows with foods rich in the factor. "Milk fortified with vitamin D," to be accepted by the Council of Foods of the American Medical Association, must contain from 135 to 400 U.S.P. units per quart of milk.

Requirements.   See Table 46, p. 318.

Vitamin D does not decrease the requirements for calcium and phos-

---

* The D provitamins, such as ergosterol and 7-dehydrocholesterol, show ultraviolet absorption characteristics of conjugated dienes, with the double bonds in the same ring. In the corresponding vitamins, the absorption spectra typify conjugated trienes.

phorus; the vitamin cannot produce good retention of these elements when they are present in insufficient amounts.

A number of clinical reports suggests that the administration of vitamin D preparations in unusually large dosages is not unaccompanied by danger. It is true that for all ordinary purposes one may speak of vitamins as being nontoxic, and taking into consideration the relatively small quantities consumed, the problem of toxicity rarely arises. However, a consumption of excessive quantities of vitamin D (and other vitamins) may produce harmful effects.

While this subject has not been investigated in great detail, some approximate figures which have appeared in the literature may be of value. The ratio of the "normal" or "optimal" quantity to the lethal dose for vitamin D has been given as 1:2000. For some other vitamins the figures are the following: vitamin A, 1:7500; thiamine, 1:25,000; niacin, 1:5000; pyridoxine, 1:60,000; and vitamin E, 1:600.

VITAMIN E (TOCOPHEROLS)

Until 1922 it was supposed that a synthetic diet for rats could be used which would cause normal growth and reproduction. Such a diet included casein, starch or sucrose, lard, salts, cod-liver oil, and yeast. Evans and Bishop, and then Sure, showed that while this diet allowed for apparently normal growth, the reproductive process was very definitely interfered with. Only by incorporating in this diet small quantities of certain natural foods—cereal grains, green leaves, legumes, nuts, and particularly the oil from wheat germ—could reproductive disturbances be avoided. The necessary factor is known as vitamin E. It is also known as the "antisterility" vitamin. In the absence of vitamin E the germinal epithelium of the testes of rats is destroyed. In the female rat, ovulation and fertilization take place, but also there is death and resorption of the fetus. This situation can be repaired by incorporating vitamin E in the diet.

Properties. Vitamin E, like vitamins A and D, is soluble in fat solvents and insoluble in water. It is resistant to heat (up to 200° C.) but is fairly easily oxidized and is destroyed by ultraviolet rays. However, it can also act as an "anti-oxidant" to prevent the oxidation of relatively unstable vitamins. Like vitamins A and D, it is found in the nonsaponifiable fraction of fats and oils. Out of the nonsaponifiable fraction of wheat-germ oil, Emerson and Evans succeeded in isolating and crystallizing two substances, to which the names α-tocopherol and β-tocopherol were given (*tokos* = childbirth, *phero* = to bear, *ol* = alcohol). The α form was biologically much the more active of the two: as little as from 1 to 3 mg. doses proved effective. Somewhat later the α modification was also isolated from cottonseed oil. A γ-modification has also been obtained.

Since the α-form is biologically the most potent and is now readily available as a synthetic product, this modification is the one that is almost invariably used.

Vitamin E is easily absorbed from the intestinal tract and stored, to some extent, in body fats, muscles, etc.

The international unit is the vitamin E activity of 1.0 mg. of the standard preparation (synthetic racemic tocopherol acetate in olive oil).

Source.   The vitamin is found in green lettuce leaves, whole cereals (oats and wheat), beef liver, egg yolk, wheat embryo, etc. Wheat germ oil is one of the richest sources.

Chemical Structure.   The three tocopherols are derivatives of chromane:

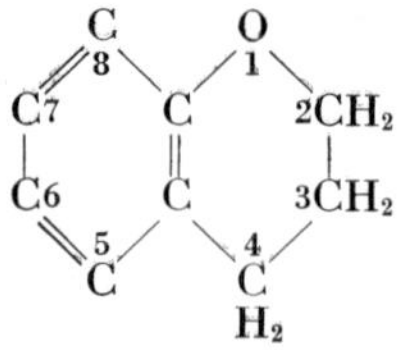

Chromane

and their formulas are

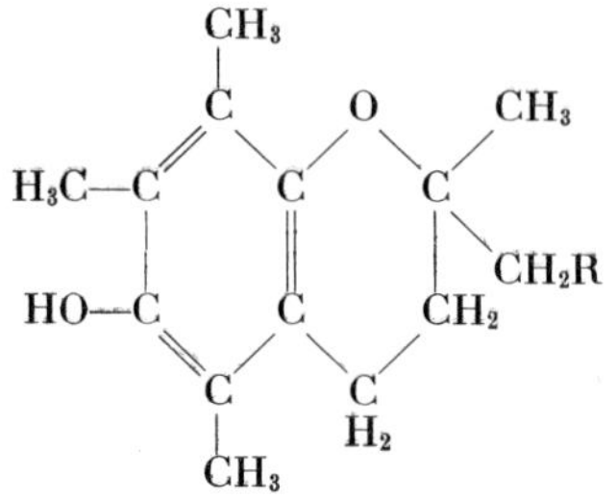

α-Tocopherol

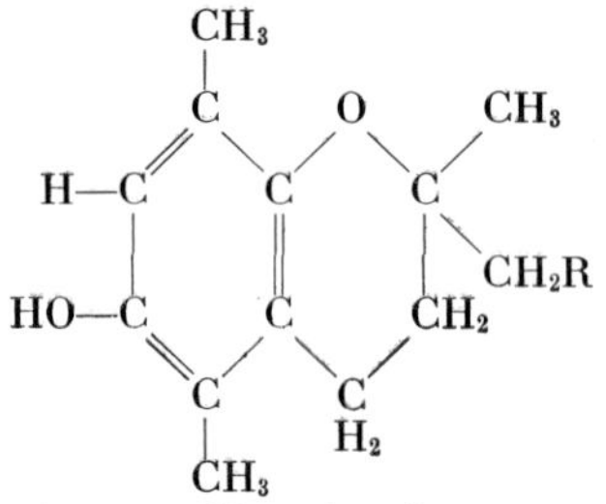

β-Tocopherol

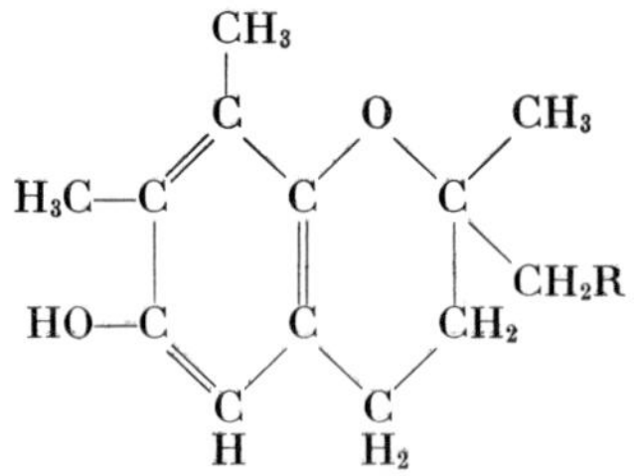

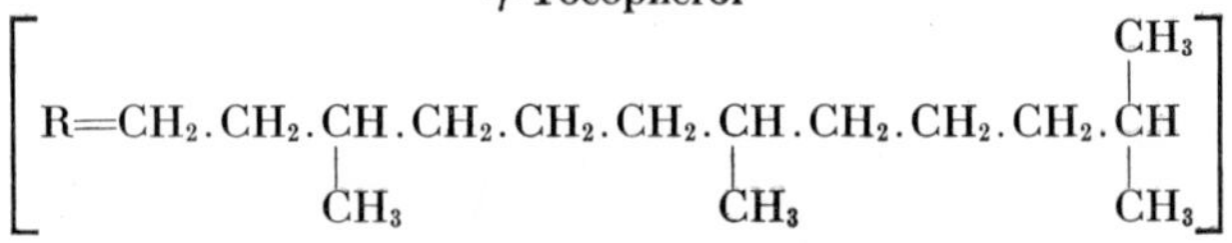

γ-Tocopherol

$$\left[R{=}CH_2.CH_2.CH.CH_2.CH_2.CH_2.CH.CH_2.CH_2.CH_2.\overset{\displaystyle CH_3}{\underset{\displaystyle CH_3}{CH}} \right]$$

It will be seen that the structural differences of these three compounds are confined to the benzene ring.

More recently another tocopherol has been isolated from soybean oil, to which the name δ-tocopherol has been given. It has but one methyl group—position 8—in the benzene ring.

The tocopherols have not only been isolated but also synthesized.

Structure and Biological Activity.   The methyl groups in the benzene ring are important. The β- and γ-tocopherols, with two methyl groups in the ring, are less active than α-tocopherol, with three methyl groups. Karrer has shown that the monomethyl derivative (which he synthesized) is quite inactive.

Physiological Functions.   These functions seem many-sided. Aside from the influence that vitamin E has on the reproductive system, it has also been connected with the physiology of the muscular and vascular systems.

What the significance of vitamin E is in human nutrition is not clear. It has been used in habitual and threatened abortion, toxemias of pregnancy, and various muscular dystrophies, but with no very marked success. The vitamin is useless in the treatment of sterility in humans.

A possible relationship of vitamin E to the metabolism of nucleic acid is suggested by the observation that vitamin E–deficient rabbits excrete large quantities of allantoin.

Assay.   The vitamin activity is expressed as milligrams of material, fed in a single dose, required to cure the sterility and produce litters in 50 per cent of the animals used.

A vitamin E–deficient diet, used by Evans and his co-workers, is the following:

```
Casein, commercial, precipitated with HCl...................  27
Cornstarch (cooked).......................................  35
Salts (McCollum 185)......................................   4
Lard......................................................  22
Cod-liver oil (Squibb's)..................................   2
Brewer's yeast............................................  10
```

The mixed diet without the cod-liver oil is allowed to stand for two weeks at room temperature to permit the rancid substances of the lard to destroy incipient traces of vitamin E. The cod-liver oil is added just before feeding.

Besides the biological assay, other methods have been suggested: measurement of the absorption maximum (294 mμ); potentiometric titration with gold chloride; oxidation of the tocopherols with ferric chloride, the conversion of the resulting ferrous ion to a red complex with α,α'-dipyridyl and measuring the red color,* oxidation of the tocopherols with nitric acid to form red-colored compounds, the color of which can be measured.

The chemical methods make no distinction among the three tocopherols. Since biologically the α-tocopherol is the most potent of the three, the rat assay, which does distinguish biological activity, still has to be used.

VITAMIN K

Dam and later Almquist described a hemorrhagic disease in chickens due to a food deficiency. The disease is associated with a decrease in the

* Mild oxidation—with gold chloride or ferric chloride—breaks the oxygen ring in tocopherol and converts the benzene ring into a quinone.

amount of prothrombin (p. 162) in the blood. The factor missing from such a diet, which is associated with the fat-soluble fraction, has been given the name *vitamin K* (after Dam, who named it "Koagulations vitamin").

Vitamin K and the Clotting Process.   The theory of the blood clotting process as at present understood is that thromboplastin, liberated from wounded tissue cells or from disintegrated blood platelets, together with calcium ions, converts prothrombin into thrombin, and once the thrombin is formed it converts the fibrinogen of the plasma into insoluble fibrin (blood clot). Vitamin K is necessary for the formation of prothrombin, a process which occurs in the liver.

Vitamin K–Deficient Diet.   As a rule, chicks are used because the disease is easily produced. Vitamin E should be included. To prevent perosis, choline and manganese are added. Almquist has shown that for optimal growth, glycine, creatine, and glucuronic acid should also be included. Glycine may be offered in the form of gelatin and glucuronic acid as gum arabic. Yeast supplies the vitamin B complex. Vitamins A and D are given in the form of cod-liver oil, and vitamin E as wheat germ oil or pure DL-alpha-tocopherol acetate.

Other basic material may be supplied by fish meal (ether extracted) or sardine meal (ether extracted), or polished rice, sucrose, calcium carbonate, sodium chloride, ferric citrate, and copper sulfate.

Since vitamin K is synthesized during putrefaction, chicks must be prevented from soiling their food and water with feces.

The synthesis of vitamin K in the intestinal tract during putrefaction has made it difficult to produce a vitamin K deficiency in the rat. This has now been overcome by adding to the diet one of the more insoluble "sulfa" drugs, such as sulfaguanidine or succinylsulfathiazole, which most probably prevents bacterial synthesis of the vitamin.

Assay.   One method is to place day-old chicks on a vitamin K–deficient diet. Bleeding is performed at the end of twelve days. If 90 per cent of the ten or twelve birds selected for the bleeding show a coagulation time of sixty minutes or more, the flock is considered ready for assays. The substance to be tested for vitamin K is added to the diet, and the effect on the reduction of clotting time is noted.

An effective dose is the minimum amount of material which will reduce the clotting time of 60 to 80 per cent of the vitamin K-deficient birds to less than ten minutes. Fieser and Tishler find that 0.3 micrograms of 2-methyl-1,4-naphthoquinone is such an effective dose.

Methods other than the biologic assay with chicks have been suggested. One deals with the ultraviolet absorption of the vitamin (or rather vitamins, for there are two of them). Another involves the red-brown color produced with sodium ethylate. Still another method employs the catalytic hydrogenation of the quinone to the corresponding hydroquinone and the titration of the latter with 2,6-dichlorophenolindophenol.

Occurrence.   The green leaf and chlorophyll-containing plants (alfalfa, spinach, etc.) are rich in vitamin K. With the exception of tomatoes, fruits contain little. Small quantities are found in cereals and beans, and practically none in carrots and potatoes.

Some bacteria contain considerable quantities of the vitamin. Yeast contains practically none of it.

Among substances tested, spinach, cabbage, kale, and cauliflower are good sources.

Vitamin K occurs less abundantly in the animal than in the plant world. Liver may be—but is not always—fairly rich in this vitamin. Milk—whether human or cow's—is a poor source.

The feces are rich in vitamin K.

Function. Though the part vitamin K plays in blood clotting is undoubtedly important, the fact that the vitamin is so widespread suggests other as yet unknown functions.

The vitamin is powerless in hemophilic conditions. Since many believe that in hemophilia the primary disturbance is due to difficulty in forming thromboplastin, and since vitamin K is primarily concerned with the formation of prothrombin, the result is not unexpected.

Just how vitamin K helps in the formation of prothrombin is not known, but we do know that the reaction takes place in the liver.

Clinical Application. Vitamin K has proved valuable in treating cases of obstructive jaundice (where there is an obstruction in the flow of bile) and in a number of liver diseases. In both examples we find deficient quantities of prothrombin in the plasma. This deficiency is explained partly on the ground that when bile is excluded from the intestinal tract, the absorption of fats (and hence fat-soluble substances, like vitamin K) suffers; another partial explanation is that the liver needs vitamin K for the synthesis of prothrombin.

Hemorrhagic disease in the newborn, often a fatal disease, can now be prevented by giving vitamin K to the mother before delivery or by direct ingestion by the baby.

Requirements. Though needed by all animals, the daily requirements are not known. It is probable that intestinal synthesis of the vitamin supplies the necessary amount. For cases of hypoprothrombinemia, 1 to 2 mg. of menadione (p. 390) daily suffices.

Chemistry. Starting with alfalfa, the fat-soluble vitamin K was isolated as an oil, but when the source was putrefied fish meal, the vitamin was obtained in crystalline form. This immediately suggested two forms of vitamin K: vitamin K_1, manufactured by the green leaf, and vitamin K_2, formed during the course of putrefaction.

Ozonolysis of K_1 led to the isolation of a product which could also be obtained from phytol, and another product which was finally identified as 2-methyl-1,4-naphthoquinone-acetic acid. The presence of a benzene ring adjoining the quinone part of the molecule was shown by oxidation with chromic acid, yielding, as one product, phthalic acid.

Synthesis of vitamin K_1 was accomplished by condensing phytyl bromide with the sodium salt of 2-methyl-1,4-naphthoquinone.

Vitamin K_2 yields the same quinone and also phthalic acid, but the side chain is more unsaturated and is longer.

Vitamin K_1 is 2-methyl-3-phytyl-1,4-naphthoquinone.*

* For the phytol group in chlorophyll, see p. 283.

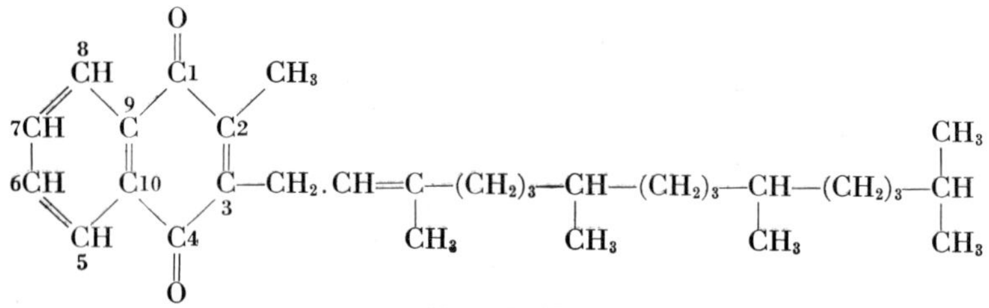

Vitamin K₁

Vitamin K_2 is also a derivative of 2-methyl-1,4-naphthoquinone, but with a side chain at position 3 other than phytyl. The formula is

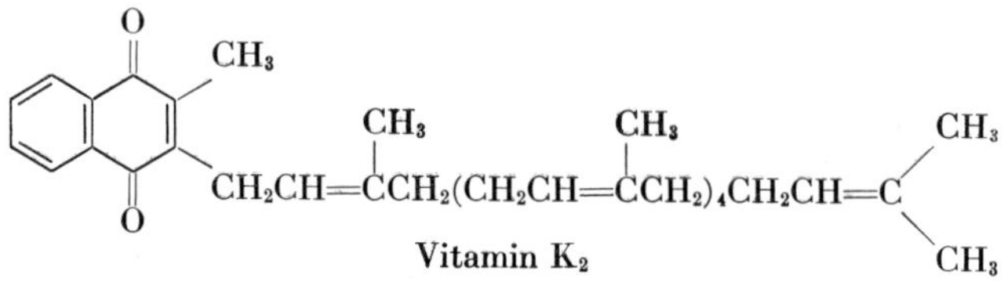

Vitamin K₂

1,4-Naphthoquinone itself shows vitamin K activity. It is also of interest that phthiocol, isolated by Anderson and associates as the pigment in human tubercle bacilli, and a 1,4-naphthoquinone derivative, shows slight antihemorrhagic properties.

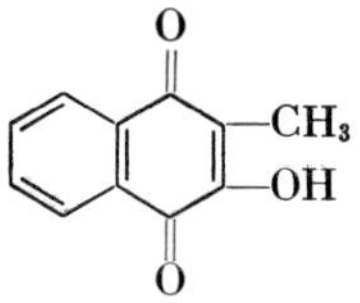

Phthiocol
(2-methyl-3-hydroxy-1,4-naphthoquinone)

However, 2-methyl-1,4-naphthoquinone (known as *menadione*) shows a biological activity which is higher than vitamin K_1 itself and is the one commonly used for treatment. Because of its insolubility in water, it is given together with bile salts. Menadione sodium bisulfite, though not so potent, is also used because it is soluble in water and does not require bile salts.

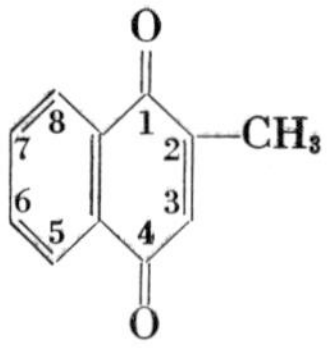

2-Methyl-1,4-naphthoquinone (Menadione)

Comparative Activities of Some Antihemorrhagic Compounds. Table 57 points to the fact that menadione is about three times as potent as vitamin K_1 or K_2.

In many cases the activity seems to be associated with the ease with which each compound can be converted to menadione in the body.

Table 57   COMPARATIVE ACTIVITIES OF THE MORE IMPORTANT ANTIHEM-
ORRHAGIC COMPOUNDS BASED ON RECENT CHICK 5-DAY ASSAYS
AND EXPRESSED IN 2-METHYL-1,4-NAPHTHOQUINONE UNITS PER
MILLIGRAM
(Almquist: Physiol. Rev., *21:* 194.)

	Units per milligram
2-methyl-1,4-naphthoquinone (menadione)	1000
2-methyl-1,4-naphthohydroquinone	930
2-methyl-1,4-naphthohydroquinone diacetate	450
2-methyl-4-amino-1-naphthol hydrochloride	470
2-methyl-1,4-naphthohydroquinone-diphosphoric acid ester (tetra sodium salt + 6 molecules water)	490
2-methyl-3-phytyl-1,4-naphthoquinone (vitamin K_1):	
Natural	300
Natural, dihydro diacetate	100
Synthetic	290
vitamin K_2	240

Cattle sometimes suffer from a deficiency of vitamin K owing to feeding upon spoiled sweet clover hay which contains the hemorrhagic substance *Dicumarol.*

REFERENCES

General. For critical reviews of recent work, see Ann. Rev. Biochem., *19:* 277, 319, 1950 (*Snell and Wright; Moore*); *20:* 265, 559, 1951 (*Dam; Emerson and Folkers*); *21:* 333, 633, 1952 (*Kemmerer; Welch and Nichol*); *Baumann, Bessey, Lowe, and Salomon: 22:* 527, 543, 1953.

For a review of vitamins from the clinical standpoint: New and Nonofficial Remedies, 1951, p. 427; *Butt:* J. Am. Med. Assoc., *143:* 236, 1950; *Youmans:* Ibid., *144:* 34, 1950.

Vitamin requirements of the growing rat: *Brown and Sturtevant:* Vitamins and Hormones, *7:* 171, 1949.

For the relationship of vitamins to enzymes, see *Sizer:* American Brewer, March, 1950.

Biological assay: *György:* Vitamin Methods, volumes 1 and 2, 1950.

Harris's Vitamins, 1952, is a readable and instructive book.

We are indebted to *Snell:* Physiol. Rev., *28:* 255, 1948, for a comprehensive review of the use of microorganisms for the assay of vitamins.

For the use of sulfonamides to inhibit biosynthesis of vitamins by intestinal microorganisms, see Borden's Review of Nutrition Research, 7: No. 5, No. 6, 1946.

Vitamin A. For the results of excessive intake of vitamin A (in rats), see *Rodahl:* J. Nutrition, *41:* 399, 1950.

Carotenoids specifically are renewed by *Mackinney:* Ann. Rev. Biochem., *21:* 473, 1952.

For the site of conversion of carotene into vitamin A (in chick), see *Cheng and Deuel, Jr.:* J. Nutrition, *41:* 619, 1950.

For details of one method of synthesizing vitamin A, see Chem. Eng. News, *29:* 3962, 1951; *Wendler, Slates, Trenner, and Tishler:* J. Am. Chem. Soc., *73:* 719, 1951.

For a review of the biochemistry of vision see *Wald:* Ann. Rev. Biochem., *22:* 497, 1953.

Wendler, Rosenblum and Tishler: J. Am. Chem. Soc., *72:* 234, 1950, describe an in vitro method for converting β-carotene into vitamin A.

Some articles dealing with the visual process are the following: *Krehl:* Borden's Review of Nutrition Research, *13:* No. 4, 1952; *Wald:* J. Chem. Educ., *29:* 259, 1952; *Hubbard and Wald:* Proc. Nat. Acad. Sci. U. S., *37:* 69, 1951; Science, *115:* 60, 1952; *Collins and Morton:* Biochem. J., *47:* 3, 10, 18, 1950; *Collins, Love, and Morton:* Ibid., *51:* 292, 1952; *52:* 669, 1952; *Wald:* Federation Proceedings, *12:* 606, 1953.

That carotene is converted into vitamin A in the intestinal wall is maintained by *Mattson, Mehl, and Deuel, Jr.:* Arch. Biochem., *15:* 65, 1947; *Wiese, Mehl, and Deuel, Jr.:* Ibid., *15:* 75, 1947; Nutr. Rev., *6:* 92, 1948.

The possible deleterious effects of mineral oil on the absorption of carotene and vitamin A are described in Nutr. Rev., *6:* 170, 1948. See also Ibid., *6:* 248, 1948.

Vitamin B complex. An authoritative review of the vitamin B complex will be found in the J. Am. Med. Assoc., *138:* 960, 1948 by *Elvehjem.* See also *Youmans:* Ibid., *144:* 307, 1950.

Beadle in the Scientific American for Sept., 1948, reviews his work on *Neurospora.* See also *Beadle:* American Scientist, *34:* 31, 1946; and *Tatum:* Federation Proceedings, *8:* 511, 1949.

Thiamine. The story of the chemistry of the beriberi vitamin is related by *Williams* in Ind. Eng. Chem., *29:* 980, 1937. The original papers by *Williams, Clarke,* et al. are to be found in the J. Am. Chem. Soc., from 1935 on.

The physiological availability of thiamine is discussed by *Woods:* Borden's Review of Nutrition Research, *9:* No. 6, 1948.

In the Nutr. Rev., *8:* 339, 1950, there is a discussion of beriberi in Japan.

For α-lipoic acid, see *O'Kane and Gunsalus:* J. Bact., *56:* 499, 1948; *Stokstad, Hoffman, Regan, Fordham, and Jukes:* Arch. Biochem., *20:* 75, 1949; *Reed, De-Busk, Gunsalus, and Hornberger:* Science, *114:* 93, 1951; *Reed, DeBusk, Gunsalus, and Schnakenburg:* J. Am. Chem. Soc., *73:* 5920, 1951; *Bullock:* J. Am. Chem. Soc., *74:* 3450, 1952.

Riboflavin. For general reviews, see *Parsons:* Federation Proceedings, *3:* 162, 1944 (human requirements); Riboflavin: *Vitamin Reviews,* Merck and Co.; *Therapeutic Notes,* Parke, Davis and Co., March, 1943, p. 76; Borden's Review of Nutrition Research, *5:* No. 8, 1944.

For the effect of riboflavin deficiencies (in humans, etc.), see *György and Sebrell* in *Evans'* The Biological Action of Vitamins (1942), pages 54 and 73; and *Keys, Henschell, Michelson, Brozek, and Crawford:* J. Nutrition, *27:* 165, 1944.

Tishler, Wellman, and Ladenburg: J. Am. Chem. Soc., *67:* 2165, 1945, describe the synthesis of riboflavin.

Kearney and Englard: J. Biol. Chem., *193:* 821, 1951, describes the enzymic phosphorylation of riboflavin.

Photochemistry of riboflavin: *Halwer:* J. Am. Chem. Soc., *73:* 4870, 1951; *Galston:* Science, *111:* 619, 1950.

Niacin. Nicotinic Acid. Yanofsky and Bonner: Proc. Nat. Acad. Sci., U. S., *36:* 167, 1950 (kynurenine as intermediate in biosynthesis of niacin).

Bonner and Wasserman: J. Biol. Chem., *185:* 69, 1950 (conversion of indole, containing N^{15}, to niacin).

Metabolism of quinolinic acid: *Henderson:* J. Biol. Chem., *178:* 1005, 1949; *Henderson and Hirsch:* Ibid., *181:* 667, 1949; *Henderson:* Ibid., *181:* 667, 1949; *Henderson and Ramasarma:* Ibid., *181:* 687, 1949.

A review of the tryptophan-niacin relationship, based on work with mutant strains of *Neurospora,* will be found in J. Nutrition, *44:* 603, 1951, by *Bonner and Yanofsky;* see also Nutr. Rev., *11:* 70, 1953.

Bean, Vilter, and Blankenhorn: J. Am. Med. Assoc., *140:* 872, 1949, discuss the incidence of pellagra. For clinical symptoms, see *Youmans:* Ibid., *144:* 386, 1950.

The relationship of niacin and tryptophan in the metabolism of humans is stressed by *Holman and de Lange:* Nature, *165:* 112, 604, 1950; *166:* 468, 1950.

The identification of some six metabolites of niacin is recorded by *Leifer, Roth, Hogness, and Corson:* J. Biol. Chem., *190:* 595, 1951.

For the effect of niacin and tryptophan on the amounts of pyridine nucleotides in man, see *Duncan and Sarett:* J. Biol. Chem., *193:* 317, 1951.

For mechanism of niacin formation, see Nutr. Rev., *8:* 211, 291, 1950.

Lewis and Musselman: J. Nutrition, *32:* 549, 1946, describe an outbreak of pellagra among American war prisoners in Japanese camps.

Pyridoxine. A clinical report on vitamin B_6 is to be found in J. Am. Med. Assoc., *147:* 322, 1951.

For the preparation of pyridoxal phosphate, see *Wilson and Harris:* J. Am. Chem. Soc., *73:* 4693, 1951; *Heyl, Luz, Harris, and Folkers:* Ibid., *73:* 3430, 1951.

The effect of vitamin B_6 deficiency on the absorption of iron and copper is discussed in Nutr. Rev., *8:* 15, 1950. The effect of a deficiency of this vitamin in man is also described in the same journal, *8:* 182, 1950.

For vitamin B_6 and the metabolism of

D-amino acids, see Nutr. Rev., *8:* 202, 1950.

For the biological assay of the vitamin B₆ group, see *Sarma, Snell, and Elvehjem:* J. Biol. Chem., *165:* 55, 1946.

Pantothenic Acid. For methods of estimating free and bound pantothenic acid, see *Neilands, Higgins, King, Handschumacher, and Strong:* J. Biol. Chem., *185:* 335, 1950. See also Nutr. Rev., *9:* 78, 1951. *Novelli, Kaplan, and Lipmann:* J. Biol. Chem., *177:* 97, 1949, are the authors of an article on the liberation of pantothenic acid from coenzyme A.

For the isolation of coenzyme A, see *Lipmann, Kaplan, Novelli, Tuttle, and Guirard:* J. Biol. Chem., *186:* 235, 1950.

The part played by coenzyme A in carbohydrate metabolism is discussed by *Ochoa and Stern:* Ann. Rev. Biochem., *21:* 565, 1952.

Biotin. For the functions of biotin, see *Lichstein:* Vitamins and Hormones, *9:* 27, 1951.

For papers dealing with biocytin, see *Wright, Cresson, Skeggs, Wood, Peck, Wolf, Folkers, Valiant, and Liebert:* J. Am. Chem. Soc., *74:* 1996, 1999, 2002, 2004, 1952. See also *Chang and Peterson:* J. Biol. Chem., *193:* 587, 1951.

Para-aminobenzoic Acid. As a growth factor for microorganisms it is discussed in Nutr. Rev., *3:* 108, 1945. For the use of para-aminobenzoic acid in the treatment of typhus, see *Yeomans, Snyder, Murray, Zarafonetis, and Ecke:* J. Am. Med. Assoc., *126:* 349, 1944; and for its use in the treatment of Rocky Mountain spotted fever, see Ibid., *132:* 911, 1946; *Ravenel:* Ibid., *133:* 989, 1947.

Inositol. For reviews on inositol, see *Woods:* Borden's Review of Nutrition Research, *9:* No. 1, No. 2, 1948. For an account of *Woolley's* contributions, see J. Biol. Chem., *139:* 29, 1941; Ibid., *140:* 453, 1941; Ibid., *142:* 963, 1942; Proc. Soc. Exp. Biol. Med., *49:* 540, 1942.

For a general review, see *György:* Ann. Rev. Biochem., *11:* 338, 1942.

For the importance of inositol in nutrition, see Nutr. Rev., *3:* 88, 1945; and J. Nutrition, *28:* 305, 1944.

Woolley: J. Biol. Chem., *147:* 581, 1943, has shown that the phosphatide obtained from soybean contains inositol.

Choline. For a review of choline, see *Best:* Science, *94:* 523, 1941; *Elvehjem:* J. Am. Med. Assoc., *138:* 966, 1948.

Horowitz: J. Biol. Chem., *162:* 413, 1946, describes the isolation of a natural precursor of choline. See also *Horowitz, Bonner, and Houlahan:* Ibid., *159:* 145, 1945; *Beadle:* American Scientist, *34:* 49, 1946; *Bonner:* Symp. Quart. Biol., *11:* 17, 1946. The importance of choline in the prevention of perosis in chicks is emphasized by *Scott:* J. Nutrition, *40:* 611, 1950.

Folic Acid. The literature on folic acid and its analogues has assumed enormous proportions. Here are some references: *Snell:* Nutritional Observatory, *12:* 53, 1951 (the citrovorum factor); *Woods:* Borden's Review of Nutrition Research, *12:* No. 6, 1951 (citrovorum factor); *May, Bardos, Barger, Lansford, Ravel, Sutherland, and Shive:* J. Am. Chem. Soc., *73:* 3067, 1951 (structure of folinic acid); *Pohland, Flynn, Jones, and Shive:* Ibid., *73:* 3247, 1951 (structure of folinic acid); *Woods:* Borden's Review of Nutrition Research, *12:* No. 7, 1951 (studies with the citrovorum factor); *Keresztesy and Silverman:* J. Am. Chem. Soc., *73:* 5510, 1951 (crystalline citrovorum factor); Research To-day (Eli Lilly), No. 1, 1952 (the folinic acid group); *Petering:* Physiol. Rev., *32:* 197, 1952 (folic acid antagonists); *Welch and Nichol:* Ann. Rev. Biochem., *21:* 633, 1952 (folic acid, CF and ascorbic acid); Nutr. Rev., *8:* 260, 1950 (review of folic acid); Ibid., *9:* 24, 1951 (review of CF); Ibid., *10:* 283, 1952 (CF conjugate); *Roth, Hultquist, Fahrenbach, Cosulich, Bronquist, Brockman, Jr., Smith, Parker, Stokstad, Jukes, Allen, Pasternak, and Seaman:* J. Am. Chem. Soc., *74:* 3247, 3252, 3264, 1952 (chemistry of leucovorin); *Broquist, Brockman, Jr., Fahrenbach, Stokstad, and Jukes:* J. Nutrition, *47:* 93, 1952 (biological activity of leucovorin and folic acid).

Vitamin B₁₂. For a review of vitamin B₁₂, see *Shorb:* J. Biol. Chem., *169:* 455, 1947; Science, *107:* 397, 1948.

The literature on vitamin B₁₂ is already enormous. Here are some selected references: *Emerson and Folkers:* Ann. Rev. Biochem., *20:* 559, 1951 (chemistry); *Welch and Nichol:* Ibid., *21:* 645, 1952 (chemistry); *Folkers:* Chem. Eng. News, *28:* 1634, 1950; *Bethell, Swendseid, Miller, and Cintron-Rivera:* Annals Internal Medicine, *35:* 518, 1951 (vitamin B₁₂ and intrinsic factor); *Smith:* British J. Nutrition, *6:* 295, 1952 (story of vitamin B₁₂); *Lewis, Tappan, and Elvehjem:* J. Biol. Chem., *194:* 539, 1952 (new form of vitamin B₁₂); Nutr. Rev., *9:* 281, 1951 (absorption and excretion); Ibid., *9:* 251, 1951 (chemical determination); *Fields and Hoff:* Merck Report, Oct., 1952, p. 3 (the vitamin and neurological disturbances); Nutr. Rev., *8:* 139, 1950 (vitamin B_{12} and growth).

Ascorbic Acid. The chemistry of ascorbic acid is described by *Haworth, Hirst,* et al. in the J. Chem. Soc., September and October, 1933.

See Nutr. Rev., *4:* 259, 1946 for a review of ascorbic acid.

Detailed methods of determining ascorbic acid are discussed by *Reid:* Biological Symposia, *12:* 393, 1947; *Satterfield:* Ibid., *12:* 397, 1947.

For the relationship of vitamin C to the metabolism of tyrosine and phenylalanine, see *Levine:* Harvey Lectures, 1946–7, p. 303; *Basinski and Sealock:* J. Biol. Chem., *166:* 7, 1946.

See also *King:* J. Am. Med. Assoc., *142:* 563, 1950 (review); *Youmans:* Ibid., *144:* 388, 1950 (review); *Sealock and Goodland:* Science, *114:* 645, 1951 (ascorbic acid and tyrosine oxid.); *Jackel, Mosbach, Burns, and King:* J. Biol. Chem., *186:* 569, 1950 (synthesis of ascorbic acid in rat); *Dunn and Dawson:* Ibid., *189:* 485, 1951 (ascorbic acid oxidase); *Vickery, Nelson, Almquist, and Elvehjem:* Science, *112:* 628, 1950 (recommended that term "vitamin P" be dropped); *Clark and MacKay:* J. Am. Med. Assoc., *143:* 1411, 1950 (rutin and related Flavonoid substances); *Woods:* Borden's Review of Nutrition Research, *8:* No. 3, 1947 (vitamin P).

Vitamin D. For general descriptions, see *Youmans:* J. Am. Med. Assoc., *144:* 39, 1950; and *Jeans:* Ibid., *143:* 177, 1950. See also *Dam:* Ann. Rev. Biochem., *20:* 273, 1951.

Studies dealing with alkaline phosphatase are to be found in Nutr. Rev., *9:* 271, 1951; *Motzok and Wynne:* Biochem. J., *47:* 187, 193, 196, 1950.

For the possible enzymic action of vitamin D, see Nutr. Rev., *10:* 25, 1952.

An editorial in the J. Am. Med. Assoc., *148:* 1227, 1952, deals with the relation of vitamin D milk to the incidence of rickets.

The conversion of cholesterol into 7-dehydrocholesterol in vivo is described by *Glover, Glover, and Morton:* Biochem. J., *51:* 1, 1952.

The chemistry of vitamin D is treated by, among others, the following: *Heilbron:* J. Soc. Chem. Ind., *55:* 129, 1936; *Butenandt:* J. Soc. Chem. Ind., *55:* 753, 891, 990, 1936.

The effects of hypervitaminosis (D) are discussed by *Freeman, Rhoads, and Yeager:* J. Am. Med. Assoc., *130:* 197, 1946; and *Hendricks, Morgan, and Freytag:* Am. J. Physiol., *149:* 319, 1947.

Vitamin E. For a very extensive discussion of vitamin E, see Annals N. Y. Acad. Sciences, *52:* 63–428, 1949. For briefer reviews, see Nutr. Rev., *10:* 225, 1952; *Butt:* J. Am. Med. Assoc., *143:* 239, 1950; *Kemmerer:* Ann. Rev. Biochem., *21:* 344, 1952.

A possible relationship of vitamin E to nucleic acid metabolism is discussed by *Young and Dinning:* J. Biol. Chem., *193:* 743, 1951.

For chemical structure in relation to vitamin E function, see *Boyer, Rabinovitz, and Liebe:* J. Biol. Chem., *192:* 95, 1951.

A survey of the chemistry of vitamin E is given by *L. I. Smith* in *Visscher's* Chemistry and Medicine, 1940, p. 57. See, also, *Fieser and Fieser:* Organic Chemistry, 1944, p. 1020.

The isolation of the tocopherols is described by *Evans, Emerson, and Emerson:* J. Biol. Chem., *113:* 319, 1936; *Emerson, Emerson, Mohammad, and Evans:* Ibid., *122:* 99, 1937.

For methods of determining vitamin E, see *Mason and Harris:* Biol. Symposia, *12:* 459, 1947; *Baxter:* Ibid., 484, 1947; *Quaife and Harris:* Anal. Chem., *20:* 1221, 1948; *Stern and Baxter:* Ibid., *19:* 902, 1947.

Vitamin K. A comprehensive review is given by *Dam:* Adv. in Enzym., *2:* 285, 1942. See also *Youmans:* J. Am. Med. Assoc., *144:* 44, 1950; *Butt:* Ibid., *143:* 240, 1950; *Dam:* Ann. Rev. Biochem., *20:* 286, 1951.

For a discussion of vitamin K and blood coagulation, see Nutr. Rev. *9:* 36, 1951.

The assay of vitamin K is discussed by *Almquist:* Biol. Symposia, *12:* 508, 1947.

Aɴ ᴇxᴀᴍɪɴᴀᴛɪoɴ of the head, the trunk, and the limbs of the body reveals certain similar types of substance in each of them, such as bone,
cartilage, muscle, nerve. These similar types, composed as they are of
groups of similar cells, are called *tissues*. In this chapter we shall discuss
the chemical composition of these tissues.

MUSCLE TISSUE

This tissue consists of three varieties: striped or striated muscle (volun-
tary), such as is found in the skeletal muscles of the body and which forms
almost one-half of the total weight of the body; smooth or nonstriated
muscle (involuntary), such as we see in the walls of the bladder, skin,
arteries, and veins; and cardiac muscle, which forms the main part of the
wall of the heart.

Chemical examination of muscle reveals it to be composed of 75 per cent
water and 25 per cent solids. Twenty per cent of the solids consist of proteins; the rest includes carbohydrates, salts, and nitrogenous compounds
(also called "extractives"). Among the latter are creatine, phosphocreatine,
purine bases, uric acid, adenylic acid and its derivatives (such as ADP and
ATP), carnosine and anserine. The last two are peptides; little is known
about them physiologically.

$$HC\!=\!\!=\!\!C\!-\!CH_2\!-\!CH.COOH$$
$$HN \qquad N \qquad NH.CO.CH_2.CH_2.NH_2$$
$$\diagdown\quad\diagup$$
$$CH$$

Carnosine (dipeptide of histidine and β-alanine)

$$HC\!=\!\!=\!\!C\!-\!CH_2.CH.COOH$$
$$CH_3.N \qquad N \qquad NH.CO.CH_2.CH_2.NH_2$$
$$\diagdown\quad\diagup$$
$$CH$$

Anserine (dipeptide of methyl histidine and β-alanine)

Creatine.　　Creatine, largely in the form of phosphocreatine, is found
in muscle (Table 58), brain and blood. Its role in muscular contraction and
carbohydrate metabolism has already been mentioned and its functions
will be further discussed.

Creatine appears to be confined to vertebrates; in invertebrates, arginine
plays a similar role.

In the urine of vertebrates we find creatinine, the anhydride of creatine.

$$
\begin{array}{ccc}
\text{NH}_2 & \text{NH.PO(OH)}_2 & \text{NH} \\
\diagup & \diagup & \diagup \\
\text{HN}=\text{C} & \text{HN}=\text{C} & \text{HN}=\text{C} \\
\diagdown & \diagdown & \diagdown \\
\text{N.CH}_2.\text{COOH} & \text{N.CH}_2.\text{COOH} & \text{N.CH}_2.\text{CO} \\
| & | & | \\
\text{CH}_3 & \text{CH}_3 & \text{CH}_3 \\
\text{Creatine} & \text{Phosphocreatine} & \text{Creatinine}
\end{array}
$$

The former is the stronger base.

When creatine is treated with acid it is converted to creatinine. In an alkaline medium, a partial reversal of the process takes place, resulting in an equilibrium mixture. In N/2 HCl, at a temperature of 117° C., the change from creatine to creatinine is practically complete in 15 minutes.

BIOSYNTHESIS OF CREATINE. When isotopic guanidoacetic acid (glycocyamine) is fed to rats, both isotopic creatine and creatinine are formed. Creatine is formed in two steps: (a) the production of guanidoacetic acid, and (b) the methylation of the compound produced.

Table 58   DISTRIBUTION OF PHOSPHOCREATINE AND ATP IN MUSCLE (IN MOLS PER GM. OF TISSUE)
(Mommaerts, in McElroy and Glass: Phosphorus metabolism, 1951, vol. I, p. 551.)

	Skeletal	Cardiac	Smooth
ATP	5×10^{-6}	1.5×10^{-6}	2×10^{-6}
Phosphocreatine	20×10^{-6}	2×10^{-6}	0.7×10^{-6}

Borsook, working with liver slices, showed that guanidoacetic acid is converted into creatine, but at a very slow pace. However, the addition of methionine, supplying additional methyl groups, accelerated the process a great deal.

Using isotopic compounds, Bloch and Schoenheimer found that among various compounds, arginine and glycine were the most effective creatine formers. By degrading the creatine formed, the particular nitrogen supplied to creatine could be located:

$$
\begin{array}{l}
\text{NH}_2 \\
| \\
\text{C}=\text{NH} \quad \xrightarrow[\text{(2H}_2\text{O)}]{\text{Ba(OH)}_2} \; 2\text{NH}_3 + \text{CO}_2 + \text{HN.CH}_3 \\
| \\
\text{N}-\text{CH}_3 \qquad\qquad\qquad\qquad\quad\; | \\
| \qquad\qquad\qquad\qquad\qquad\quad \text{CH}_2.\text{COOH} \\
\text{CH}_2\text{COOH} \;\; \text{(boil)} \qquad\qquad \text{Sarcosine} \\
\quad \text{Creatine}
\end{array}
$$

All of the N in the amidine group of creatine is recovered as NH_3, and the remaining N is recovered in the form of sarcosine.

When isotopic glycine was fed, the isotope was located in the sarcosine fraction of creatine. On the other hand, the feeding of isotopic arginine concentrated the isotope in the ammonia fraction obtained from creatine.

In this way it could be shown that the amidine group in creatine is derived from arginine, and the sarcosine portion, from glycine.

The origin, then, of creatine, can be summarized as follows:

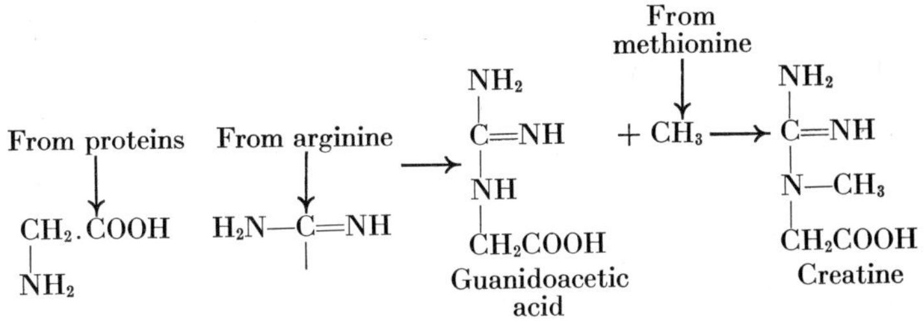

$$
\begin{array}{ccccc}
& & & \text{From} & \\
& & & \text{methionine} & \\
& & \text{NH}_2 & \downarrow & \text{NH}_2 \\
& & | & & | \\
\text{From proteins} \quad \text{From arginine} & \rightarrow & \text{C}{=}\text{NH} \quad + \text{CH}_3 \rightarrow & \text{C}{=}\text{NH} \\
\downarrow \qquad\qquad \downarrow & & | & & | \\
\text{CH}_2.\text{COOH} \quad \text{H}_2\text{N}{-}\text{C}{=}\text{NH} & & \text{NH} & & \text{N}{-}\text{CH}_3 \\
| \qquad\qquad\qquad | & & | & & | \\
\text{NH}_2 & & \text{CH}_2\text{COOH} & & \text{CH}_2\text{COOH} \\
& & \text{Guanidoacetic} & & \text{Creatine} \\
& & \text{acid} & &
\end{array}
$$

While the methyl group of methionine is used for the building of the creatine of muscle, neither creatine, nor creatinine, nor sarcosine can supply its methyl group to convert homocystine to methionine.

CREATINE-CREATININE RELATIONSHIPS. The feeding of labelled creatine leads to the isolation from the urine of labelled creatinine. It can be assumed, therefore, that creatinine arises from creatine. However, the feeding of isotopic creatinine does not result in the formation of isotopic creatine, but in the elimination of unchanged creatinine.

Folin was among the first to show that the amount of creatinine excreted in the urine of a normal individual remains remarkably constant. What happens to the creatine other than that which is excreted as creatinine is still a question. There may, indeed, be other pathways for the metabolism of creatine.

The normal male adult excretes no creatine. However, the base does appear in the urine in periods of starvation, fevers, and when muscle atrophies. In the female adult one meets with intermittent creatinuria. During pregnancy, creatine appears in the urine. Until puberty, children of both sexes excrete both creatine and creatinine.

Proteins in Muscle.   Table 59 gives the percentages of proteins in muscle.

Table 59   PROTEIN FRACTIONS OF WHITE MUSCLE
(Mommaerts: Muscular Contraction, 1950.)

Protein	Per Cent of Total Protein
Myogen	9
Globulin X	18
Myosin	57
Stroma	16

Myogen is the so-called albumin fraction of muscle which is soluble in the absence of salts. It represents a mixture of several proteins; two of them, myogen A and myogen B, have been isolated in crystalline form.

This myogen fraction contains a number of enzymes; isomerase, aldolase, triosephosphate dehydrogenase and phosphorylase constitute some 16 per cent of the fraction.

Little is known about globulin X. The substance precipitates when the salts are removed by dialysis.

"Stroma" is the protein fraction of muscle which remains after several extractions with salt solutions. It is believed to be the source of actin which, in combination with myosin, yields actomyosin, the contractile protein.

Muscle Contraction.   Our present knowledge of the chemistry of the contractile proteins in muscle is based largely on the work of Szent-Györgyi.

Inside the muscle there are present bundles of small fibers called myofibrils; a series of these make up a muscle fiber, which contracts under the influence of a nerve impulse.

If ground muscle is extracted for short periods of time with salt solutions, the extract contains myosin; or, as we now know, a mixture of myosin and

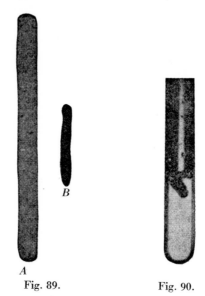

A
Fig. 89.   Fig. 90.

Fig. 89. *A*, Actomyosin thread. *B*, The same contracted. Magn. 1:30.
Fig. 90. Contraction of an actomyosin solution. (Szent-Györgyi: Chemistry of Muscular Contraction.)

actomyosin. If, however, the muscle is extracted for a longer period and with concentrated salt solutions, a complex protein, actomyosin, is obtained. This actomyosin is presumably the result of the reaction between myosin and actin.

Actomyosin is a viscous substance and displays, in solution, the property of birefringence (double refraction). When a salt solution of actomyosin is extruded into a more dilute salt solution, threads of actomyosin precipitate. These threads contract in the presence of ATP and K and Mg ions (Figs. 89 and 90).

The contraction is similar to that which occurs in muscle in vivo. By comparing the in vitro contraction of actomyosin threads with the optical properties of the myofibrils in the intact muscle fiber, it appears fairly certain that the shortening during contraction is due to the actomyosin in the myofibril.

Myosin has been crystallized and found to have a molecular weight of 900,000. Actin can exist in two forms: globular actin (G-actin), which is converted to fibrillar actin (F-actin), which, in turn, is highly polymerized. This conversion needs ATP:

$$\text{G-actin} + \text{ATP} \longrightarrow \text{F-actin} + \text{ADP} + \text{PO}_4^=$$

Agents which block sulfhydryl groups (such as p-chloromercuribenzoate), inhibit both fibril contraction and polymerization, which probably means that the contractile protein requires free —SH groups for its activity.

Mommaerts has proposed the following sequence of events during muscle contraction: Muscle at rest contains G-actomyosin which reacts with ATP to form F-actin. The latter polymerizes and combines with myosin to yield F-actomyosin, which then contracts and liberates ADP. During the relaxation of muscle, ADP is reconverted to ATP via the action of phosphocreatine, or other energy-rich phosphate compounds.

Myosin and Adenosinetriphosphatase (ATPase). The discovery associating the enzyme ATPase with myosin we owe to Engelhardt and Lyubimova. They believe the enzyme to be myosin itself. As evidence, it is pointed out that the enzymic properties of myosin are unchanged throughout a series of mild reactions—reprecipitation, dilution, and salting out. No protein fraction other than myosin itself shows these enzyme properties to anywhere near such an extent. Any reaction, however mild, which denatures myosin also destroys the properties of the enzyme.

Subsequent work by Meyerhof, Cori, and others, has thrown some doubt on these views. While it is agreed that the enzyme ATPase is closely associated with myosin, yet the latter is not the enzyme itself. Meyerhof has, in fact, completely separated a second ATPase, activated by magnesium, from myosin. He claims that this magnesium-activated enzyme is mainly responsible for the ATPase activity of fresh myosin.

Mommaerts has shown that with a highly purified preparation of myosin, the ATPase activity remains low within the physiological range of pH, and that it accounts for but 1 per cent of the dephosphorylation of ATP during muscle contraction.

Myosin has also been digested by trypsin, and as a result of such treatment it no longer reacts typically with actin. The ATPase activity, however, remains unchanged. It is possible, therefore, that myosin may form a complex with ATPase, and that the enzyme is liberated by the action of trypsin (Gergely).

Myoglobin. In muscle we also find a compound similar to hemoglobin: myoglobin. It may appear in the urine after injury to the limbs. It has been obtained in crystalline form and has an iron content of 0.34 per cent, similar to human hemoglobin (see p. 176).

NERVE TISSUE

The nerve tissue includes the brain, spinal cord, peripheral nerves, ganglia, and plexuses. Its importance lies in its ability to respond to stimuli and to conduct impulses.

Composition. The gray matter of the brain may contain as much as 80 per cent—and even more—of water. Of the solids present in nerve tissues, some 50 per cent may be due to proteins, of which collagen and neurokeratin are the most abundant, according to Block. Neurokeratin itself, though possibly different from the keratin found in epidermal tissue, is similar to the latter in so far as its general insolubility and its resistance to peptic and tryptic digestion are concerned. Block believes that neurokeratin is possibly the protein in the neurofibrils, the filaments in the nerve cells, and their axons.

Relatively small quantities of alkaline phosphates, phosphocreatine, adenosinetriphosphate, hexosephosphate and chlorides, carbohydrates, extractives (creatine, etc.), and inositol are also present. But aside from the proteins, the materials present in largest quantity (in nerve fibers, at least), and in many ways the most characteristic materials, are the lipids.

The brain of a rat embryo contains 10 per cent of fatty acids; so does the liver. When thirty days old, the fatty acids of the liver still remain 10 per cent, but those of the brain have increased to 20 per cent.

The turnover of these lipids in the brain is a slow process by comparison with other tissues of the body. Using deuterium as the tracer, it can be shown that in the adult brain, some 20 per cent of the fatty acids are replaced in a week. In the liver, on the other hand, the turnover is as high as 50 per cent in one day.

The chemistry of these lipids has already been discussed (Chap. 3). These substances include lecithin, cephalin, sphingomyelin, cerebrosides, and sterols (particularly cholesterol), besides the true fats. While not peculiar to nervous tissue, some, like the cerebrosides, are rarely found in any other part of the body; and they are certainly present in abundance. Furthermore, Thannhauser has found that the fatty acids of the sphingomyelin in brain differ from those present in the sphingomyelin of other organs (lung and spleen).

A disease of childhood, known as *Niemann-Pick disease*, is characterized by an increase in the sphingomyelin of the brain.

The "cephalin" in brain is not a definite compound, as was supposed, but apparently a mixture of several compounds. Folch has shown that it is a mixture of three different phosphatides: one contains ethanolamine, another serine, and a third inositol.

The principal constituent of the sheath, "myelin," is a mixture of substances. The principal lipid constituents are free cholesterol, cerebroside, and sphingomyelin, rather than cephalin and lecithin, as was thought at one time.

The distribution of lipids in the peripheral nerves resembles that of the lipids in the white matter of the brain rather than that of the gray matter.

Both brain white matter and peripheral nerves contain more cerebroside, free cholesterol, and sphingomyelin than brain gray matter.

When a peripheral nerve is cut, the portion of the nerve distal to the point of section soon loses its ability to transmit a nerve impulse. This is associated with histological changes known as *Wallerian degeneration*.

With the degeneration of the nerve, the myelin, rich in lipids, which surrounds the axon of the nerve, is ultimately completely destroyed.

The Metabolism of Nerves.   The unit of the nervous system, the neuron, consists of the cell, the dendrites, and the axon (Fig. 91). The axon (or axis-cylinder) is the central core of a nerve fiber. The nervous impulse is propagated along the nerve with a velocity of 27 meters per second in the frog, and more rapidly in the mammal. There is a change in electric potential: the portion of the nerve in action is electrically negative, as compared to "resting" portions, in front and behind. The fatigue of the nerve comes only after relatively long periods of activity.

It is possible, particularly when working with cold-blooded animals, to excise a nerve and keep it "in action" for some time, assuming a temperature which is low enough, and provided, also, that the moisture is suitable. Under such conditions, it is possible, by the use of instruments delicate enough, to measure the production of heat generated during the course of the activity of the nerve and to examine a number of electrical properties.

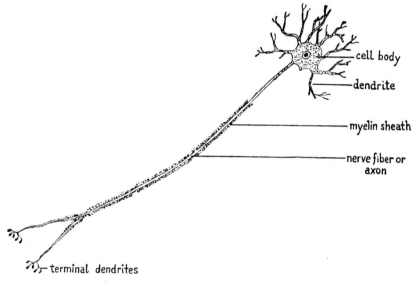

Fig. 91. A nerve cell or neuron. (Dawson.)

The fact that heat is produced during the conduction of an impulse is evidence of a metabolic process. Such a condition is not merely a physical, but also a chemical, phenomenon. Although the amount of heat produced is small enough, it has been measured; it amounts to 141×10^{-5} calories per gram of nerve for a stimulus lasting ten seconds. The heat is evolved in two stages; a small amount of heat—from 2 to 3 per cent of the total—is produced; and the remainder is evolved over a period which may last half an hour or so after the stimulation.

Oxygen is absorbed by the nerve at rest, but during and following stimulation much more is absorbed. The Q_{O_2}* of resting frog nerve at 15°

* Q = quantity of substance produced or consumed per milligram of dry weight of tissue per hour. A negative sign indicates absorption: a positive sign, evolution. The gas in question is expressed in cubic millimeters at N. T. P. For example, if the cortex of a rabbit's brain yields the figure $Q\dfrac{N_2}{CO_2} = +19$, it means that using the cortex (in nitrogen), 19 cu.μ or 19 μl of carbon dioxide is produced per milligram of dry weight per hour.

is -0.08, and of stimulated frog's nerve, -0.3. The nerve, it is known, will conduct for a comparatively long time in an atmosphere of nitrogen. Upon the admission of oxygen, however, this gas is consumed in larger quantities than would have taken place without the preliminary treatment with nitrogen. This process is spoken of as "going into oxygen debt."

The nerve can produce lactic acid from carbohydrate in the absence of oxygen. The lactic acid is oxidized very slowly. It is still uncertain as to whether the stimulation of a nerve involves a glycogen–lactic acid metabolism at all comparable to what takes place in muscle. One would expect that under the stimulation of oxygen, an increased amount of lactic acid would disappear, but the results do not support this view.

A somewhat mysterious effect is the production of ammonia when the nerve is stimulated. What the significance of this ammonia is, is not clear; nor has the origin of this compound been settled. There are two substances present in brain tissue which might give rise to ammonia: one is adenylic acid and the other is glutamine. Adenylic acid may lose ammonia, yielding inosinic acid. Here the change involved is a change of the adenine (in adenylic acid) to hypoxanthine (in inosinic acid).

Glutamine, also, may break down to glutamic acid and ammonia:

$$CONH_2 . CH_2 . CH_2 . CHNH_2 . COOH \longrightarrow NH_3 + COOH . CH_2 . CH_2 . CHNH_2 . COOH$$

There is reason to believe that glutamine itself is first formed by the reverse process: the combination of glutamic acid and ammonia. In any case, gray cortex can "bind" large quantities of ammonia, provided glutamic acid is present; and, what is very significant, no other amino acid can take the place of glutamic acid.

As a result of stimulation in oxygen, this gas is consumed and carbon dioxide, ammonia, and inorganic phosphate are liberated.

It is believed that potassium ions are involved in the electrical phenomena of nerve. Bathing a nerve in oxygenated sea water does not change the content of potassium in the nerve, despite the fact that the concentration of the element inside is ten times that of the element outside. Such a difference in concentration would give rise to a difference in electrical potential. But should the nerve be stimulated, or should it be deprived of oxygen, it begins to lose its potassium. It is of interest to find that so long as the potassium ions are retained by the tissue, so long can a potential difference be noted between the inside and the outside of the fiber. But the loss of potassium, resulting from stimulation, or oxygen deprivation, causes the potential difference to disappear.

Brain.   The brain—and all nervous tissue—is characterized by a high lipid content. Table 60 compares the distribution of various lipids among a number of tissues:

The gross composition of human (whole) brain is: water (per cent fresh weight), 76.9; protein (per cent dry weight), 37.7; lipid, 54.4; extractives, 7.9.

Where, as in the above case, $Q_{O_2} = -0.3$, it means that with the nerve under stimulation, $0.3 \, \mu l$ of oxygen, calculated at N. T. P., is consumed per milligram of dry weight per hour.

The brain gets its energy practically exclusively from the oxidation of carbohydrate; its R. Q. is 1. It does not store glycogen though it needs glucose (and oxygen). Glycolysis occurs in brain tissue and many of the enzymes and phosphorylated intermediates active in glycolysis are known to be present, though it is not certain that the pathway of carbohydrate metabolism here is altogether comparable to what happens in muscle or liver.

The Membrane Theory of Conduction.   This theory assumes that the nerve is surrounded by a polarized membrane, the outside of which carries a positive charge and the inside a negative charge, due to the fact that the concentration of potassium ions is higher inside than outside the membrane. This selective permeability to potassium ions, and the leakage of potassium

Table 60   LIPIDS IN OX TISSUES AS PERCENTAGE OF DRY WEIGHT
(Kaucher, Galbraith, Button, and Williams: Arch. Biochem., 3: 203, 1943.)

	Brain	Liver	Kidney	Heart	Muscle	Lung
Total lipid	51.60	23.99	17.25	16.45	11.99	14.83
Neutral fat	2.97	5.81	4.45	4.06	7.57	2.41
Phospholipin	26.38	16.22	10.32	9.83	3.24	9.79
Sphingomyelin	4.97	0.76	1.67	0.53	0.20	2.28
Cerebroside	12.01	0	0.71	2.00	0.95	0.44
Cholesterol, free	10.00	0.44	1.44	0.34	0.18	1.34
Cholesterol, esters	0.25	0.53	0.34	0.23	0.07	0.89

ions during nerve activity, is the basis for the membrane theory of nerve conduction. When a stimulus is applied to the surface membrane, a reversal of charge takes place and the outside surface becomes negative to an adjacent point on the membrane. In this way a flow of current results which stimulates an adjacent point. There is, apparently, an exchange of potassium ions across the nerve membrane even during the resting stage, thus establishing a dynamic concentration gradient with respect to this ion, as well as to sodium ions, which are more concentrated outside than inside the membrane. The flow of current in an isolated nerve after a suitable stimulus has been applied can be seen and measured with the aid of the cathode ray oscilloscope. The current which is produced is called the "action potential."

Role of Acetylcholine and ACh-esterase in Nerve Transmission.   Of the two types of nerve endings, the sympathetic release epinephrine (Adrenalin) and norepinephrine, whereas the parasympathetic release acetylcholine. We owe to Hunt and Dale our knowledge of the relationship of acetylcholine to the parasympathetic nerves. The first clear-cut observation that acetylcholine could be a mediator of nerve impulse transmission was that of Otto Loewi in 1921, who found that following stimulation of the vagus nerve of an isolated frog heart, a substance appeared in the perfusion fluid which, when applied to a second frog heart, had the same effect as vagal stimulation. This "Vagusstoff" was soon identified as acetylcholine.

The work of the earlier nerve physiologists was largely confined to the study of the electrical signs of nerve activity. Nachmansohn and his group are responsible for the biochemical studies involving the enzymes which synthesize and split acetylcholine.

The biosynthesis of acetylcholine is associated with oxidative metabolism and requires an enzyme, choline acetylase, together with coenzyme A. In addition, a source of ATP is also required, and can be furnished by those metabolic reactions in the cell which incorporate the high energy phosphate bond to form ATP, e.g., phosphocreatine breakdown. In the electric eel, the chemical energy released by the breakdown of phosphocreatine is adequate to account for the electrical energy released by the action potential.

Nachmansohn assumes that acetylcholine is present in the cell in an inactive form bound to protein or lipoprotein and is thus protected from the action of acetylcholine esterase (ACh-esterase). When, during the flow of current, a stimulus reaches this point, acetylcholine is released. Having produced its effect, it is then hydrolyzed by ACh-esterase to form acetate and choline. During the recovery phase, more acetylcholine would be synthesized. This picture is similar in many respects to our present concept of muscle contraction.

One of the most important criteria for chemical mediation of nerve impulse transmission is the exceedingly great speeds involved, since we are dealing with electrical currents. Nachmansohn states that such a chemical reaction would have to take place within less than 100 microseconds. ACh-esterase does, in fact, split acetylcholine at speeds which satisfy this requirement. Thus, the enzyme from the electric tissue of the electric eel has been purified to the extent that 1 mg. protein splits 75 gm. acetylcholine per hour. An approximate molecular weight of such material is 3,000,000, according to sedimentation rate studies with the ultracentrifuge. It can be calculated that one molecule of enzyme would split one molecule of acetylcholine in 3 to 4 microseconds.

ACh-esterase is localized in nerve tissue and in the muscle at the motor end plate. In the electric eel, there is a parallel relationship between the action potential and ACh-esterase concentration in the electric tissue, as well as a correlation between voltage and ACh-esterase concentration.

One of the most fruitful studies of ACh-esterase has centered around its inhibition by a variety of chemical agents. The administration of such highly specific ACh-esterase inhibitors results in the accumulation of acetylcholine and block nerve conduction. In vivo, the death of the animal treated with such agents is associated with a complete inhibition of its brain ACh-esterase. In vitro, the addition of such an inhibitor to the medium bathing the nerve results in an alteration of the action potential. Physostigmine (eserine) and prostigmine are reversible inhibitors, so that they may be removed from the nerve by washing, with a restoration of conduction. Diisopropyl fluorophosphate, an irreversible inhibitor, if used for a sufficient period of time, causes an irreversible abolition of nerve conduction. In vivo, the latter compound is a powerful nerve poison.

Vitamins.   A number of vitamins are necessary for the prevention of

$$C_3H_7O \diagdown \underset{C_3H_7O \diagup}{\overset{O}{\overset{\|}{P}}} \diagdown F$$

Diisopropyl
fluorophosphate

$$CH_3.NH.CO.O \diagdown \underset{\overset{|}{CH} CH_2}{\overset{CH_3}{\underset{|}{C}} \text{---} CH_2} \diagup \underset{N N.CH_3}{}$$

Physostigmine

$$\underset{CH_3}{\overset{CH_3}{N}} \text{---} CO.O \diagdown \diagup \text{---} \underset{SO_4CH_3}{\overset{CH_3 CH_3 CH_3}{\overset{|}{N}}}$$

Prostigmine

degenerative changes in the central nervous system; they belong almost exclusively to the vitamin B complex. Of this group, the one which has received most attention so far is vitamin B_1, or thiamine.

The brain oxidizes carbohydrate almost exclusively; and for this purpose, insulin is not required—unlike other organs, such as muscle, heart, kidney, and liver. Then, too, the path of carbohydrate metabolism may follow the path outlined in Chap. 12, or it may take some other form; or, at different times, it may take several forms.

The metabolic defects on a vitamin B_1-deficient diet—which also appear elsewhere (heart and kidney) besides the nervous system—appear before there is any degeneration of tissue, which means that a fairly prompt supply of the missing factor restores the animal to normal health.

The development of beriberi is accompanied by an increase in the amount of pyruvate present in the brain and also by a decrease in the amount of oxygen consumed (Peters). It is assumed that the oxidation of glucose in the brain may follow the path: glucose $\longrightarrow$ lactic acid $\longrightarrow$ pyruvic acid $\longrightarrow$ carbon dioxide; and it is believed that vitamin B_1 (thiamine) as well as CoA and α-lipoic acid are concerned with the change of pyruvic acid to acetic acid and CO_2 by a process of oxidative decarboxylation:

$$CH_3CO.COOH \underset{+O}{\overset{-CO_2}{\longrightarrow}} CH_3.COOH + CO_2$$

A cocarboxylase, as well as carboxylase itself, is necessary for the proper functioning of this system. This coenzyme is none other than a pyrophosphoric ester of vitamin B_1 (Lohmann).

$$\underset{\underset{N \text{---} C.H}{\overset{\|}{}}}{\overset{N=C.NH_2}{CH_3 \text{---} C C \text{---} CH_2 \text{---} N}} \diagup \underset{\underset{Cl CH \text{---} S}{}}{\overset{CH_3}{\overset{|}{C}} = C \text{---} CH_2.CH_2 \text{---} O \text{---} \underset{\overset{\|}{O}}{\overset{OH}{\overset{|}{P}}} \text{---} O \text{---} \underset{\overset{\|}{O}}{\overset{OH}{\overset{|}{P}}} \text{---} OH}$$

Cocarboxylase (vitamin B_1—or thiamine—pyrophosphate)

From the work of Peters and his associates it seems clear that not only is carboxylase active in the oxidation of pyruvic acid in brain, but that the C_4 acids (succinic, fumaric, malic, oxaloacetic) play an essential role in this transformation. In other words, the C_4 acids are important whether we deal with oxidations in muscle or oxidations in brain.

Hormones. We will presently (Chap. 23) touch upon the subject of insulin in hypoglycemic shock, and we have referred to the probability that nerves themselves liberate substances which may be regarded as hormones. A study of one or two hormones, generated in other parts of the body, in their possible effect on the activity of the brain has been made. Thyroxine, for example, increases the respiration of both nerve and brain. This is presumably brought about by inducing an increased production of dehydrogenases, the enzymes involved in processes of oxidation.

Extracts from the adrenal cortex have a profound effect on the metabolism of sodium in the body, and it is not surprising to find that they influence the potassium and sodium balance in the brain.

Effect of Drugs. It has been emphasized that, from the point of view of metabolism, the brain is not a homogeneous tissue. Neither is it homogeneous in its anatomical or chemical structure. The multiplicity of results obtained by the use of different chemicals is not surprising.

To cite a few examples: cocaine paralyzes sensory nerve endings; atropine paralyzes the nerve endings of the parasympathetic system only; morphine depresses the centers dealing with pain perception; analgesics and antipyretics (salicylates, aspirin, etc.) depress the pain-perceiving and temperature-regulating mechanisms; alcohol depresses the power of judgment and releases inhibitions; etc.

EPITHELIAL TISSUE

The epithelial tissue is found in the covering of the surface of the body (the skin), in the lining of the respiratory tract, as an essential part of glandular organs, etc.

Keratin. The characteristic substance present in this tissue is the albuminoid keratin. Among proteins, it is the most resistant to chemical action. It is insoluble in any of the solvents which dissolve other proteins and is not attacked by gastric or pancreatic juice. This protein is further characterized by its high sulfur content, of which most is in the form of cystine. Human hair, for example, contains from 16 to 21 per cent of this amino acid.

Though normally resistant to chemical and enzymic action, by exhaustive grinding keratin becomes more digestible. For example, if wool fibers (rich in keratin) are first ground in a ball mill, they can be digested by both pepsin and trypsin. Significantly enough, after grinding, these wool fibers if extracted with water show larger quantities of nitrogen and sulfur constituents in solution than before grinding. Similar results are obtained with keratins from human hair, turkey feathers, duck feathers, chicken feathers, and porcupine quills.

That such mechanical grinding, aside from increasing surface area and so enabling the proteolytic enzymes to come into more intimate contact with substrate, is accompanied by some chemical change is made probable by the fact that, after the operation, there is a decrease in cystine sulfur, and one-half to one-fourth of the water-soluble sulfur is in the form of inorganic sulfates, a change which suggests some oxidation.

Suggestive, too, are experiments with animals which lead to the conclusion that such finely ground keratin can be utilized to some degree as the protein constituent in the diet of animals. Supplementing the diet with tryptophan, methionine, and histidine—amino acids present in very small quantities—improved the condition of the animals. To convert what has always been considered a purely waste product from the point of view of food—keratin—into a useful animal "feed" would be an important practical achievement.

Male hair, it seems, contains more cystine than female hair; and dark hair contains more cystine than light hair.

According to Edwards and Duntley, the color of normal skin is due to several pigments: melanin, a closely related substance which the authors call "melanoid," carotene, reduced hemoglobin, and oxyhemoglobin. "Our studies confirm the idea that the colored races owe their characteristic color only to variations in the amount of melanin present. . . . No pigments other than those found in the whites are encountered in the dark races. . . ."

Human red hair yields a red iron pigment of unknown constitution. This pigment cannot be obtained from human hair unless it is bright red in color.

CONNECTIVE TISSUE

Under this heading we shall discuss collagen (white fibrous tissue), elastin (yellow elastic tissue), chondromucoid (mucoprotein of cartilage) and the variety of substances which make up the "ground substances" of the cell (Fig. 92).

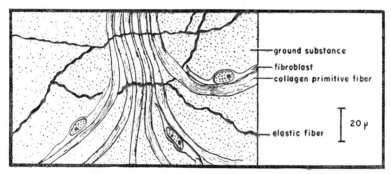

ground substance
fibroblast
collagen primitive fiber

20 μ

elastic fiber

Fig. 92. The distinctive components of connective tissue. (*Bear*, in Anson and Edsall's Advances in Protein Chemistry, *7:* 69, 1952.)

Collagen. The main organic constituent of white fibrous tissue is the albuminoid *collagen*, which, like keratin, is chemically resistant, but not to the same degree. Collagen is also found in bone, skin, and the walls of blood vessels. It is formed from precollagenous material in maturing connective tissue—a process which ceases to some extent in scurvy.

Collagen is fairly well digested by pepsin, but only slightly by trypsin. Preliminary treatment with alkali makes the albuminoid more digestible by trypsin. It contains much less sulfur (in the form of cystine or methionine) than does keratin. By boiling with water, the collagen is converted to *gelatin*, a much more easily digestible protein. The chemical nature of this interconversion is still not clear; the tendency is to regard the change in the nature of an intramolecular rearrangement.

Radioactive studies show a low turnover for collagen, unlike, say, the proteins in liver and muscle.

In rheumatoid diseases there develop degenerative changes in the collagen.

An analysis by Gies of the tendo achillis of the ox—an example of white fibrous tissue—reveals that the solids constitute from 35 to 40 per cent, only a fraction of a per cent of which is inorganic matter. The organic matter is composed of the following (in per cent): collagen, 31.6; elastin, 1.6; mucoid, 1.2; fatty substance, 1.0; etc.

The elastin is referred to in the next section. The mucoid (tendomucoid) resembles the mucin of the saliva; which means that it is a glucoprotein.

Elastin.   According to Gies, the analysis of ligamentum nuchae—an example of yellow elastic tissue—yields some 40 per cent of solids, composed of the following (in per cent): elastin, 31.6; collagen, 7.2; fatty substance, 1.1; mucoid, 0.5; inorganic matter, 0.4; etc.

The elastin, like keratin and like collagen, belongs to the class of proteins known as albuminoids; which means that it is, relatively speaking, a chemically resistant protein. In general, it resembles collagen in its properties, although, unlike the latter, it is not changed to gelatin when boiled with water.

Elastin is that which is left over when everything else is hydrolyzed by dilute acid or alkali. Lowry hydrolyzes tissue with 0.1 N NaOH at 95° C. for 20 minutes, resulting in an insoluble material which is the elastin.

Elastin is slowly digested by pepsin and trypsin.

Table 61 gives the amino acid composition of collagen and elastin. Collagen is characterized by an unusually high concentration of hydroxyproline.

Cartilage.   This rather tough and firm material, popularly known as "gristle," is composed almost exclusively of collagen and chondroitin sulfate. The major portion of cartilage is a protein salt of chondroitin sulfate.

If we define, with Meyer, a mucopolysaccharide as a hexoseamine-containing polysaccharide which occurs either free or loosely combined with protein, then chondroitin sulfate, mucoitin sulfate, hyaluronic acid, and heparin are examples.

Chondroitin sulfate, which, in addition to cartilage, can also be isolated from umbilical cord tissue, spongy bone, and skin, is made up of equimolar parts of acetyl galactosamine, ester sulfate, and glucuronic acid.

Mucoitin sulfate is a monosulfuric acid ester of hyaluronic acid.

Heparin, the substance in liver which prolongs the clotting time of blood, is also a mucopolysaccharide containing more than one ester sulfate group.

Hyaluronic acid is a straight chain polymer of a disaccharide composed of 1 molecule of N-acetylglucosamine and 1 molecule of glucuronic acid. It is found, among other places, in synovial fluid (viscid fluid of a joint cavity), vitreous humor (fluid between the retina and lens of the eye) and umbilical cord. When prepared under suitable conditions it has a high viscosity.

Hyaluronidase is an enzyme which can break down hyaluronic acid, a process which leads to a decrease in viscosity of the acid (a depolymerization) and to its hydrolysis. In the native state, hyaluronic acid is present as a gel. When made acid, the hyaluronic acid precipitates (together with protein in the extract) to form a clot.

The importance of the hyaluronic acid–hyaluronidase system is evident from a list of reactions with which it has been associated:

Table 61   AMINO ACID COMPOSITION OF BOVINE COLLAGEN
AND ELASTIN (GM. IN 100 GM. PROTEIN)
(Bowes and Kenton: Biochem. J., *43:* 358, 1948 [collagen]; Graham, Waitkoff, and Hier: J. Biol. Chem., *177:* 529, 1949 [elastin].)

Amino Acid	Collagen	Elastin
Glycine	19.9	22.5
Alanine	7.6	15.1
Phenylalanine	3.7	4.4
Leucine(s)	4.8	10.1
Valine	2.9	12.5
Proline	12.7	13.4
Hydroxyproline	12.1	1.7
Glutamic acid	10.0	2.4
Aspartic acid	5.5	0.35
Arginine	7.9	0.88
Lysine	4.0	0.39
Hydroxylysine	1.1	. . . .
Histidine	0.7	0.04
Serine	2.7	0.68
Threonine	2.0	0.87
Methionine	0.7	0.18
Cystine	0.0	0.28
Tyrosine	1.3	1.4
Tryptophan	0.0	0.0
Total	99.6	87.2
Total N	18.6	16.9
Amide N	0.65	0.04

A. The "spreading reaction" of hyaluronidase, which brings about a decrease in viscosity of tissue fluids and allows for the invasion or "spreading" of chemical substances throughout the tissue.

B. Decapsulation of mucoid strains of streptococci.

C. During fertilization it is believed that hyaluronidase disperses the viscous substance cementing the cumulus cells of the ova, facilitating the process of fertilization. Only mature spermatozoa contain relatively large amounts of the enzyme.

D. Capillary permeability.

BONE * (*Osseous Tissue*)

The organic matrix is similar to that found in cartilage and connective tissues in general. We find collagen, a glycoprotein, and an osseoalbuminoid.

* Compare this section with the section devoted to teeth (p. 412).

The normal mature bone contains nearly one-half its weight of water, and sometimes as much as 24 per cent of fat. Using the dry, fat-free material, some 30 to 40 per cent of this substance is organic in nature. The chief inorganic constituents are calcium, phosphate, and carbonate (Table 62).

Among the organic constituents is citric acid, a substance which was overlooked for a long time, probably because in the ordinary analysis of bone as "bone ash" the citrate had been converted into carbonate and recorded as such.

Dickens has found citric acid—probably as the calcium salt—in bone to the extent of about 1 per cent. In fact, more than 90 per cent of the citric acid in the body is located in bony structure. It may be of use to the organism in two ways: as a reserve supply of citrate in the course of the metabolism of carbohydrate, and to form soluble calcium salts, probably as a preliminary step in the active metabolism of bone.

Table 62   COMPOSITION OF BONE
(Morgulis: J. Biol. Chem., 93: 455; Hammet: Ibid., 64: 693.)

Animal	Condition	Calcium	Magnesium	Phosphorus	CO_2
		In per cent of total bone ash			
Dog.....................	Normal	35.7	0.46	15.8	5.6
Cow.....................	Normal	36.1	0.74	16.4	4.6
Rabbit.................	Normal	36.3	0.53	16.0	5.7
Hen.....................	Normal	37.2	0.51	16.4	5.5
Rat.....................	Normal	37.5	0.85	18.5	

Inorganic Salts.   The principal inorganic constituents of bone are calcium, phosphate, and carbonate, with lesser quantities of magnesium and sodium. The x-ray diffraction pattern of bone is similar to that of the mineral apatite, which is sometimes written as $Ca_{10}(PO_4)_6F_2$. Substitutions of $(OH)^-$ for F^- and Mg^{+2} for Ca^{+2} occur with only minor changes in the diffraction pattern.

Various formulas for the main phosphate substance of bone have been suggested, but none has been found convincing. For example, the suggestion has been made that this substance is a carbonate apatite, $Ca_{10}(PO_4)_6.$-CO_3; or that it is a hydroxyapatite, $Ca_{10}(PO_4)_2(OH)_2$; or that it is hydrated tricalcium phosphate, $3Ca_3(PO_4)_2.2H_2O$; or that it is apatite with occluded phosphate ion.

In any case, the composition of the inorganic constituents of bone is by no means constant. Changes occur with age, in rickets, in acidosis and alkalosis, as a result of change in diet, etc. If, for the sake of convenience, we confine ourselves for the moment to a basic formula which has often been used, $CaCO_3.nCa_3(PO_4)_2$, the most frequent changes occur in the percentage of carbonate.

Sobel and Kramer have shown that the calcium and phosphorus content, and the vitamin D content of the diet, influence the $CO_3:Ca$ ratio of bone.

That there is active metabolism in bone was shown by Hevesy who used labelled (radioactive) phosphorus and found that some of the phosphorus atoms of the mineral constituents of the bone exchange rapidly with those present in the plasma. Within fifty days, 29 per cent of the mineral constituents of the femur and tibia epiphyses were found to be renewed.

Absorption of Calcium and Phosphorus.   The normal adult absorbs only 50 per cent of the calcium ingested with his food, and about two-thirds of his ingested phosphate. Only the water-soluble form of calcium will be absorbed and inasmuch as neutral or alkaline pH favors the formation of insoluble calcium compounds, the pH of the intestinal contents plays an important role in calcium absorption. The absorption of calcium is aided by the presence of amino acids, fats, bile salts and by vitamin D.

The absorption of inorganic phosphate is intimately connected with that of calcium. Most of the excreted calcium is in the form of the insoluble calcium phosphate.

Factors Affecting Calcification.   (a) THE CALCIUM AND PHOSPHORUS OF THE BLOOD. The concentration of the calcium and phosphorus is important since it affects the composition of fluid in immediate contact with tissues undergoing calcification. More specifically, we are here interested in the ion product which determines precipitation of mineral material.

Of the 9 to 11 mg. per cent calcium in the plasma, 2 mg. is ionizable, and from 3 to 5 mg. is associated with the plasma proteins and is non-diffusible; the remainder is non-ionized but diffusible, the nature of which is in dispute. Even the 2 mg. per cent of ionizable calcium is theoretically enough to yield a supersaturated solution.

Intermediate carbohydrate metabolism plays its role here, since it makes available organic phosphorus compounds from which phosphorus ions are liberated by action of alkaline phosphatase.

Of the total phosphorus in the blood, 2 to 5 mg. per cent is inorganic phosphate, and together with the organic ester phosphorus (14 to 29 mg. per cent) makes up the "acid-soluble" phosphorus. The remainder includes the phospholipid P (8 to 18 mg. per cent), together with a small quantity of nucleic acid P. The inorganic P is equally distributed between the plasma and corpuscles, the ester P is mostly in the corpuscles and the lipid P is higher in the corpuscles than in the plasma.

From the work of Robison and others, it seems clear that an important factor in the process of calcification is the presence of the enzyme *phosphatase*. This enzyme, present in bones, teeth, and ossifying cartilage of young animals, hydrolyzes hexosemonophosphoric ester and glycerophosphoric ester, liberating inorganic phosphate. A rachitic bone, cut longitudinally and placed in a solution of calcium hexosemonophosphate or calcium glycerophosphate, absorbs calcium phosphate and deposits the salt in the zones prepared for calcification. The conclusion has been drawn from this work that the bone phosphatase acts on the organic phosphorus ester liberating inorganic phosphate which, in turn, affects the product of the calcium and phosphate ions in solution to such a degree that the solubility product is exceeded, and the excess calcium phosphate is deposited.

Gutman has accumulated evidence which makes it likely that glycolysis, the utilization of glycogen in hypertrophic cartilage cells, plays an important role in calcification. Thus, enzyme inhibitors block the calcification of bone slices in vitro. Marks and Shorr inhibited calcification by the use of iodoacetamide, which interferes with the enzyme 1,3-diphosphoglyceric aldehyde dehydrogenase, and also showed that the removal of glycogen from cartilage slices markedly impaired the calcification process when inorganic phosphate was used, but not when glucose-1-phosphate was used. It has also been demonstrated that a number of enzymes and their substrates of the glycolytic cycle are present in cartilage. The process of calcification appears to be anything but a simple precipitation of calcium phosphate.

(b) THE CALCIUM AND PHOSPHORUS IN FOOD. The diet should include the following daily amounts (in grams):

	Ca	P
Children (3–13 years of age)	1.0	1.16–1.46
Adults	1.0	1.5
Pregnancy	1.5	1.5
Lactation	2.0	2.0

(c) VITAMIN D. See p. 379.

(d) REACTION OF THE INTESTINAL TRACT. Dogs fed a normal diet show a pH in the small intestine varying from 5.7 to 6.6. When these animals are fed a rickets-producing diet, the pH of the intestine is changed to 6.4 to 7.4. The addition of cod-liver oil, or irradiation of the animal, lowers the pH more to the acid side (Grayzel and Miller). Apparently, in a more acid medium, the calcium salts are more soluble, and, therefore, more easily absorbed.

(e) POTENTIAL ACIDITY AND ALKALINITY OF THE DIET. This may be a factor in pH changes in calcifying tissues. Also, a large excess of acid-forming food may be a drain on the fixed base of the body, including calcium.

(f) ENDOCRINE GLANDS. (The relation of calcium and the parathyroid hormone is discussed on p. 442). Especially important are the parathyroids, thyroid, anterior pituitary, and sex glands.

These factors may affect calcification by their influence, directly or indirectly, on one or more of the following: by acting directly on the calcifying cells, thereby altering the rate of deposition or solution of the inorganic or organic substances; by varying the absorption of calcium and phosphorus from the intestinal tract; by regulating the excretion of calcium and phosphorus; and by altering the composition of the fluid in contact with the calcifying tissues.

Teeth. The tooth consists of three calcified parts: the dentin, the chief substance of the tooth surrounding the tooth pulp; the cementum, covering the root of the tooth; and the enamel, the hardest of the three, covering the dentin (Fig. 93). These three, the dentin, the cementum, and the enamel, contain both inorganic and organic matter.

ORGANIC MATTER. The approximate percentages of organic matter are enamel, 1; dentin, 18; cementum, 23. The main constituent in enamel is keratin, with smaller quantities of cholesterol and phospholipids. In dentin we find mainly collagen, with less elastin and small quantities of lipids. Collagen is found in cementum.

THE INORGANIC MATTER. The inorganic matter (in percentage, and on a dry basis) is approximately 96 for enamel, 70 for dentin, and 65 for cementum. The water content (in percentage) is approximately 3, 12, and 27 for enamel, dentin, and cementum, respectively. The following figures give the average results of analysis of human enamel and dentin (Karshan), and for comparison, an analysis of human bone (Gabriel).

	Enamel	*Dentin*	*Bone*
Calcium............................	35.8	26.5	23.84
Magnesium.........................	0.38	0.79	0.30
Phosphorus.........................	17.4	12.7	10.41
Carbon dioxide (from carbonate)........	2.9	3.1	3.81

Enamel also contains (in per cent) 0.7 of sodium, 0.3 of potassium, 0.3 of chlorine, 0.0112 of fluorine and 0.0218 of iron; and dentin (in per cent) 0.19 of sodium, 0.07 of potassium, 0.03 of chlorine, 0.0204 of fluorine, and 0.0072 of iron.

Analyses of whole, sound teeth (human) give the following figures (in percentages and on a dry basis): Ca, 29.7; Mg, 0.06; P, 14.2; CO_2 (from

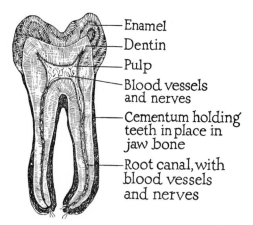

Fig. 93. Molar tooth cut lengthwise. (U. S. Dept. Agriculture.)

Enamel
Dentin
Pulp
Blood vessels and nerves
Cementum holding teeth in place in jaw bone
Root canal, with blood vessels and nerves

carbonate), 2.9 (Lefevre and Hodge). The average of inorganic and organic matter in whole human teeth is 85 and 15 per cent, respectively.

As in the case of bone, the exact nature of the main mineral substance in teeth has not as yet been completely clarified. In general, what was stated for bone holds for teeth. With regard to tooth enamel, it may be noted that the x-ray diffraction patterns of this tissue and of hydroxyapatite are strikingly similar.

The view held at one time that enamel is a "lifeless, inert, mostly inorganic substance" has undergone modification. This has become possible because of the application of radioactive isotopes for the study of mineral metabolism.

A contribution to the metabolism of teeth was made by Hevesy who showed that when compounds of radioactive phosphorus were injected into animals, radioactive phosphorus was found in the whole teeth. The enamel contained about 10 per cent of the radioactive element present in dentin.

For the teeth to calcify properly, the diet must include enough calcium and phosphorus and some of the vitamins (A, C, D). Some of the hormones are also important.

FLUORINE AND DENTAL CARIES (see p. 309). It has been maintained that fluorine is related to resistance to dental caries. This conclusion is based mainly on the fact that there is less dental decay in localities where the drinking water contains about one part per million of fluorine. Ordinarily, the amount of fluorine in water is much less than this amount. It has also been found that topical application of sodium or potassium fluoride solution to the teeth may reduce caries by as much as 40 per cent.

Another important fact is that treatment of enamel with fluoride solutions reduces the solubility of enamel in acid.

The fluorine content of the water is relatively high in areas of endemic mottled tooth enamel. Further, the teeth of rats develop less caries when fluorine is added to the diet, either during the time of development of the teeth or after the teeth are mature.

REFERENCES

Muscle. Borsook and Dubnoff: J. Biol. Chem., *132:* 559, 1940 (biosynthesis of creatine); *Bloch and Schoenheimer:* Ibid., *133:* 633, 1940; *138:* 167, 1941 (biosynthesis of creatine); *Du Vigneaud:* Harvey Lectures (1942–43), p. 55 (creatine).

Szent-Györgyi: Chemistry of Muscular Contraction, 1951; *Mommaerts:* Muscular Contraction, 1950.

Engelhardt and Lyubimova: Nature, *144:* 668, 139 (myosin and ATPase); *Gergely:* J. Biol. Chem., *200:* 543, 1943 (myosin and ATPase); *Astbury:* Proc. R. S. (London), Series B, *134:* 303, 1947 (structure of myosin); *Straub:* Ann. Rev. Biochem., *19:* 371, 1950 (review); *Dubuisson:* Ibid., *21:* 387, 1952 (review); *Szent-Györgyi:* Bull. N. Y. Acad. Med., *28:* 3, 1952 (contraction in heart muscle); *Szent-Györgyi:* Scientific American, June, 1949, p. 22 (muscle research); *Helwig and Greenberg:* J. Biol. Chem., *198:* 695, 1952 (myoglobin); *Rossi-Fanelli:* Science, *108:* 15, 1948 (myoglobin).

Nerve tissue. Metabolism and Function in Nervous Tissue: Biochemical (English) Society Symposia, No. 8, 1952; *Nachmansohn* in *Green:* Currents in Biochemical Research, 1946, p. 335, Annals N. Y. Acad. Sciences, *47:* 395, 1946; *Loewi:* American Scientist, July, 1945, p. 159; J. Am. Med. Assoc., *139:* 788, 1949 (cholinesterase inhibitors in myasthenia gravis); *Nachmansohn:* Electrical Engineering, March, 1950 (electric currents in nerve tissue); *Nachmansohn:* Bull. Johns Hopkins Hospital, *83:* 463, 1948 (acetyl-

choline); *Nachmansohn:* Ann. N. Y. Acad. Sciences, *47:* 395, 1946 (chemical mechanism of nerve activity); *Sacks and Culbreth:* Amer. J. Physiol., *165:* 251, 1951 (phosphate turnover in brain); *Peters and Wakelin:* J. Physiol., *119:* 421, 1953 (pyruvate oxidase system); *Dale:* Endeavour, *12:* July, 1953, p. 117 (transmission of nervous effects).

Epithelial tissue. Lang and Lucas: Biochem. J., *52:* 84, 1952 (analysis of hair keratin).

Connective tissue. Neuberger and Slack: Biochem. J., *53:* 47, 1953 (metabolism of collagen); *Rogers, Weidmann, and Parkinson:* Ibid., *50:* 537, 1952 (collagen content of bone); J. Am. Med. Assoc.. *150:* 220, 1952 (collagen diseases); *Einbinder and Schubert:* J. Biol. Chem., *188:* 335, 1951 (collagen).

Wolfrom, Madison, and Cron: J. Am. Chem. Soc., *74:* 1491, 1952 (structure of chondroitin sulfate); *Rapport, Meyer, and Linker:* Ibid., *73:* 2416, 1951 (action of hyaluronidase on hyaluronic acid; *Meyer and Rapport:* Adv. Enzym., *13:* 199, 1952 (hyaluronic acid and hyaluronidase); *Sieve:* Science, *116:* 373, 1952 (antifertility factor); Annals N. Y. Acad. Sciences, *52:* 945–1192, 1952 ("ground substance" and hyaluronidase); J. Am. Med. Assoc., *147:* 1570, 1951 (hyaluronidase); *Jeanloz and Forchielli:* J. Biol. Chem., *186:* 495, 1950; *188:* 361, 1951; *190:* 537, 1951 (hyaluronic acid); *Gerarde and Jones:* J. Biol. Chem., *201:* 553, 1953 (cortisone and collagen synthesis); *Robertson and Schwartz:* J. Biol. Chem., *201:* 689, 1953 (ascorbic acid and collagen).

Bone. Hendricks and Hill: Proc. Nat. Acad. Sci. U. S., *36:* 731, 1950 (composition); Nutr. Rev., *11:* 118, 1953 (citric acid in bone); *Dixon and Perkins:* Biochem. J., *52:* 260, 1952 (metabolism of citric acid); *Neuman, Neuman, Main, O'Leary, and Smith:* J. Biol. Chem., *187:* 655, 1950 (F in bone); *Evans:* Ibid., *187:* 273, 1950 (metabolism); *Rogers, Weidmann, and Jones:* Biochem. J., *54:* 37, 1953 (metabolism).

Albaum, Hirshfeld, and Sobel: Proc. Soc. Exp. Biol. Med., *78:* 719, 1951 (calcification): *Yu and Gutman:* Ibid., *75:* 481, 1950 (calcification); *Marks and Shorr:* Science, *112:* 752, 1950 (calcification); *Howard:* Bull. N. Y. Acad. Med., Jan., 1951, p. 24 (metabolism of Ca and P).

Roche in *Sumner and Myrbach's* The Enzymes, 1950 (phosphatase); *Neuman, Di Stefano, and Mulryan:* J. Biol. Chem., *193:* 227, 1951 (phosphatase).

Teeth. Nutr. Rev., *9:* 268, 1951 (composition of enamel and dentin); Ibid., *9:* 228, 1951 (diet and tooth development); Ibid., *10:* 76, 1952 (mechanism of fluoride action); Ibid., *10:* 114, 1952 (F in caries control); Ibid., *10:* 28, 1952 (F content of teeth); *Munroe:* Ind. Eng. Chem., *45:* 105, 1953 (review of fluoridation); *Russell and Elvove:* Public Health Reports, *66:* 1389, 1951 (water and dental caries); *McClure and Folk:* Proc. Soc. Exp. Biol. Med., *83:* 21, 1953 (rat caries); *Leicester:* Ann. Rev. Biochem., *22:* 341, 1953 (teeth).

Chapter 22   *Biochemistry of the Kidneys—Urine*

THE KIDNEYS; FORMATION OF URINE

THE KIDNEY is the chief organ of the body for the elimination of water and a number of compounds in blood of relatively low molecular weight. The chief functions of this organ might be said to be the maintenance of electrolyte composition of the body and the regulation of its acid-base balance.

In a very general way, the kidney serves the function of maintaining the composition of the fluids of the body at a certain level. This function is shared with the respiratory system, the skin, and the gastrointestinal tract. To maintain a fluid of constant composition within the body, the kidney eliminates urine which, from time to time, varies very much as to composition, and which also varies as to rate of production. A constituent such as urea is found in far higher concentration in urine than in blood; and, under normal conditions, not more than a trace of glucose is found in the urine, although there are appreciable quantities in the blood.

The kidney represents a complex organ made up of innumerable small tubes, the uriniferous tubules. From each kidney a tube, the ureter, carries urine to the bladder (Fig. 94), and by means of another tube, the urethra, the urine is voided.

At the beginning of the uriniferous tubule is a capsule, known as "Bowman's capsule," which surrounds a tuft of capillaries, the glomerulus. What is known as a "malpighian corpuscle" is made up of such a glomerulus and a Bowman's capsule.

To each capsule is attached a long tubule including a convoluted tubule terminating in the loop of Henle, and an ascending loop which ultimately connects with a main collecting tube opening into the renal pelvis (Fig. 95).

There have been many theories to explain the process by which urine is formed. It is generally agreed that at least two processes are involved: one includes a filtration process through Bowman's capsule, and the other, a process of concentration as the liquid passes along the tubules, until what is known as "urine" is formed. Richards emphasizes these facts as follows: the kidney, first of all, has to separate a filtrate from the blood so enormous in volume as to contain the waste products of metabolism and the unneeded salts and water. But were the activities of the kidney to stop here, death would result from dehydration and loss of Na^+. This is prevented by a process of reabsorption along the different segments of the tubules. In this way the water, salts and other diffusible compounds are maintained at a constant level of concentration in the plasma.

Glomerular Filtration. The first step in the formation of urine is filtration of the non-protein substances across the glomerulus. Richards,

416

using microtechniques, showed this to represent an ultrafiltration of plasma, with a composition similar to plasma except for its proteins. This filtration process occurs when the blood pressure in the glomeruli is greater than the sum of the osmotic pressure of the plasma proteins and the pressure in Bowman's capsule. This is referred to as the "filtration pressure."

Tubular Reabsorption.   If the glomerular filtrate is of a composition similar to the non-protein portion of blood, it is obvious that much of the

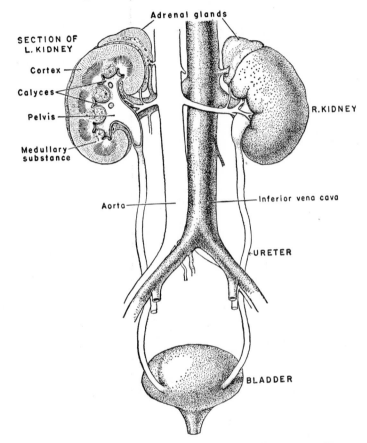

Fig. 94. Gross anatomy of the human urinary system. (Hunter and Hunter: College Zoology.)

water and dissolved substances must be returned to the blood before urine as such can be formed. This reabsorption takes place along the renal tubules. The glomeruli (both kidneys) filter 170 liters of solution per day. Since the volume of urine excreted in a day is about 1.5 liters, 168.5 liters, or 99 per cent of the glomerular filtrate, is reabsorbed.

Some 80 to 87 per cent is reabsorbed along the upper (proximal) portion of the tubule; this fraction is referred to as "obligatory" reabsorption. Along this section of the tubule the urine remains isosmotic with blood plasma. Concentration of urine takes place along the lower (distal) portion

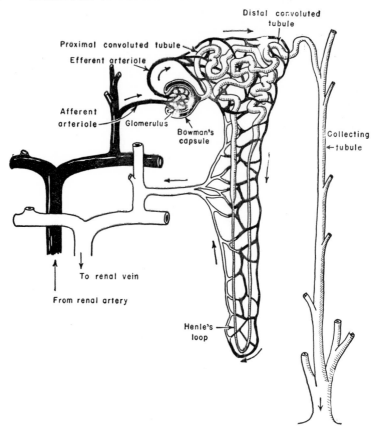

Fig. 95. The microscopic anatomy of a single kidney tubule, showing its blood supply. (Hunter and Hunter: College Zoology.)

of the tubule; this is known as "facultative" absorption. This fraction amounts to 13 to 20 per cent of the total filtrate. It is reabsorbed against the osmotic pressure of urine, and it requires energy. This energy is provided by the metabolic activity of the renal tubular cells.

Energy Expenditure by the Kidney.   Table 63 shows the energy expended.

Table 63   THE TOTAL WORK PERFORMED BY THE HUMAN KIDNEY
IN THE PRODUCTION OF THE 24-HOUR URINE
(Borsook and Winegarden: Proc. Nat. Acad. Sci., U. S., *17:* 3, 13, 1931.)

Kind of Work Performed	Quantity of Work $(-\Delta F)$
	(gm. calories)
Concentration	−1126
Transport of water	+267
Formation of ammonia from urea	+155
	−704

The kidney must expend 704 calories in order to form 1 to 1.5 liters of urine. This corresponds to 70 gm. calories per gram of nitrogen, or 0.7 gm. calories per milliliter of urine. A further calculation showed that the energy consumed by the kidney in the production of this urine is equal to 6 to 11 calories per gram of nitrogen excreted. Calculating the ratio of work performed and energy used, we get an efficiency of 1 to 2 per cent—a very low figure, considering that we are dealing with a healthy kidney.

Tubular Excretion.   In addition to a flow of substances from the plasma across the glomeruli, and a flow of substances across the tubular cells back into the plasma, there is also a flow from the plasma directly across the tubular cells into the lumen of the tubule. Figure 96 shows that glucose, under normal conditions, is completely reabsorbed along the proximal length of the tubules, whereas creatinine is filtered both via the glomerulus and also via the proximal tubules to join the urine.

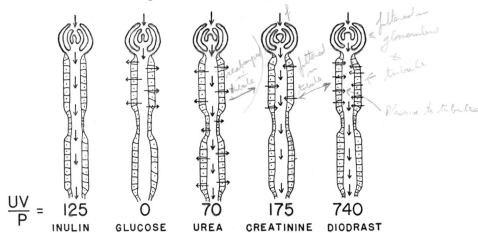

$$\frac{UV}{P} = \quad 125 \qquad 0 \qquad 70 \qquad 175 \qquad 740$$

INULIN   GLUCOSE   UREA   CREATININE   DIODRAST

Fig. 96. Results of clearance studies with five different test substances. (Gamble: Extracellular Fluid, 1950.)

Acid-Base Regulation.   Table 64 illustrates the substances of the plasma which constitute its ionic constituents. Except for carbonic acid, which is regulated by the respiration, and the plasma proteins, all the other constituents are regulated by the kidney.

The acidity of the urine can be expressed either in terms of pH, or concentration of H^+, or as titratable acidity, which expresses the total free acid present.

The pH of normal urine varies from 5.0 to 7.0, with a mean of 6.0. This pH is maintained largely by the relative amounts of NaH_2PO_4 and Na_2HPO_4 present. The change from a pH of 7.4 in the plasma to a pH of 6.0 in the urine is accomplished by a change in the proportion of these phosphates. In the plasma, $\frac{NaH_2PO_4}{Na_2HPO_4} = \frac{1}{5}$, whereas in the urine the ratio is 9/1. In this way a large quantity of Na^+ of the body is conserved at the time when pH changes take place during the passage of the urine through the distal tubules.

Table 64   IONIC COMPOSITION OF BLOOD PLASMA*
(Gamble: Extracellular Fluid, 1950.)

Cations		Anions	
(milliequivalents per liter of plasma)			
Na^+	142	HCO_3^-	27
K^+	5	Cl^-	103
Ca^{++}	5	HPO_4^-	2
Mg^{++}	3	SO_4^-	1
	155	Org. acids	6
		Protein	16
			155

* Cations are often referred to as "fixed base," and anions as "fixed acid."

Among the theories suggested to explain this change in pH, there is one by Pitts, who suggests that the secretion of acid by the tubules is due to an ionic exchange: the H^+ in the plasma, derived from H_2CO_3, is exchanged for Na^+ across the cell wall (Fig. 97).

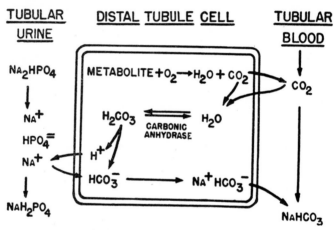

Fig. 97. Nature of the cellular mechanism for acidification of the urine. (Pitts and Alexander: Federation Proceedings, 7: 422, 1948.)

Kidney Function Tests.   Methods for the determination of renal function are important for two reasons: in the first place, they help to locate the site of impairment of renal function; secondly, they add to our information concerning the normal biochemical function of the cells of the kidney.

Analyses of both blood and urine are performed during a specified time and under controlled conditions. The substance to be determined in blood and urine may be one normally present, such as urea, or may be one which is foreign to the body and is intravenously injected. The result is expressed in terms of amount of substance found in urine (over a unit of time) to the volume of plasma which it would occupy at the existing plasma concentration.

Figure 96 illustrates five such "test" substances used in these "clearance" studies. In the calculation—"urea clearance"—a comparison is made between the concentration of urea in the blood and the rate of its excretion in the urine.

$$C = \frac{UV}{P}$$

where C is the volume of plasma cleared per minute, U is the concentration of substance in urine, V is the volume of urine excreted per minute, and P is the concentration of substance in blood.

Inulin, a polysaccharide which yields fructose on hydrolysis and has a molecular weight of 5000, is completely filtered by the glomerulus. It is not reabsorbed or excreted by the tubules and is, therefore, an index of glomerular filtration. Diodrast, 3:5-diiodo-4-pyridone-N-acetic acid

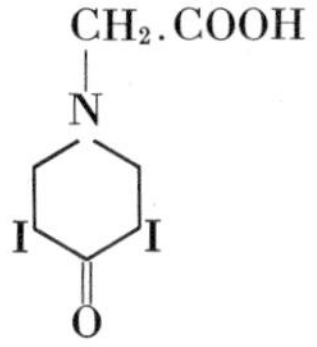

is excreted by the tubules as well as by the glomerulus. Its clearance rate is high, as the figure indicates.

Renin. One of the commonest diseases suffered by man is arterial hypertension. Goldblatt discovered that persistent hypertension could be induced in the dog by constriction of both main renal arteries or by the constriction of one renal artery and the excision of the opposite kidney. That some active substance was discharged by the kidney into the blood was made probable by several experiments. One of these consisted in transplanting a kidney to the neck, with no nervous connections with the rest of the body; a rise of blood pressure still occurred when the main artery to the kidney was constricted. This indicates that some active substance is released by the kidney into the systemic circulation.*

The substance responsible for this rise in blood pressure has been given the name *renin.*

COMPOSITION OF URINE

A diagram representing comparative concentrations of substances in blood plasma and urine is instructive (Fig. 98).

The kidney is the main organ of regulation of extracellular fluid, which, as may be remembered, consists of plasma and interstitial fluid including lymph. A substance like urea is in far higher concentration in urine than in blood. Substances like protein and glucose are not found in normal urine to any appreciable extent. Ammonia (in the form of ammonium salt) is present in urine and probably absent in blood.

Using very rough figures, and always working with a twenty-four hour

---

* "Although the kidney is not generally looked upon as an endocrine organ, there is no reason to deny the possibility of its performing such a function; for the elaboration of humoral substances is not limited to specifically endocrine organs" (Grollman, Harrison, and Williams, Jr.).

sample of urine, we may say that the average amount of urine voided during this period would be about 1500 ml. In this 1500 ml. of fluid would be found some 60 gm. of solids. Roughly, one-half (or 30 gm.) is due to urea, and one-quarter (or 15 gm.) is due to sodium chloride. The remaining 15 gm. includes the various organic and inorganic constituents (uric acid,

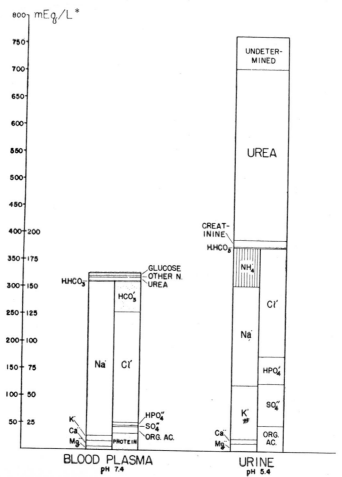

Fig. 98. Comparison of composition of blood plasma and urine. (Gamble: Extracellular Fluid, 1950.)

creatinine, amino acids, hormones, enzymes, vitamins, ammonia, sulfates, phosphates, etc.).

Under pathological conditions, substances appear in the urine which are normally absent, or, if anything, present in traces; these include proteins, sugar, acetone bodies, bile, hemoglobin, etc.

Quantity.   As has already been stated, the quantity of urine voided in twenty-four hours may be some 1500 ml. Of course, this figure varies

* mEq/L = milliequivalents per liter. For sodium ion, for example, milliequivalents per liter is obtained by multiplying the mg. per 100 ml. by 10 and dividing by 23.

considerably with different individuals. The fluctuations for a normal adult are probably from 800 to 2300 ml. (40–50 ounces). Increases beyond the normal amount (polyuria) occur in a number of diseases—chronic nephritis, diabetes insipidus, etc. The amount of urine voided in twenty-four hours is from 2 to 5 liters, and, in very rare cases, it may even reach 20 liters. The reversed condition, the elimination of a decreased quantity of urine (oliguria), occurs in diarrhea, fevers, etc.

The renal excretion of water is in part under the control of the anti-diuretic hormone of the pituitary.

Color. The color of the urine, usually from yellow to reddish yellow, will vary with the amount of urine voided. The chief pigment is urochrome (yellow in color). Small quantities of urobilin and hematoporphyrin are also present. With the presence of abnormal constituents, the color may change considerably. The presence of hemoglobin will give rise to a brown to red color. Bile in the urine may produce a yellow foam when the sample is shaken, and the color of the urine may become a pronounced brown. Rhubarb, cascara, and some other cathartics produce a brown color, which changes to red upon the addition of alkali.

Fresh urine is transparent. After a time, a cloud appears, due to the separation of mucus, leukocytes, and epithelial cells. Where there is much cloudiness, the effect may be due to phosphates, urates, pus, blood, or bacteria. It must be emphasized at this point that normal urine, on standing, becomes alkaline, and this itself causes a precipitation of phosphates.

Odor. The peculiar odor of urine is ascribed, rather vaguely, to "volatile acids." Urine undergoing decomposition has an ammoniacal odor. Certain dietary ingredients and a number of drugs influence the odor. For example, the eating of asparagus will give rise to a urine with a particularly offensive odor.

pH. The reaction of normal urine is usually on the acid side (about pH 6), but the variations are considerable, even in normal samples. An excess of protein in the diet, producing increased quantities of sulfate and phosphate, will tend to increase the acidity of the urine. The acidity is also increased in acidosis and in fevers (with a concentrated urine).

As has already been stated, the urine becomes alkaline on standing, owing to the gradual conversion of the urea into ammonia. Where the freshly voided urine is alkaline, the reason must be sought elsewhere. It may be due to decomposition in the bladder—a decomposition of urea after the urine is secreted. It may also be the result of frequent vomiting. It may, on the other hand, signify nothing more than a temporary "alkaline tide," due to a full meal, or it may be the result of eating excessive quantities of fruit. In the latter case, the salts of organic acids give rise to an alkaline ash when oxidized in the body.

The ingestion of from 3 to 5 gm. of sodium bicarbonate is enough, in a normal individual, to produce an alkaline urine.

Specific Gravity. The usual range is from 1.010 to 1.030. It varies, in general, inversely with the quantity of urine voided.

The specific gravity is low in chronic nephritis and in diabetes insipidus, and it is high in fevers and in diabetes mellitus.

Some General Considerations. The organic substances present undergo decomposition rapidly when the urine is left standing. For example, urea is changed to ammonia. It is important, therefore, in examining urine with a view to a quantitative analysis of its constituents, to work with fresh urine; or, since that is usually difficult, to use urine to which a preservative has been added. Such preservatives include boric acid, Formalin, thymol, toluene, chloroform, etc. All of them are objectionable. The objection is usually due to some interference with a chemical test. Thymol and toluene are probably the most widely used.

Normal Constituents. The variations within normal limits are given in Table 65.

Table 65   COMPOSITION OF NORMAL URINE
(Lang: Handbook of Chemistry, 1949.)

Color: slightly yellow to amber
Quantity: 1000 to 1500 ml./24 hrs.
Specific Gravity: 1.008 to 1.030$^{15°}$
pH: 5.5 to 7.5
Sugar: 0.015%
Nitrogen { Total: 7 to 20 gm./24 hrs.
          Amino Acid: 0.15 to 0.30 gm./24 hrs.
Urea: 12 to 35 gm./24 hrs.
Ammonia: 0.6 to 1.2 gm./24 hrs.
Creatinine: 0.8 to 2.0 gm./24 hrs.
Creatinine Coefficient: 22 to 30 mg. creatinine per kg. per day.

Uric Acid: 0.3 to 0.8 gm./24 hrs.
Hippuric Acid: 0.7 gm./24 hrs.
Chlorides (NaCl): 10 to 15 gm./24 hrs.
Phosphorus (P): 1.2 gm./24 hrs.
Sulfur (S) { Total: 1.2 gm./24 hrs.
            Inorganic: 1.0 gm./24 hrs.
            Ethereal: 0.1 gm./23 hrs.
Sodium (Na): 2.5 to 4.0 gm./24 hrs.
Calcium (Ca): 0.1 to 0.3 gm./24 hrs.
Potassium (K): 1.5 to 2.0 gm./24 hrs.
Magnesium (Mg): 0.1 to 0.2 gm./24 hrs.

A brief description of a number of these constituents will now be given.

UREA. This substance represents the principal nitrogenous end product. This is not true of all animals, as Baldwin has once again emphasized (Table 66).

Table 66   NITROGEN END PRODUCT OF VARIOUS ANIMALS
(Baldwin: Comparative Biochemistry, Cambridge Univ. Press, London.)

Animal	Nitrogen End Product
Sharks, dog-fishes	Urea
Bony fishes (teleostei)	Ammonia
Frogs, newts	Urea
Turtles	Urea
Snakes, lizards	Uric acid
Birds	Uric acid
Mammals	Urea

However, in man, for example, the output of urea varies directly with the protein intake, and usually constitutes from 80 to 90 per cent of the total nitrogen excretion. On a low protein diet, this ratio (80–90 per cent) is lowered (Table 67).

The formation of urea in the body has already been discussed (p. 249).

Urea is soluble in water and alcohol and insoluble in ether and chloroform. It forms biuret when heated.

It is oxidized by hypobromite in alkaline solution:

$$CO(NH_2)_2 + 3NaOBr \longrightarrow 3NaBr + N_2 + CO_2 + 2H_2O$$

which forms the basis for a rough quantitative estimation of urea by measuring the volume of nitrogen eliminated. A much more accurate method for estimating this substance is based on the action of the enzyme *urease* (found in soy and jack beans), which quantitatively converts urea into ammonia.

Characteristic crystals of urea nitrate, $CO(NH_2)_2.HNO_3$, and urea oxalate, $CO(NH_2)_2.H_2C_2O_4$, are easily obtained by mixing urea with the respective acids; these salts are valuable for identification.

Table 67   SHOWING THE AVERAGE AMOUNT OF DIFFERENT FORMS OF NITROGEN EXCRETED WHEN LOW, NORMAL AND HIGH PROTEIN DIETS WERE INGESTED
(Beard.)

Substance	Normal diet			High protein diet			Low protein diet		
Volume of urine	1364 ml.			1472 ml.			1408 ml.		
Specific gravity	1.022			1.023			1.019		
	Amount	Nitrogen content	Per cent of total N	Amount	Nitrogen content	Per cent of total N	Amount	Nitrogen content	Per cent of total N
	gm.	gm.		gm.	gm.		gm.	gm.	
Total nitrogen................	....	11.16	....	....	15.28	....	....	7.97	....
Urea........................	20.38	9.51	85.21	28.29	13.20	86.36	13.20	6.16	77.29
Ammonia....................	0.66	0.54	4.83	0.83	0.68	4.45	0.52	0.43	5.39
Uric acid...................	0.57	0.19	1.70	0.63	0.21	1.37	0.54	0.18	2.26
Creatinine..................	1.70	0.63	5.64	1.78	0.66	4.32	1.67	0.62	7.78
Undetermined nitrogen by difference.......	....	0.29	2.62	....	0.53	3.50	....	0.58	7.28

The amount of urea excreted is increased in fevers, diabetes (with little acidosis), etc. In diseases of the liver (acute yellow atrophy, cirrhosis, etc.), with a decreased formation of urea, there is less excreted. This is also true in cases of acidosis, where some of the nitrogen which would be normally converted into urea is changed to ammonia.

Aside from a decreased formation of urea with a subsequent decreased output, a retention of urea (as in nephritis) also leads to a smaller output. Here, for diagnostic purposes, the estimation of urea in the blood is of great importance.

CREATININE. This substance—and its relationship to creatine—has already been discussed (p. 396). Creatinine is a normal constituent of urine; it is, according to Folin, relatively independent of the amount of protein ingested. Its amount, however, is decreased in many pathological conditions.

Creatinine is soluble in water and alcohol and forms a characteristic double salt with zinc chloride, $(C_4H_7N_3O)_2.ZnCl_2$, which is used for the purpose of isolating the base. With picric acid, in an alkaline solution, it forms a red color, which is the basis for a colorimetric determination (Jaffe, Folin). Greenwald is of the opinion that the reaction is due to the formation of a red tautomer of creatinine picrate. In addition to this test, originally due to Jaffe, there is the test in which the urine (containing creatinine) is mixed with alkali and sodium nitroprusside, yielding a red color which turns yellow (Weyl); and if acetic acid is now added to the yellow solution and heated, a green, and finally a blue color (Prussian blue) is obtained (Salkowski).

URIC ACID. This substance represents one of the final stages in the oxidation of the purines in the body and is the chief nitrogenous end product in birds, snakes, and lizards (Table 66). It is derived from the nucleoproteins of the food and from the breakdown of nucleoprotein within the cells of the body.

Uric acid acts as an acid and forms salts with sodium and potassium to give the corresponding urates. It is these urates, very largely, which are found in the urine, the highly insoluble free acid being obtained on strong acidification. The acid itself, however, is probably also present to some degree. The urates—the acid salts particularly—are thrown out of solution when urine is concentrated, giving the sediment of "amorphous urates."

In leukemia, with destruction of leukocytes, the uric acid output is very much increased. This is also true in diseases associated with the liver, an organ rich in nuclein material. Gout has long been popularly associated with a disturbed metabolism of uric acid; but the connection is not altogether clear. Before an attack, the output is somewhat decreased, and for several days after the attack, the output is definitely increased.

A characteristic test for uric acid is the *murexide reaction*. This is obtained by evaporating the uric acid with nitric acid and treating the residue with ammonia; a reddish violet product (murexide, or ammonium purpurate) is obtained. The nitric acid oxidizes uric acid to dialuric acid and alloxan, which then condense:

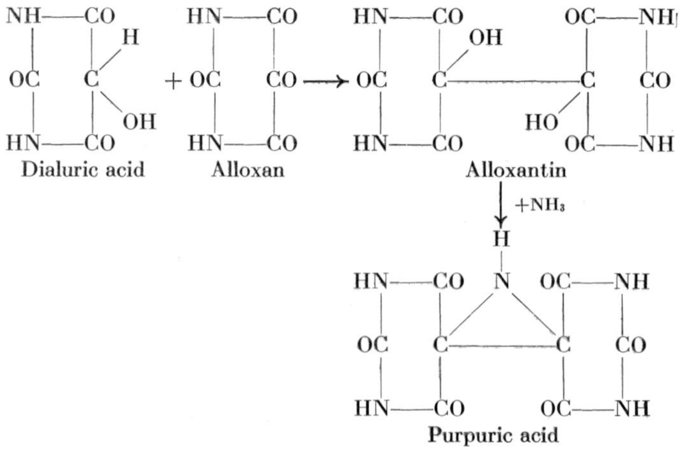

Dialuric acid   Alloxan   Alloxantin

Purpuric acid

Uric acid also reduces silver solutions in an alkaline medium (Schiff test) and gives a blue color with phosphotungstic acid (Folin), which serves as the basis for one quantitative procedure.

AMINO ACIDS. The small quantity normally in urine is much increased in impairment of hepatic function (as in yellow atrophy of the liver), eclampsia, and in certain types of poisoning (such as that due to chloroform, phosphorus, arsenic, or carbon tetrachloride).

The use of protein hydrolysates in nutritional disturbances has made the study of amino acid excretion important. Methods based on microbiological technique or paper chromatography are used extensively.

Normal urine is usually considered protein-free. However, very small quantities are present. On an average, some 15 mg. of albumin and 26 mg. of globulin (per 24 hours) are found (Rigas and Heller).

CHLORIDES. Next to urea, chlorides are the most abundant substances. The chlorides, mainly as sodium chloride, are derived chiefly from the food, and the output, therefore, fluctuates depending upon the intake. During starvation the output may be almost abolished, and yet the chlorides in the blood will maintain for a time their normal concentration.

There is a decrease in the elimination of chlorides in several forms of nephritis and in fevers.

SULFATES. Most of the sulfur has its origin in protein. Much of it is derived from the protein in the food, and some of it has its source in cellular activity.

The sulfur appears in the urine in three forms: inorganic sulfate, ethereal sulfate, and neutral sulfur.

INORGANIC SULFATES. Roughly speaking, the output of sulfate is proportional to the output of total nitrogen, the ratio $N:SO_3$ is about $5:1$. Since the amount of nitrogen eliminated (as urea, etc.) is a measure of the amount of protein metabolized, estimations of inorganic sulfate as well as of nitrogen are valuable in studies dealing with protein metabolism.

ETHEREAL SULFATES. Of the total preformed sulfates present in urine, about nine-tenths is in the inorganic form (combined with Na, K, Ca, and Mg). About one-tenth, however, is in the form of an ester: a combination of sulfuric acid with phenols:

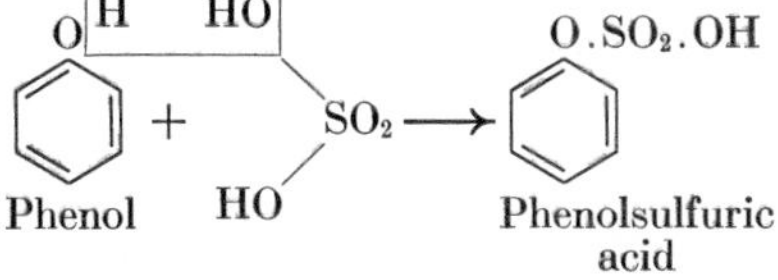

Other substances combined with the acid are p-cresol, indole (as indoxyl) and skatole (as skatoxyl). All these are included under the name "ethereal sulfates."

The ethereal sulfates represent, to some extent, the putrefactive products in the intestine which are detoxified in the liver and then eliminated. To a large extent, these substances are the result of normal protein metabolism in the body, but the exception, according to Folin, is indican, which really represents putrefactive activity. Indican is the potassium salt of indoxyl sulfuric acid (Chap. 24).

Indicanuria (a substantial increase in the output of indican) is common in diseases of the small intestine (intestinal obstruction, for example), and in intestinal indigestion ("biliousness"). Simple constipation of the large intestine is not, as a rule, followed by an indicanuria. Increases in indican are also noted in diseases of the stomach in which there is a subnormal amount of hydrochloric acid (gastritis, cancer).

The tests used in detecting indican in the urine depend upon its decomposition and oxidation to indigo-blue (Jaffe, Obermayer):

Indoxyl   Indigo-blue

In the Obermayer method, the urine is mixed with the reagent (ferric chloride and concentrated hydrochloric acid), chloroform is added, and the mixture is shaken. The chloroform turns blue, the intensity depending upon the amount of indican present.

Acidification of urine with hydrochloric acid and the addition of barium chloride precipitates inorganic sulfates. This precipitate is filtered off, and the filtrate is heated. If an excess of barium chloride has been added, a second precipitate will be formed. The hot acid hydrolyzes the ethereal sulfates, and the sulfate ion combines with the barium ion. This method is used not only qualitatively for the detection of the two types of sulfur, but as the basis for a quantitative determination.

NEUTRAL SULFUR. This represents sulfur in an incomplete state of oxidation, possibly in the form of cystine, taurine, sulfides, thiocyanates, etc. Its amount seems to be independent of the amount of protein ingested, and in this sense it resembles creatinine.

This type of sulfur can be tested for by adding zinc and hydrochloric acid to a sample of urine. The hydrogen combines with the sulfur, and the hydrogen sulfide which is liberated is identified with a strip of paper soaked in a solution of lead acetate. Black lead sulfide is formed.

The quantitative determination of neutral sulfur is carried out by evaporating a sample of urine to dryness, heating the residue with an oxidizing mixture (a mixture of copper nitrate and potassium chlorate, or just sodium peroxide alone), thereby converting all the sulfur to sulfate. By precipitating with barium chloride, the total sulfate can be determined. If we now subtract the inorganic and ethereal sulfates from the total sulfate, the difference represents the neutral sulfur.

PHOSPHATES. These substances are very largely derived from the foods we eat, though a small quantity has its origin in cellular metabolism. There are two types of phosphates, the alkaline and the earthy phosphates. The alkaline phosphates, which make up some two-thirds of the whole, are salts of sodium and potassium, and the earthy phosphates are combinations of calcium and magnesium. In alkaline urines, the "amorphous" phosphate precipitates are due to the alkaline earth variety. The ammonia formed when urine is exposed for a time combines with the magnesium and the phosphate to form ammonium magnesium phosphate, or "triple phosphate," which is an insoluble and characteristically crystalline product.

From the clinical point of view variations in the phosphate content of urine are not very important; here studies in blood chemistry yield results of greater significance. But it should be mentioned that in bone diseases (rickets, osteomalacia) there is an increased excretion of phosphorus; and sometimes a decreased output has been noted in infectious diseases and in diseases of the kidneys.

The two types of phosphates can be detected by first precipitating the earthy phosphates by the addition of ammonium hydroxide, filtering, adding magnesia mixture (magnesium sulfate + ammonium chloride + ammonium hydroxide) to the filtrate, and warming; the white precipitate so obtained represents the alkaline phosphates.

Several methods are available for the determination of phosphate. One such method depends upon the addition of molybdate solution (sodium molybdate in sulfuric acid) to form phosphomolybdate, which is then reduced to a blue compound by means of stannous chloride; the intensity of the blue color can be estimated colorimetrically.

AMMONIA. Ammonia is excreted as ammonium salts in amounts which tend to adjust the acid-base balance of the body. Unless ammonia (as ammonium ion) were available, acids might use too much of the basic ions of the blood and so endanger blood neutrality. This adjustment comes admirably into play when acids or foods yielding acids in the body are fed; the amount of ammonia excreted is increased. On the other hand, when alkali or foods yielding bases in the body are ingested, the excretion of ammonia is decreased.

The origin of this ammonia was explained in this way: normally amino acids are deaminated and most of the ammonia which results is converted into urea, a small portion escaping as ammonia. The danger of acidosis diverts some of the ammonia which normally would be used to form urea into combination with acid radicals, resulting in increased ammonia and decreased urea output.

The discovery that the kidneys as well as the liver could deaminate amino acids suggested that the source of urinary ammonia could be traced to amino acids in general.

The work of Van Slyke and his associates suggests further and newer possibilities. Using explanted kidneys, they determined the amounts of materials removed from the blood per unit of time. All of the urea in the blood found its way into the urine; there was apparently no conversion into ammonia. The small amount of α-amino acids removed from the blood failed to account for the amount of ammonia in the urine.

However, one amino acid in the form of its amide, glutamine, is apparently one source of urinary ammonia. The amount of glutamine in the blood is enough to account for much of the ammonia in the urine (conversion of glutamine to glutamic acid plus ammonia); the remainder is derived from the amino acids of plasma.

The enzyme glutaminase, present in the kidney, catalyzes the conversion of glutamine to glutamic acid and ammonia. Under suitable conditions, this process is also reversible. The hydrolytic process is prevalent in the kidney, whereas the synthetic process is dominant in other tissues.

When glutamine or various amino acids were administered to a dog suffering from experimentally induced acidosis (with HCl), the amount of ammonia excreted was increased. On the other hand, in a dog suffering from alkalosis—induced with sodium bicarbonate—the amount of glutamine removed from renal blood decreased.

The deamination of amino acids can also occur in the kidney, because three deaminating enzymes are present here: glycine oxidase and D- and L-amino acid oxidases.

One method of estimating the ammonia in the urine is to liberate it from its ammonium salt (by the addition of alkali), and to aerate the ammonia so liberated into an excess of standard acid. The acid left unneutralized is titrated with standard alkali.

ALLANTOIN. This is a partial oxidation product of uric acid. It is present in very small quantities in human urine, but in other mammals (except the anthropoid ape) it is the chief end product of the metabolism of purines. It will be remembered that in the human being, the chief end product of purine metabolism is uric acid.

The efficacy of the rather ancient treatment of healing wounds with maggots is now attributed to the formation of allantoin.

OXALIC ACID $(COOH)_2$. This rather insoluble salt is found in the form of calcium oxalate, and is kept in solution by the presence of the acid phosphate. The source of the acid is believed to reside in the food we eat. Cabbage, grapes, lettuce, tomatoes, etc., contain oxalates.

CITRIC ACID. Though easily oxidized by the body, citric acid is nevertheless found in the urine. The excretion increases in cases of alkalosis (Östberg).

PURINE BASES. Several purine bases, representing substances which have not been oxidized to uric acid, are found. Some of them are derived from the caffeine and theobromine found in coffee and tea.

Abnormal Constituents. Under pathological conditions, a number of substances are found in the urine which, normally, are hardly found at all. Among such substances are glucose, protein, acetone bodies, etc. Brief descriptions of some of these will now be given.

PROTEINS. What is known as the "albumin" of the urine is really a mixture of serum albumin and serum globulin. "Albuminuria" is commonly attributed to damaged kidneys (nephrosis), such as an inflamed organ (nephritis). As much as 20 gm. of protein may be eliminated in twenty-four hours.

Addis and Longcope speak of hemorrhagic, degenerative, and vascular nephritis as several forms of what is commonly called "Bright's disease."

The first, hemorrhagic (glomerular) nephritis, is the most common. It usually results from an infection due to a hemolytic streptococcus, such as in scarlet fever.

The degenerative form, a complication of the hemorrhagic variety, has an obscure origin.

The vascular form (nephrosclerosis) is related to the problem of arterial hypertension. Patients suffering from arterial hypertension sometimes succumb to uremia (the toxic condition of urinary constituents in the blood).

The albumin may be detected by heating the urine, then adding a little dilute acetic acid; a white cloud (or precipitate) is formed. The several methods of estimating the protein depend upon a preliminary precipitation of the protein with trichloracetic acid or some other "alkaloidal" reagent. In one such method (Van Slyke), the protein is precipitated with trichloracetic acid, dissolved in sodium hydroxide, and copper sulfate added. The intensity of the color formed ("biuret") is estimated colorimetrically.

Bence Jones proteinuria, often associated with multiple myeloma (tumor-like hyperplasia of the bone marrow), is due to a peculiar protein in urine which precipitates at a low temperature (50 to 60° C.) and is dissolved—to a greater or less extent—when heated above 80° C., the precipitate forming once again upon cooling.

An analysis of the hydrolytic products of the protein—by paper chromatography—reveals the presence of the common amino acids, except for methionine. Since all the main fractions of plasma protein—from which, presumably, the Bence Jones variety is derived—contain some methionine, the abnormal character of the Bence Jones variety becomes more pronounced. Dent suggests that multiple myelomatosis may be due to an infection by a virus "which stimulates the plasma cells to reproduce rapidly, as in the case of the white cells in fowl leukemia." Possibly the Bence Jones protein is the protein which, when attached to a nucleic acid, is the virus itself.

It may be significant too, in this connection, to recall that virus proteins are usually free of methionine.

GLUCOSE. Appreciable quantities of this sugar in the urine indicate glycosuria. What is known as "renal glycosuria" is due to a lowered renal threshold, which means that although sugar appears in the urine, there is no increase of sugar in the blood. An increase of sugar in the blood (hyperglycemia), with a corresponding elimination of sugar in the urine, is found in diabetes. In most instances, glycosuria is indicative of diabetes. In this condition, the sugar will vary from 3 to 5 per cent, although sometimes it is even higher.

The Benedict test for glucose has already been discussed (Chap. 2). This is also the basis for a quantitative estimation.

ACETONE BODIES. These have been discussed in connection with fat metabolism. While these substances are present in normal urine in traces, in pathological conditions they may increase from 0.02 to 6 gm., of which β-hydroxybutyric acid often forms a large percentage. This last substance, together with acetoacetic acid, is eliminated as a salt, and so depletes the alkali reserve of the body, giving rise to an acidosis. To meet the crisis, more ammonia is formed in the kidney.

The qualitative tests for acetone bodies are, as a rule, tests for acetone, and as acetoacetic acid very easily decomposes into acetone, the tests also include this acid. One such test is based on the transformation of acetone into iodoform; the urine is heated with sodium hydroxide and iodine, and a precipitate of iodoform is formed.

If the urine is fresh, a test for acetoacetic acid may be shown by obtaining a reddish-colored solution with ferric chloride. The test for β-hydroxy-butyric acid is seldom carried out, since it is somewhat involved, necessitating, first, the removal of the other two acetone bodies.

One method of determining these substances quantitatively is to convert the two acids to acetone and precipitate the latter as a basic mercuric sulfate (Van Slyke). Given a mixture containing acetone, acetoacetic acid, and β-hydroxybutyric acid, the mere heating of such a mixture will convert acetoacetic acid into acetone; and if, in addition to the heating, an oxidizing agent is present (such as dichromate), β-hydroxybutyric acid is also converted to acetone. This procedure, then, gives "total acetone bodies." If we wish to determine acetone and acetoacetic acid alone, the dichromate is omitted. On the other hand, by making use of the relative volatility of acetone and acetoacetic acid—they may be removed by heating the acidified urine—β-hydroxybutyric acid itself may be determined.

BILE. An obstruction in the bile duct, preventing the normal outflow of bile and forcing it back into the general circulation, gives rise to jaundice, or icterus. The yellowness of the skin is due to the bile pigments, which also appear in the urine. The pigments may be detected by the play of colors obtained on the addition of concentrated nitric acid (Gmelin), the various colored products representing stages of oxidation of bilirubin.

Another test is based upon the green color obtained when methylene blue is added to urine containing bile. The bilirubin (of the bile) and the methylene blue react to form a green compound.

The pigment related, chemically, to bilirubin and normally found in urine is urobilin.

BLOOD. Blood in the urine (hematuria) may result from a lesion in the kidney or the urinary tract. This is more common than "hemoglobinuria," in which hemoglobin without the red corpuscles is recognized. Where the destruction of red blood cells is very great (as in bad burns), the liver cannot change all of the hemoglobin into bile pigments, and some of the blood pigment appears in the urine. The tests for hemoglobin have already been given (Chap. 9).

PORPHYRINS. These iron-free pyrrole substances, under normal conditions, build hemoglobin and various oxidizing enzymes (cytochromes, for example). In the plant world, together with magnesium, they form the building blocks for chlorophyll. There are several varieties of these porphyrins. Under normal conditions, the daily output of one of them—called coproporphyrin—is from 14 to 99 micrograms in the urine and from 100 to 200 micrograms in the feces.

PORPHYRIA. This metabolic disturbance, involving the excretion of abnormal amounts of porphyrins, may occur in cirrhosis, obstructive jaundice, etc.

Hans Fischer, who has done much of the chemical work on these substances, was able to isolate two of these porphyrins, known as copro- and uroporphyrin, from cases of congenital porphyria, and he showed that these two differed in chemical structure from those found in the urine and feces of normal subjects.

WATER

Of all compounds in the body, water is the most abundant. It constitutes some 70 per cent of the total weight of the body. A loss of 10 per cent of the water content (in man) results in illness, and a loss of 20 per cent may cause death. We find water in cellular and vascular spaces, and small portions are also deposited in conjunction with protein and carbohydrate. The storage of fat, however, is accompanied by little water.

Water is present in every tissue, but the amounts vary considerably.

The following data, collected by Rowntree, give some figures (in percentages): saliva, 99.5; cerebrospinal fluid, 99; vitreous humor, 98.5; embryonic brain, 91; milk, 88; brain (gray matter), 86; kidney, 83; thyroid, 82; thymus, 81; adrenals, 80; blood, 79; pancreas, 78; muscle, 75; spleen, 76; liver, 70; skin, 72; brain (white matter), 68 to 70; tendon, 68; cartilage, 67; elastic tissue, 50; bones, 50; fat, 20; dentin, 10.

Function.   A very large percentage of the water is of the utmost importance physiologically—as solvent, as a carrier in transporting foods to tissues, and wastes from tissues, and as a regulator of body temperature.

Water helps to maintain the electrolyte balance of the body. A state of health is possible only so long as the osmotic pressure exerted by solutes remains in equilibrium.

Within the body we have intracellular and extracellular compartments. The latter may be further divided into intravascular and interstitial compartments. The fluid representing the intravascular part circulates through blood vessels and lymphatics; the interstitial fluid surrounds the cells representing the tissues of the body.

Of the total content of body water (some 70 per cent of the body weight), the extracellular fluid represents 20 per cent of the body weight. Of this amount, 25 per cent represents plasma, and the rest is interstitial fluid.

Heat is gained by the oxidation of foodstuffs in the body. Heat is lost through the following channels (in percentages): urine and feces, 1.8; warming of expired air, 3.5; vaporization from lungs, 7.2; evaporation from skin, 14.2; radiation and conduction from skin, 73.0.

Amount Needed.   The needs of the body for water are met in two ways: by direct intake, and by the oxidation of the foodstuffs in the body. By "direct intake" we mean water as such and water present in foods. Roughly speaking, on a diet equivalent to 3000 calories, probably 2000 ml. of water is derived from the water in foods and from the products of the oxidation of foodstuffs in the body. Since the requirement may be some 3000 ml. per day, another liter of water must be supplied.

The amount of water liberated as a result of the oxidation of foodstuffs is approximately 10 to 14 gm. per 100 Calories. For example, 100 gm. of fat, when oxidized, produces 107 ml. of water. The 100 gm. of fat is equivalent to 930 Calories, which means that fat equivalent to 100 Calories will produce 11.5 ml. of water. Similarly, carbohydrate and protein equivalent to 100 Calories each will produce 13.5 and 10.1 ml. of water, respectively.

Regulation.   Since the amount of water in the body tends to vary but little, the regulation of the water balance in the body is a very important matter. Not only is water taken into the system in the manner already referred to, but it also leaves the body through several channels—urine, sweat, expired air, feces, and, in much smaller quantities, tears.

Reference has already been made to the reabsorption of water and dissolved compounds. This phase of water reabsorption is regulated by a hormone of the posterior lobe of the pituitary, the antidiuretic hormone (p. 449). This hormone (ADH) is believed to act directly on the distal tubular cells, increasing the rate of water reabsorption. When the hypophyseal stalk is cut or the neurohypophysis removed, the hormone is no longer secreted and the animal develops polyuria, an excessive excretion of urine (diabetes insipidus). A similar condition is observed in man when the posterior pituitary fails to secrete ADH.

Diuresis, the excretion of excessive amounts of water, occurs after the ingestion of large quantities of water or of concentrated salt solutions. A transitory, though marked, diuresis is caused by drugs such as caffeine, mercurial compounds, and phloridzin. The last substance also produces a glycosuria and probably acts largely on the proximal tubular cells.

The intake and output of water is summarized in the following:

Intake:		Output	
Drink	1200 ml.	Urine	1400 ml.
Water in food	1000 ml.	Stool	200 ml.
Water of oxidation	300 ml.	Insensible water *	900 ml.
Totals	2500 ml.		2500 ml.

* Vaporized through skin and lungs.

The water loss through the lungs is quite constant, but the loss through the sweat glands is associated with their function as regulators of body heat.

Dehydration.   This term is applied to the loss of fluid from the body. When water is lost, electrolytes (Na,K, etc.) are also lost. If insufficient water is consumed, some electrolyte must be eliminated so as to maintain the ionic concentrations of the body fluids. From this it also follows that the removal or loss of electrolyte requires the removal of some water.

The removal of sweat and the loss of gastrointestinal secretions removes not only water but electrolyte. "Dehydration," writes Gamble, "is an incomplete term since it does not indicate the accompanying loss of electrolyte." The treatment of "dehydration," then, means not only replacing the water lost but also the electrolyte lost.

As showing fine internal adjustments, some 10 per cent of the body's weight may be lost owing to depriving the individual of water without any appreciable reduction in blood volume.

Shock.   Traumatic shock, usually produced by burns, wounds or severe hemorrhage, causes disturbances in body fluids (see under Blood, p. 162).

REFERENCES

For practical handbooks dealing with the analysis of urine, see *Todd, Sanford, and Wells:* Clinical Diagnosis by Laboratory Methods, 1953, Chap. 3; *Simmons:* Laboratory Methods of the U. S. Army, 1935, p. 1; *Hawk, Oser, and Summerson:* Practical Physiological Chemistry, 1947, Chaps. 28–32.

Theories dealing with the secretion of urine are reviewed by *Cantarow and Trumper:* Clinical Biochemistry, 1949, p. 336; *Richards:* Harvey Lectures, Ser. 30, 1934–1935, p. 93; Bull. N. Y. Acad. Med., Jan., 1938; Proc. R. S. (London), Series B, *126:* 398, 1938; *Smith:* Scientific American, Jan., 1953, p. 40; What's New (Abbott Labs.), March, 1949; J. Am. Med. Assoc., *141:* 994, 1949; *Miller and Hayman* in *Duncan's* Diseases of Metabolism, 1952, p. 1035.

Renin. Arch. Biochem., *42:* 368, 1953.

Excretion of water. Smith: Bull. N. Y. Acad. Med., April, 1947, p. 127; *Gamble:*

Extracellular Fluid (Harvard Medical School, 1950); *Peters:* Physiol. Rev., *24:* 491, 1944; *Darrow:* Bull. N. Y. Acad. Med., March, 1948, 147 (disturbances in electrolyte metabolism); *Moore:* Science. *104:* 157, 1946 (determination of total body water with isotopes); *Smith:* Bull. N. Y. Acad. Med., April, 1947, p. 177; *Darrow and Pratt:* J. Am. Med. Assoc., *143:* 365, 1950 (fluid therapy); *Pinson:* Physiol. Rev., *32:* 123, 1952; *Schroeder:* J. Am. Med. Assoc., *147:* 1109, 1951 (use of diuretic reagents); *Steele:* Bull. N. Y. Acad. Med., Nov., 1951, p. 679 (body water in man); *Robinson:* Biol. Rev. *28:* 158, 1953 (water transport in living systems).

Acidity of urine. Pitts: Federation Proceedings, *7:* 418, 1948 (review); *Menaker:* Am. J. Physiol., *154:* 174, 1948.

Uric acid and gout. J. Am. Med. Assoc., *139:* 1268, 1949 (review).

Amino acids in urine. Nutr. Rev., *6:* 6, 1948; *Wright:* Trans. N. Y. Acad. Sciences, *10:* 271, 1948; Nutr. Rev., *7:* 68, 115, 1949; *Westall:* Biochem. J., *52:* 638, 1952; *Stein:* J. Biol. Chem., *201:* 45, 1953.

Sulfate. Dziewiatkowski: J. Biol. Chem., *178:* 389, 1949; *Berenbohm and Young:* Biochem., J., *49:* 165, 1951.

Ammonia. Mylon and Heller: Am. J. Physiol., *154:* 542, 1948 (renal glutaminase); *Van Slyke, Phillips, Hamilton,*

Archibald, Futcher, and Hiller: J. Biol. Chem., *150:* 481, 1943; J. Am. Med. Assoc., *124:* 577, 1944; *Davies and Yudkin:* Biochem. J., *52:* 407, 1952 (source of NH_3); *Kamin and Handler:* J. Biol. Chem., *193:* 873, 1951 (source of NH_3); *Ferguson:* J. Physiol., *112:* 420, 1951.

Protein. Seegal and Wertheim: Bull. N. Y. Acad. Med., Oct., 1949, p. 605 (nephritis); Nutr. Rev., *8:* 17, 1950 (Bence-Jones protein); *Bayrd and Heck:* J. Am. Med. Assoc., *133:* 147, 1947 (multiple myeloma).

Bile. Reinhold and Fowler: J. Biol. Chem., *167:* 401, 1947 (reaction of bile and methylene blue); *Watson:* Harvey Lectures (1948–49), p. 41 (urobilin).

Blood. Wolbarst: Merck Report, Oct., 1947, p. 19 (blood in urine).

Porphyrins. Watson and Larson: Physiol. Rev., *27:* 478, 1947 (review); *Cantarow and Trumper:* Clinical Biochemistry, 1949, p. 421; *Rimington and Miles:* Biochem. J., *50:* 202, 1951 (porphyria); *Gray and Neuberger:* Ibid., *47:* 81, 1950; *Gray, Neuberger, and Sneath:* Ibid., *47:* 87, 1950 (porphyria); *McSwiney, Nicholas, and Prunty:* Ibid., *46:* 147, 1950 (porphyria); *Gibson and Harrison:* Ibid., *46:* 154, 1950 (porphyria).

Creatinuria. Wilder and Morgulis: Arch. Biochem., *42:* 69, 1953.

Chapter 23   *Hormones*

Most of the glands of the body have ducts. The secretions which these glands manufacture are poured out through such ducts. Typical examples are the salivary and gastric glands. Another group of glands (the endocrine organs, Fig. 99) discharge their secretions directly into the blood (ductless glands); these secretions usually contain hormones. *Hormones* are chemical substances which are carried by the blood to various organs of the body to

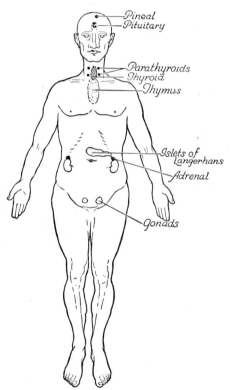

Fig. 99. The location of some of the glands of internal secretion. (Williams.)

influence the activities of such organs. They are the "chemical messengers" of the body. We have reasons for believing that the hormones act by influencing enzyme systems.

Some of the hormones are proteins (insulin, for example), others are related to the steroids (sex and adrenal hormones), and still others are relatively simple compounds (epinephrine and thyroxine).

We shall discuss these hormones in connection with the glands which manufacture them.

436

THE THYROID

(See also under Iodine, p. 308.) The thyroid gland is made up of two lobes on both sides of the trachea and the larynx. It weighs, on an average, about 25 gm. in the adult and contains about 10 mg. iodine—about one-fifth of the total in the body. Through its hormone it regulates, among other things, the rate of metabolism within the body. It also has other profound effects, as is seen in cases of cretinism, where we have individuals who are mentally and physically retarded, and who suffer from a deficiency of the hormone (Fig. 100). Thyroxine, the hormone used, will

Fig. 100. Cretinism. A group of seven cretins at Urnatsch, Switzerland, showing their appearance and stunted growth compared to the normal individual in the center background. (Photographed by and reproduced through the courtesy of Professor J. F. McClendon. Grollman: Essentials of Endocrinology. J. B. Lippincott Co.)

cause remarkable cures. An enlargement of the gland, known as a *goiter*, may be of two kinds: "endemic goiter," due to insufficient iodine; or one due to an abnormally high activity of the thyroid gland, as in exophthalmic goiter and Graves' disease. The endemic goiter lends itself to treatment with iodine. Both hypo- and hyperactivities of the thyroid affect the basal metabolism.

The treatment of endemic goiter—endemic because it occurs in places where the soil or water is deficient in iodine—with sodium iodide has been markedly successful. Marine and Kimball, pioneers in this field, discovered in the Akron-Cleveland district that about 45 per cent of the school girls from the fifth to twelfth grades and about 18 per cent of the boys showed goiter symptoms in various degrees. Treatment which involved the use of 2 gm. of sodium iodide, given in doses of 0.2 gm., and distributed over two weeks, caused complete cures. Iodized salt—sodium chloride containing 0.01 per cent of potassium iodide—is used quite extensively.

As early as 1895, Baumann made the discovery that the thyroid contains iodine—an element which until then was not suspected as one of the elements of the body. The active substance present in the thyroid gland is thyroxine, which was first isolated by Kendall and later by Harington. We owe to Harington its correct formula, as well as its synthesis.

$$HO\text{—}\underset{I}{\overset{I}{\bigcirc}}\text{—}O\text{—}\underset{I}{\overset{I}{\bigcirc}}\text{—}CH_2.CH.COOH$$
$$\underset{NH_2}{|}$$

Thyroxine

β-[3,5-diiodo-4-(3′,5′-diiodo-4′-hydroxy-phenoxy)-phenyl]-α-amino-propionic acid

Iodine in the Body.   Iodine circulates in the body in two forms: as iodide and as thyroid hormone. The inorganic iodide in plasma is largely trapped and utilized by the thyroid gland to build up the hormone. The concentration of iodide in the thyroid gland is several hundred times that in circulating blood. Iodide is evenly distributed throughout the body fluids (including the brain); the hormonal iodine is associated with the plasma proteins.

Some 90 per cent of the iodine in the thyroid is in organic combination as thyroxine and diiodotyrosine. These two organic compounds are bound to protein and can be freed (and isolated) by first hydrolyzing the tissue.

Using the radioisotope of iodine, I^{131}, Chaikoff showed that fifteen minutes after the injection, some 95 per cent of the radioactivity present in the thyroid could be precipitated with trichloracetic acid, which meant that 95 per cent of the substance containing this iodine was in organic combination. At this stage, some 80 per cent of the activity was in the diiodotyrosine fraction, and 10 to 15 per cent in the thyroxine fraction.

The amount of iodine in the blood may prove of diagnostic value. Normally, the total iodine in blood may vary from 3 to 20 micrograms per 100 ml. of blood. This blood iodine is increased in exophthalmic goiter and also in several diseases not caused by thyroid dysfunction. In hypothyroidism, the iodine in the blood may show normal values, but the acetone-insoluble fraction (containing the circulating hormone) is about one-half the normal amount.

The urinary excretion of iodine may vary as much as 72 to 340 micrograms per day in nongoitrogenous regions, and from 27 to 64 micrograms in goitrogenous regions. In hypothyroidism (and in several diseases not caused by thyroid dysfunction) there is a tendency to increase the amount of iodine lost in the urine.

Thyroxine.   ORIGIN.   Thyroxine is not found as such in the thyroid gland but in the form of a protein, thyroglobulin. Harington is of the opinion that the gland manufactures this protein by first forming 3,5-

$$HO\text{—}\underset{I}{\overset{I}{\bigcirc}}\text{—}CH_2.CH.COOH$$
$$\underset{NH_2}{|}$$

3,5-Diiodotyrosine

diiodotyrosine from iodine and tyrosine, which is then converted into thyroxine by the union of two molecules:

$$\text{HO}\langle\bigcirc\rangle\text{CH}_2.\text{CH}.\text{COOH} + \text{H}\text{O}\langle\bigcirc\rangle\text{CH}_2.\text{CH}.\text{COOH}$$

(with I substituents on the rings and NH₂ on the side chains)

The thyroxine so formed, together with unchanged diiodotyrosine and other amino acids, finally forms a molecule of thyroglobulin.

That thyroxine is formed from diiodotyrosine has been made probable by the actual conversion of the latter into the former in vitro. Tyrosine was first converted into the diiodo salt, the latter dissolved in sodium hydroxide and maintained at a pH of 8.8 and a temperature of 70° C. for fourteen days. Thyroxine was precipitated with acid, purified, and separated as the potassium salt.

Thyroid slices incubated for two hours in Ringer's solution, to which radioactive iodide (I^{131}) had been added, resulted in the formation of an organically bound compound of which 85 per cent contained I^{131}. Some 75 per cent of this was diiodotyrosine and 10 per cent was thyroxine.

The biosynthesis of thyroxine probably involves these steps: fixation of the inorganic iodine by the gland; incorporation of iodine by tyrosine to form diiodotyrosine; and the conversion of the latter to thyroxine.

THYROXINE FROM IODINATED PROTEINS. If casein (or some other protein) is "iodized"—if, in other words, it is treated in an alkaline solution with iodine—the product shows definite thyroid activity. When this iodized protein is hydrolyzed and fractionated, diiodotyrosine and thyroxine can be separated (Fig. 101).

As might be anticipated, casein is not the only protein which, by iodination and subsequent treatment, yields thyroxine. Soybean protein serves equally well. Apparently the value of the protein for this purpose lies in its content of tyrosine.

Thyroxine and diiodotyrosine are the only two compounds of iodine known to exist in the thyroid. About 30 per cent is in the form of the hormone and about 70 per cent as the iodinated tyrosine.

(Highly purified thyroglobulin, when analyzed, yields: cystine, 4.30 per cent; methionine, 1.31 per cent; tryptophan, 1.88 per cent; tyrosine, 3.00 per cent; diiodotyrosine, 0.67 per cent; thyroxine, 0.28 per cent; and glucosamine, 2.20 per cent.)

One of the hormones of the anterior pituitary, the *thyrotropic hormone* (TSH) (p. 447), influences the activity of the thyroid gland. An injection of the thyrotropic hormone into a normal animal gives rise to hypertrophy and hyperactivity of the thyroid.

THERAPEUTIC USE. In cases of hypothyroidism, as in cretinism and myxedema, thyroxine or desiccated thyroid can be administered. These materials can be given orally, though, of the two, the thyroid is the more easily absorbed and utilized. With the probable exception of one or two of the sex hormones, thyroxine is the only hormone which is so readily active when given orally, for insulin and other hormones have to be given parenterally.

Where there is hyperfunction of the thyroid, an increased elimination (in the urine) of iodine results. Sometimes the increase is from three to four times the normal amount. Estimations of iodine in blood and in urine may therefore be of value. The treatment is often one of surgery. Some four-fifths of the gland is removed, with the idea of lessening the production of thyroxine.

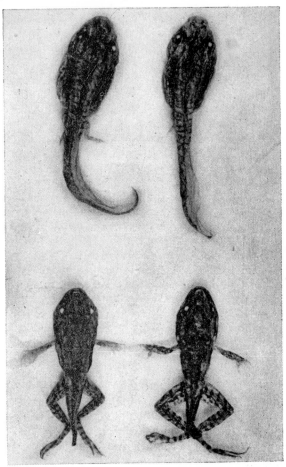

Fig. 101. The response of large frog tadpoles (60 mm. size) to the injection of artificial thyroproteins.
    The tadpoles at the top are normal controls. The two at the bottom illustrate the striking degree of metamorphosis occurring within four days after the injection of 0.1 mg. of iodinated casein. (From Reineke and Turner: Agr. Exp. Sta. Mo., Res. Bull. *355*.)

Radioactive iodine is also used. "As the radioactive atoms disintegrate within the thyroid, they emit beta and gamma rays, producing the same kind of tissue reaction as x-rays, but the irradiation is largely confined to the gland itself" (Werner, Quimby, and Schmidt). The normal uptake is 20 to 30 per cent of the administered tracer dose. Above 40 per cent is regarded as hyperthyroid; below 20 per cent, as hypothyroid.

ANTITHYROID COMPOUNDS.   Thiouracil and several other compounds possess the property of inhibiting the production of thyroxine. This property has led to the use of such compounds in hyperthyroidism.

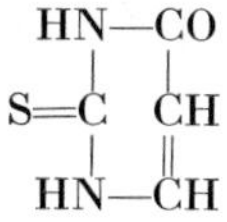

$$
\begin{array}{c}
\text{HN——CO} \\
| \quad\quad | \\
\text{S}\!=\!\text{C} \quad \text{CH} \\
| \quad\quad || \\
\text{HN——CH}
\end{array}
$$

Thiouracil

Thiouracil itself is relatively toxic; less so are propylthiouracil, thiourea, and methylthiouracil. Among these, propylthiouracil has been used most

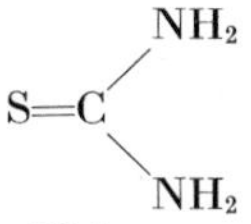

$$
\text{S}\!=\!\text{C}\begin{array}{c} {}^{NH_2} \\ {}_{NH_2} \end{array}
$$

Thiourea

extensively. It is three times more active than thiouracil and much less toxic.

These substances and their uses have an interesting history. In the attempt to prevent the synthesis of some vitamins by intestinal flora, several investigators used sulfaguanidine. After several weeks a hypertrophy of the thyroid gland was noticed. The glands were several times larger than those of animals which had not received sulfaguanidine. There was at the same time a lowering of the basal metabolism. Administering iodine had no effect, but thyroxine reversed the process: the gland approached normality again and the basal metabolic rate was restored. Many compounds were now tried in the attempt to duplicate the action of sulfaguanidine. Thiourea and thiouracil were picked as the most promising at the time.

It is possible that the antithyroid action of a compound is related to its reducing power and preferential reactivity with iodine, thereby inhibiting the formation of diiodotyrosine and thence thyroxine (Pitt-Rivers).

ANALOGUES OF THYROXINE.   With the view of relating structure to physiological action, several compounds closely related chemically to thyroxine have been prepared, and the biological action of such compounds has been tested. The diiodo compound, $3^1,5^1$-diiodothyronine (I) (thyronine is the

I

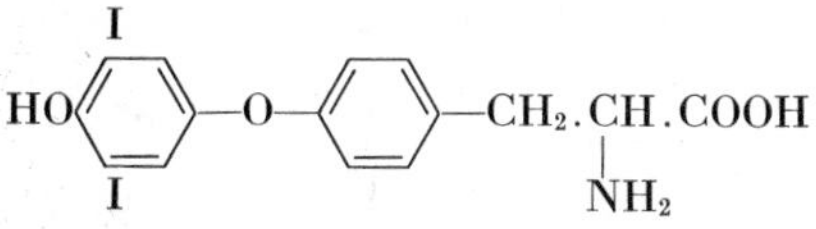

HO—⟨ ⟩—O—⟨ ⟩—CH$_2$.CH.COOH with I substituents and NH$_2$

name given to thyroxine without its iodine atoms) is but one-fourth as active as thyroxine. 3:5:3′-triiodothyronine is said to be more active than thyroxine itself.

Of two isomers of thyroxine, the one with the OH group in the meta position (II) was inactive, and the other with the OH group in the ortho position (III) showed slight activity.

II

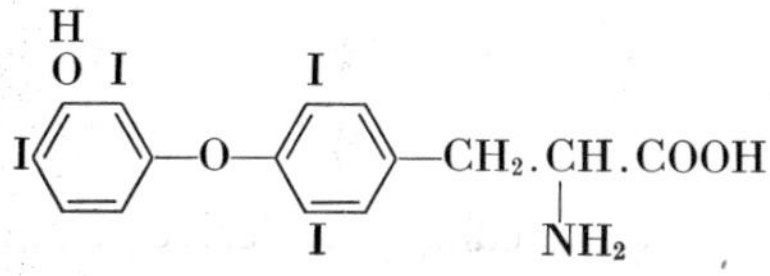

I—⟨ ⟩—O—⟨ ⟩—CH$_2$.CH.COOH with OH, I substituents and NH$_2$

III

$$O_2N \text{ (structure III)} \quad CH_2CH.COOH \quad NH_2$$

Niemann suggests the necessity of a potential quinoid structure for the compound to show physiological activity (IV):

IV

$$O= \text{ (structure IV)} =O- \quad CH_2CH.COOH. \quad NH_2$$

As in the case of vitamins, some attempts have been made to show that certain structural analogues of hormones exhibit physiological antagonism. In one such experiment, Woolley synthesized several ethers of N-acetyl-diiodotyrosine. As a test method, he made use of the fact that thyroxine is a lethal agent for tadpoles (though minute quantities of the hormone accelerate metamorphosis). Relatively large amounts of the hormone cause rapid metamorphosis and ultimate death. The derivatives of diiodotyrosine were able to protect tadpoles against the lethal action of thyroxine.

THE PARATHYROIDS

Attached to the thyroid are four small organs, the parathyroids, which for a long time were confused with the thyroid itself. The combined weight of the glands varies from 0.05 to 0.3 gm.

The removal of the parathyroids gives rise to two types of change: neuromuscular and chemical. There develop muscular twitchings (tetany) leading to convulsions. The calcium in the plasma steadily decreases. The tetany can be relieved by the administration of a soluble calcium salt.

Tetany develops when the calcium in plasma falls from 10 mg. per 100 ml. (normal) to 7 mg. per 100 ml.; convulsions occur when the calcium is further decreased to 3.5 to 5 mg. per 100 ml. plasma.

As the calcium declines in the blood there is a decrease in the urine; however, during this period the phosphorus in plasma increases from a normal of 5 mg. per 100 ml. to 9 mg. per 100 ml., and even higher.

Collip and Hanson prepared an extract, obtained by the acid hydrolysis of the gland, which when injected into a parathyroidectomized animal restored its health and, at the same time, raised the percentage of calcium in the blood. It was shown subsequently that the injection of a potent extract into a normal dog doubled the amount of blood calcium normally present (the normal amount being about 10 mg. per 100 ml.). The plasma calcium shows the first signs of an increase in about four hours, and then reaches a maximum in from twelve to eighteen hours; from then on a decrease sets in until the normal level is reached in from twenty to twenty-four hours.

The increase in plasma calcium is followed by an increased urinary excretion of calcium and inorganic phosphate and a decrease in blood phosphate.

It is believed that this extra calcium is derived from the bones by a withdrawal of the element. Under such conditions of hypercalcemia, the kidney undergoes pathological changes and abnormal deposits of calcium salts accumulate in soft tissues.

Parathyroid preparations have been used successfully in the treatment of tetania parathyreopriva (tetany caused by removal of parathyroids) and of infantile tetany. Occasionally, in operations on the thyroid gland, tetany may develop due to removal of or injury to the parathyroid glands or their blood supply.

The hormone has not, as yet, been prepared in a pure condition, but the evidence points to its being a protein. The most potent preparations show an ultraviolet absorption spectrum almost identical with that of many simple proteins. Further, the action of pepsin or trypsin completely inactivates the material.

THE PITUITARY (HYPOPHYSIS)

This gland, no larger than the end of the little finger, situated at the base of the skull, seems to have a multiplicity of functions. There are three distinct portions to this gland, the anterior, the pars intermedia, and the posterior; and while all three may be important enough, it is the anterior portion which seems to be actually essential to life.

Clinically, types of gigantism and acromegaly (examples of hyperpituitarism) and dwarfism (a possible example of hypopituitarism) have been known for some time. But more recently, extracts have been obtained which show a multiplicity of actions. Since the active substances show the properties of proteins, the difficulties of separating them are great.

Table 68   SOME CHARACTERISTICS OF ANTERIOR PITUITARY HORMONES

Hormones	Molecular Weight	Isoelectric Point	Mannose	Hexoseamine
			(per cent)	(per cent)
ICSH (sheep)	40,000	4.6	4.5	5.8
Prolactin (sheep)	26,500	5.7	0.0	0.0
Thyrotropic hormone	10,000	. .	3.5	2.5
ACTH (sheep)	20,000	4.7	0.0	0.0
Growth hormone (ox)	44,250	6.9	0.0	0.0

Anterior Pituitary.   We shall first take up the question of the anterior pituitary, which is responsible for the following hormones:

(a) Growth hormone.
(b) Gonadotropic (gonadotrophic) hormones:
   1. Interstitial cell–stimulating hormone (ICSH).
   2. Follicle-stimulating hormone (FSH).
(c) Lactogenic hormone (prolactin).
(d) Thyrotropic (thyrotrophic) hormone (TSH).
(e) Adrenocorticotropic (adrenocorticotrophic) hormone (ACTH).

After hypophysectomy the thyroids, the adrenal cortex, and the gonads are much affected and their functional activity is greatly lessened. Lactation ceases. In general, atrophy of many of the endocrine glands and a deficient output of glandular secretions are evident.

While survival for a time is possible without the anterior lobe of the hypophysis, a normal life span is probably not possible.

In rats, as little as 10 per cent of the original gland will prevent the various deficiencies.

A number of the hormones have been highly purified and some even crystallized. Table 68 gives a summary of their properties.

GROWTH HORMONE. Hypophysectomy in young animals gives rise to dwarfism and sexual infantilism (Fig. 102). Cretinic dwarfs may also be

Fig. 102. Effects of pituitary removal on body growth in animals. The two small pups were operated on when five days old and grew little thereafter though their littermate is shown to have made good growth when all were photographed four months later (Kapran). (Riddle: Scientific Monthly, *47*: 97.)

the result of a depression of the pituitary function (Fig. 103). Evans succeeded in preparing active material which when injected into rats produced definite gigantism (Fig. 104).

Such growth appears to resemble normal growth and is not the result, for example, of an accumulation of water and fat. The hormone influences, in the main, skeletal growth by stimulating the epiphyseal cartilages, but it also affects the soft tissues, etc. It promotes the synthesis of tissue protein from the circulating amino acids.

A case of acromegaly is shown in Fig. 105.

The extracts originally used by Evans were essentially dilute aqueous alkaline solutions which, in addition to containing the active growth hormone, retained varying quantities of a number of other hormones present in the anterior portion of the pituitary; but such extracts have been very much purified since then. In fact, Evans, Li, and Simpson obtained the hormone as a chemically pure protein. Assays were made on female rats hypophysectomized when twenty-seven days old. Injections were begun fourteen days later, once daily for ten days. They found that 0.010 mg. of the purified product gave an increase of 10 gm. in body weight.

As evidence of the purity of the product, the injection of as much as 5 gm. of the product failed to show the presence of any of the other hormones in the anterior portion of the pituitary (such as those dealing with lactogenic, thyrotropic, adrenotropic and follicle-stimulating properties).

The activity of the hormone is destroyed by peptic or tryptic digestion. It is unstable at the temperature of boiling water and is more stable in alkaline than in acid solutions. Iodination of the hormone destroys its biological activity, which is an indication that tyrosine groups are essential.

Fig. 103. Sebastian de Morra. A painting by Velasquez. This is one of the most famous of the numerous paintings of dwarfs and endocrine types by Velasquez.

It should be pointed out that several investigators object to this conception of a "growth hormone," for, as Smith points out, "growth is such a complex process, that it is difficult to conceive of its being due to a single hormone." However, that there is some "principle" or hormone in the hypophysis which is essential for general body growth seems well established.

GONADOTROPIC (GONAD-STIMULATING) HORMONES. P. E. Smith and Aschheim and Zondek discovered that when a piece of anterior pituitary tissue is implanted under the skin of an immature rat, the ovaries develop within a few days. Zondek later postulated that the growth of the ovarian follicles is due to a "follicle-stimulating hormone" ("prolan A"), and the development of lutein tissue, to a luteinizing hormone.

In 1931 Hisaw and Leonard separated the pituitary gonadotropic fractions into two components: ICSH (interstitial cell–stimulating hormone) and FSH (follicle-stimulating hormone). ICSH increases the ovarian weight

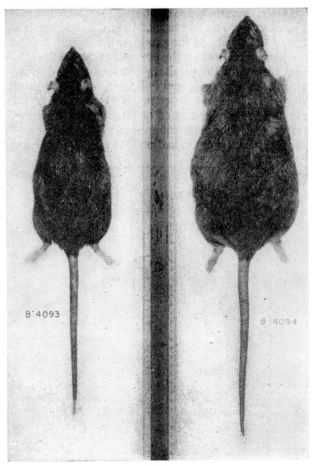

Fig. 104. Typical photograph of a normal plateau female rat receiving growth hormone for 432 days as compared with the control. B 4093, Control. B 4094, Injected. (Li and Evans: Vitamins and Hormones, 5: 197.)

Fig. 105. A case of acromegaly. A, The patient at age twenty-four, before the onset of the malady; B, at age twenty-nine, at the time of onset; C, at age thirty-seven; and D, at age forty-two, when outspoken acromegalic changes are evident. (Cushing: The Pituitary Body and Its Disorders. J. B. Lippincott Co.)

of the normal immature female rat, stimulates the repair of ovarian interstitial tissues of hypophysectomized rats, increases the weight of the seminal vesicles of the normal immature male rat and increases the weight of the ventral lobe of the prostate in hypophysectomized male rats.

ICSH has been prepared in a pure state and is a protein which remains homogeneous when tested electrophoretically, by the ultracentrifuge and by solubility tests. The hormone (in sheep) has a molecular weight of 40,000 and contains 4.5 per cent of mannose and 5.8 per cent of hexoseamine.

FSH stimulates follicular growth, thereby increasing ovarian weight, and causes the enlargement of ovarian follicles in the hypophysectomized rat. It also behaves as a single protein in experiments involving electrophoresis, diffusion and ultracentrifugation. It contains 1.2 per cent hexose and 1.51 per cent hexoseamine.

Gonadotropins other than those obtained from the pituitary are known. These substances may be classified as follows: (1) Human chorionic * gonadotropin (present in blood, urine, and tissues of pregnant women); (2) human nonchorionic gonadotropin (present in blood and urine of ovariectomized and post-menopausal women); and (3) equine gonadotropin (present in blood and placental tissue of the pregnant mare). There is evidence which indicates that extracts of human placenta, pregnancy blood, and pregnancy urine contain gonadotropic substances which are not the same as those in the pituitary. However, pregnant mare's serum contains a substance more comparable to the gonadotropins in the pituitary and different from human placental gonadotropic hormones.

Zondek and Aschheim originally discovered a gonadotropic hormone in the urine of pregnancy, which led them to their now well established pregnancy test. The principle involved in the pregnancy test is to inject immature mice with the suspected urine, kill the animals on the fourth day, and examine the ovaries for hemorrhagic spots and yellowish protrusions (developed corpora lutea).

During pregnancy, we find a relative abundance of an estrogenic (female) hormone and the gonadotropic hormone in the urine. The latter appears in recognizable quantity by the first missed period (the Aschheim-Zondek test), and reaches its maximum between the second and third months of pregnancy; the former appears somewhat later, but lasts until birth, and then decreases very rapidly.

LACTOGENIC HORMONE. Riddle was among the first to prepare an extract of the pituitary which stimulates the enlargement and functioning (formation of "crop milk") of the crop glands in pigeons (Fig. 106). This hormone, which initiates lactation, is known as *prolactin*.

It is believed that a female hormone produced by the placenta during pregnancy stimulates the growth of the mammary gland and at the same time inhibits the secretion of prolactin. At parturition, the inhibiting influence of the placenta is removed, the prolactin is released, and the secretion of milk is fostered.

Crystalline products have been obtained by Evans, White, and Riddle.

THYROTROPIC HORMONE [also called *thyroid-stimulating hormone* (TSH)].

* Pertaining to the more external of the two fetal membranes.

An appropriate extract of the pituitary injected into normal animals results in the enlargement and hyperplasia of the thyroid. There is an increase in the metabolism and in the heart rate and the development of an exophthalmos resembling Graves' disease. Smith was among the first to show that the extirpation of the pituitary results in the atrophy of the thyroid. This condition can be improved by implanting fresh pituitary into a hypophysectomized animal.

Active extracts injected into rabbits or guinea-pigs—rats are more immune—results in symptoms of exophthalmic goiter: the thyroid is increased

Pigeon Crop Gland   Mammary of Rabbit

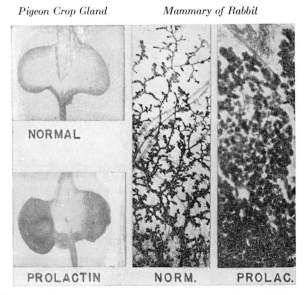

Fig. 106. Showing the action of prolactin on crop sacs and on mammary gland. When unstimulated by prolactin, the walls of the pigeon's crop are very thin and transparent. But either the release of prolactin by the bird's own pituitary or injection of prolactin from a hen, a calf, or a whale causes the lateral pouches of the crop wall (and these parts only) to thicken greatly and produce "pigeon milk." After the cells and ducts of rabbit mammary glands have developed properly, from two to four injections of prolactin will cause them to form and store milk. Other pituitary hormones do not stimulate milk secretion. (Riddle: Scientific Monthly, *47:* 97.)

in size, the iodine is decreased, there is a loss of colloid and the cells are enlarged, or hypertrophied. There is also a rapid rise in basal metabolism.

The relation between the pituitary and the thyroid is regarded as reciprocal. When thyroxine is administered, there results a reduction of TSH in the pituitary; and when TSH is administered, the content of thyroid hormone is reduced.

The hormone, a protein, contains 3.5 per cent hexose, 2.5 per cent glucosamine and 1.0 per cent sulfur. It has a molecular weight of approximately 10,000. The purity of the isolated product is still in question.

ADRENOCORTICOTROPIC HORMONE (ACTH). Hypophysectomy results in the atrophy of the adrenal cortex. Improvement is possible by using pituitary implants or by injecting appropriate pituitary extracts; but no improvement results when the adrenal cortical hormone is injected. The injection of ACTH results in an enlargement of the adrenals of both normal as well as hypophysectomized animals.

White and Long, and Evans, have isolated the hormone in presumably pure form. It is a protein and has been found to have a molecular weight of about 20,000.

The hormone has been prepared in a pure state by Li, who obtained a yield of 70 mg. per gram of sheep gland. It contains no carbohydrate.

Digestion of the ACTH by pepsin, even to the extent when the protein is hydrolyzed 50 per cent, does not alter its activity. A polypeptide has been isolated from the degradation products which still possesses adrenal-stimulating activity, and which contains but eight amino acid residues. Its molecular weight is about 1,200 to 2,000.

ACTH is used with success in arthritic conditions. The explanation is that it stimulates the production of cortisone (p. 457).

OTHER ANTERIOR PITUITARY HORMONES.   Particularly since the discovery of insulin, it has been believed that blood sugar was regulated primarily, if not exclusively, by the pancreas. It has already been pointed out that the removal of the pancreas leads to diabetes. However, Houssay showed that if the pituitary is also removed, the rise in blood sugar can be prevented. Both Houssay and Evans have since shown that the injection of anterior pituitary extracts into normal animals produces hyperglycemia and glycosuria.

Largely through the work of Young, it has been established that the anterior pituitary contains a "diabetogenic hormone" which causes a rise in blood-sugar level. But even more arresting is the observation that by increasing the daily dose of the pituitary extract (equivalent to 25 gm. of fresh ox anterior lobe), and then stopping the injections, the diabetic condition continues and presumably becomes permanent. This is true—in many cases but not in all—of the dog, but it apparently does not apply to the cat.

Dogs made permanently diabetic with the diabetogenic hormone exhibit injury of the islands of Langerhans in the pancreas (the place where insulin is manufactured); and it is possible that some cases of diabetes in man may be due to an overactivity of the hypophysis.

In addition to affecting carbohydrate metabolism, Funk and others are of the opinion that the pituitary also harbors a "fat-metabolism" hormone. Extracts have been obtained which, when injected, cause a very marked increase in the acetone body production.

Extracts from urine have been obtained which have a hyperglycemic function and which can also give rise to acetone bodies. It is not clear whether such active material has its origin in the pituitary (Harrow).

The preparations of those various extracts are still in an unsatisfactory state. They involve various acid and alkaline extracts, sometimes fractional precipitations, sometimes adsorption procedures, sometimes delicate pH adjustments, etc.

Posterior Lobe of the Pituitary.   Aqueous extracts of this portion of the gland (pituitrin) have long been used in labor. Two substances have been separated by Kamm and others: one, *vasopressin* (Pitressin), raises blood pressure and decreases the secretion of urine (antidiuretic); the other, *oxytocin* (Pitocin), contracts the muscles of the uterus and perhaps functions during parturition to remove the products of conception.

Vasopressin stimulates the peripheral blood vessels and causes a rise in blood pressure. It has been used to combat the low blood pressure of shock following surgery. The claim has been made that, under certain conditions, vasopressin has the advantage over epinephrine in that the former gives rise to a more gradual increase in blood pressure, and that this pressure is of longer duration.

It has been shown that the injection of vasopressin in cases of diabetes insipidus—a disease characterized by the elimination of large quantities of urine—checks the flow of urine; it is an antidiuretic substance.

By means of electrophoretic studies, using the principle of electrical transport and the relative migration velocities of different molecules, du Vigneaud and his associates have shown that, starting with the juice of the posterior gland, "the pressor activity travelled at a faster rate than the oxytocic activity, thus demonstrating that the activities . . . were manifestations of different chemical entities."

Du Vigneaud has isolated both the oxytocic and vasopressor material, each free of the other. Both preparations contain but eight amino acids; six of these are common to both: tyrosine, proline, glutamic acid, aspartic acid, glycine, cystine and three equivalents of ammonia. Oxytocin also contains leucine and isoleucine, while vasopressin contains arginine and phenylalanine (beef).

Further work by Du Vigneaud and co-workers has enabled them to synthesize an octapeptide amide, with a molecular weight of approximately 1000, which shows the hormonal activity of oxytocin.

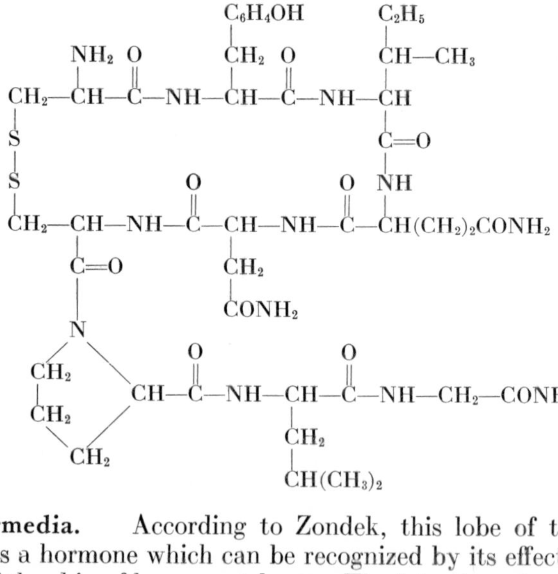

$$CH_2-CH-C-NH-CH-C-NH-CH$$

Pars Intermedia.   According to Zondek, this lobe of the pituitary manufactures a hormone which can be recognized by its effect on the pigment cells of the skin of lower vertebrates. The injection of an extract into a minnow (*Phoxinus laevis*) causes a red color at the point of attachment of the thoracic, abdominal, and anal fins. Beyond its exerting an influence on the chromatophores of cold-blooded animals, the significance of this hormone, called *intermedin*, is not clear.

THE PANCREAS (See also p. 203)

Insulin.   As has already been stated, the pancreas has two distinct functions: it secretes a juice (pancreatic juice) which flows into the intestine and which contains digestive enzymes, and it secretes a hormone which finds its way into the blood and which plays an important role in the regulation of carbohydrate metabolism.

The removal of the pancreas results in the following: (*a*) hyperglycemia (rise in blood sugar) and glycosuria (increase in urinary sugar); (*b*) depletion of the glycogen stores of liver and muscle; (*c*) lowering of the respira-

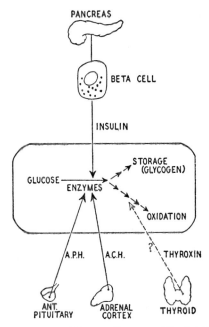

Fig. 107. Endocrine factors in diabetes. (Lazarow, Physiol. Rev., *29:* 48, 1949.)

tory quotient; (*d*) increased NPN excretion; (*e*) increased formation of acetone bodies. Death results in about three weeks. Banting, Macleod, Best, and Collip prepared an acid alcoholic extract of the pancreas which prevented these symptoms in a pancreatectomized animal, and which could be used to relieve diabetic sufferers among human beings. The hormone is called *insulin*. (See Fig. 107.)

When injected into normal animals, insulin lowers the blood sugar and finally convulsions occur. This discovery led to a method for standardizing the hormone.

The effects attributable to the administration of insulin are (*a*) acceleration of glucose oxidation in the tissues; (*b*) increased rate of conversion of glucose to glycogen or fat in the tissues; (*c*) inhibition of carbohydrate formation in the liver from non-carbohydrate sources; (d) inhibition of excessive formation of ketone bodies.

Starting with highly active commercial fractions, Abel and his co-workers obtained crystalline insulin. Crystalline preparations of insulin contain zinc.* In any case, apart from the zinc, the hydrolysis of insulin yields nothing but amino acids, among which cystine and glutamic acid are prominent. Tryptophan has not been detected.

Proteolytic enzymes attack insulin and, indeed, the hormone has to be injected rather than be given by mouth. It has been claimed that during peptic hydrolysis of insulin, the decrease in its activity runs parallel with a decrease in its tyrosine content.

Insulin is easily destroyed by alkali but is relatively stable in slightly acid solutions.

Stern and White acetylated insulin with ketene, $CH_2{=}C{=}O$. They found that when ketene acted on insulin for five minutes at room temperature and at pH 5.7, only free amino groups were acetylated. If the reaction is continued beyond this time, the hydroxyl groups of tyrosine are slowly acetylated. In this way, it could be shown that acetylating the free amino groups of insulin has no appreciable effect on its activity; but, on the other hand, when the hydroxyl groups on tyrosine were acetylated, there was marked reduction in the activity of the hormone.

These results are of special interest, since Northrop and Herriott showed that the tyrosine group plays an analogous role in so far as the activity of pepsin is concerned.

Insulin contains its sulfur (cystine) in the —S—S— form; if reduced to the —SH modification, it loses its activity.

Protamine Insulin, Etc.   A notable advance in insulin therapy was made by Hagedorn and Jensen, who, by combining insulin with protamine (one of the basic proteins), prepared a product which, when injected, is absorbed more slowly than insulin itself, and whose effects are therefore more lasting. Instead of two and three injections a day, often but one suffices. The addition of zinc to protamine insulin was suggested by Scott and Fischer. This "protamine zinc insulin" prolongs the effective action of insulin; it lowers the blood sugar for more than twenty-four hours. A further modification, "NPH insulin," differs from protamine zinc insulin by containing less protamine and less zinc and by being crystalline. The blood sugar–lowering action is intermediate between globin insulin and protamine zinc insulin.

Globin insulin with zinc has also come into use. The globin is the protein derived from hemoglobin. The action time is intermediate between that of insulin alone and protamine zinc insulin. This globin insulin with zinc is a "twelve-to-fifteen-hour insulin" (the action lasts that long) and in certain cases, involving careful regulation of diet, is preferred.

In the use of protamine zinc insulin, a drop in blood sugar begins in four to six hours; with insulin alone, the action is immediate; with globin insulin and zinc, the lowering occurs within two hours.

Mechanism of Diabetic Activity.   Two theories have been advanced: (a) This is sometimes called the "non-utilization theory." It states that

* It may be significant that normal pancreatic tissue is relatively rich in zinc.

in the absence of insulin, the capacity of the peripheral tissue to metabolize glucose is greatly decreased. Several of the hormones from the anterior pituitary and the adrenal cortex depress the utilization of glucose and also stimulate glucose production in the liver from protein.

(b) This is sometimes called the "overproduction theory." It states that the utilization of glucose in the tissues is not affected to any great extent by insulin or by hormones of the pituitary or adrenals. In the absence of insulin, excess glucose is due to a stimulation of glucose production, not only from amino acids but also from fatty acids in the liver, and this stimulation develops from the activity of hormones in the pituitary and the adrenals.

Insulin Shock.   Another advance we owe to Sakel, who finds that insulin injections almost up to the point of shock often have a beneficial effect in certain mental disorders (schizophrenia or dementia praecox).

Insulin and the Pituitary.   The pituitary and possibly the adrenals are involved in the activity of insulin. As has been pointed out elsewhere (p. 207), Cori and his co-workers have claimed that the enzyme hexokinase, which promotes the formation of glucose-6-phosphate (in the carbohydrate cycle) is inhibited by certain fractions from the anterior pituitary, and that the inhibition is removed by insulin. This has been challenged by Mirsky.

Alloxan Diabetes.   Alloxan, a substance structurally related to uric acid, produces diabetes in various animals. A single injection will often produce the disease in twenty-four to twenty-eight hours.

$$
\begin{array}{ccc}
\text{HN} & \text{---} & \text{CO} \\
| & & | \\
\text{CO} & & \text{CO} \\
| & & | \\
\text{HN} & \text{---} & \text{CO}
\end{array}
$$

Alloxan

The disease is brought about by the destruction of pancreatic tissue (selective necrosis of the islets of Langerhans) with a lessening production of insulin.

While it is also possible to produce experimental diabetes in the animal by the injection of the diabetogenic hormone from the pituitary (p. 449) or by partial pancreatectomy, the diabetes so obtained is considered as due to overwork of the beta cells; alloxan diabetes brings about their actual destruction. As evidence for this view, in the early stages of the disease, starvation or treatment with insulin will prevent the diabetes due to surgical operation or the injection of the anterior pituitary extract; but this is not true of diabetes due to alloxan.

Lazarow showed that the injection of large amounts of glutathione immediately preceding a dose of alloxan protects rats from diabetes. While substances other than glutathione are known to do this, glutathione is a natural constituent of cells. It is known that glutathione reacts with alloxan to change it to a compound which is not diabetogenic.

Hyperglycemic Hormone (H-G Factor).   Funk   and   others   have shown that the islet tissue of the pancreas is not only responsible for insulin, which depresses blood glucose, but for another hormone which increases blood glucose. Crude extracts of the pancreas, when injected, give rise to an initial increase of the blood sugar, followed by a drop below normal levels—a result of the combined action of the H-G factor and insulin.

If the animal is first treated with alloxan, the pancreatic extracts contain just the H-G factor (manufactured by the alpha cells) and insulin is absent. Cori, etc., have purified this H-G factor.

THE ADRENALS

There are two distinct parts to the adrenals, the medulla and the cortex. The medulla, an offshoot of the sympathetic nervous system, contains the hormone epinephrine; and the cortex, essential to life, contains several hormones which have been isolated.

The Adrenal Medulla. Epinephrine (Adrenalin). This was first isolated by Abel and Takamine. The method employed by Takamine in isolating the hormone was to extract the glands with warm acidulated water, filter, concentrate the filtrate, precipitate inert material with an excess of alcohol, and finally precipitate the epinephrine with ammonia. Its formula is:

$$HO \quad \text{—} \quad CHOH . CH_2NHCH_3$$
$$HO$$

Epinephrine or Adrenalin

which means that it is catechol to which a hydroxyethylmethylamine group is attached.

Using methyl-labelled epinephrine, it can be shown that in the body (the rat) some 50 per cent is inactivated by the loss of methylamine (probably through the action of an amine oxidase). The methylamine is partially oxidized to CO_2 but some 10 per cent is excreted in the urine in various forms.

Norepinephrine (Noradrenaline). Besides epinephrine, the adrenals also contain norepinephrine,

$$HO \quad \text{—} \quad CHOH . CH_2NH_2$$
$$HO$$

which is epinephrine minus the N-methyl group. In the adrenals of cattle both are found, in the proportion of one part norepinephrine to 4 parts epinephrine. In fact, most commercial preparations of epinephrine contain from 10 to 20 per cent of norepinephrine. The hyperglycemic effect of norepinephrine is 1/20 that of epinephrine, but the former is more active on arterial blood pressure.

It is believed that in the body norepinephrine can be converted to epinephrine by a methylation reaction involving enzymes of the adrenal, and requiring ATP.

Epinephrine constricts the splanchnic and cutaneous blood vessels, causing a rise in blood pressure; it accelerates the heart rate; it causes a temporary increase in blood sugar and blood lactic acid.

The L-form is fifteen times more effective than the D-form.

Epinephrine is used in shock and collapse, in asthmatic attacks (also as the isopropyl derivative), and in combination with local anesthetics (to prevent bleeding).

Epinephrine is the most powerful vasoconstrictor known. It is this property which makes it so useful as an adjunct in local anesthesia. The anesthetic effects are prolonged by adding epinephrine to the solution of the local anesthetic to be used. Not only does the hormone prolong the anesthetic effect but less of the anesthetic is needed.

Cannon is of the opinion that one function of epinephrine is to act in emergencies (in cold, fatigue, shock, etc.).*

It has already been mentioned (p. 203) that epinephrine plays a role in the metabolism of carbohydrates. Its effect is to increase the conversion of liver glycogen to blood sugar and to increase the conversion of muscle glycogen to lactic acid (which may be ultimately converted to liver glycogen).

REGULATION OF GLUCOSE METABOLISM BY HORMONES. Both epinephrine and the H-G factor cause an increased glycogenolysis (breakdown of glycogen) in vitro and in vivo. Cori has pointed out that of the enzyme systems involved in the formation of blood glucose by liver, the first system—phosphorylase reaction—is rate-limiting.† Epinephrine and the H-G factor would, in that case, exert their effect by increasing the activity of the phosphorylating reaction in the liver. In contrast to Cori's views, Somogyi is of the opinion that epinephrine depresses the rate of assimilation of glucose by the extrahepatic or peripheral tissues.

Stadie has shown that the rat diaphragm combines with epinephrine in vitro, thereby decreasing its ability to form glycogen from glucose. He has also shown that this muscle combines with insulin, resulting in the greater ability of the muscle to form glycogen from glucose. When the rats are injected with a crude anterior pituitary extract, or with purified growth hormone, the combination of the diaphragm with insulin is prevented. This also occurs when the rats are first made diabetic with alloxan. Such findings suggest that the main difficulty in the diabetic animal is a decreased capacity to utilize carbohydrate.

The suggestion has been made that insulin and the pituitary hormone

* "The adrenal medulla cooperates with sympathetic impulses in producing adrenalin. This sympathico-adrenal system is brought prominently and usefully into action in emotional excitement, in vigorous muscular work, in asphyxia, low blood pressure, chilling surroundings, and hypoglycemia—in brief, it serves effectively in emergencies; furthermore, this service can be given a general expression in stating that the system guards the constancy of the internal environment of the organism; and finally that secreted adrenalin itself acts to prolong the effects of nerve impulses, to accelerate metabolism, to shorten coagulation time, and to release glucose from the liver. There is no evidence that secreted adrenalin is an important agent in maintaining a high blood pressure" (Cannon).

† When one is dealing with a series of stepwise reactions, such as A $\longrightarrow$ B $\longrightarrow$ C $\longrightarrow$ D, each proceeding at a different rate, the factor which will limit the rate of conversion of A to D will be that reaction whose rate is slowest, that is, it is the "rate-limiting" reaction.

compete for combination with similar groups in muscle tissue, resulting in a regulation by these hormones of carbohydrate metabolism.

That there is an impairment in the utilization of glucose in the diabetic rat has also been advanced by Chaikoff. Using C^{14}-glucose, he reports that in the alloxan-diabetic rat the conversion of glucose to CO_2 and fatty acids is depressed. By means of C^{14}-acetate, he has shown that although the conversion to CO_2 remains normal, the conversion to fatty acids is subnormal.

The Adrenal Cortex.   The adrenal medulla produces epinephrine and norepinephrine. The cortex produces a mixture of many steroids, several of which act as hormones. Histologically the cortex is made up of three layers: zona glomerulosa (outside), zona fasciculata, and the zona reticularis (inside). These three layers are responsible for the elaboration of a number of hormones which, in the form of a crude extract of the cortex, are called *cortin*. The glomerulosa is believed to produce the hormones responsible for electrolyte and water balance, and the fasciculata, for those affecting carbohydrate and protein metabolism.

When an animal is adrenalectomized, it dies soon afterward unless supported by injections of cortin. The important chemical findings after bilateral adrenalectomy are:

1. Decreased Na^+, Cl^-, bicarbonate and glucose in the serum.
2. Increased K^+ and NPN in the serum.
3. Decreased Na^+ in the muscle.
4. Increased K^+ and water in the muscle.
5. Decreased glycogen in the liver and muscle after fasting.
6. Increased excretion of Na^+, Cl^- and bicarbonate.
7. Decreased excretion of K^+ and total N.
8. Inability to excrete ingested water.

These findings are quite similar to those observed in *Addison's disease* in man. Addison's disease is characterized by the loss of function of the adrenals for a variety of reasons. The chemical alterations are very similar to those which take place in the adrenalectomized animal. It has been successfully treated with extracts from the cortex of the adrenals, and with 11-desoxycorticosterone (p. 457).

ADRENAL CORTICOSTEROIDS. As a result of work by many investigators over a period of 25 years, some 28 steroids have been isolated from the adrenal glands, and many from the urine, which appear to be related to adrenal metabolism, especially when associated with diseases of the adrenals. Only six of these steroids from the adrenals possess biological activity; the others probably represent metabolic intermediates. Of especial interest is an amorphous fraction, still uncharacterized, which has considerable activity.

Figure 108 gives the formulae for the six most important of the adrenal steroids. They are characterized by the fact that they contain 19 or 21 carbon atoms and in all instances C_{11} is either unsubstituted (11-desoxy series) or bears a ketonic or alcoholic function (11-oxygenated series). Several are active with respect to only one metabolic dysfunction produced by adrenalectomy. Thus 11-desoxycorticosterone causes a retention of Na^+ and water but is without effect in maintaining normal carbohydrate metabolism. On the other hand, 17-hydroxycorticosterone is active in its effect on carbohydrate metabolism but has no effect on sodium retention. The following illustrates the importance of the various steroid hormones of the adrenal in a series of tests designed to show the repair of function in the adrenalectomized animal:

1. Recovery of fatigued muscle in the adrenalectomized rat: The most potent is 11-desoxycorticosterone.

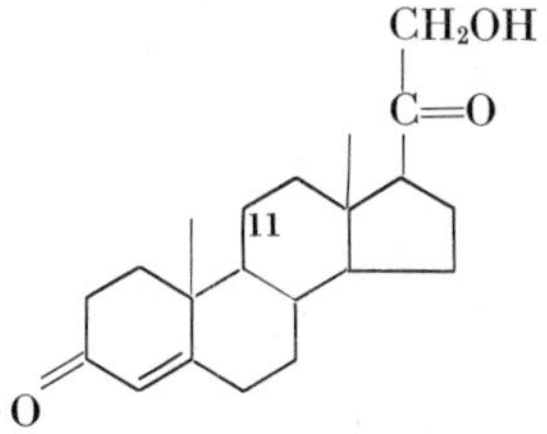

11-Desoxycorticosterone

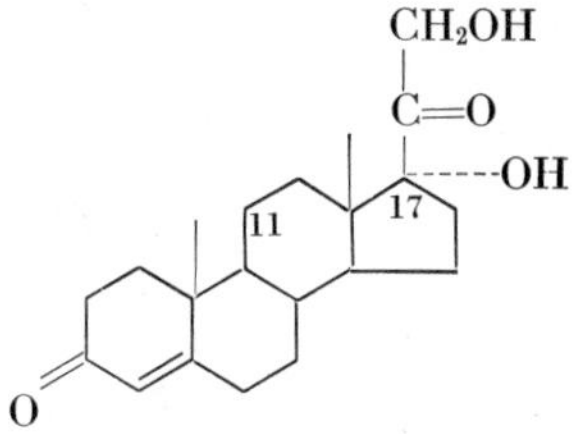

17-Hydroxy-11-desoxycorticosterone

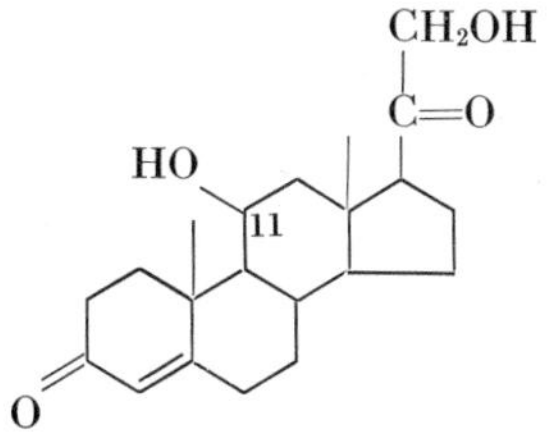

Corticosterone

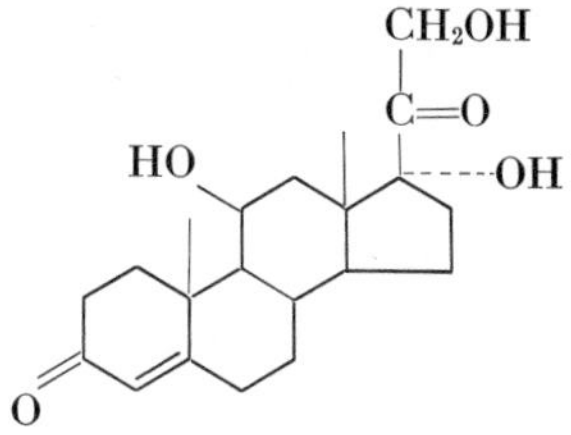

17-Hydroxycorticosterone (compound F)

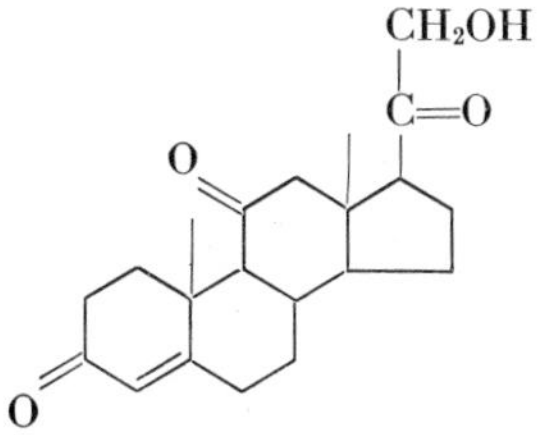

11-Dehydrocorticosterone

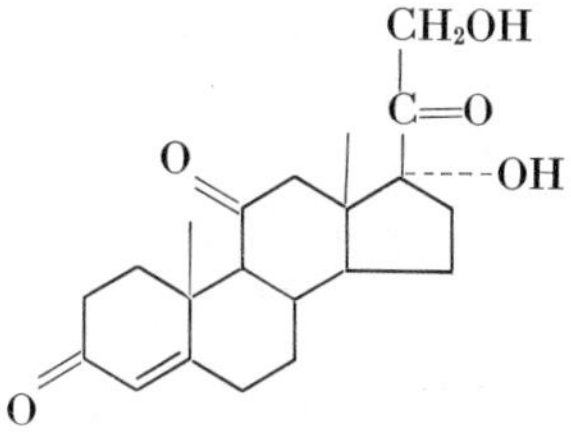

17-Hydroxy-11-dehydrocorticosterone (compound E) ("Cortisone")

Fig. 108. Adrenal steroids.

2. Survival of adrenalectomized rats: All are active, but the most active is 11-desoxycorticosterone.

3. Na^+ and Cl^- retention in the dog: Again 11-desoxycorticosterone (DCA, as the acetate) is active, with corticosterone about $\frac{1}{2}$ as active. 17-Hydroxycorticosterone and 17-hydroxy-11-dehydrocorticosterone are inactive.

4. Work performance under the influence of repeated electrical stimuli in the adrenalectomized rat: The most active are the 17-hydroxy steroids.

5. Prevention of insulin convulsions in the intact rat: Both of the 17-hydroxy compounds are most active, whereas the corticosterone and 11-

dehydrocorticosterone are slightly less active. 11-Desoxycorticosterone is inactive.

6. Diabetogenic action: Increased glycosuria in partially depancreatized and in adrenalectomized-depancreatized rats. Corticosterone and 17-hydroxy corticosterone are most active.

7. Glycogen deposition in fasted adrenalectomized rats: The 17-hydroxy steroids are most active, the others less so.

On the basis of such experimental findings, the following conclusions may be drawn in terms of the relationship of structure to activity:

1. For life maintenance and salt and water balance, one needs an α,β-unsaturated 3-ketone with a reducing α-keto grouping in the side chain and a stable orientation of the side chain at C_{17}.

2. For glycogenic potency, one needs a ketonic oxygen atom substituted at C_{11}.

Metabolites of the adrenal steroids appear in the urine. In man, two groups of urinary steroids are associated with adrenal metabolism: the 17-ketosteroids and the glycogenic corticoids. Analysis of 17-ketosteroids determines the adrenal and testicular steroids of androgenic activity and their metabolic end products. These are concerned with nitrogen (protein) metabolism. The glycogenic steroids are concerned with carbohydrate metabolism.

The function of ACTH of the pituitary is believed to be one of stimulation of the adrenal to secrete 17-hydroxy-11-dehydrocorticosterone (compound E, cortisone). Both ACTH and this adrenal steroid have been used with success in the treatment of rheumatoid arthritis.

ORIGIN OF THE CORTICAL HORMONES. Based on some experimental evidence, the suggestion has been made that cholesterol may eventually prove to be the mother substance. Bloch has shown that when cholesterol (tagged with deuterium) is fed to pregnant women, pregnanediol containing the isotope could be recovered from the urine. Now pregnanediol is the normal urinary excretory product of progesterone, one of the female hormones, and this progesterone has even been isolated from the adrenals by Reichstein.

Also, in this connection, it may be noticed that when the adrenocorticotropic hormone of the pituitary (which controls the secretory activity of the adrenals) is injected, the cholesterol (and, incidentally, the ascorbic acid) is decreased; at the same time, there is an increased rate of secretion of the adrenal cortical hormones. All this suggests that the adrenal cholesterol is a direct precursor of the adrenal cortical steroids (Long).

ADRENALS AND SEX. The cortex of the adrenals also elaborates substances belonging to the group of sex hormones.* Abnormal changes in sex may sometimes be due to disturbances in the adrenal cortex involving sex hormones. The female assumes male secondary sex characteristics and at the same time certain female characteristics become repressed. This is a type of masculinity or virilism known as "adrenal virilism." The cases are less frequent in the male, but when they do occur, the tendency is towards feminization—enlargement of breasts, genital atrophy, etc.

---

* The following paragraphs might be read in conjunction with the section dealing with the sex hormones.

These developments are due, first, to the fact that the adrenals manufacture androgens and estrogens, male and female hormones (which is, apparently, a perfectly normal function); but, second, that owing to some unknown cause, the hormones may be produced in excessive amounts, or their normal metabolism may be disturbed—in any case, giving rise to these sex changes.

Reichstein and others have isolated several compounds from beef adrenals which are androgens, or male hormones. One of them, adrenosterone, shows a capon comb test equivalent to one-fifth that of androsterone. Adrenosterone has been obtained artificially from 11-dehydro-17-hydroxycorticosterone, a compound which has already been included among the cortical hormones and which is effective to some extent in maintaining life after adrenalectomy.

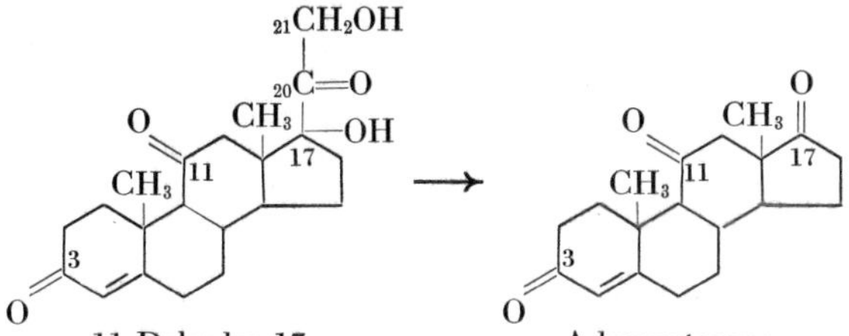

11-Dehydro-17-
hydroxycorticosterone

Adrenosterone

It is also of interest to note that often malignant cortical tumors (adrenal carcinoma, for example) give rise to the excretion in excessive quantities of androgens; and this irrespective of the sex of the patient.

One of a number of these androgens isolated from the urine is dehydroisoandrosterone, a compound which is excreted in small amounts by normal men and women and which, even here, probably means that its source is in the adrenals rather than in the reproductive organs.

From such observations it seems reasonable to conclude that not all of the androgens excreted by normal subjects have their source in the gonads, but some of them, at least, are derived from the adrenal cortex. It is significant that the urine of eunuchs and of ovariectomized women still shows the presence of androgens.

High amounts of estrogens, or female hormones, are sometimes excreted in cases of virilism. Here, too, it may be noted that the urine of male and female castrates shows some estrogenic activity, suggesting the adrenal cortex as the origin of such substances. The typical estrogen, estrone, has actually been isolated from adrenal glands.

Are the compounds in the adrenals which are related to the sex compounds merely by-products of truly cortical substances manufactured by the gland? Or are they specifically manufactured by the adrenal cortex to help regulate normal sex functions?

THE SEX HORMONES

Under the stimulation of hormones from the anterior pituitary (gonadotropic hormones), the sex hormones in the testes and in the ovary are secreted.

The genital tract and the accessory male organs are influenced by the male hormones. One method of detecting the presence of an active extract is to observe its effect on the growth of comb and wattles in a capon. The cocks are castrated; this is followed by a shrivelling of the comb and wattles. The injection of a potent extract causes a renewal of growth of these secondary sex organs (Funk and Harrow, Koch).

In the female, two types of hormones are found to function. One type, as represented by estradiol, is a product of the ovary; the other, progesterone (progestin), is derived from the corpus luteum, which is formed after the ovum is ruptured and expelled. Both hormones control the uterine cycle.

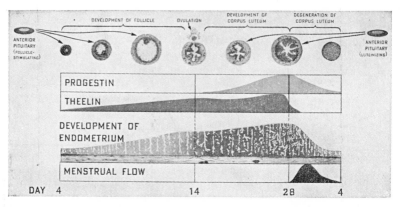

Fig. 109. Normal menstrual cycle. Rapid regeneration of endometrium (following menstrual flow of previous cycle) under the influence of estradiol, elaborated by the developing follicle (4th to 14th day)—ovulation (14th day) followed by slight decrease in estradiol—steady increase in amounts of estradiol and progesterone during development of the corpus luteum (15th to 28th day); under the influence of progesterone the highly vascular endometrium is changed to the secretory type (these changes are considered essential to subsequent rapid destruction of the endometrium following withdrawal of progesterone)—sudden degeneration of the corpus luteum (if conception does not occur) and withdrawal of estradiol and progesterone (28th day)—rapid destruction of the endometrium and subsequent sloughing (1st to 4th day of new cycle). (Therapeutic Notes, courtesy of Parke, Davis & Co.)

Under the influence of the hormones from the anterior pituitary (the sex-stimulating hormones, or gonadotropins), the ovary elaborates female hormone (estradiol) which causes the endometrium—the membrane that lines the uterus—to grow; and it also elaborates progesterone, or corpus luteum hormone, which causes the endometrial glands to secrete and transforms connective tissue (stroma) into decidua-like cells. These changes are necessary for the implantation of the fertilized ovum.

The normal menstrual cycle occurs only when conception has not taken place. Here the hormones involved ultimately decrease in concentration and the endometrium degenerates (Fig. 109).

Where impregnation has occurred, the corpus luteum increases in size and continues to function until nearly the end of pregnancy.

Figure 110 shows the comparative concentration of three of the hormones eliminated (in the urine) during pregnancy. One of them, a gonadotropic hormone found in pregnancy urine, is used as the basis for the Aschheim-Zondek test for pregnancy. One method is to inject the urine into immature mice. On the fourth day, the animals are killed and the ovaries examined for hemorrhagic spots (blutpunkte) and yellowish protrusions (developed corpora lutea).

The Friedman test for pregnancy, a modification of the Aschheim-Zondek test, makes use of the rabbit. The urine under examination is injected into the marginal ear vein of a mature female rabbit. The ovaries

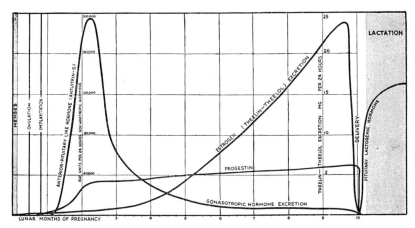

Fig. 110. Hormone excretion in pregnancy. Three important hormones, which profoundly influence physiologic conditions in pregnancy, are excreted by the kidneys. Chorionic gonadotropin (p. 447) appears in the urine; twenty-four-hour excretion rises from less than 20,000 rat units to about 200,000 rat units during the first two lunar months. After a rapid decrease in excretion a level of approximately 10,000 rat units is reached at the sixth lunar month and maintained until delivery.

Combined estrogen excretion in twenty-four hours does not rise beyond 5 mg. during the first half of pregnancy; it increases rapidly during subsequent months, reaching a peak of more than 20 mg. during the tenth lunar month. Precipitous decline occurs during the last week, values reaching the nonpregnant normal at or shortly after parturition.

Corpus luteum hormone is essential to early pregnancy and plays a vital role in the pregravid phase of each menstrual cycle; it is excreted as pregnanediol. After the second lunar month, the level of progesterone mounts slowly until parturition, after which it drops sharply. (Therapeutic Notes, July, 1938, p. 197, courtesy of Parke, Davis & Co.)

are examined twenty-four hours later. The presence of ruptured or hemorrhagic follicles is an indication of pregnancy.

The hormones of the estrin type, of which estradiol, found in the ovary, is the most potent, are detected by the Allen and Doisy test: the production of estrus (with complete cornification of the vaginal mucosa as judged from a smear) in ovariectomized sexually mature rats. The basis of the test for progesterone (progestin), as developed by Corner and Hisaw, is that it exerts a specific proliferative action on the uterine endometrium.

One method of obtaining active extracts from pregnancy urine involves, first, the fact that the active factors are soluble in fat solvents; second, that the hormones can be saponified without destruction; and third, that they can be recovered after saponification by first acidifying and extracting with ether.

In an alcohol-benzene mixture, most of the estriol (see below) is taken up by alcohol and almost all the estrone by benzene.

Doisy and also Butenandt, in 1929, isolated the follicular hormone (estrone) from pregnancy urine. In 1931, Butenandt obtained a hormone from male urine (androsterone). In 1934, W. Allen, Wintersteiner, Butenandt, and others obtained a crystalline corpus luteum hormone (progesterone) from swine ovaries.

Ovarian Hormones (Estrogens).   So far, five substances of the estrone group have been isolated: (1) estrone (pregnancy urine, stallion urine, mare urine, and palm kernels); (2) estradiol (ovaries and mare urine); (3) estriol (placenta, pregnancy urine); (4) equilin (mare urine); (5) equilenin (mare urine).

The principal hormone produced by the ovary is estradiol. Estriol is the

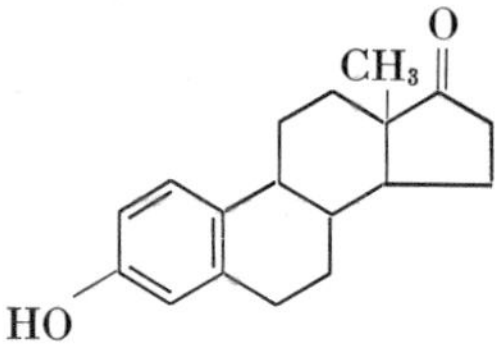

Estrone, $C_{18}H_{22}O_2$
(Theelin)
(3-Hydroxy-17-keto-Δ1,-
3,5-estratriene)

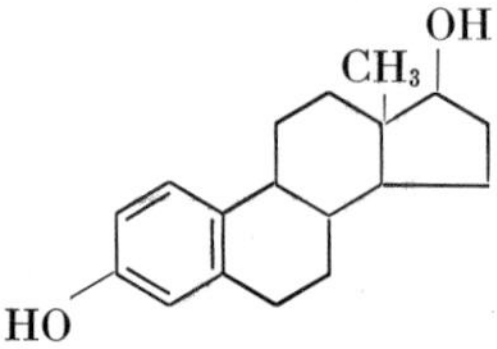

Estradiol, $C_{18}H_{24}O_2$
(Dihydrotheelin)
(3,17-Dihydroxy-Δ1,3,5-
estratriene)

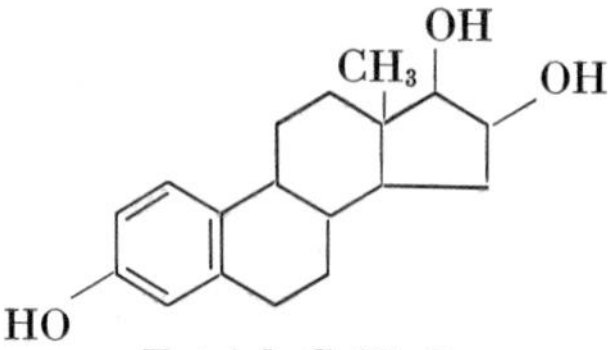

Estriol, $C_{18}H_{24}O_3$
(Theelol)
(3,16,17-Trihydroxy-Δ1,3,5-
estratriene)

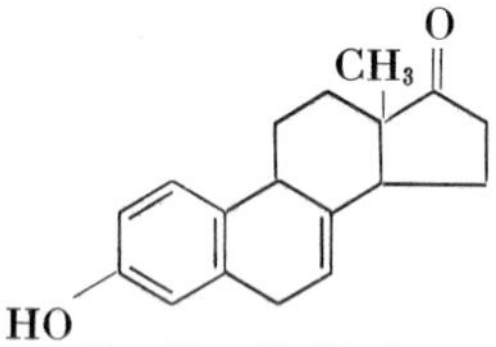

Equilin, $C_{18}H_{20}O_2$
(3-Hydroxy-17-keto-Δ1,3,-
5,7-estratetraene)

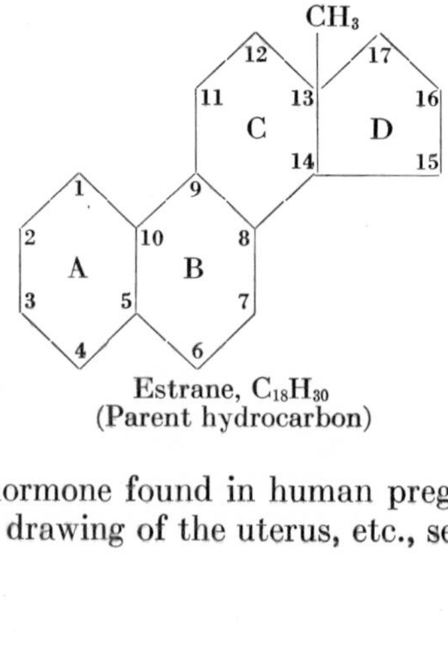

Estrane, $C_{18}H_{30}$
(Parent hydrocarbon)

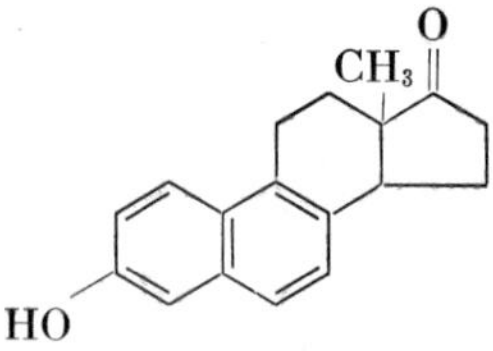

Equilenin, $C_{18}H_{18}O_2$
(3-Hydroxy-17-keto-Δ1,3,-
5,6,8-estrapentaene)

chief hormone found in human pregnancy urine and in human placenta. (For a drawing of the uterus, etc., see Fig. 111.)

Since some of the rings in the compounds are true benzene rings and others are hydrogenated, one of them, estrone, is rewritten as follows:

$$
\begin{array}{c}
\text{O} \\
\text{H}_2 \quad\quad\quad \| \\
\text{C} \; \text{CH}_3 \; \text{C} \\
\end{array}
$$

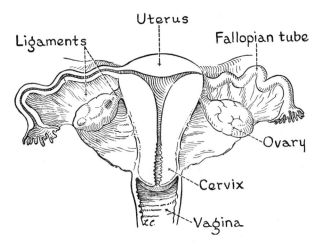

In all of these compounds the first ring is a truly aromatic one, and the OH represents a phenolic hydroxyl group. In equilenin, the second ring is

Fig. 111. Vertical section of the uterus and its appendages. (Etheredge: Health Facts.)

also aromatic. At the other end of the molecule, we find (*a*) carbonyl, (*b*) hydroxyl, or (*c*) glycol arrangements:

(*a*)   (*b*)   (*c*)

That these compounds have the four-ring structure given to them was made highly probable by Butenandt when he obtained 1,2-dimethyl-phenanthrene from estriol by fusion with alkali and reduction with selenium and zinc dust. But further confirmation came from the work of Cook,

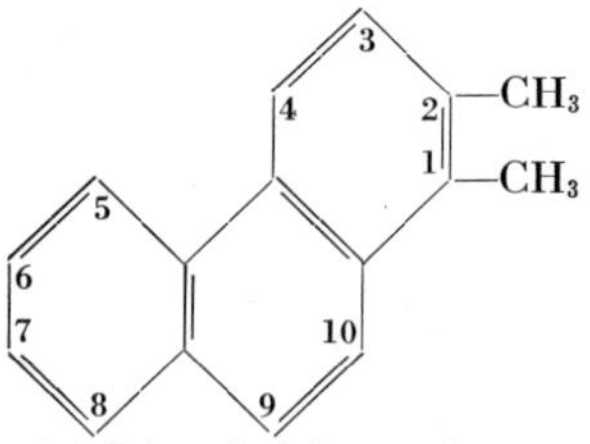

1,2-Dimethylphenanthrene

who converted estrone into a derivative of cyclopentanophenanthrene (A), the structure of which was proved by synthesis:

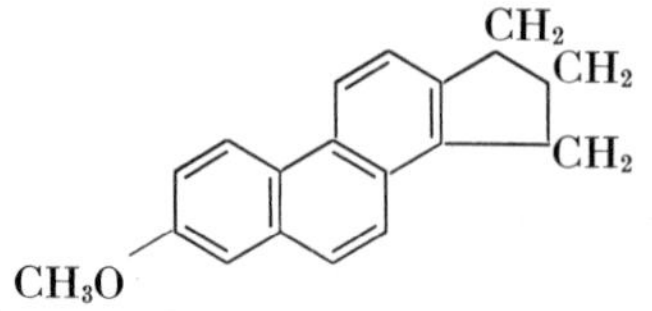

7-Methoxyl-1, 2-cyclopentanoperhydrophenanthrene (A)

(Notice that phenanthrene compounds are numbered differently from compounds derived from estrone.)

This chemical work made it clear that the female hormones belonged to the steroid group, of which cholesterol is so prominent a member. This also means that these estrogens are chemically related to androgens (p. 469), to hormones in the adrenal cortex, to progesterone (p. 446), and to bile acids.

ESTRADIOL. As has been pointed out, estradiol is found mainly in the ovaries, and it is believed to be the mother substance of estrone and estriol.

Estradiol occurs in two forms, the α-estradiol and the β-estradiol, the difference between the two depending on the space relationship of the OH group at position 17. When estrone is reduced to estradiol, the α-form is the chief product. The α-form is thirty times more potent than the β-variety.

METABOLISM. There is much which is conflicting in this field. The simplest hypothesis is to suggest that estradiol, the main product of the ovary, and the most potent of the various estrogenic substances, is changed and ultimately eliminated as estrone and estriol. To begin with, however, there is evidence to show that the conversion of estradiol to estrone is a reversible process in the human body. Furthermore, the administration of estrone (in large doses, to be sure) enables one to extract estriol from the urine. These and other reactions have suggested the following pathways:

$$\beta\text{-Estradiol}$$
$$\updownarrow$$
$$\alpha\text{-Estradiol} \rightleftarrows \text{Estrone} \longrightarrow \text{Estriol}$$

Confirmation that the liver is involved in several of these metabolic changes came with the demonstration that when estradiol was perfused through the liver, it was converted—partly, at least—to estrone and estriol. When, however, estrone was perfused through the liver, it was partly converted into estradiol and estriol. Repetition of the experiment, using estriol as the starting material, did not lead to the production of any more active product. Finally, continued perfusion of these estrogens destroyed all estrogenic activity (Schiller).

It has also been possible to show that an enzyme system in the liver catalyzes the conversion of α-estradiol to estrone.

Some two-thirds of the estrogen transported by the blood to the tissues is said to be bound to protein, and as such is biologically inactive. This protein-estrogen combination is in equilibrium with free estrogen or estrogen-glucuronide (see below), which when removed by tissues causes a partial dissociation of the protein-estrogen complex to create a new equilibrium. It is suggested that the liver is involved in the formation of this complex.

The estrogens are largely excreted in a combined form with glucuronic acid. The combined form is more water-soluble and less biologically active than the original estrogen. There is evidence, too, that the estrogens may be partly eliminated in combination with sulfuric acid.

As in most conjugations of this kind, the reaction probably occurs in the liver. (See under Detoxication, p. 493.)

STILBESTROL. Several derivatives containing the p-hydroxyphenyl group have proved themselves potent estrogens. The best known of these compounds is stilbestrol

$$HO - \left\langle \bigcirc \right\rangle - \underset{\underset{C_2H_5}{|}}{C} = \underset{\underset{C_2H_5}{|}}{C} - \left\langle \bigcirc \right\rangle - OH$$

a substance which can be synthesized at relatively low cost, and which, if given in sufficient dosage, is potent orally. Its possible disadvantage is that it may prove somewhat toxic. However, in relation to its high estrogenic potency, it may not be any more toxic than natural estrogens.

Stilbestrol is eliminated, at least partly, as the glucuronide, and, to a much smaller extent, as the ethereal sulfate.

Stilbestrol has also proved of some value in the treatment of cancer of the prostate. Colston and Brendler claim that 75 per cent of patients under this treatment will show "objective regression of the primary growth." The malignant cells require androgen (male hormone) "for their viability"; and it is possible that the stilbestrol neutralizes the effect of the androgen.

Whether we are dealing with the natural or with the synthetic estrogens, the compounds are often administered in the form of their esters (as benzoates or propionates) to allow for a more prolonged action.

Corpus Luteum Hormone (Progesterone).   This hormone is found in the female during the second stage of the monthly cycle. It makes its appearance in the cavity of the ruptured follicle after the egg has developed and continues the action of the female hormone in the development of the mucous membrane of the uterus. It acts on the uterus so that this organ may receive and nourish the fertilized ovum. "When an ovum begins its journey through the fallopian tube, the follicle from which it took origin gives place to the corpus luteum, and this organ thereupon delivers into the blood stream a substance, progesterone, that has the property of causing extensive development of the endometrium, preparing the uterus for the reception and nutrition of the embryo." (Corner.)

ISOLATION. The hormone has been prepared in crystalline form from ovarian extracts by a number of workers (Butenandt, W. Allen, Wintersteiner, Slotta, etc.). Its formula is $C_{21}H_{30}O_2$ and it is a tetracyclic diketone. It has been prepared artificially from several substances: from cholesterol, from pregnanediol (Marrian) found in pregnancy urine, and from stigmasterol, a plant sterol.

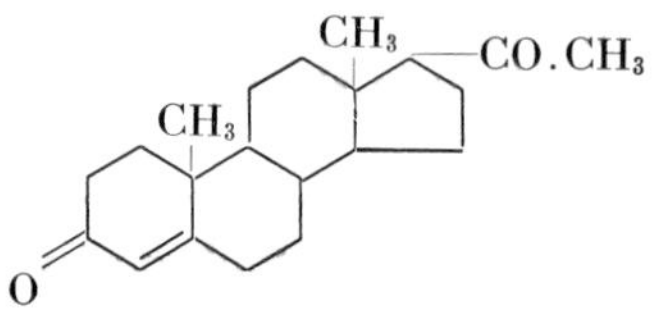

Progesterone

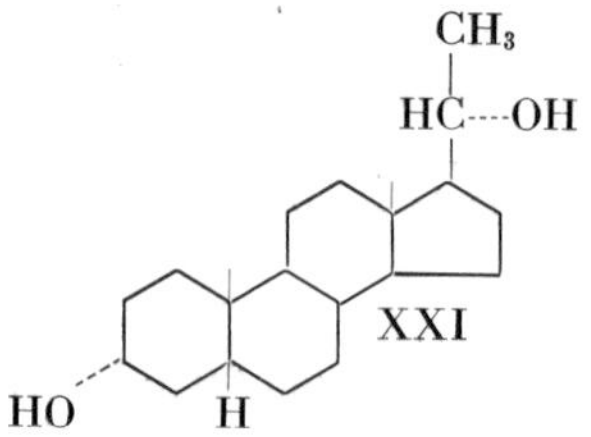

Pregnane-3(α), 20(α)-diol
(Pregnanediol)

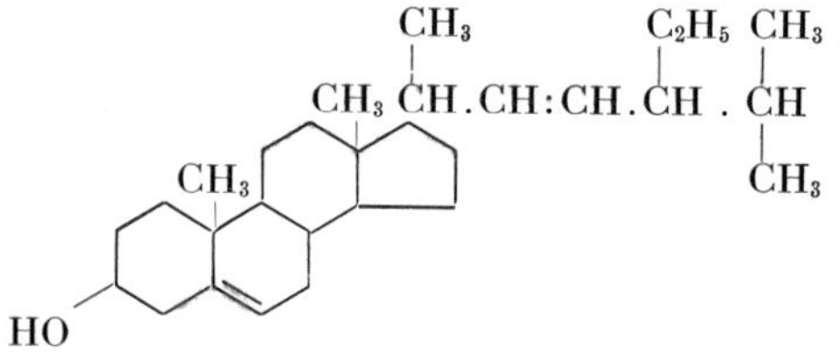

Stigmasterol

METABOLISM. Pregnanediol is the chief product of excretion of the corpus luteum hormone. During the latter half of the menstrual cycle, from 1 to 10 mg. daily of sodium pregnanediol glucuronidate may be recovered from the urine. The presence of pregnanediol in the urine indicates a progestational endometrium, and its absence, a follicular endometrium.

An important contribution to the metabolism of progesterone was made by Bloch. Cholesterol, containing deuterium in the side chain and in the nucleus, was fed to a woman in the eighth month of pregnancy. At this stage enough pregnanediol glucuronidate was excreted in a day for a deuterium analysis. The glucuronidate was isolated and found to contain significant concentrations of the isotope.

Since pregnandiol, in this instance, is a metabolic product of progesterone, this experiment implies that cholesterol can be transformed in the body into progesterone.

The same author had already shown that bile acids can be formed from cholesterol.

Cholesterol, then, may perhaps be regarded as a precursor of steroid hormones and bile acids, though the quantities of cholesterol used for such conversions are negligible as compared to those present in animal tissues.

These metabolic activities of cholesterol apply to tissues other than the brain, for though relatively large quantities of the sterol are found in the brain, such cholesterol has been shown to be metabolically inert: "it is not regenerated at a detectable rate."

The female secretes not only estrogens (female hormones) and progesterone, but a considerable amount of androgens (male hormones). Androgens are probably formed by the adrenal cortex rather than by the ovaries.

THERAPEUTIC USE. The therapeutic use of the estrogens is based upon the following: (a) developmental action of the reproductive organs (e.g. hypogenitalism, or sexual infantilism); (b) inhibition of pituitary hormones (e.g., excessive lactation after delivery and in treatment of menopausal syndrome); and (c) constitutional effects (e.g., increase in muscle strength, etc.). This last one is more open to doubt.

The therapeutic use of the corpus luteum hormone may include the production of secretory endometrium (often indicated by functional uterine bleeding), and inhibition of uterine motility (as a possible protection during pregnancy).

Steroid Structures and Nomenclature.   Just as it is possible to have cis and trans forms of the compound 2-butene,

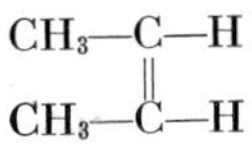

$$CH_3—C—H$$
$$CH_3—C—H$$
Cis-2-butene

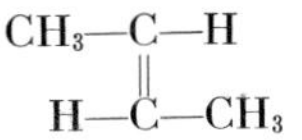

$$CH_3—C—H$$
$$H—C—CH_3$$
Trans-2-butene

So it is possible to have a similar type of stereoisomerism in ring structures, as the decalins:

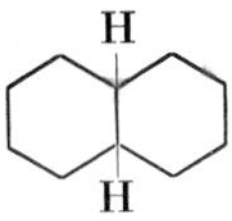

H

H
Cis-decalin

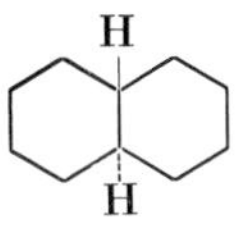

H

H
Trans-decalin

The dotted line indicates that the H atom is related to the upper H atom in a different space relationship than when there is a solid line.

Among the steroids, isomerism is possible in a number of places, since there are many asymmetric carbon atoms. Thus, isomerism around C_3 concerns the relationship of the OH group at this position to the angular methyl group attached to C_{10}. If the OH group among the androgens is cis to this methyl group, it is called a member of the β series; if it is trans, it is called a member of the α series. The same holds for the OH group at position 17.

The following formulae indicate the relationships of androsterone and isoandrosterone to various compounds related to cholesterol (Fig. 112).

In the cholesterol series, the prefix epi- refers to the trans configuration of the OH group at C_3 relative to the methyl group at C_{10} (which is the opposite of that of the natural, or typical, steroid).

Male Hormones (Androgens).   "The testicle," writes Moore, "exercises two principal functions; it produces spermatozoa, which are necessary for fertilization, and secretes a substance or substances (hormone) that plays an important role in the organism. This hormone places in function numerous special accessory reproductive organs: epididymis, vas, prostate, seminal vesicles, penis, etc., that make possible the delivery of spermatozoa to the place where fertilization can occur; and at least in sub-primate vertebrates the hormone initiates the sexual drive, or inclinations to mate with females. The sex urge in man is not so clearly or exclusively dependent upon hormone action since imitation, custom, and psychology play such a great role in human conduct." (See Fig. 113.)

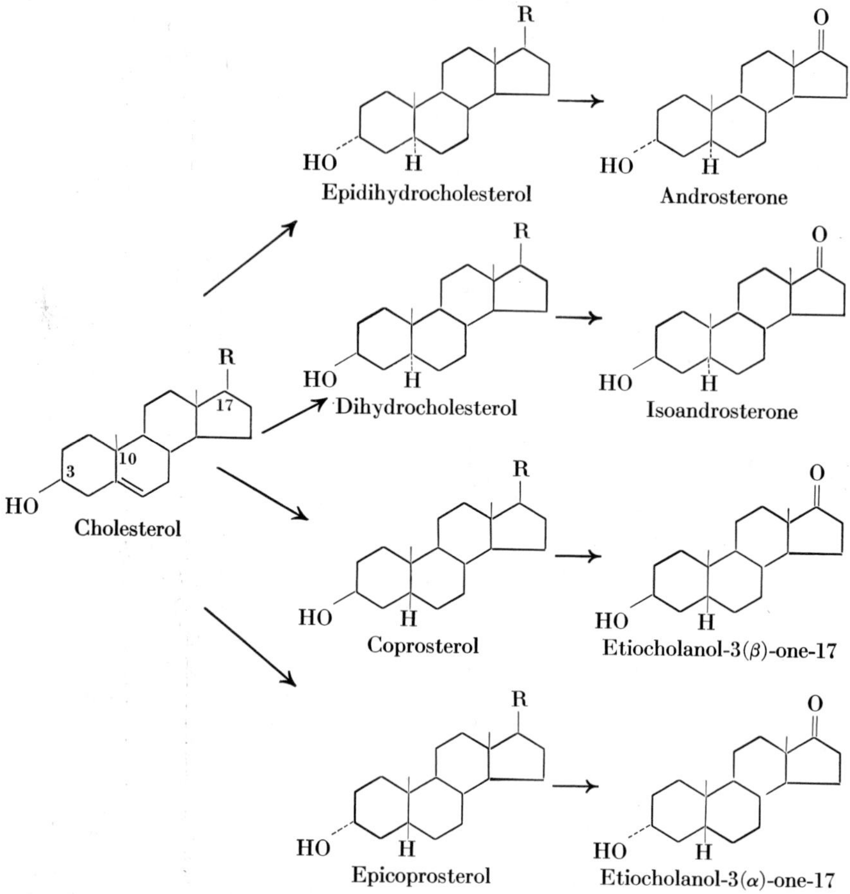

Fig. 112. Schematic representation of the partial synthesis of androsterone and three isomers. R = a side group. (From Dorfman in Pincus and Thimann: The Hormones, 1950, p. 476.)

A number of extracts respond to the male hormone tests (comb growth in the capon, for example). An active extract, responding to the comb test, may be prepared from the urine of males by extracting an acidified portion with an organic solvent, such as chloroform, evaporating the chloroform from the extract, heating the residue with sodium hydroxide, extracting the active material with ether, evaporating the ether, and incorporating the residue with oil (Funk, Harrow, and Lejwa).

A potent extract injected into a castrated cock (Fig. 114) over a period of eighteen days will produce the result (comb and wattles) shown in Figure 115.

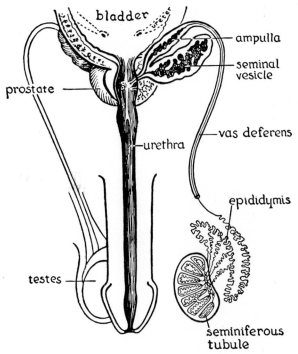

Fig. 113. The male reproductive system. (Drawn by E. M.) (Gerard: The Body Functions. John Wiley and Sons.)

Among the naturally occurring compounds belonging to the male hormone group are androsterone, $C_{19}H_{30}O_2$, in male urine; dehydroandrosterone, $C_{19}H_{28}O_2$, in testes; androstanedione, $C_{19}H_{28}O_2$, in testes; and testosterone, $C_{19}H_{28}O_2$, in testes.

Androstane, $C_{19}H_{32}$
(Parent hydrocarbon)

Androsterone, $C_{19}H_{30}O_2$
(Androstanol-3(α)-one-17)

Dehydroisoandrosterone,
$C_{19}H_{28}O_2$
(Δ^5-Androstenol-3(β)-one-17)

Androstanedione,
$C_{19}H_{28}O_2$
(Androstanedione-3,17)

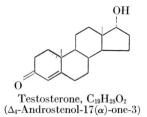

Testosterone, $C_{19}H_{28}O_2$
(Δ_4-Androstenol-17(α)-one-3)

Fig. 114.

Fig. 115.

Figs. 114, 115. (Koch: Harvey Lectures, Ser. 33, p. 205, Williams and Wilkins Co., Publishers.)

Of these substances, testosterone is physiologically the most powerful and is considered the parent hormone in the testes.

METABOLISM AND ELIMINATION. A number of products of the metabolism of testosterone are found in the urine. The principal product is androsterone, which has a very marked physiological potency, though not so powerful as testosterone. Androsterone and some five other chemically closely related substances belong to the group known as the 17-ketosteroids (because of a ketone group in position 17) and are all metabolic products of testosterone.

The estrogens, it has been seen, are eliminated, at least partly, as glucuronides and as sulfate. This is also true of the androgens.

Androsterone and other 17-ketosteroids are found in both male and female urines. Since these substances have been isolated from the urine of eunuchs and from the urine of ovariectomized women, the genital glands are not always necessarily the originators of such compounds. There is reason to believe that under certain conditions the adrenal glands manufacture these substances.

CHEMISTRY. Based on chemical work somewhat analogous with that on the female hormones, it was possible for Butenandt to predict the tetracyclic nature of these substances. This view was further strengthened by the successful reduction of estrone into octahydroestrone (absorption of eight hydrogen atoms), giving a product which responded to male hormone tests:

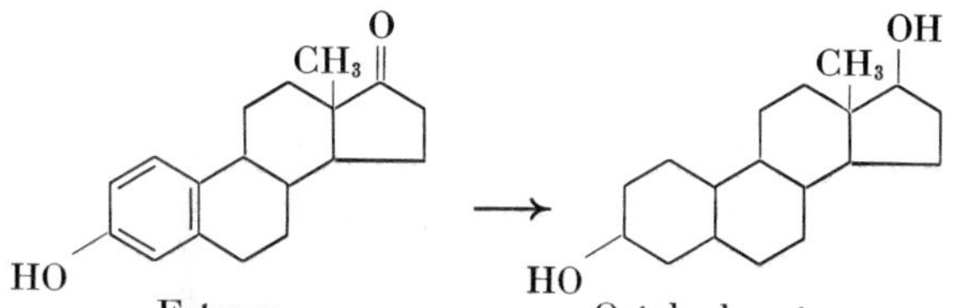

Estrone   Octahydroestrone

A very important advance in our knowledge of these structures was the success attained by Ruzicka in converting a cholesterol derivative into androsterone, one of the male hormones.

Testosterone has also been prepared artificially, starting with dehydroandrosterone.

The biosynthesis of testosterone has been accomplished by showing that testicular tissue slices can convert labelled acetate to the hormone.

THERAPEUTIC USE. Clinically, the androgen favored is testosterone in the form of the propionate (in which form, absorption and elimination are delayed). Here, as in the case of the natural estrogens, injections are much

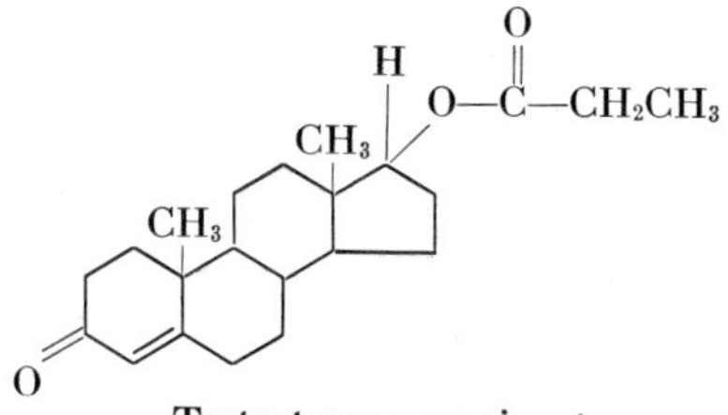

Testosterone propionate

more effective than when the hormone is given orally. In this connection, methyl testosterone (where the H at C_{17} in testosterone is replaced by CH_3) is said to be much more active than the mother substance.

The testosterone in use is derived from cholesterol. This is in contrast to estradiol which, so far, cannot be made cheaply enough by any synthetic process.

Testosterone propionate is of value in eunuchoidism, serving as replacement therapy, but many other claims are hardly warranted. It has practically no effect in psychic impotence or as an aphrodisiac.

SYNTHETIC SUBSTANCES SHOWING PHYSIOLOGICAL PROPERTIES

Slight modifications in structure—the change of a carbonyl group to a secondary alcoholic group—may markedly change the physiological activity of the compound. Many compounds have been made which can produce estrus; some are but distantly related to the original estrane structure. For example, a derivative of dibenzanthracene (A) corresponds in its activity to the natural estriol.

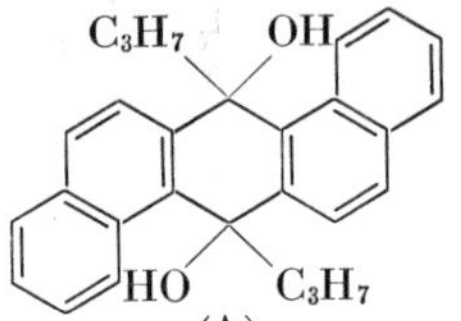

(A)

This substance (A), incidentally, shows not only estrogenic properties but also cancer-producing activities, for, when applied continuously to a mouse over a period of time, there develops a malignant tumor. The same is true of a compound, methylcholanthrene, which may be obtained artificially from desoxycholic acid, one of the acids of the bile (Fieser).

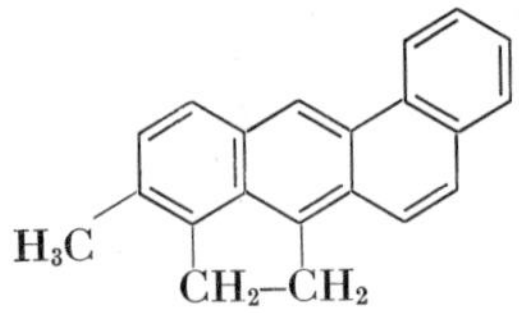

Methylcholanthrene

We have already discussed stilbestrol, a synthetic compound with powerful estrogenic properties.

Butenandt has also interested himself in modifying structures to bring about a reversal in physiological action. For example, 6-oxo-testosterone, derived from testosterone, shows no testicular action, but a very definite

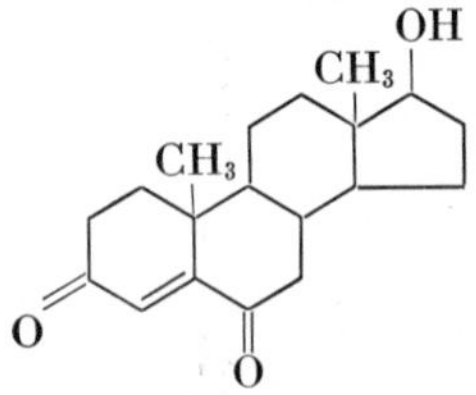

6-Oxo-testosterone

follicular action. This change from male hormone to female hormone activity is also illustrated by the conversion of androstanedione to $\Delta^{1,2}$-androstenedione, which shows complete estrus in a castrated female mouse when

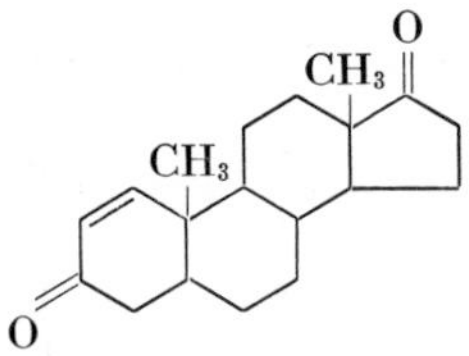

Δ¹,²-Androstenedione

injected in 4 × 500γ amounts; but even 4 mg. of the material still fails to show growth in the comb of the capon. "In this example," as Butenandt says, "the difference between a male and female substance is merely the position of the double bond in ring I." But he has even gone one step further. He has obtained a substance, androstenediol, from dehydroandrosterone, which shows both male and female properties.

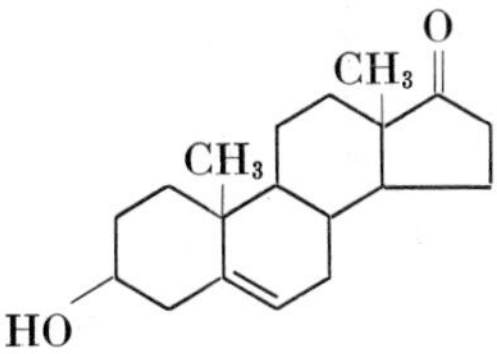

Dehydroandrosterone
♂

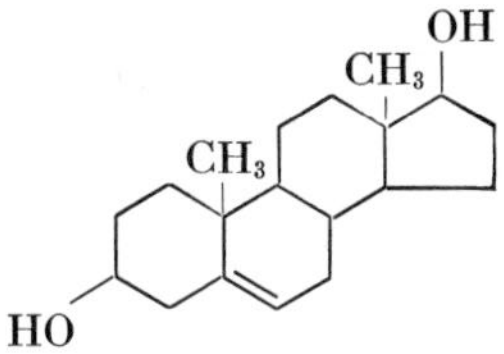

Androstenediol
♂   ♀

HORMONES AND CARCINOGENESIS

It has already been pointed out that a derivative of dibenzanthracene and methylcholanthrene exhibit cancer-producing activities. It has also been observed that in adrenal cortical tumor, resulting in adrenal virilism, large amounts of male hormones are excreted.

In one case, Fieser points out, the amount of dehydroandrosterone excreted was 100 times as much as in the normal. Fieser is of the opinion that in abnormal metabolism—such as the example just cited—a sterol compound (represented by one of the sex compounds or cholesterol) may, perhaps, be transformed into a "carcinogen," or cancer-producing product, of the cholanthrene type.

"An abnormal process leading to the formation of a carcinogen may be only slightly differentiated from normal sex hormone metabolism. Suspicion as to the point of origin of a 'degenerated biocatalyst' centers around the adrenal cortex partly because steroids of the adrenal cortical type appear to be the likely precursors of all the sex hormones and partly because this gland, particularly when hyperactive, appears to maintain conditions favorable for dehydrogenative processes." (Fieser.)

Reference has been made to a treatment in cancer of the prostate with estrogens. Some work has also been done on the use of testosterone in the treatment of cancer of the breast; the results have been conflicting. At best, there is temporary relief. Cortisone and ACTH have been used in leukemia with some success, if only temporary.

Studying the inciting factors which play a role in the genesis of spontaneous mammary cancer in mice, Bittner lists them as three: inherited susceptibility, hormonal stimulation, and the mammary tumor milk agent (the agent transferred in the mothers' milk); the last represents Bittner's discovery of a substance—probably a virus—which is normally obtained by nursing.

The study of neoplastic cells—cells showing abnormal growth, such as a tumor—has been pushed very vigorously (see references at the end of the chapter). The claims of a conjugated form of folic acid in the treatment of cancer are very much in dispute.

On the other hand, the toxic effect of "nitrogen mustard" compound on

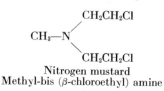

Nitrogen mustard
Methyl-bis (β-chloroethyl) amine

neoplastic tissue of the hematopoietic system is the basis for the treatment of Hodgkins' disease and leukemia; though, to be sure, the relief afforded is but temporary.

In studying the effect of nitrogen mustard on neoplastic tissue, the discovery was made that it arrests mitosis and causes mutations (in *Drosophila* and *Neurospora*). In low concentrations, the nitrogen mustard inhibits the synthesis of cellular nucleic acid (which, according to one hypothesis, is needed for the synthesis of tissue proteins and, presumably, enzymes).

GASTROINTESTINAL HORMONES *

In so far as the secretion of saliva is concerned, a hormone mechanism seems to play no part. A humoral mechanism may, in part, be involved in gastric secretion. The injection of an acid extract of the pyloric mucosa stimulates secretion. This stimulation is attributed to a hormone, *gastrin*.

Komarov obtained histamine-free extracts from the pyloric mucosa which contains two active materials: one of these stimulates the gastric glands (gastrin), and the other stimulates the external secretion of the pancreas (similar to secretin).

Enterogastrone, a substance which inhibits gastric secretion, has been obtained in concentrated form from the upper intestinal mucosa. A probable excretory product, showing some of the properties of the mother substance, is *urogastrone*.

The mucosa of the upper part of the intestine is responsible for two hormones, *secretin* and *cholecystokinin*. Bayliss and Starling obtained an acid extract of the mucosa, which, when injected, caused a flow of pancreatic juice. The active material in this acid extract was named "secretin," and substances of the type represented by secretin were called "hormones" (from the Greek, "to excite").

Crystalline products of secretin have been obtained by Hammarsten and Ågren. The substance is probably a basic polypeptide.

Extracts from the mucosa of the upper part of the intestine (freed from histamine and choline) give, when injected, a prolonged contraction of the gallbladder with evacuation. The substance which stimulates this contraction of the gallbladder is called "cholecystokinin" (Ivy) which, chemically, resembles secretin, though it is not identical with it. There is also said to

* Refer to Chap. 7.

be still another hormone, *pancreozymin*, released by the upper intestinal mucosa, which stimulates the secretion of enzymes by the pancreas.

PLANT HORMONES *

While plant hormones belong, more specifically, to plant biochemistry and not to animal biochemistry, plant and animal hormones may be related. At any rate, plant hormones have been obtained from the urine of human beings and a "female hormone" has been obtained from plant extracts.

In plants the hormones do not originate in certain glands (as in the animal kingdom), but in buds or other growing centers. These plant hormones—or growth-promoting substances—stimulate root cuttings, induce production of seedless fruits in tomatoes and cucumbers, prevent potatoes from sprouting during storage, control the pre-harvest fall of apples, and act on selective weed-killers.

In one series of experiments, conducted by Kögl, a substance was isolated in a chemically pure state which affects the curvature (cell stretching) in plants. The "growth substance" to be tested—which, for example, is found in the tips of the coleoptile of oats—is placed in contact with cubes of agar-agar, which allow the active material to diffuse into it. If such cubes are placed on the cut area of the coleoptile, curvature results, and the extent of such curvature is proportional to the concentration of active material produced (Fig. 116).

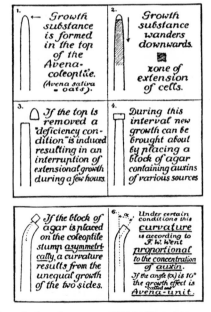

Fig. 116. Estimation of plant hormone. (Kögl: Chemistry and Industry, *57:* 49.)

* One finds various names in the literature: Auxins, growth hormones, growth regulators, phytohormones, growth substances. These include true hormones, like the auxins and indole-3-acetic acid, which are found in the plant, and many substances which affect growth (positively and negatively), but which are not necessarily part of the plant structure.

While the tips of oats and corn, fungi and yeast contain the hormone, Kögl found urine (male and female) to be the most convenient source material. He isolated an active acid, $C_{18}H_{32}O_5$, which formed a lactone and contained three hydroxyl groups. To this was given the name "auxin A." From malt and from maize germ, another acid, $C_{18}H_{30}O_4$, isomeric with the lactone from auxin A, was obtained; this substance was called "auxin B." Exhaustive and beautiful chemical investigation by Kögl, recalling the

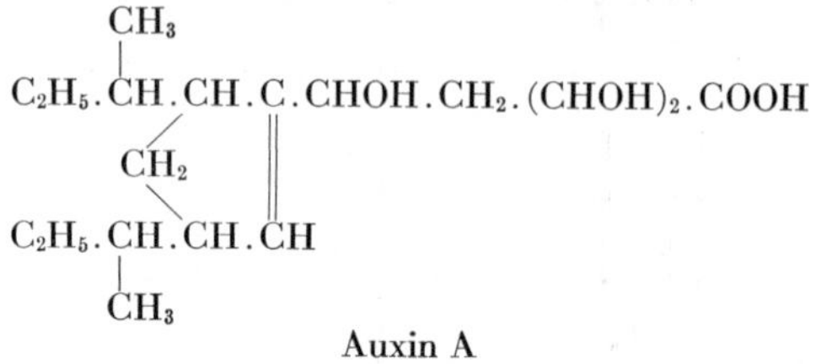

$$CH_3$$
$$|$$
$$C_2H_5.CH.CH.C.CHOH.CH_2.(CHOH)_2.COOH$$
$$CH_2$$
$$C_2H_5.CH.CH.CH$$
$$|$$
$$CH_3$$

Auxin A

$$CH_3$$
$$|$$
$$C_2H_5.CH.CH.C.CHOH.CH_2.CO.CH_2.COOH$$
$$CH_2$$
$$C_2H_5.CH.CH.CH$$
$$|$$
$$CH_3$$

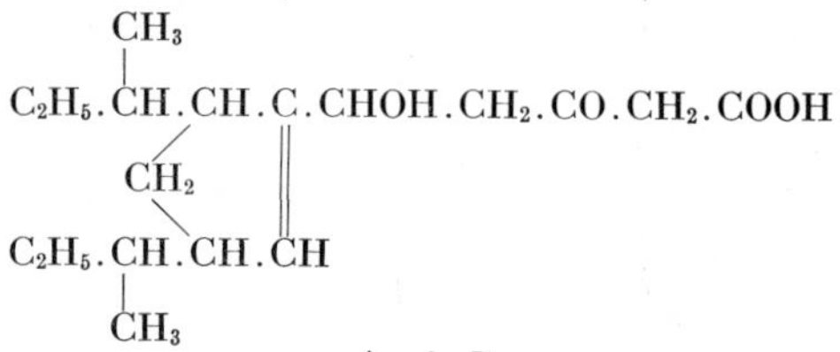

Auxin B

work of Butenandt on the sex hormones, led to structural formulas for these two substances.

Auxin B is the β-keto acid of auxin A.

The auxins probably occur in the plant as protein complexes.

To regulate the effect of auxin, plants also show "antiauxin" effects. One such "antiauxin" has been isolated.

The term "auxin" is now used not only for the natural substances just described, but also for synthetic substances which induce hormone-like responses.

Commoner and Thimann have shown that a close connection exists between growth and respiration. Using the *Avena* coleoptile for their experiments, they have shown that auxin provides a link between growth and respiration. The link is the four-carbon acid respiratory system: malate, fumarate, etc.

The growth of *Avena* coleoptile sections in sucrose solutions is retarded by substances which inhibit dehydrogenase action; for example, iodoacetic acid. This retardation is overcome by malate and fumarate. Respiration is considerably increased if auxin is added to sections of coleoptile soaked in malate and fumarate.

Substances Showing Growth-Promoting Properties. Many substances possess this growth-promoting activity. Kögl isolated from urine a third substance, indole-3-acetic acid, which exhibited marked activity. Curiously enough, this substance is a bacterial decomposition product of proteins derived, more specifically, from tryptophan. Thimann has shown that the growth-promoting substance in mold cultures is this indole deriva-

$$_3C.CH_2.COOH$$
$$_2CH$$
$$N$$
$$H$$

Indole-3-acetic acid

tive; and Haagen-Smit has isolated it from wheat germ. This indole-3-acetic acid, also called "heteroauxin," shows a growth-promoting activity comparable to the auxins themselves.

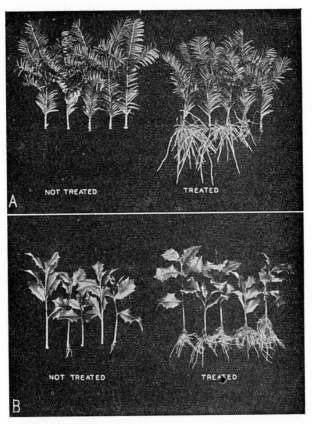

Fig. 117. Cuttings treated with water solution of indolebutyric acid for twenty-four hours, then planted in the rooting medium. *A*, Taxus. *B*, Holly. (Zimmerman: Ohio J. Science, *37:* 333.)

Hitchcock and Zimmerman have tried many substances for their growth-promoting properties and find them very widely distributed—from such a simple substance as ethylene to indole, benzene, naphthalene, and even anthracene derivatives. They found effective root-forming substances to be α-naphthalene acetic acid and indole-3-butyric acid (Fig. 117), although they were not as effective as indole-3-acetic acid for epinastic * response of leaves.

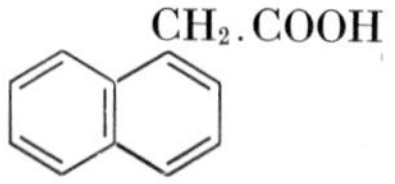

CH$_2$.COOH

—C.CH$_2$.CH$_2$.CH$_2$.COOH
‖
CH

N
H

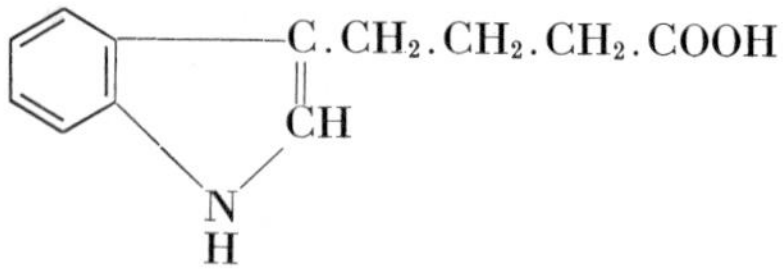

α-Naphthalene   Indole-3-butyric acid
acetic acid

(This property of accelerating root growth is, incidentally, a property possessed by ethylene, which, in addition, can accelerate the ripening of fruit.)

In studying the relation between chemical structure and growth-promoting activity, the following conclusions have been drawn: that the essential groups are an unsaturated or an aromatic ring, a carboxyl group, or one converted to a carboxyl by the plant; and that the carboxyl group must be separated from the ring by one carbon (or oxygen) atom. It is believed that energy-rich phosphate bonds are involved in the growth-promoting effects.

The auxins are also used to prevent premature drop of apples and pears; and a particular auxin, 2,4-D(2,4-dichlorophenoxyacetic acid), is used as a weed-killer.

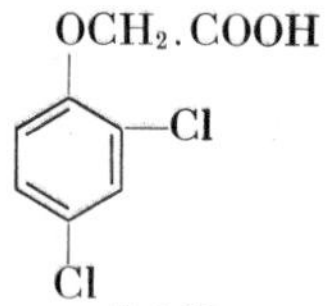

OCH$_2$.COOH

—Cl

Cl
2,4-D

Hormone units in terms of 1 mg. quantities are given below:

Androsterone	10 CU	(a; j)	Estrone	10,000 IU	(b; j)
Benzestrol	25,000 IU	(b)	Estrone	2,666 RU	(c; p)
Benzestrol	1,250 RU	(c)	Estrone	1,000 RU	(c; k; q)
Estradiol	70,000 to 120,000 IU	(b; k)	Estrone		
Estradiol	12,000 RU	(c; m)	benzoate	10,000 IBU	(d)
Estradiol			Insulin	22 IU	(e)
benzoate	70,000 to 120,000 IBU	(d; k)	Progesterone	1 IU	(f)
Estradiol			Progesterone	1 CAU	(g)
benzoate	6,000 RU	(c; m)	Progesterone	2 CIU	(h; q)
Estradiol,			Progesterone	4 to 6 ECU	(i; q)
ethinyl	100,000 IU	(c; n)	Testosterone	70 to 75 CU	(a; m)
Estradiol,			Testosterone		
ethinyl	20,000 IU	(b; n)	propionate	50 CU	(a; m)
Estriol	16,000 IU	(b; n; q)	Testosterone,		
Estriol	1,600 RU	(c; k; q)	methyl	15 CU	(a; m; n)

(a) Capon Units of androgenic potency; (b) International Units of estrogenic potency or Estrone Units; (c) Rat Units of estrogenic potency by Allen-Doisy method; (d) International Benzoate Units of estrogenic potency; (e) International Units of insulin activity; (f) International Units of progestational activity; (g) Corner-Allen Units;

* Downward curvature of a plant member induced by a more active growth on its upper side.

(*h*) Clauberg Rabbit Units; (*i*) European Clinical Units; (*j*) by definition; (*k*) by calculation; (*m*) by experimental finding; (*n*) for oral use only; (*p*) chemical determination, J. Biol. Chem. *116*, 415 (1936); (*q*) conversion data unreliable. (Lange's Handbook of Chemistry, 1949.)

REFERENCES

References to Hormones in General. Turner: General Endocrinology, 1948; *Pincus and Thimann:* The Hormones, 1948, 1950, two volumes; *Emmens:* Hormone Assay, 1950 (methods of estimating hormones); *Bodansky and Bodansky:* Biochemistry of Disease, 1951, chapters 7–11, 13–14; *Harrow:* One Family: Enzymes, Vitamins and Hormones, 1950.

Reviews dealing with progress in the field may be found in Progress in Hormonic Research, edited by *Pincus;* Ann. Rev. Biochem., *19:* 111, 261 (*Pincus; White*); *20:* 227, 343, 1951 (*Lieberman and Dobriner; Barrón*); *21:* 411, 603, 1952 (*Zamecnik; Li and Harris*).

For the assay of hormones, see *Thayer:* Vitamins and Hormones, *4:* 311, 1946.

Thyroid. A book by the foremost authority is *Harington's:* The Thyroid Gland, 1933. *Kendall,* himself a pioneer in the field, is the author of Thyroxine, 1929.

The formation of diiodotyrosine and thyroxine from iodine, using the radioactive isotope, and with the help of thyroid tissue, is described by *Morton and Chaikoff:* J. Biol. Chem., *147:* 1, 1943.

Further references are the following: *McGavick:* The Thyroid, 1951; *Barker:* Physiol. Rev., *31:* 205, 1951 (mechanism of action); *Greer:* Ibid., *30:* 513, 1950 (nutrition and goiter); *Curtis and Fertman:* J. Am. Med. Assoc., *139:* 28, 1949 (iodine in nutrition); *Salter:* Annals N. Y. Acad. Sciences, *50:* 358, 1949 (metabolic circuit of thyroxine); *Chaikoff and Taurig:* Ibid., *50:* 377, 1949 (formation of organically-bound iodine); *Gordon, Gross, O'Connor, and Pitt-Rivers:* Nature, *169:* 19, 1952 (nature of circulating material).

Reineke: Annals N. Y. Acad. Sciences, *50:* 450, 1949 (thyroxine from iodenated proteins); *Weiss and Rosetti:* Proc. Nat. Acad. Sci. U. S., *37:* 540, 1951 (metamorphoses in tadpoles); *Clark, Rule, Trippel, and Cofrin:* J. Am. Med. Assoc., *150:* 1269, 1952 (radioactive iodine in hyperthyroidism).

Pitt-Rivers: Physiol. Rev., *30:* 194, 1950 (mode of action of antithyroid substances); *Astwood:* Annals N. Y. Acad. Sciences, *50:* 418, 1949 (mode of action of antithyroid substances); *Barr:* Bull. N. Y. Acad. Med., May, 1948, p. 287 (thiouracil, etc.).

Parathyroids. The review by *Thompson and Collip:* Physiol. Rev., *12:* 309, 1932, should be consulted. For further work, the following should be consulted; *Albright:* J. Am. Med. Assoc., *117:* 527, 1941 (general review); *Jaffe:* Bull. N. Y. Acad. Med., May, 1940, p. 291 (hyperparathyroidism); *L' Heureux, Tepperman, and Wilhelmi:* J. Biol. Chem., *168:* 167, 1947 (preparation of the hormone).

Anterior Pituitary Hormones. White: Bull. N. Y. Acad. Med., Jan., 1953, p. 11.

Growth Hormone. Li: Harvey Lectures (1950–51), p. 185; *Li, Simpson, and Evans:* J. Biol. Chem., *176:* 843, 1948 (iodination); J. Am. Med. Assoc., *150:* 1602, 1952 (G. H. and carbohydrate metabolism); *Reinhardt and Li:* Science, *117:* 295, 1953 (production of arthritis with G. H.); *Greene:* J. Am. Med. Assoc., *147:* 1096, 1951 (pituitary dwarfism).

Follicle-Stimulating Hormone. Li and Pederson: J. Gen. Physiol., *35:* 629, 1952 (properties of FSH).

Lactogenic Hormone. Li: J. Biol. Chem., *178:* 459, 1949 (amino acid composition).

Thyrotropic Hormone. Albert: Annals N. Y. Acad. Sciences, *50:* 466, 1949; *Rawson:* Ibid., *50:* 491, 1949.

Adrenocorticotropic Hormone. Li: Harvey Lectures (1950–51), p. 196; *Lesh, Fisher, Bunding, Koesis, Walaszek, White, and Hays:* Science, *112:* 43, 1950; *Geschwind, Hess, Condiffe, and Williams:* Ibid., *111:* 625, 1950.

Brink, Meisinger, and Folkers: J. Am. Chem. Soc., *72:* 1040, 1950; *Li, Ash, and Papkoff:* Ibid., *74:* 1923, 1952 (activity of of peptides); *Ingle:* Annals Internal Medicine, *35:* 652, 1951 (relation of anterior pituitary to adrenal cortex); Bull. N. Y. Acad. Med., April, 1950 (ACTH and cortisone).

Posterior Pituitary Hormones. J. Am. Med. Assoc., *151:* 914, 1953; *Turner, Pierce, and Du Vigneaud:* J. Biol. Chem., *191:* 21, 1951 (vasopressin); *Pierce, Gordon, and Du Vigneaud:* Ibid., *199:* 929, 1952; *Du Vigneaud, Ressler, Swan, Roberts,*

Katsoyannis, and Gordon: J. Am. Chem. Soc., *75:* 4879 (1953) (oxytocin).

Insulin. Stetten, Jr.: Bull. N. Y. Acad. Med., June, 1953, p. 466 (metabolism); *Chaikoff:* Harvey Lectures (1951–52), p. 99 (metabolism); *Ricketts:* J. Am. Med. Assoc., *150:* 959, 1952 (diabetes); *Sherry:* Bull. N. Y. Acad. Med., March, 1953 (diabetes); *Heard, Lozinski, and Stewart:* J. Biol. Chem., *172:* 857, 1948 (α-cell hormone); *Sutherland, Cori, Haynes, and Olsen:* Ibid., *180:* 825, 1949 (H-G factor); *Staub, Sinn, and Behrens:* Science, *117:* 628, 1953 (H-G factor); *Zimmermann and Donovan:* Am. J. Physiol., *153:* 197, 1948 (H-G factor); J. Am. Med. Assoc., *148:* 373, 1952 (NPH insulin); *Fisher:* Canadian Medical Assoc. J., *65:* 20, 1952 (NPH insulin); Nutr. Rev., *9:* 82, 1951 (alloxan and insulin secretion); *Sutherland and Cori:* J. Biol. Chem., *188:* 531, 1951; *Somogyi:* Ibid., *186:* 513, 1950; *Stadie, etc.:* Ibid., *188:* 173, 1951; *Chaikoff, etc.:* Ibid., *193:* 459, 1951 (regulating glucose metabolism by hormones).

Epinephrine. Gurin and Delluva: J. Biol. Chem., *170:* 545, 1947 (phenylalanine $\longrightarrow$ epinephrine); *Schayer, Smiley, and Kaplan:* Ibid., *198:* 545, 1952 (metabolism).

Norepinephrine. Goldenberg, Apgar, Deterling, and Pines: J. Am. Med. Assoc., *140:* 776, 1949; *Goldenberg, Faber, Alston, and Chargaff:* Science, *109:* 534, 1949; *Shepherd and Best:* J. Physiol., *120:* 15, 1953; *Burn:* Irish J. Medical Science, Aug., 1951, p. 345; *Crawford:* Biochem. J., *48:* 203, 1951.

Adrenal cortex. Annals N. Y. Acad. Sciences, *50:* 509–678, 1949; *Mulholland:* Surgical Clinics of North America, *32:* 347, 1952; Nutr. Rev., *8:* 25, 1950 (adrenals and ascorbic acid); Ibid., *8:* 173, 1950 (protein and carbohydrate metabolism); Ibid., *11:* 41, 1953 (Na^+ metabolism); *Zaffaroni and Burton:* J. Biol. Chem., *193:* 749, 1951 (identifying corticosteroids by paper chromatography).

For a review of Reichstein's work on the chemistry of the corticosteroids, see Chimia, *4:* 21, 47, 1950; and Bulletin der Schweizerischen Akadamie der Medizinischen Wissenschaften, *7:* 359, 1951 (both in German).

For cortisone and ACTH, see Bull. N. Y. Acad. Med., April 1950; Scope (Upjohn Co.), Spring, 1952; *Kendall:* Federation Proceedings, *9:* 501, 1950 (compounds in adrenal cortex and arthritis);

Kendall: Chem. Eng. News, *28:* 2074, 1950 (cortisone); *Bunim:* Bull. N. Y. Acad. Med., Feb., 1951, p. 75; *Hench, Slocumb, Polley, and Kendall:* J. Am. Med. Assoc., *144:* 1327, 1950 (cortisone and ACTH in rheumatic diseases); Merck Report, Oct., 1950, pp. 4, 9 (cortisone—its history).

17-Ketosteroids, etc. Mason and Engstrom: Physiol. Rev., *30:* 321, 1950; *Koets:* Stanford Medical Bulletin, Feb., 1947, p. 42; *Pincus:* J. Clinical Endocrinology, *5:* 291, 1945 (analysis of urines for steroids).

For the literature dealing with compound E in arthritis, see Nutr. Rev., *7:* 290, 1949; *Boland and Headley,* J. Am. Med. Assoc., *141:* 301, 1949; *Addinall,* Merck Report, Oct., 1949, p. 4; *Marker and Applezweig,* Chem. Eng. News, *27:* 3348, 1949.

Sex Hormones. For a general review, see *Allen:* Sex and Internal Secretions, 1943 (articles by specialists), in which the biological aspect is stressed. See also *Burrow:* Biological Action of the Sex Hormones, 1950. The chemistry of the compounds is emphasized by *Fieser:* The Chemistry of Natural Products Related to Phenanthrene, 1937, Chap. 5.

Estrogens. J. Am. Med. Assoc., *141:* 390, 1949 (estradiol, the benzoate and the dipropionate); *Lodogar and Jones:* Science, *112:* 536, 1950 (estradiol $\longrightarrow$ estrone); *Heard and Saffran:* Recent Progress in Hormone Research, 1949, pp. 25, 43 (metabolism of estrogens); *Albert, Heard, Leblond, and Saffron:* J. Biol. Chem., *177:* 247, 1949 (metabolism); *Coppedge, Segaloff, and Sarett:* Ibid., *182:* 181, 1950 (DPN necessary for metabolism); *Axelrod:* Ibid., *201:* 59, 1953 (separation of estrogens by paper chromatography); *Grant and Marrian:* Biochem. J., *47:* 1, 1950 (isolation from urine as glucuronide); *Johnson, Banerjee, Schneider, Gutsche, Shelberg, and Chinn:* J. Am. Chem. Soc., *74:* 2832, 1952 (synthesis of estrone).

Hochster and Quastel: Nature, *164:* 865, 1949 (stilbestrol as a competitive hydrogen carrier).

Mason: J. Clinical Endocrinology, *8:* 190, 1948 (steroid nomenclature).

Androgens. Samuels, Sweat, Levedahl, Pottner, and Helmreich: J. Biol. Chem., *183:* 231, 1950; *West and Samuels:* Ibid., *190:* 827, 1951 (metabolism of testosterone); *West, Reich, and Samuels:* Ibid., *193:* 219, 1951 (urinary metabolites); *Brady:*

Ibid., *193:* 145, 1951 (biosynthesis of testosterone).

Hormones and Cancer. J. Am. Med. Assoc., *146:* 471, 1951 (mammary cancer); *Sicé and Mednick:* J. Am. Chem. Soc., *75:* 1628, 1953 (hormonal antimetabolites); J. Am. Med. Assoc., *149:* 1400, 1952 (review); *Funk, Tomashefsky, Soukup, and Ehrlich:* British J. Cancer, *5:* 280, 1951; *Craver:* Bull. N. Y. Acad. Med., June, 1952, p. 385 (review); *Taylor, Ayer, and Morris:* J. Am. Med. Assoc., *144:* 1058, 1950 (use of cortical steroids).

Gastrointestinal Hormones. Grossman: Physiol. Rev., *30:* 33, 1950.

Plant Hormones. Went and Thimann: Phytohormones, 1937; *Kögl:* J. Society of Chemical Industry, *57:* 49, 1938; *Schocken:* Scientific American, May, 1949, p. 40 (review); *Rhodes and Ashworth:* Nature, *169:* 76, 1952 (mode of action); *Roberts:* Science, *117:* 456, 1953 (antiauxin); *Smith and Wain:* Proc. R. S. (London), Series B, *139:* 118, 1951 (growth activity of α [2-napthoxy] propionic acid).

Chapter 24   *Detoxication*

THAT detoxication is not always a conversion of a toxic to a nontoxic body is made clear by one or two examples. For instance, the female sex hormone is eliminated (to some extent, at least) as a glucuronate and the male sex hormone (also to some extent) as the sulfate. Obviously, neither of these hormones, of importance to the body, can be considered as a toxic substance. Again, as Quick points out, the formation of taurocholic acid from cholic acid and glycine—a normal metabolic process—cannot, in reality, be distinguished from a detoxication involving glycine in other reactions.

The word "detoxication" has been used for so many years that it may be convenient to retain it. However, it should be made clear that under this term we cover "the chemical changes which foreign organic compounds undergo in the animal body" (Williams). In fact, "detoxication" deals very largely (though not entirely) with the metabolism of substances other than fat, protein, and carbohydrate.

The toxic substances produced in the large intestine and discussed in Chap. 7 are largely eliminated in the stool; those which are not, are detoxified—that is, absorbed, combined in the liver or kidney with perhaps sulfuric or glucuronic acid, and then eliminated through the kidneys into the urine.

In a general way, it may be said that, in the attempt to detoxify a substance introduced into the body, several methods are employed; toxic material may be oxidized or the toxic substance may combine with glucuronic acid, sulfuric acid, one of the amino acids, etc., and thereby bring about a detoxified product.

In Chap. 7 we discussed the production of indole from tryptophan, a bacterial change brought about in the large intestine. Much of the indole is eliminated in the feces. Some of it is absorbed, partially oxidized, and combined with sulfuric acid to form indican, which is eliminated in the urine.

The amount of indican in the urine may be indicative of the extent of putrefaction in the large intestine.

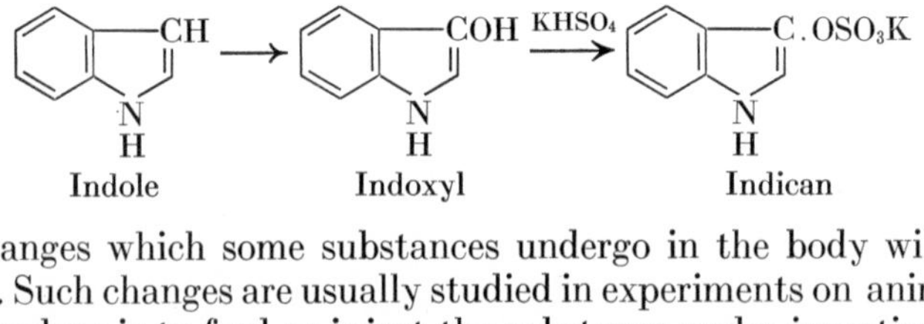

| Indole | Indoxyl | Indican |

The changes which some substances undergo in the body will now be discussed. Such changes are usually studied in experiments on animals. The usual procedure is to feed or inject the substance under investigation into the animal (dog, rabbit, etc.), collect the urine over a given period of time, and recover from it changed and unchanged material. The practical difficulties are often very great, and much of the information at present is in a very incomplete state.

The tissue slice technique developed by Warburg is also employed.

ENZYMES

It should be emphasized at the very outset that the chemical changes which these substances (described in this chapter) undergo in the body are brought about by the action of enzymes. If no mention is made of such enzymes, it is merely because few enzymic studies have been undertaken. Until recently investigators were content with studying the chemical changes involved, and this important phase of the work is still being pursued, but a more complete answer will be obtained when, together with the chemical work, enzymic studies are made of such reactions.

In connection with such enzyme studies, the question at once arises whether these catalysts are specific for the many *un*physiological compounds which constitute this chapter. Two possibilities exist, which are not mutually exclusive. One possibility is that the enzyme which catalyzes a reaction involving a foreign compound also carries out a similar function with physiological compounds, provided both the foreign and the physiological compound contain similar chemical groupings. One such example is the enzyme which brings about the acetylation of sulfanilamide (p. 492)— a "foreign" compound, in so far as the body is concerned—and requires coenzyme A for the transfer of the acetyl group and acetylations involved in such cases as the formation of acetylcholine (p. 404).

Another possibility is that the enzyme which acts on the "foreign" compound is normally not an enzyme at all but merely some protein; and the "foreign" substance fits in certain groupings of the protein. A possible example is the discovery in the liver and kidney of rabbits of an enzyme which is capable of catalyzing the hydrolytic cleavage of the phosphorus-fluorine linkage in diiosopropyl fluorophosphate.

OXIDATION

In a general way, it may be said that aliphatic compounds are more easily oxidized than aromatic ones. It is true that this does not apply to α-amino acids attached to aromatic nuclei. These are, of course, foods and not poisonous products. For example, so far as we know, phenylalanine and tyrosine, both containing the benzene nucleus, are quite readily oxidized in the animal organism. On the other hand, the fate of benzene itself is still largely a matter of dispute. Many years ago, Jaffe claimed to have isolated muconic acid as a result of feeding benzene; this has been confirmed by Drummond and others.

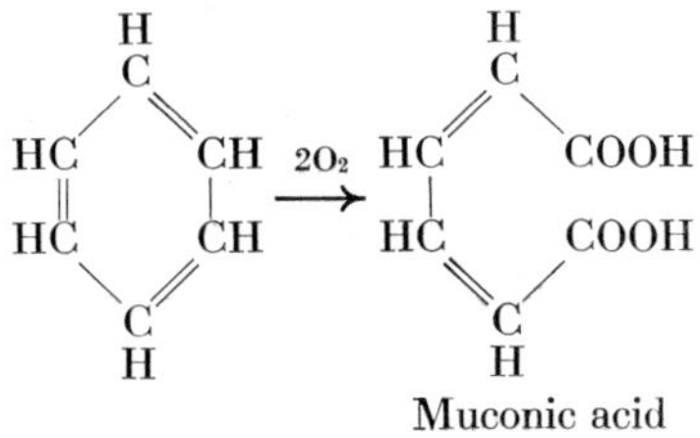

Muconic acid

However, some of this benzene is converted into phenol by both man and the dog. Some of the phenol, in turn, is excreted in conjugated form, partly with sulfuric acid and partly with glucuronic acid and with cystine.

Using benzene labelled with C^{14}, Williams has shown that 45 per cent of the dose is eliminated in expired air: 43 per cent as unchanged benzene, and some of the rest as CO_2. At the same time, 35 per cent of the benzene appears in the urine as the following end products (in per cent of dose): phenol, 23; quinol, 5; catechol, 2; hydroxyquinol, 0.3; phenylmercapturic acid, 0.5; and muconic acid, 1.3.

Toluene and ethylbenzene are oxidized to some extent to benzoic acid. With m-xylene, $C_6H_4(CH_3)_2$, containing two methyl groups, one methyl group is oxidized to a carboxylic acid group. This is also true of mesitylene, the symmetrical trimethylbenzene, $C_6H_3(CH_3)_3$, which, when ingested, has but one of its CH_3 groups converted to COOH.

Among the aliphatic alcohols, methyl alcohol is oxidized in the body to formaldehyde and then to formic acid. It is a highly toxic substance and often gives rise to incurable blindness.

A large part of ethyl alcohol is first oxidized to acetaldehyde and then to acetic acid; this takes place largely in the liver. The ultimate oxidation products are carbon dioxide and water. Ninety per cent of the radioactive carbon-14 in ethyl alcohol, for example, is excreted as radioactive CO_2 in the expired breath in the course of ten hours.

Primary aromatic alcohols are often oxidized to the corresponding carboxylic acids. For example, benzyl alcohol, $C_6H_5.CH_2.OH$, is converted to benzoic acid, C_6H_5COOH; and phenylethyl alcohol, $C_6H_5.CH_2.CH_2.OH$, to phenylacetic acid, $C_6H_5.CH_2.COOH$.

Aromatic aldehydes are usually oxidized to the corresponding carboxylic acids. Benzaldehyde, $C_6H_5.CHO$, for example, is converted into benzoic acid. Vanillin is oxidized to vanillic acid:

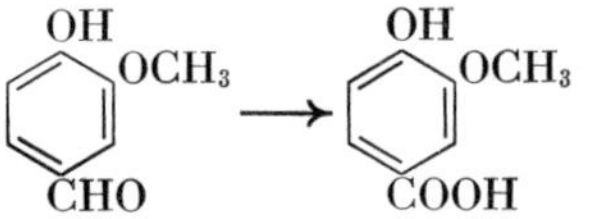

Vanillin   Vanillic acid

Whereas aliphatic amines—like aliphatic compounds, in general—are apt to be destroyed by the body, aromatic amines are sometimes converted to carboxylic acids. Benzylamine, $C_6H_5.CH_2NH_2$ is oxidized to benzoic acid. Where, however, the NH_2 group is attached to the benzene nucleus, the results are different. For example, aniline, $C_6H_5.NH_2$, itself, is oxidized to p-aminophenol,

p-Aminophenol

though it is finally excreted in combination with sulfuric acid and possibly glucuronic acid.

Histamine, the important pharmacological base derived from the amino acid histidine (p. 57), has been studied using the base labelled with C^{14} in the imidazol ring. The major excretory products appear to be compounds whose imidazol ring has been modified.

Acetanilid, $C_6H_5 \cdot NH \cdot CO \cdot CH_3$, is oxidized to p-acetylaminophenol, $HO \cdot C_6H_4 \cdot NH \cdot CO \cdot CH_3$, and is excreted as the glucuronide and ethereal sulfate.

Naphthalene, 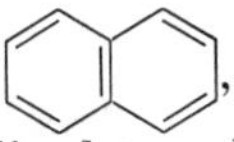 , phenanthrene, 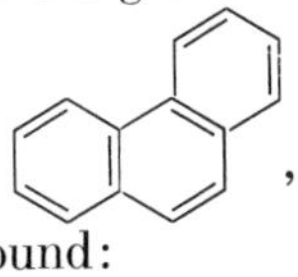 , and anthracene are partially oxidized to a dihydroxy compound:

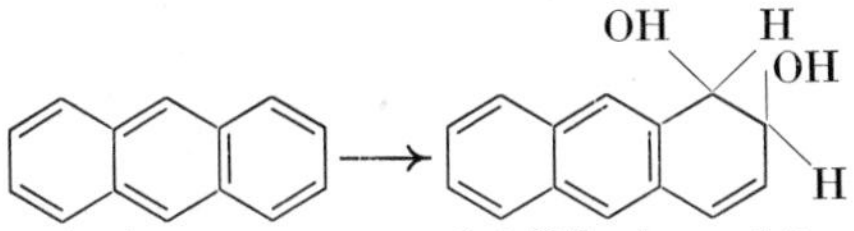

Anthracene   1,2-Dihydroxy-1,2-dihydroanthracene

although some also combines with glucuronic acid.

REDUCTION

Though less common than oxidation, reduction of substances in the animal body does occur. (We exclude here reactions in the large intestine, where reducing bacteria are very active.) A classic example of this type of reaction is the conversion of picric acid into picramic acid:

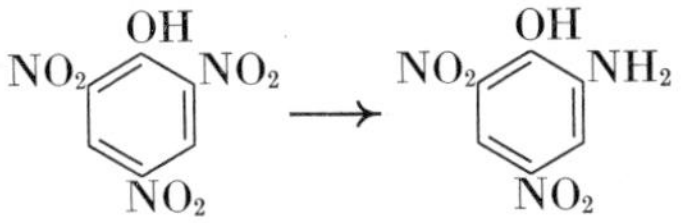

Picric acid Picramic acid

Sometimes a simultaneous reduction and oxidation within the same compound will occur; for example, when rabbits are fed p-nitrobenzaldehyde they excrete appreciable quantities of p-aminobenzoic acid:

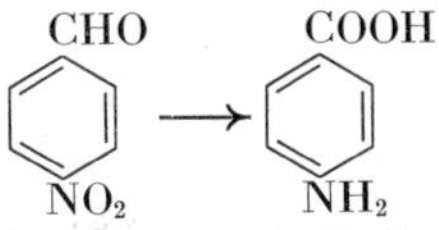

p-Nitroben- p-Aminoben-
zaldehyde zoic acid

Nitro compounds, as a fairly general rule, are converted to the corresponding amino compounds. The simplest aromatic nitro derivative nitrobenzene, $C_6H_5NO_2$, reacts similarly to p-nitrobenzaldehyde, because reduction and oxidation occur, to give rise to p-aminophenol:

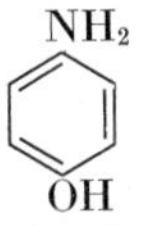

p-Aminophenol

It is interesting to note that both aniline and p-nitrophenol, $HO \cdot C_6H_4 \cdot NO_2$, also form p-aminophenol.

2,4-Dinitrophenol, one of a number of nitrophenols which affect basal metabolism, yields a mixture of compounds.

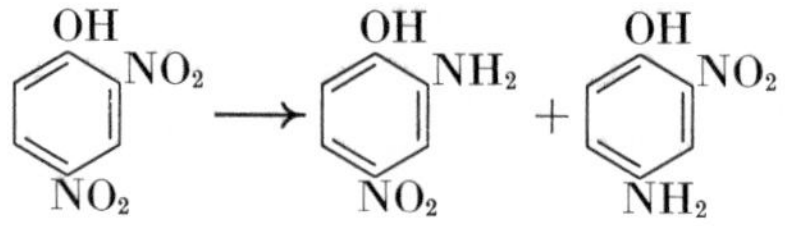

2,4-Dinitrophenol   2-Amino-4-   2-Nitro-4-
nitrophenol   aminophenol

2,4,6-Trinitrotoluene (T.N.T.) is partially reduced to 2,6-dinitro-4-aminotoluene:

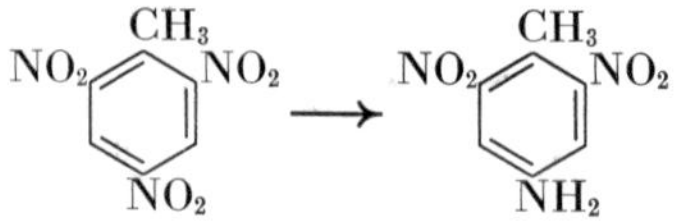

and also partially excreted as the glucuronide.

CONJUGATION

Where oxidation fails, conjugation becomes an alternate (or added) procedure. (As we have seen, a substance like anthracene can be partly oxidized and partly conjugated.) Conjugation involves the combination of the toxic product with some substance available to the body to form a detoxified product which is then eliminated. The substances known to be used by the body for detoxifying purposes are glycine, glutamine, ornithine, cysteine, sulfuric acid, glucuronic acid, acetic acid, and the methyl group.

Glycine. This amino acid seems to attach itself to acids in particular. The well-known example is the production of hippuric acid by feeding benzoic acid:

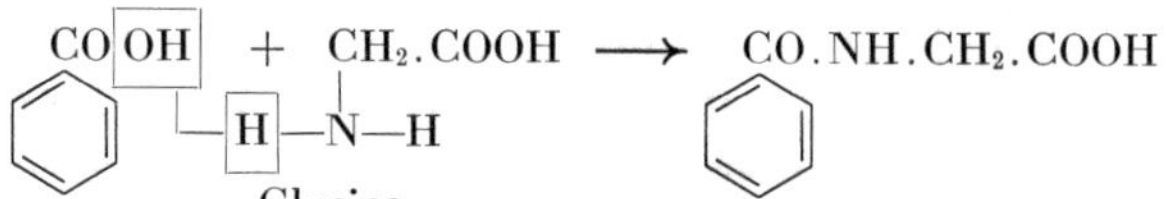

Benzoic acid   Glycine   Hippuric acid

However, combination of acids with glucuronic acid is also common.

It might be expected that o-hydroxybenzoic acid, which is the compound of pharmacological importance known as salicylic acid, would also be detoxified in the body by combining with glycine; and, in fact, the main product in man is salicyluric acid,

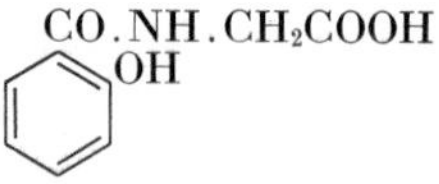

Salicyluric acid

(the combination of salicylic acid and glycine). Some gentisic acid,

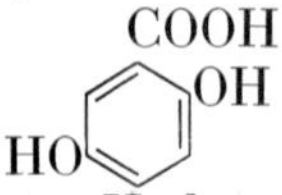

is also formed.

p-Hydroxybenzoic acid is excreted partly uncombined and partly conjugated with glycine.

In dealing with detoxifying agents, it should be pointed out that because the horse forms hippuric acid when it is fed benzoic acid, one cannot necessarily conclude that hippuric acid will always be formed, irrespective of the animal used. As a matter of fact, in this instance, with one exception, every vertebrate so far tried forms hippuric acid. The one exception is the fowl, which uses ornithine in the place of glycine.

Niacin is partly conjugated with glycine in the body to form nicotinuric acid:

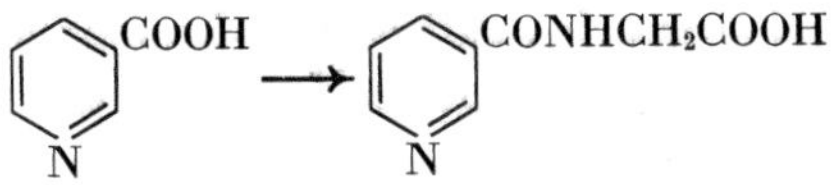

Glutamine.   This amide of glutamic acid is an active detoxifying agent only in human beings and in the chimpanzee, at least so far as the record up to the present is concerned. The ingestion of phenylacetic acid by a human being will cause the production of phenylacetylglutamine, a product which can be isolated from the urine:

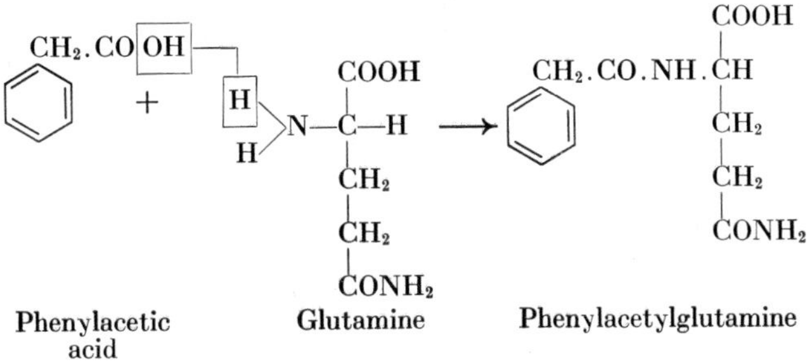

Phenylacetic   Glutamine   Phenylacetylglutamine
acid

As illustrating once again the difference in behavior depending upon the animal used, in the fowl, phenylacetic acid combines with ornithine, and in most other animals, phenylacetic acid combines partly with glycine and partly with glucuronic acid.

Ornithine.   As has already been indicated, the fowl is the one animal that utilizes ornithine for detoxifying purposes. With phenylacetic acid the reaction is as follows:

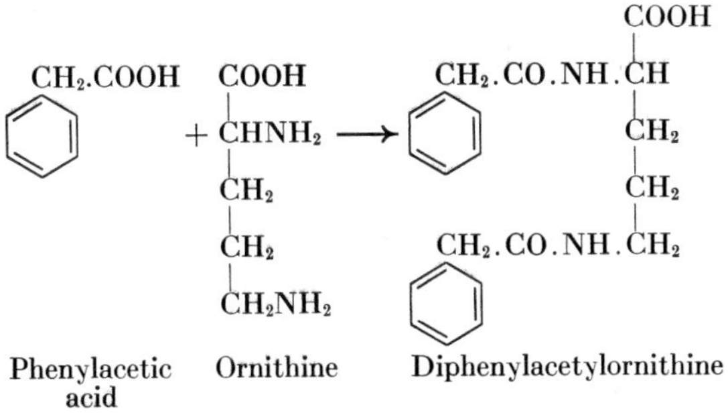

Phenylacetic   Ornithine   Diphenylacetylornithine
acid

Cysteine.   The feeding of bromobenzene to dogs results in the formation of a mercapturic acid; which means that cysteine is used for detoxifying purposes. (The amino group of the cysteine is acetylated at the same time.)

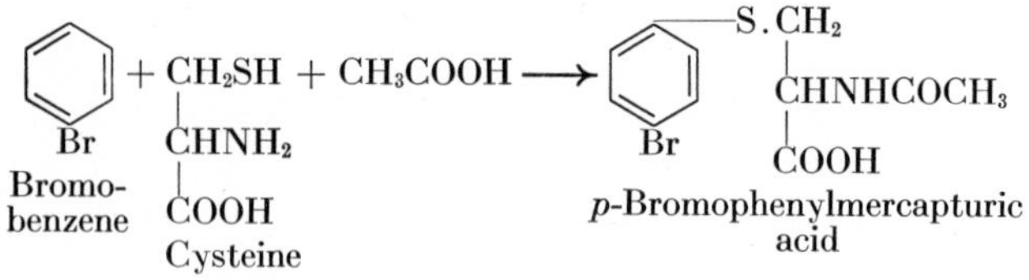

Some of the bromobenzene is oxidized to p-bromophenol, and the latter is excreted partly in combination with sulfuric acid and partly in combination with glucuronic acid.

Chlorobenzene, iodobenzene, and fluorobenzene are converted into the corresponding mercapturic acid derivatives.

An important contribution to cysteine as a detoxifying agent we owe to Bourne and Young. They discovered that in rabbits naphthalene is partially converted into its mercapturic acid:*

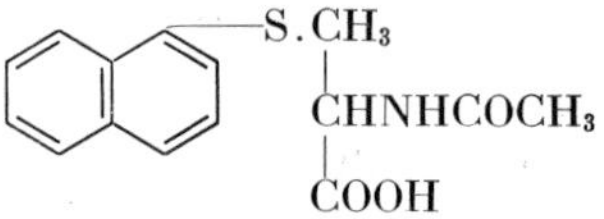

Naphthylmercapturic acid

Some of the napthalene is also excreted in combination with glucuronic and sulfuric acids.

There is evidence at hand that anthracene is detoxicated in a similar manner; and some claim this to be true also of phenanthrene.

Small quantities of phenylmercapturic acid have been isolated by Young after administering benzene to rats.

The evidence for the formation of mercapturic acid with benzene and phenanthrene is an increased neutral sulfur excretion when they are administered. Further evidence is afforded by the fact that on certain synthetic diets the growth of rats is inhibited when phenanthrene (or naphthalene or bromobenzene) is added to the diet. Probably the explanation is that phenanthrene attaches itself to cystine (or other sulfur-containing compounds), thereby making the latter unavailable to the animal. If phenanthrene and cystine (or methionine) are simultaneously added to the diet, no deficiency occurs.

Ethereal Sulfates.   The well-known example of the formation of indican from indole (p. 482) is an instance of this type of detoxication. Phenol behaves similarly:

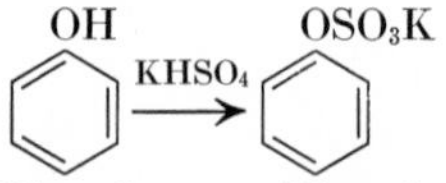

* When naphthalene is repeatedly administered to rabbits, the crystalline lens of the eye undergoes degeneration—a process which resembles that observed in human senile cataract.

In general, phenolic hydroxy compounds have a tendency to form such sulfate combinations, although androsterone, one of the male hormones and a secondary alcohol, combines with sulfuric acid.

Not only is part of the phenol conjugated (with sulfuric and glucuronic acids) but part of it is oxidized and part of it excreted unchanged. (In many of these detoxication experiments one finds very appreciable quantities of the ingested material in the urine.)

In the case of a methyl substituted phenol, such as p-cresol, $HO.-C_6H_4.CH_3$, this substance, when ingested, is first converted to p-hydroxy-benzoic acid, $HO.C_6H_4.COOH$, and then probably converted to the corresponding sulfate or glucuronate salts.

α-Naphthol, 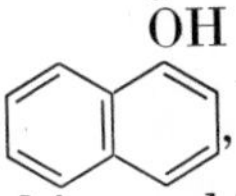 , and β-naphthol, 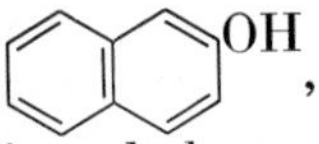 , like phenol itself, are excreted in combination with sulfuric and glucuronic acids.

Acetanilid is first oxidized to p-acetaminophenol and finally excreted in combination with sulfuric and glucuronic acids.

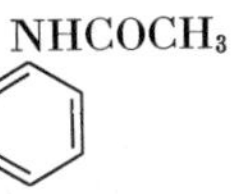

Acetanilid

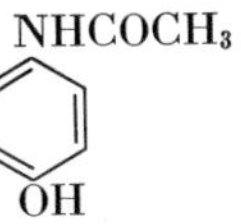

p-Acetaminophenol

It would seem that the administration of epinephrine markedly increases the elimination of ethereal sulfates. This suggests that the inactivation of epinephrine in the body is not necessarily accomplished by, say, oxidative destruction, but by coupling it with sulfuric acid.

Glucuronic Acid.   Combinations with this acid are extremely common. Many compounds containing hydroxyl or carboxyl groups—or compounds which are first changed in the body to such derivatives—form conjugates with glucuronic acid.

Benzoic acid combines not only with glycine but also with glucuronic acid to form 1-benzoylglucuronic acid:

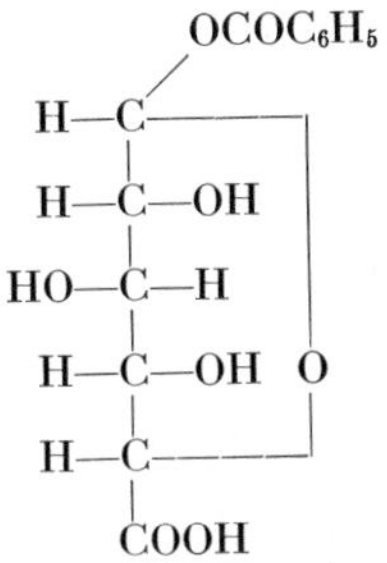

1-Benzoylglucuronic acid

The same is true of phenol; it also combines with glucuronic acid (as well as with sulfuric acid) to form phenolglucuronic acid:

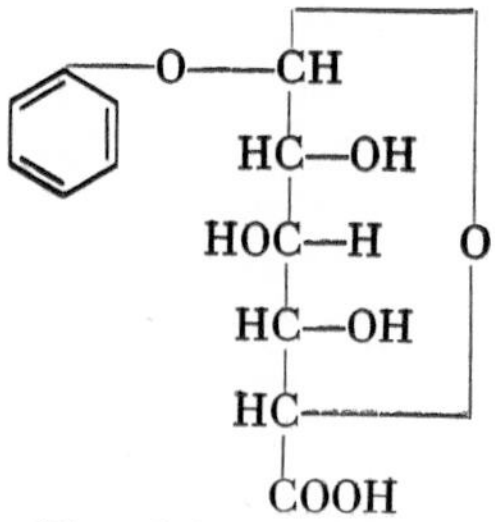

$$\begin{array}{c} \text{C}_6\text{H}_5\text{---O---CH} \\ \text{HC---OH} \\ \text{HOC---H} \quad \text{O} \\ \text{HC---OH} \\ \text{HC---} \\ \text{COOH} \end{array}$$

Phenolglucuronic acid

The combination of benzoic acid with glucuronic acid can be shown in the pig, the dog, the sheep, and in humans. In humans, some 5 per cent may be eliminated as the glucuronide. The maximum excretion occurs in the first three hours, and detoxication is complete in nine to fifteen hours, depending on the amount of benzoic acid ingested.

Phenylacetic acid, the first homologue of benzoic acid, is also eliminated as a glucuronide to the extent of about 7.5 per cent.

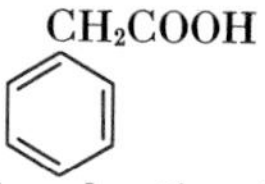

$$\text{CH}_2\text{COOH}$$

Phenylacetic acid

The synthetic female hormone, stilbestrol, is partly converted into the monoglucuronide:

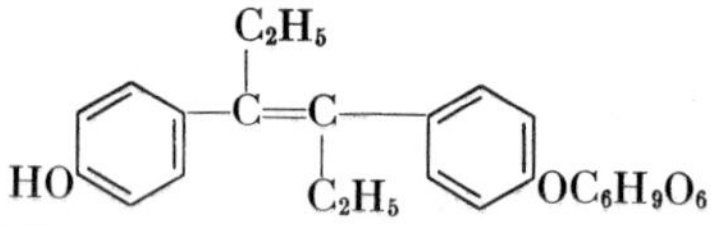

$$\text{C}_2\text{H}_5$$
$$\text{HO}\text{---}\text{C}=\text{C}\text{---}\text{OC}_6\text{H}_9\text{O}_6$$
$$\text{C}_2\text{H}_5$$

The indicator (and drug) phenolphthalein is detoxified, to some extent at least, as its glucuronide.

Anthracene is not only partially oxidized, as we have seen, but combines to some extent with cysteine to form a mercapturic acid, and combines to some extent with glucuronic acid to form a glucuronide.

Marrian has shown that the female sex hormones are eliminated, to a certain extent, as glucuronates.

Borneol, the secondary alcohol obtained from camphor when the latter is reduced, combines almost exclusively with glucuronic acid. In humans,

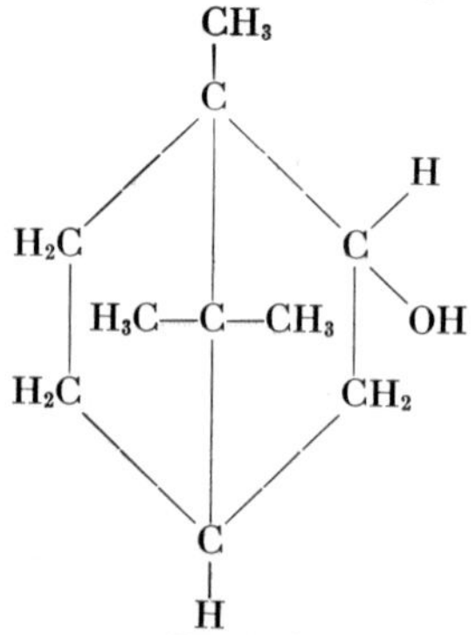

$$\begin{array}{c} \text{CH}_3 \\ \text{C} \\ \text{H}_2\text{C} \qquad \text{C---H} \\ \text{H}_3\text{C---C---CH}_3 \quad \text{OH} \\ \text{H}_2\text{C} \qquad \text{CH}_2 \\ \text{C} \\ \text{H} \end{array}$$

Borneol

the ingestion of borneol results in the excretion in twenty-four hours of some 90 per cent or more in the form of its glucuronide. The maximum excretion occurs in from three to six hours, and the detoxication is complete in about fifteen hours.

The combination of borneol (and menthol or phenol) with glucuronic acid may also be shown by using liver slices in a saline medium (at pH 7.4), to which borneol is added, and shaking the mixture in a Warburg apparatus.

Sulfapyridine is eliminated, to some extent, as a glucuronide of a hydroxysulfapyridine.

Glycoside formation in plants might correspond to the formation of glucuronides in animals, in the sense that, as a rule, less toxic substances are produced.

The mechanism of the biosynthesis of glucuronic acid really involves two problems: the mechanism of the synthesis of glucuronic acid itself, and the mode of conjugation. If glucuronic acid itself is conjugated with the substance, then the two problems are distinct. However, it is possible that conjugation occurs not directly with glucuronic acid but with some precursor. That glucose itself may be such a precursor has been suggested. One such experiment involved the use of $1\text{-}C^{14}\text{-}$glucose, which was administered to a rabbit with menthol; the menthol glucuronide isolated from the urine showed most of the radioactivity on C_1 of the glucuronic acid portion.

It has also been suggested that the origin of glucuronic acid may be traced to the combination of two trioses, one a lactate and another formed from glucose.

An enzyme, β-glucuronidase, hydrolyzes glucuronides, and some claim has been made that it can also act in the reverse direction by causing "coupling" of glucuronic acid with various substances.

Glucuronidase is present in animal tissues, mostly in the spleen and liver. Interest in this enzyme has centered about its ability to hydrolyze glucuronides of the estrogens (female sex hormones) which are normally present in the animal organism. In fact, it has been shown that there is a correlation between the tissue glucuronidase activity and the process of cell proliferation.

Acetic Acid.   This acid is used by the organism for the detoxication of amino groups. One such example has already been given in the formation of the mercapturic acids. Another well-known example is the acetylation of p-aminobenzoic acid:

	COOH		COOH
	$\rightarrow$		
	NH$_2$		NHCOCH$_3$
	p-Amino- benzoic acid		p-Acetylamino- benzoic acid

Insulin markedly increases the output of p-acetylaminobenzoic acid. That this is a result of a stimulating effect on carbohydrate metabolisms seems probable.

Reduced glutathione alone has no effect upon the acetylation process.

But the simultaneous injections of insulin and glutathione very definitely inhibit the output of p-acetylaminobenzoic acid. Such a result is probably due to the inactivation of insulin by glutathione.

Approximately 25 per cent of the p-aminobenzoic acid can be accounted for as the acetylated product. Some of the acid is also eliminated in the form of the glucuronate.

Sulfanilamide is largely excreted in the form of the acetylated derivative:

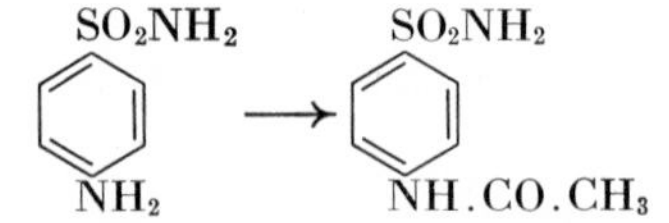

Sulfanilamide (p-aminobenzene-sulfonamide) → p-Acetylamino-benzene-sulfonamide

From 50 to 90 per cent of the sulfanilamide administered can be accounted for by the acetylated and the free drug which is eliminated in the urine. However, there is an increase in the output of ethereal sulfate, and this suggests that some of the sulfanilamide is changed in the body to a hydroxy compound, possibly a phenol (p-aminophenol?), which is then eliminated in the combined form with sulfate.

Lipmann has shown that the acetylation of sulfanilamide—and acetylations in general—is brought about by an enzyme system which includes coenzyme A, a derivative of pantothenic acid (p. 367).

The derivatives of sulfanilamide, such as sulfapyridine and sulfathiazole (p. 506), are also eliminated to some extent as their acetylated compounds, though—like sulfanilamide itself—they are partly oxidized to phenolic compounds which then combine with sulfuric and glucuronic acids.

The acetylation process is carried out not only by animals but even by a mold, *Neurospora crassa*.

Methylation.   It was supposed for a time that this type of detoxication was not common. One of the few examples quoted was the conversion of pyridine to a methyl derivative:

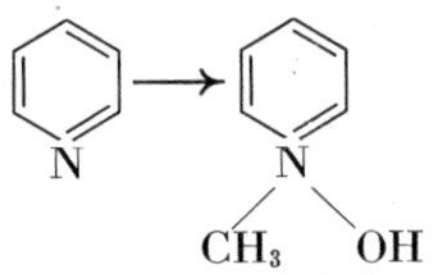

Pyridine   Methyl hydroxy-pyridine

However, it has now been shown that methylation in the body is very common. Both choline and methionine, for example, can supply their methyl groups for various needs.

In this connection it may be mentioned that a compound closely related to pyridine, namely niacin, is methylated to some extent in the body, forming N'-methylnicotinamide:

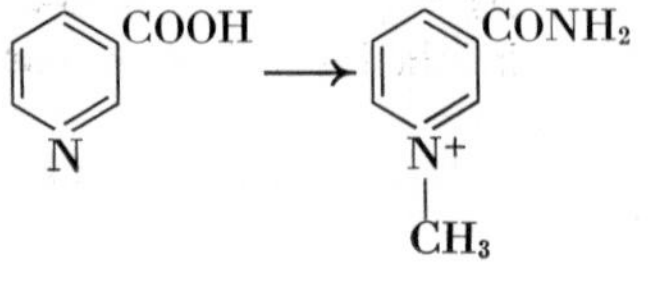

The methyl group required for this reaction is probably derived from methionine.

Thiocyanate.   The thiocyanate found in saliva, etc., is derived from cyanides (which are derived from fruits, the breakdown of proteins, and tobacco smoke). Since the cyanides are toxic whereas the thiocyanates are not, this is indeed a detoxication process.

The conversion of cyanide to thiocyanate is brought about by an enzyme (rhodanase) in the presence of a suitable compound of sulfur.

THE LIVER AND DETOXICATION

In the main, the liver seems to be the seat for the detoxicating process, although experiments are not wanting to prove that often the kidney and other organs function also.

Using the tissue slice technique, Borsook has found that in the guinea-pig, rabbit, and rat, hippuric acid synthesis (conjugation of benzoic acid and glycine) can occur in both kidney and the liver, whereas in the dog it occurs in the kidney but not the liver.

It is interesting to note that when the tissue cell structure is destroyed by maceration or poisoned with toluene or cyanide, no synthesis takes place.

Detoxicating reactions have been suggested at various times for testing organic function. They have met with varying success.

GLUTATHIONE

Aside from a possible role which glutathione plays in oxidative mechanisms, the suggestion has been advanced that it may be of importance as a detoxifying agent. It is, to say the least, extremely suggestive that this polypeptide consists of three amino acids (glycine, cysteine, glutamic acid), each one of which is known to act as a detoxifying agent. Evidence in favor of this view has been presented.

REFERENCES

A masterly introduction to the subject is by *Williams:* Detoxication Mechanisms, 1947.

A review of recent work will be found in the article by *Williams:* Ann. Rev. Biochem., *20:* 441, 1951.

References to the metabolism of benzene and other aromatic hydrocarbons are *Williams:* Ann. Rev. Biochem., *20:* 453, 1951. See also *Williams:* Biochem. J., *48:* 621, 624, 1951; *Parke and Williams:* Ibid., *51:* 339, 1952; *Parke and Williams:* Ibid., *46:* 236, 1950; *54:* 231, 1953.

For the pharmacology and the metabolism of methyl and ethyl alcohol, see *Sollmann:* A Manual of Pharmacology, 1948, p. 607. A detailed discussion of the metabolism of ethyl alcohol is presented by *Jacobsen:* Nature, *169:* 645, 1952.

For a discussion of the metabolism of aniline, see *Williams:* Ann. Rev. Biochem.,

20: 455, 1951; for histamine, see *Schayer:* J. Biol. Chem., *196:* 469, 1952; for acetanilide, see *Williams:* Ann. Rev. Biochem., *20:* 444, 1951.

Young: Biochemical Society Symposia, No. 5, p. 27, 1950, discusses the oxidation of polycyclic hydrocarbons in the animal body. See also *Young:* Biochem. J., *41:* 417, 1947 (metabolism of naphthalene); *Boyland and Wolf:* Ibid., *47:* 64, 1950 (metabolism of phenanthrene).

For a description of the detoxication of nitro compounds, see *Robinson, Smith and Williams:* Biochem. J., *50:* 221, 228, 1951.

The synthesis of hippuric acid from benzoic acid and glycine is discussed by *Arnstein and Neuberger:* Biochem. J., *50:* 154, 1951, and by *Bray, Thorpe, and White:* Ibid., *48:* 88, 1951. See also the synthesis of p-aminohippuric acid, from p-aminobenzoic acid and glycine, by *Kielley and*

Schneider: J. Biol. Chem., *185:* 869, 1950.

The formation of gentisic acid from salicylic acid is reported by *Roseman and Dorfman:* J. Biol. Chem., *192:* 105, 1951.

The conjugation of phenol in the body is described by *Meio and Tkacz:* J. Biol. Chem., *195:* 175, 1952, and by *Bray, Humphris, Thorpe, White, and Wood:* Biochem. J., *52:* 419, 1952. For the conjugation of the naphthols, see *Berenbom and Young:* Biochem. J., *49:* 165, 1951.

References to glucuronic acid as a detoxicating agent are many. See, for example, *Wagreich, Bernstein, Pader, and Harrow:* Proc. Soc. Exp. Biol. Med., *46:* 582, 1941; *Ottenberg. Wagreich, Bernstein, and Harrow:* Arch. Biochem., *2:* 63, 1943; *Bray, Humphries, Thorpe, White, and Wood:* Biochem. J., *52:* 416, 1952.

The much-debated origin of glucuronic acid is discussed by the following: *Eisenberg and Gurin:* J. Am. Chem. Soc., *73:* 4440, 1951; *Mosbach and King:* J. Biol. Chem., *185:* 491, 1950; *Doerschuk:* Ibid., *195:* 855, 1952; *Bidder:* J. Am. Chem. Soc., *74:* 1616, 1952; *Packham and Butler:* J. Biol. Chem., *194:* 349, 1952; *Douglas and King:* Ibid., *198:* 187, 1952.

Articles dealing with the enzyme glucuronidase are by *Mills:* Biochem. J., *40:* 283, 1946; *Graham:* Ibid., *40:* 603, 1946; *Levvy:* Ibid., *42:* 2, 1948; *Fishman:* J. Biol. Chem., *169:* 7, 1947; *Fishman and Fishman:* J. Biol. Chem., *152:* 487, 1944; *Levvy, Kerr, and Campbell:* Biochem. J., *42:* 462, 1948.

The problems of acetylation are discussed from various angles in the following articles: *Bloch and Rittenberg:* J. Biol. Chem., *155:* 243, 1944; *159:* 45, 1945; *Lipmann:* Ibid., *160:* 173, 1945; *Charalampous and Hegsted:* Ibid., *180:* 623, 1949; *Riggs and Hegsted:* J. Biol. Chem., *193:* 669, 1951; *Riggs and Christensen:* Ibid., *193:* 675, 1951; *Lipmann:* Harvey Lectures (1948–49), p. 104.

For the acetylation of histamine, see *Millican:* Arch. Biochem., *42:* 399, 1953; and for its oxidation, see *Tabor, Mehler, and Schayer:* J. Biol. Chem., *200:* 605, 1953.

Liver functional tests are discussed by *Cantarow and Trumper:* Clinical Biochemistry, 1949, 399.

Chapter 25 *Immunochemistry and Chemotherapy*

Microorganisms Which Cause Disease. These may be divided into three groups; animal parasites, such as protozoa; vegetable parasites, such as bacteria and fungi; and filter-passing viruses.

Amebic dysentery, malaria, and sleeping sickness—all three common in tropical countries—are caused by protozoa. Since the spirochetes are usually classed as protozoa, syphilis would be included here.

In temperate climates, the chief diseases are caused by bacteria. Some of these bacteria and the diseases they give rise to are the following:

Streptococcus pyogenes, or β-hemolytic streptococcus, includes some thirteen different strains of bacteria which give rise to septic wounds, blood-poisoning, erysipelas, scarlet fever, etc.

Diplococcus pneumoniae, or pneumococcus, includes some thirty-four strains which are the common cause of pneumonia.

Staphylococcus aureus, commonly found in the skin, usually causes boils.

Neisseria gonorrhoeae, or gonococcus, gives rise to gonorrhea.

Neisseria intracellularis, or meningococcus, causes cerebrospinal meningitis.

Various bacteria also cause diphtheria, tuberculosis, cholera, plague, lockjaw, anthrax, etc.

Bacteria are grouped under gram-positive (those that are not decolorized by alcohol in Gram's method of staining) and gram-negative (those that are decolorized by alcohol in Gram's stain).

Diseases due to viruses—particles which were once thought to be invisible bacteria but which are now known to be large protein molecules of the type of nucleoproteins—are smallpox, infantile paralysis, typhus fever, common colds, and probably measles, mumps, influenza, etc.

So far, greater success has attended the treatment of protozoal and bacterial diseases than the virus diseases.

Defenses Set Up by the Body. The skin and the acid of the stomach are among these defenses—the skin by preventing entrance of bacteria and the hydrochloric acid by destroying them. But many bacteria do get into the body. The large intestine (and the eliminated feces) is full of bacteria, but these cannot penetrate the intestinal wall to enter the body proper.

However, whether through the nose, through the throat or through a cut, or as a result of lessened resistance, bacteria do penetrate the blood and tissues. To counter this menace, certain cells, macrophages, engulf the bacteria and are usually strong enough to destroy them. The macrophages are found lining the blood vessels of the liver, bone marrow, etc. (reticulo-endothelial system), and some wander and may even circulate in the blood.

495

The white cells (leukocytes) of the blood have a function similar to the macrophages.

IMMUNOCHEMISTRY

This is a branch of the general subject of immunology; it deals with the chemistry of antigens and antibodies, and the chemical basis underlying immunity and resistance to disease.

Antigens and Antibodies.   We have seen how the body handles certain toxic substances by detoxicating them and then eliminating the detoxified products. When, however, the toxic substance which enters the blood stream is chemically of a sufficiently complex nature—approaching, say, that of a protein in complexity—the body tries to resist the effects of such toxicity by building up for its defense antibodies (proteins related to serum gamma globulin), which tend to combine with, and so nullify the effects of, the toxic substance.

The substances which give rise to these antibodies are called "antigens." The antigens include bacteria, protozoa, molds, and "foreign" proteins.

In general, proteins which are "foreign" to the body—that is to say, proteins which are not normally found in the animal—give rise to antibodies. Certain polysaccharides may also stimulate antibody production.

When a suspension of living or dead bacteria (pneumococci, for example) is injected into an animal in increasing doses, an immunity to further infection by subsequent injection of bacteria may be acquired, and the serum of the animal reacts characteristically when mixed with an extract of the bacteria. The characteristic reaction resulting from the mixing of the serum with the bacteria originally used for the injection may give rise to a clumping, or agglutination; to a dissolving, or lysis; or to a precipitate, or precipitin, depending upon conditions. The agglutinins, lysins, and precipitins are all antibodies.

Heidelberger, and also Marrack, consider specific immune precipitation and specific agglutination of bacteria as due to the combination of antigen and antibody in such a way that molecules of antigen may become attached to molecules of antibody through one or more linkages.

As this concept postulates several reactive groupings in the molecules, an antigen-antibody complex may combine with other antigen or antibody molecules, or with preformed antigen-antibody combinations to build up large aggregates which separate from solution (or, in the case of bacteria, clump together and settle).

The process of immune combination is a reversible one. Aggregates may dissociate into uncombined antigen and antibody molecules. This dissociation, however, is relatively small.

The antigenic properties of the bacteria are usually ascribed to the proteins which they contain. Proteins, in general, with the notable exception of gelatin, give rise to antibodies, and these substances are removed from the serum with the fraction containing the globulins—a fact which is used as evidence that the antibodies resemble the serum globulins.

These antibodies, then, are globulins, but differ from the ordinary serum globulins in one important respect: their reactivity with the antigen, which means that the antibody molecule differs in some structural way from the serum globulins.

Complement.   For lysis, or solution, of bacteria to occur, the serum must be fresh. The use of old serum, or serum which has been heated to 56° C. for one-half hour, prevents this lysis. This lytic action can be restored by the addition of fresh serum. The factor so easily destroyed by heating or on standing is known as "complement," and the action of antigen and antibody in the presence of complement is called "complement fixation."

Estimating Antibody.   A method of estimating the amount of antibody is based on the specificity of immunological reactions and on the fact

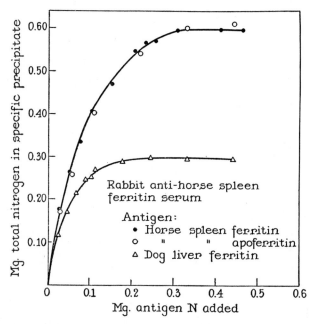

Fig. 118. Quantitative precipitin curves for rabbit antiserum to crystalline horse spleen ferritin. (Mazur and Shorr: J. Biol. Chem., *182:* 607, 1950.)

that antibodies are proteins. The precipitate of antigen-antibody is analyzed for its total nitrogen content. By subtracting the nitrogen content of the antigen from that of antigen-antibody, the nitrogen content of antibody is obtained.

In a specific example, the antibody prepared against horse ferritin (p. 310) was treated with increasing quantities of this ferritin (antigen) and the precipitates analyzed for nitrogen (Fig. 118). Reactions of a similar kind were done, but apoferritin—differing from ferritin by being free of iron (p. 310)—was substituted for ferritin as the antigen. It will be noticed that the values both for ferritin and apoferritin fall on the same curve, which is an indication that, immunologically, the two are identical, and that the iron does not interfere in the reaction of antigen with antibody.

On the other hand, when the same antibody is reacted with *dog* ferritin as the antigen, a different curve is obtained.

It is true that the antibody to horse ferritin did react to some extent with dog ferritin—a "cross reaction"—but the extent of this reaction was much less than with the homologous antigen-antibody pair. The "cross reaction" actually indicates immunological similarity but not identity, a conclusion borne out by differences in the electrophoretic behavior of these two species of ferritins.

Many are the theories which have been advanced to explain the formation of antibodies in response to injection of antigen. Porter writes: "All accept the principle that combination of antibody with antigen depends on the configuration of parts of the antibody molecule being complementary to parts of the antigen molecule."

Specificity.   Some idea of the specificity of these reactions may be obtained by using chemically altered antigens. For example, azo proteins may be formed by coupling the diazotized product of sulfanilic acid with the tyrosine groups of crystallized egg albumin:

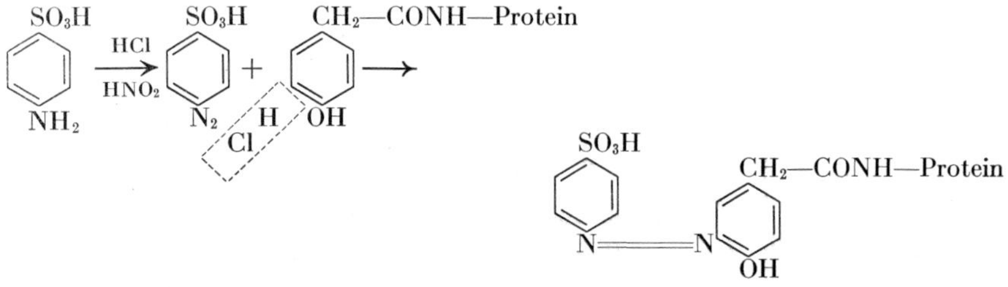

Rabbits immunized with this azo protein form antibodies which react with sulfanilic acid joined to some other protein and react but slightly with egg albumin alone.

The specificity of these immunological reactions is remarkable. The immunological test for human blood has already been given. Here is another example: if crystallized egg albumin is injected, the antibodies produced, present in the serum, will not precipitate solutions of another albumin, such as crystalline horse serum albumin.

With the help of the electron microscope, we can actually visualize the antigen-antibody reaction. Tobacco mosaic virus was selected as the antigen. The result of the injection in the rabbit caused the serum of the animal to develop the corresponding antibody. The rabbit antiserum was the source, then, of the antibody (Figs. 119 and 120).

Toxins.   Certain bacteria—those causing diphtheria and tetanus, for example—produce toxic proteins, or toxins. Injection of such toxins in relatively small quantities, or injection of the *toxoid* (the detoxified product made by treating the toxin with formaldehyde), gives rise to antitoxins in the serum. These antitoxins when mixed with their respective toxins tend to neutralize the toxic effects of the latter. These toxins, then, are antigenic poisons.

Botulinal and tetanal toxins and several toxoids have been isolated in crystalline form.

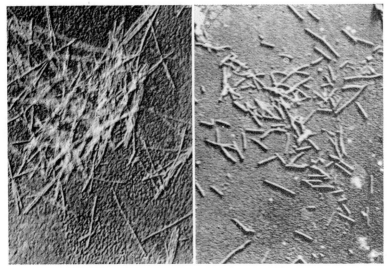

Fig. 119.   Fig. 120.

Fig. 119. Electron photomicrograph of the antibody-antigen complex of tobacco mosaic virus and homologous rabbit antibody. The virus was taken from an aqueous solution. The mount was prepared with gold by the shadow-casting technique. The magnification is 34,800.

Fig. 120. Electron photomicrograph of untreated purified tobacco mosaic virus in phosphate buffer. The mount was prepared with gold by the shadow-casting technique. The magnification is 34,800. (Malkiel and Stanley: J. Immunology, *57:* 31.)

Anaphylaxis.   In contradistinction to prophylaxis, anaphylaxis is the lack of protective effects, and the term was coined by Richet in 1902 to describe this experiment: Using toxic extracts of certain sea anemones, but in sublethal doses, and working with dogs, Richet found that the first injection produced no obvious symptoms; a second injection, however, given sometime after the first, caused illness and often death of the animal.

Subsequently it was shown that the substance causing this anaphylaxis need not be a toxic substance. Similar results could be produced by the use of normal serum from a different species, or by the use of such a food as egg white.

This anaphylaxis also represents an antibody-antigen reaction.

In the attempt to explain the phenomenon, some investigators believe that a toxic substance is liberated as a result of the antigen-antibody combination, which produces the "shock." The toxic substance, it has been suggested, might be histamine, or some histamine-like compound.

Allergy.   This word, meaning "changed or altered reactivity," was coined by Von Pirquet to indicate "any acquired specific alteration in the capacity to react, which occurs in living organisms or tissues upon exposure to living agents or inanimate substances." The sufferer is "hypersensitive" upon exposure to certain substances; he is "allergic."

Some believe that a hereditary factor is involved, though contact with the allergen is necessary.

The fact that the allergy may be due to a relatively simple compound e.g., drug allergy, seems to show that the antigen need not necessarily be complex. However, Landsteiner has shown that comparatively simple chemical substances may become antigenic ("haptenic") provided they are attached to proteins; and it is possible that allergenic drugs combine with the individual's own proteins.

In a somewhat narrow (and popular) sense, the word "allergy" refers to the clinical conditions of hay fever, asthma, eczema, and urticaria.*

An allergy to foods is not uncommon, particularly in infants and young children.

Histamine and Antihistaminic Agents.   It had been noticed that anaphylactic reactions in the guinea-pig showed certain similarities to reactions seen in asthma and hay fever. As far back as 1910, Dale and Laidlaw pointed out that the effects of histamine and the manifestations in anaphylactic shock have points of resemblance.

Histamine is the amine of the amino acid histidine, and has the following structure:

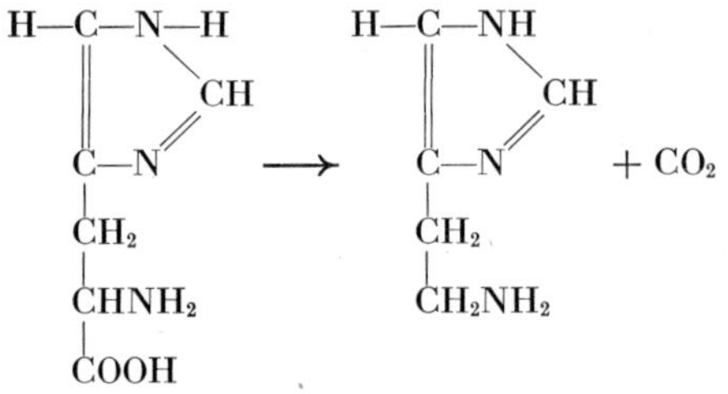

$$
\begin{array}{ccc}
\underset{\text{Histidine}}{
\begin{array}{l}
\text{H—C—N—H} \\
\quad\|\qquad\diagdown \\
\quad\|\qquad\quad\text{CH} \\
\text{C—N}\diagup \\
\;| \\
\text{CH}_2 \\
\;| \\
\text{CHNH}_2 \\
\;| \\
\text{COOH}
\end{array}}
&
\longrightarrow
&
\underset{\text{Histamine}}{
\begin{array}{l}
\text{H—C—NH} \\
\quad\|\qquad\diagdown \\
\quad\|\qquad\quad\text{CH} \\
\text{C—N}\diagup \\
\;| \\
\text{CH}_2 \\
\;| \\
\text{CH}_2\text{NH}_2
\end{array}}
& +\ CO_2
\end{array}
$$

and like the other amines of the amino acids from proteins, it is a highly potent toxicological product.

The discovery by Best in 1929 that tissues contain an enzyme, histaminase, which is capable of decomposing histamine, led to the hope that the enzyme could be used in counteracting anaphylactic reactions. The results proved disappointing.

More encouraging results have been obtained by applying the theory of metabolic antagonists (p. 362). This, in turn, is based on a theory of the action of histamine which may be stated as follows: histamine is a normal constituent of the body but present in an inactive form—perhaps bound to certain amino acid components within the cell. In the anaphylactic reaction the cell is injured in some mysterious way, following the union of antigen and antibody, and histamine is set free.

Here substances—somewhat analogous in structure to histamine—are used which can compete with histamine. These substances "supposedly prevent histamine from reaching those cells or enzymes to which histamine normally becomes anchored," writes Mayer, "and they are capable of occupying those places which histamine normally would occupy. In other words, antihistaminic substances compete with histamine for the normal histamine-receptive sites. For this reason, no histamine effects appear."

---

* In a general way, it may be stated that when the phenomena of sensitivity appear in lower animals, the reference is to "anaphylaxis"; when the sensitivity refers to humans, then we speak of an "allergy."

Among the first of these antihistaminic drugs was a phenolic ether prepared by Fourneau in 1933 and shown to have the property of counteracting the action of histamine in vivo as well as in vitro. It has the following structure:

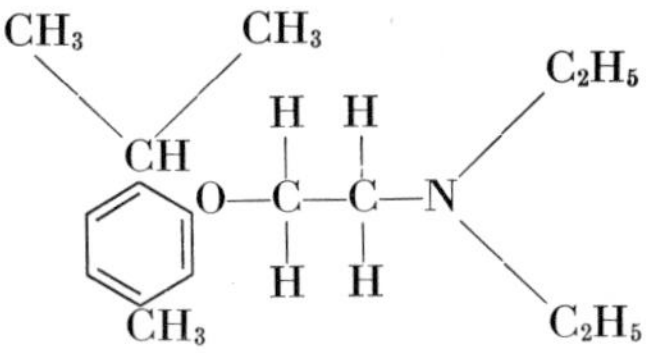

2-Isopropyl-5-methylphenoxyethyldiethylamine

However, the toxicity of this substance led to a number of modifications in the structure. Two such products, of some practical value in clinical medicine, are diphenhydramine hydrochloride (Benadryl):

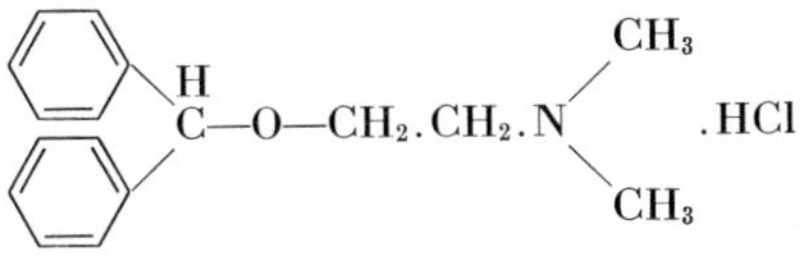

and tripelennamine hydrochloride (Pyribenzamine):

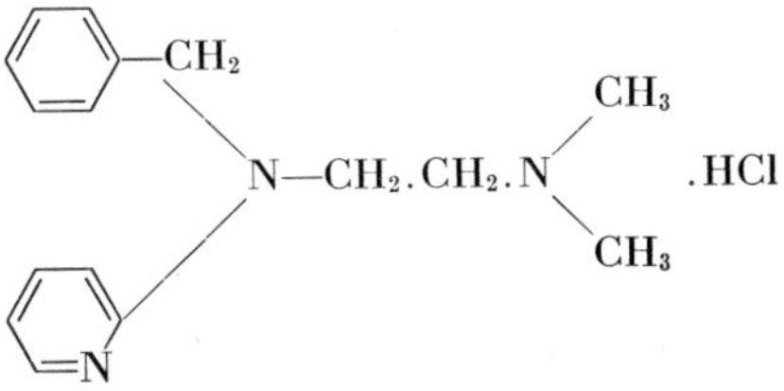

Both of these compounds have been relatively more successful in the treatment of the patient suffering from hay fever than in the treatment of asthma.

"Both drugs," writes Feinberg, "give a high incidence of side reactions, among which sedation and drowsiness are most commonly observed." A cure cannot be expected. At best, the results are a temporary alleviation of the allergenic conditions. As for the use of "antihistamines" in curing colds, the evidence is negative.

Blood Group Substances.   There are four main blood groups, referred to as A, B, AB (a mixture of A and B) and O. Red cells containing these substances are agglutinated by certain agglutenins (p. 496) present in the serum of various individuals. This agglutination is the cause of the sometimes fatal reactions which occur when blood of a "foreign" type is used for transfusion.

The blood group substances are also found in saliva, commercial peptone and hog gastric mucin. They are glycoproteins or glycopeptides containing both carbohydrates and amino acids. Some of the carbohydrates are D-galactose, D-mannose and D-glucosamine.

The Rh Factor.   Landsteiner immunized rabbits by injections with the blood of the rhesus monkey. The serum of such rabbits agglutinized about 85 per cent of human bloods. These human bloods acted as if they possessed the same immunizing or antigenic substance as the blood of the monkey; hence, the human factor was given the name rhesus or Rh factor.

The blood (red blood cells) containing the Rh factor was called Rh+ and blood not containing it (about 15 per cent), Rh—. The Rh— showed no agglutination.

Landsteiner showed that the Rh factor is transmitted as a dominant trait in heredity. "In the normal human body the Rh antigen is harmless; and its presence is important only in childbirth, blood transfusion, and paternity disputes. For example, when an Rh— woman, wedded to an Rh+ man, has an Rh+ infant, there is a possibility that the Rh factor may exert its malignant influence on the mother and child. This is accomplished by the flow of Rh+ antigenic substances through the placental barrier, from the fetus to the mother. In the mother's body the production of antibodies to Rh is thereby stimulated. When these antibodies return through the placenta to the fetus, they react with the blood cells of the fetus, destroying them and giving rise to a hemolytic disease of the fetus or newborn (erythroblastosis fetalis)." [*What's New* (Abbott Labs.), March, 1946.]

CHEMOTHERAPY

Aside from the defense mechanisms of the body for protecting itself against the effects of bacterial invasion, other possibilities suggest themselves. One method is to employ heat. Sufficient heat destroys bacteria. It is obvious, however, that it is practically impossible to increase the temperature of the body to a degree necessary to destroy the organisms without harming the tissues. The same applies to the action of many chemicals. Phenol, formaldehyde, iodine, mercuric chloride, chloride of lime, and many other chemicals are excellent disinfectants. However, they have a serious disadvantage in that they are also effective destroyers of protoplasm.

The problem, then, is to find chemicals, drugs, which will destroy the organisms without materially harming the tissues. This is the problem of chemotherapy.

A partial answer to this problem was obtained when it was shown that malaria could be cured, to some extent, at least, with quinine, and syphilis with mercury compounds. This work also suggested that a definite chemical substance was specific in its attack on a definite organism.

The triumph of chemotherapy may be said to date back to 1910 when Ehrlich made his great discovery of "606," or salvarsan, as a cure for syphilis.

Salvarsan or arsphenamine
(3,3'-Diamino-4,4'-dihydroxyarsenobenzene)

Until 1935, practically all of the successful chemical substances in use were remedies for tropical diseases caused by protozoa.

For example, one of the most striking of these diseases for which chemotherapy found an answer was malaria, a disease caused by the protozoan, *Plasmodium*, transmitted by the female *Anopheles* mosquito to man. It had been known for a long time that the bark of the cinchona tree was a remedy for malaria, but it took years to isolate quinine (one of twenty-odd alkaloids present in the bark).

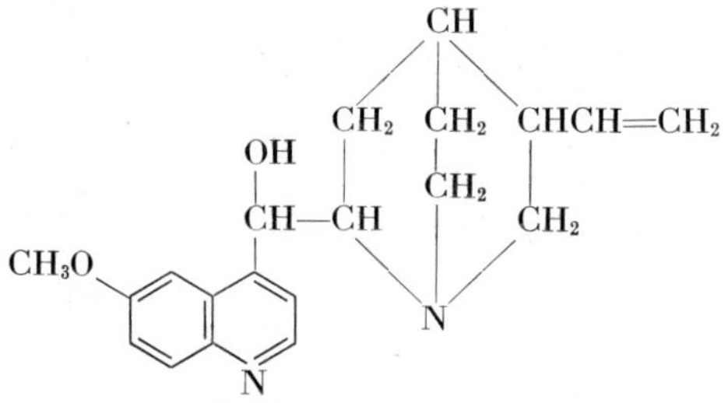

Quinine

This valuable drug is obtained largely from the Dutch East Indies. During the Second World War the occupation of these islands by the Japanese made it difficult for American health authorities to supply our troops with the needed quinine. Synthetic substitutes, such as Plasmochin (a quinoline derivative), and Atabrine (an acridine derivative) came into use.

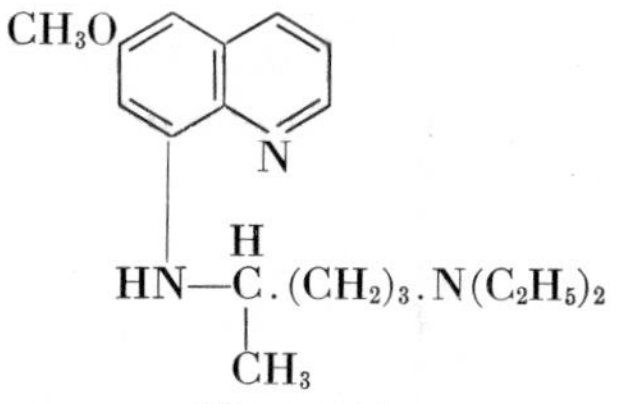

Plasmochin

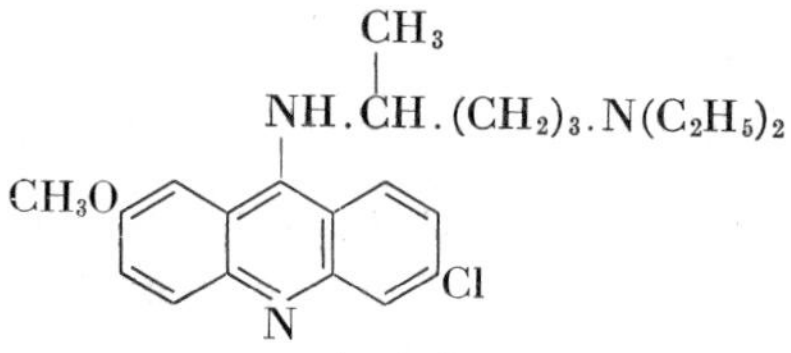

Atabrine

Chloroquine, another quinoline derivative, has also been used.

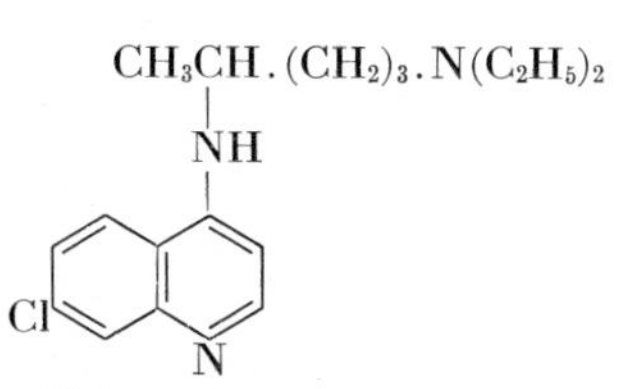

Chloroquine

The first fairly satisfactory drug for the cure of sleeping sickness was prepared by Jacobs and Heidelberger in 1919. It is known as tryparsamide and is an arsenical derivative of phenylglycineamide:

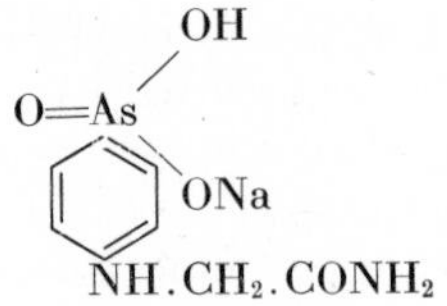

$$\begin{array}{c} OH \\ / \\ O{=}As \\ \diagdown \\ \bigcirc{}ONa \\ NH.CH_2.CONH_2 \end{array}$$

Tryparsamide

The synthesis of quinine itself, for years a stumbling block to organic chemists, was accomplished by Woodward and Doering in 1944.

Sulfonamide Compounds.   It was not until 1935, with the use of sulfanilamide, that the first of a series of substances was used which was effective against bacteria—the bacteria which give rise to the commonest diseases. Domagk, in an extension of the application of dyes to chemotherapy, discovered that Prontosil injected into mice infected with streptococci had a definitely curative effect.

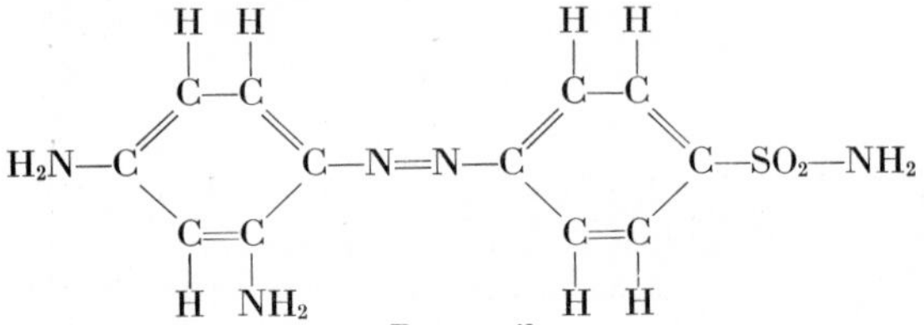

$$H_2N{-}C \overset{\overset{\displaystyle H \;\; H}{|\quad|}}{\underset{\underset{\displaystyle H \;\; NH_2}{|\quad|}}{\underset{C{=}C}{\overset{C{-}C}{\diagup\diagdown}}}} C{-}N{=}N{-}C \overset{\overset{\displaystyle H \;\; H}{|\quad|}}{\underset{\underset{\displaystyle H \;\; H}{|\quad|}}{\underset{C{=}C}{\overset{C{-}C}{\diagup\diagdown}}}} C{-}SO_2{-}NH_2$$

Prontosil
(4-Sulfonamido-2′,4′-diaminoazobenzene)

Further work made clear that in humans, Prontosil was an effective therapeutic agent against the β-hemolytic streptococcus, an agent which destroys red blood cells, or which gives rise to red rashes on the skin (erysipelas and scarlet fever).

It was next shown that Prontosil was converted in the body into *sulfanilamide*, a very well known organic substance, and that sulfanilamide itself was most potent.

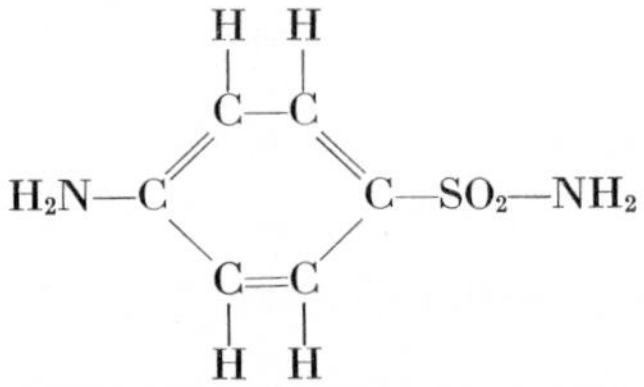

$$H_2N{-}C \overset{\overset{\displaystyle H \;\; H}{|\quad|}}{\underset{\underset{\displaystyle H \;\; H}{|\quad|}}{\underset{C{=}C}{\overset{C{-}C}{\diagup\diagdown}}}} C{-}SO_2{-}NH_2$$

Sulfanilamide (*p*-Aminobenzenesulfonamide)

Writing the skeletal form of sulfanilamide thus:

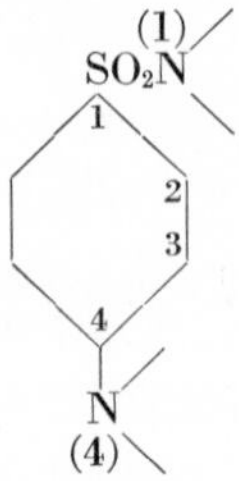

$$\begin{array}{c} (1) \\ SO_2N \diagup \\ \diagup\diagdown \\ | \quad 2 \\ | \quad 3 \\ \diagdown \;\; 4 \diagup \\ N \\ (4) \diagdown \end{array}$$

where the N in the p position is in position 4, and the other N would therefore be in position 1, we may say that the best results so far obtained are from substitution of hydrogen on the N (1) group.

Extremely effective compounds were obtained by replacing the hydrogen on N (1) with pyridine, thiazole, and other groups.

The steps in the synthesis of some of these sulfonamides are graphically shown in Fig. 121.

CLINICAL USE.   The sulfonamide drugs are administered by mouth and in fairly large quantities.

One or more of the drugs have been used, sometimes with amazing success, in septic wounds and blood poisoning, puerperal fever (disease of childbirth), erysipelas, meningitis, malignant endocarditis (infection of the heart), pneumonia, gonorrhea, certain kidney infections, etc.

But quite a number of bacterial diseases exist which, apparently, are not influenced by the "sulfa drugs." Among them are tuberculosis, typhoid, paratyphoid, cholera, bacillary dysentery, and whooping cough.

Also the main body of virus diseases are not influenced by treatment with the sulfonamides. These include smallpox, measles, infantile paralysis, colds, and influenza.

MODE OF ACTION.   An antisulfanilamide factor, obtained from an extract of yeast, was traced to p-aminobenzoic acid. Woods showed that a concentration as low as 1:10,000 was active in partially inhibiting the bacteriostatic effect of sulfanilamide at a concentration of 1:20,000.

This suggested to Woods and to Fildes a possible mechanism of the action of sulfonamide compounds. p-Aminobenzoic acid is regarded as an essential compound synthesized by the bacterial cells from amino acids, or obtained by the cells from their environment. To be properly utilized by the cell, the p-aminobenzoic acid is acted upon by an enzyme. If sulfanilamide is present, it attaches itself to the enzyme and thereby prevents the normal metabolism of the bacterial cell. The bacteria fail to get their proper nutrition and are ultimately destroyed.

EXCRETION.   The sulfonamides are detoxicated in various ways in the body, presumably in the liver. They are excreted through the kidneys and appear in the urine in one or more of the following modifications: as an N_4-acetyl derivative, as a monohydroxyl derivative, as a glucuronide, as an ethereal sulfate.

INTESTINAL ANTISEPTICS.   Sulfaguanidine and succinylsulfathiazole are very poorly absorbed; they have therefore been used as intestinal antiseptics.

Experiments on animals have shown that these sulfa compounds, by destroying organisms in the intestine, often prevent, to a large extent, the synthesis of a number of vitamins which are normally brought about with the help of these organisms. Some of these vitamins are vitamin K and a few belonging to the vitamin B complex (biotin, folic and, p-aminobenzoic acid).

Antibiotic Substances.   Florey records that as far back as 1877 Pasteur noticed that the growth of one type of bacteria may be stopped by the simultaneous growth of another adjacent to it. Later this phenomenon was shown to be due to the production of some definite chemical substance by

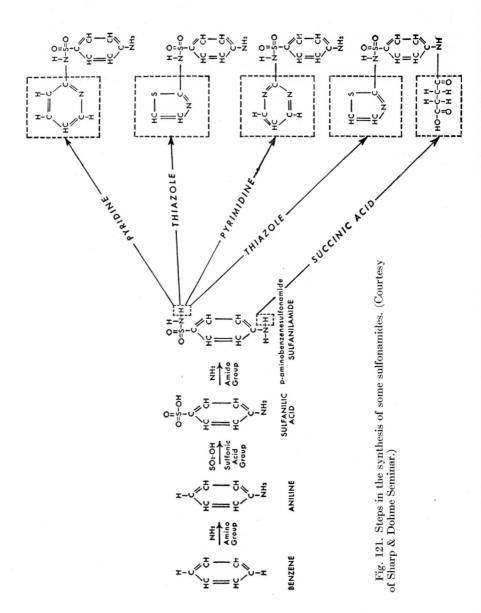

Fig. 121. Steps in the synthesis of some sulfonamides. (Courtesy of Sharp & Dohme Seminar.)

the antagonistic microorganism. These chemical inhibitors were called *antibiotic.*

These substances, antimicrobial in action, are produced by molds, soil organisms (actinomycetes) and bacteria. They inhibit the growth of bacteria—they are bacteriostatic—though they may also, and to a lesser extent, show bactericidal properties. These substances show a certain specificity in their action. Some act on gram-positive bacteria and show little action upon gram-negative ones. Others show selective action on some of each group.

Representative members of this group of substances are penicillin, streptomycin, gramicidin, tyrocidine, bacitracin, polymyxin (formerly called aerosporin), aureomycin, Terramycin and Chloromycetin. Several of these antibiotic substances have found wide clinical use.

Some of the antibiotics, such as aureomycin, bacitracin, penicillin and Terramycin, are being incorporated in the food supplied to poultry, hogs, etc., on the ground that they act as growth stimulants.

PENICILLIN. In 1929 Fleming made his great discovery while studying the growth and properties of staphylococcus. He grew the organism on a solid medium containing agar. He noticed that "in a large colony of a contaminating mold the staphylococcus colonies became transparent and were obviously undergoing lysis." This observation, due to the accidental contamination of the media by molds from the air, was the key to the discovery.

The contamination, in Fleming's case, was due to a mold colony. He cultivated the mold in liquid broth, and noticed that during growth something appeared which inhibited the growth of some organisms.

Fleming called this "something" *penicillin,* for the mold was identified (somewhat later) as *Penicillium notatum*—a mold not at all common and not the one found on bread (Fig. 122).

Fleming made the important observation that his extract containing penicillin was not poisonous to animals and did not harm white blood cells.

It was not until 1938 that this work of Fleming's was actively pursued, this time by Florey and his associates. This group developed a quick assay method and uncovered several chemical properties of penicillin, such as that it exhibited acidic properties, was unstable in acid and alkaline media and more stable in a neutral medium.

Florey and his associates found that the penicillin brew, after acidification, could be extracted with ether, and that the ether extract (containing much of the penicillin) when mixed with some water and the right amount of alkali, yielded a more stable alkaline salt.

The properties of penicillin which made it so valuable a remedy for man were also largely uncovered by the Florey group. They confirmed Fleming's observation that the substance was nontoxic to animals and to white blood cells and tissue cultures (body cells grown outside of the body). They further found that the activity of penicillin was not affected by pus, blood or breakdown products of dead tissue (which is not true of the sulfonamides), and that it was little affected by the number of bacteria present (also not true of the sulfonamides).

Florey was of the opinion at the time that penicillin could not be given orally. While it is true that the antibiotic is partially inactivated by gastric juice, by making due allowance for this and giving a sufficient amount (about four to five times as much as for injection) the oral route is effective.

It had also been observed that penicillin was rapidly excreted, which meant that comparatively large and repeated doses were necessary. It has since been shown that 60 per cent of an injected dose is excreted within one hour, and in each succeeding hour 70 per cent of the remaining penicillin is excreted.

Fig. 122. Photomicrograph ($\times$ 100) of penicillin-producing mold growing on agar. Branching ends of conidiophores give genus its name of *Penicillium*, from the Latin for brush. (*Penicillin*, Abbott.)

To retard this rapid excretion, penicillin is often incorporated with peanut or sesame oil and white wax or is used as suspensions of procaine penicillin. Sometimes substances which inhibit tubular excretion—such as *p*-aminohippurate or caronamide, *p*-benzylsulfoneamidobenzoic acid—can be used.

Florey relates one of the early tests of the substance on mice, in preparation for its application to man. Mice were inoculated with germs which normally would kill them. "We sat up all night injecting penicillin every three hours into the treated group; and I must confess it was one of the more exciting moments when we found in the morning that all the untreated mice were dead and all the penicillin-treated ones were alive."

"The discovery of penicillin," concludes Florey, "was one of the luckiest accidents . . . for, without exception, all other mold antibiotics so far examined are poisonous." *

The effect of penicillin on bacteria is graphically illustrated in Figures

* Many others have been examined since, and some are not so poisonous.

123 and 124, which represent photographs taken with the electron microscope.

ASSAY. The "cup method," devised by Florey and associates, is widely used. An agar plate is seeded with cultures of the test organisms. Cylinders

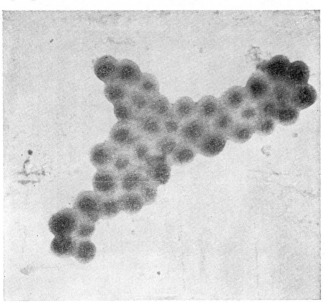

Fig. 123. *Staphylococcus aureus* prior to influence of penicillin (reduced from original electron micrograph, × 38,000). (Courtesy, Radio Corporation of America.)

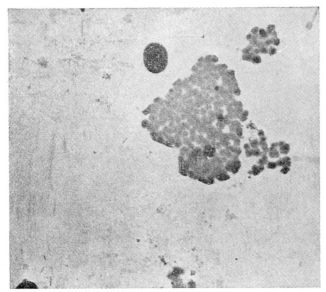

Fig. 124. Penicillin action on *Staphylococcus aureus* (reduced from original electron micrograph, × 38,000). (Courtesy, Radio Corporation of America.)

of glass, short and open at both ends, are placed on the agar, and the solutions which are to be tested are placed in the cylinders. After incubation, where the penicillin has diffused out and inhibited growth there appears a circular and clear zone around each cylinder. The diameter of the zone is related to the concentration of the penicillin (Fig. 125).

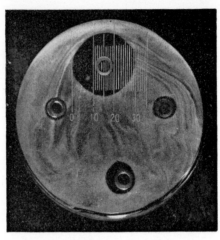

Fig. 125. The diameter of the inhibited zone—30 mm. wide in this case—is readily observed with the aid of the ruled plate and reflected light of the penicillin reader. (Fisher Scientific Co.)

The "Florey," or "Oxford," unit, widely used, is defined as "that amount of penicillin which, when dissolved in 50 cc. of meat extract broth, just inhibits completely the growth of the test strain of *Staphylococcus aureus.*"

The International Unit, based on the activity of the crystalline sodium penicillin G, is 0.6 micrograms (μg) of this salt.

CHEMISTRY.   About fifty types of penicillin are known, but only types F, G, X, and K have been produced in quantity.

The penicillins all have the empirical formula $C_9H_{11}O_4SN_2$.R.

In F-penicillin, R = Δ^2—pentenyl, $-CH_2.CH = CH.CH_2.CH_3$.
In G-penicillin, R is benzyl, $C_6H_5CH_2$.
In X-penicillin, R is *p*-hydroxybenzyl, $pHOC_6H_4CH_2$.
In K-penicillin, R is *n*-heptyl, $CH_3(CH_2)_6$.

The penicillins are strong monobasic acids of *p*K about 2.8.
The formula proposed for the penicillins is

which shows them to contain a thiazolidine ring (attached to a carboxyl and two methyl groups) joined to a β-lactam ring attached to a side chain.

CLINICAL USE. Penicillin has been used extensively, and with marked success, in the following: infections due to staphylococci (boils, carbuncles, abscesses, osteomyelitis, infected wounds, etc.); infections due to hemolytic streptococci (skin infections, mastoiditis, peritonitis, puerperal sepsis— infection associated with childbearing—etc.); pneumonia; gonorrhea; syphilis; etc.

However, penicillin has no effect in mitigating the evils of tuberculosis, malaria, typhoid fever, infantile paralysis, measles, mumps, influenza, and the like.

Blake, in comparing the action of penicillin with sulfonamides, divides the results into three groups:

1. Those in which both the sulfonamides and penicillin are more or less effective, though not necessarily equally so; namely certain gram-positive and gram-negative coccic infections: hemolytic streptococcus, pneumo-coccus, staphylococcus, *Streptococcus viridans*, meningococcus, and gono-coccus.

2. Those in which the sulfonamides are of value but not penicillin; namely gram-negative bacillary infections such as those caused by *Escherichia coli*, *Shigella dysenteriae*, *Hemophilus influenzae*, *Klebsiella pneumoniae*, and *Hemophilus ducreyi*.

3. Those in which penicillin is of value but not the sulfonamides; namely syphilis, yaws, and possibly other spirochetal infections and those due to *Clostridia*—gas gangrene.

HOW DOES PENICILLIN FUNCTION? Penicillin does not affect the resting bacterial cell but gradually inhibits the respiration of rapidly growing bacteria. Labelled with S^{35}, penicillin attaches itself to the growing bacteria.

Gale and his co-workers have demonstrated that the gram-positive bacteria (which are, as a rule, susceptible to penicillin) concentrate a large amount of amino acids, particularly glutamic acid, inside the cell. This concentration occurs only in rapidly growing cells and requires energy, which is probably obtained by the degradation of glucose during the glycolytic process.

Now penicillin prevents the transport of glutamic acid across the cell wall, so that in the presence of the antibiotic, though the cells may for a time continue to grow larger by utilizing the glutamic acid already inside the cell for protein synthesis, after a time this synthesis slows down and the cells stop multiplying because of the reduction of the glutamic acid. This would explain the bacteriostatic effect of penicillin.

Figure 126 explains how various chemotherapeutic agents may act on the cell.

PENICILLIN RESISTANCE. The work by Gale also explains the phenomena of penicillin-resistant bacteria. He started with bacteria (gram-positive *Staphylococcus aureus*) which were susceptible to as little as 0.05 units per milliliter of penicillin and grew them in media containing increasing amounts of penicillin. Mutants were harvested and a bacterial strain was obtained which required as much as 7000 units per milliliter of penicillin. Although the original bacterial strain required glutamic acid for growth, as the bacteria became increasingly resistant to penicillin, their requirement for glutamic acid decreased: they could now synthesize their own glutamic acid. Further, the penicillin-resistant strain of bacteria became gram-negative, which meant that they were unaffected by penicillin. Gale also prepared a mutant strain of *Staphylococcus aureus* in the complete absence of penicillin by growing them in media increasingly deficient in glutamic acid, so that the bacteria were trained to lose their requirement for this amino acid and gain the ability to synthesize it themselves. The bacterial strain which had lost its requirement for glutamic acid had also become greatly resistant to penicillin.

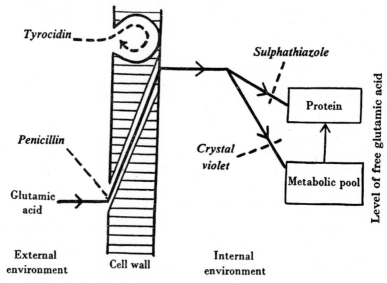

Fig. 126. Assimilation of glutamic acid by grampositive bacterial cell and action thereon of chemotherapeutic agents. (Gale: J. Gen. Microbiology, *1*: 327, 1947.)

HOW ADMINISTERED.   Penicillin may be administered orally, parenterally, by inhalation, or locally. It is essentially nontoxic, though side reactions, particularly in patients with eczematous tendency, are fairly common.

TYROTHRICIN.   Dubos isolated from the soil a sporulating bacillus which produces a soluble principle toxic for gram-positive bacteria. The substance so obtained was named tyrothricin, but this was later found to be a mixture of two crystalline compounds. The neutral, alcohol-soluble one was given the name *gramicidin* and the other basic one was called *tyrocidine*. Gramicidin has been postulated to have a minimum molecular weight of about 2000. It is a polypeptide made up of the amino acids glycine, alanine, valine (D and L), tryptophan, and D-leucine plus ethanolamine.

A dose of 0.005 mg. of gramicidin will kill in vitro 10⁹ pneumococci or group A streptococci in two hours at 30° C. One dose of 0.002 mg. of the substance injected into a mouse protects such an animal against 10,000 fatal doses of pneumococci or hemolytic streptococcus.

The mixture of gramicidin and tyrocidin—and possibly other substances—is known as *tyrothricin*, and while it is highly toxic when injected—and so cannot be considered in the same light as penicillin—it has come to be used locally in restricted cases; for example, superficial indolent ulcers, empyema (accumulation of pus in the chest or some cavity of the body), mastoiditis, and several wound infections.

D-AMINO ACIDS. L-Amino acids are found almost exclusively in nature. It may be significant that a number of antibiotics are derivatives of D-amino acids. In the penicillins we find D-penicillamine; in gramicidin, D-leucine and D-valine; in tyrocidin and bacitracin, D-phenylalanine; in polymyxin, D-leucine.

Significant, too, is that the L-analogue corresponding to the D-amino acid residue in penicillin is without activity; and that D-amino acids have been shown experimentally to inhibit bacterial growth.

STREPTOMYCIN. Penicillin has little effect on gram-negative bacteria. Among the latter are the colon bacilli, organisms of the dysentery and typhoid group, others causing undulant fever, etc. The bacillus of tuberculosis, it is true, is gram-positive, but penicillin has no effect.

A promising antibiotic is *streptomycin*, isolated by Waksman from a medium growing *Streptomyces griseus*, which is an inhabitant of garden soil, river muds, and peat and compost heaps.

Streptomycin inhibits the growth of a number of gram-negative bacteria which are not affected by penicillin, for example, *Escherichia coli*, *Hemophilus influenzae*, *Proteus vulgaris*, *Eberthella typhosa*, etc. It is not sufficiently absorbed when given by mouth and the best results are obtained by parenteral injection.

This antibiotic has been successfully used in the treatment of certain urinary tract infections, tularemia (a disease of rodents resembling plague), influenzal meningitis (due to *Hemophilus* organisms), certain wound infections, etc. Its use in the treatment of undulant fever, bacillary dysentery, and typhoid fever has not shown much promise.

Since the preliminary work by Hinshaw and Feldman on the use of streptomycin in the treatment of tuberculosis, by which it was found that the antibiotic exerts a suppressive action on the disease process, streptomycin has become a drug of extreme usefulness in the therapy of tuberculosis.

CHEMISTRY. The chemistry of streptomycin has been elucidated. It consists of a base, streptidine (a diguanido derivative of cyclohexane), linked to a nitrogen-containing disaccharide, streptobiosamine. The latter consists of streptose and N-methylglucosamine:

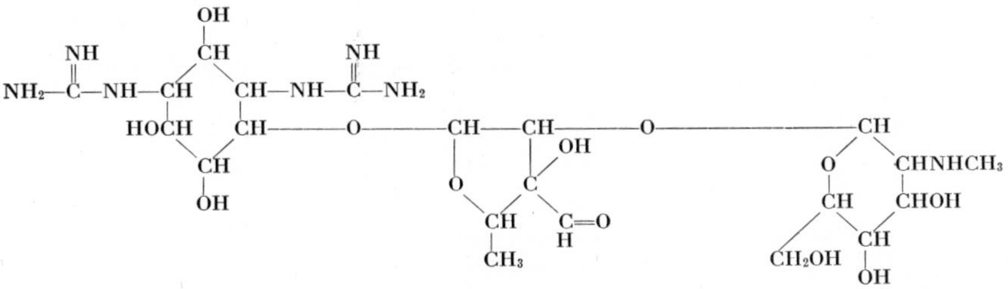

Streptidine   Streptose   N-Methyl-L-glucosamine

Streptomycin

Sometimes p-aminosalicylic acid is combined with streptomycin to minimize the development of bacilli resistant to the latter.

The recent introduction of "hydrazid" therapy—the use of hydrazide derivatives of isonicotinic acid—

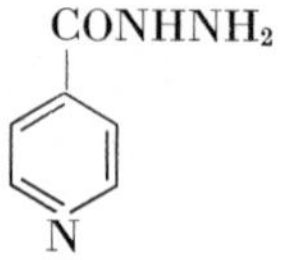

$$CONHNH_2$$

holds out some promise.

Dihydrostreptomycin, a reduction product of the parent substance, has properties similar to streptomycin. Its toxic effects develop more slowly than do those of streptomycin, which means that sometimes it can be used for longer periods and in higher dosage than streptomycin.

NEOMYCIN. In attempts to get an agent active against streptomycin-resistant bacteria, Waksman isolated an antibiotic produced by a species of *Streptomyces Fradiae*, present in the soil, to which the name "neomycin" has been given. The treatment of clinical infections, particularly those of the urinary tract, has yielded encouraging results. Neomycin is a mixture of closely related compounds.

AUREOMYCIN. This antibiotic is derived from a mold belonging to the actinomycete group—the same family that gives rise to streptomycin—and has proved effective against bacterial diseases such as undulant fever, peritonitis, urinary tract infections, gonorrhea, and the pneumococcal pneumonia. It has also yielded encouraging results in rickettsial diseases (Rocky Mountain spotted fever, typhus) and some virus diseases (primary atypical pneumonia), and the venereal disease lymphogranuloma venereum. Bacteria do not seem to become resistant to the attacks of this antibiotic, as they do with penicillin and streptomycin.

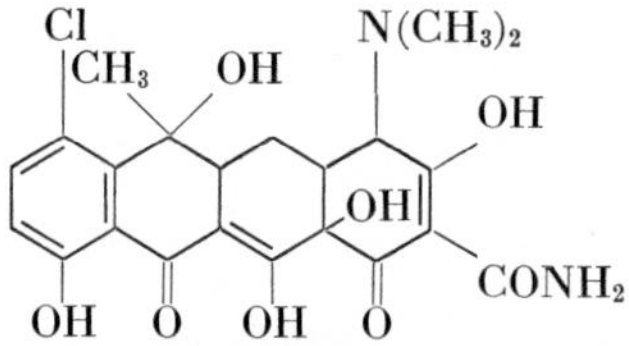

Aureomycin

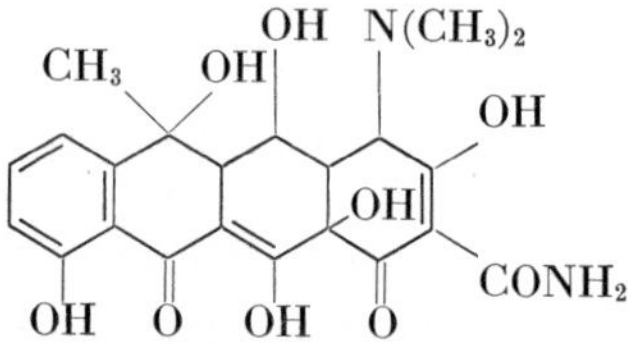

Terramycin

TERRAMYCIN. Closely allied to aureomycin, chemically and as a therapeutic agent, is terramycin.

CHLORAMPHENICOL (CHLOROMYCETIN). This antibiotic is a product of *Streptomyces venezuelae*, isolated from soil near Caracas, Venezuela. It has been effective in treating mice experimentally infected with a number of rickettsia and viruses (rickettsialpox and the viruses of psittacosis and lymphogranuloma venereum). Clinically, it has proved effective in epidemic typhus, scrub typhus, and Rocky Mountain spotted fever. Chloromycetin has been isolated and chemically identified. Its structure is

NO₂

CH.OH
|
CH.NH.COCHCl₂
|
CH₂OH

which means that it is 1-*p*-nitrophenyl-2-dichloroacetamidopropane-1,3-diol.

BACITRACIN is produced from a strain of *Bacillus subtilis*. It inhibits the growth of more gram-positive than gram-negative organisms and is effective against rickettsiae and some viruses. This antibiotic is a polypeptide and is used locally.

BACTERIAL RESISTANCE TO ANTIBIOTICS. This problem has become one of common experience. Repeated application of an antibiotic often develops a "resistance" to it by bacteria. Long suggests several possible mechanisms: (*a*) The bacteria may produce during growth a substance which antagonizes the antibacterial effect of the antibiotic; (*b*) previously sensi-

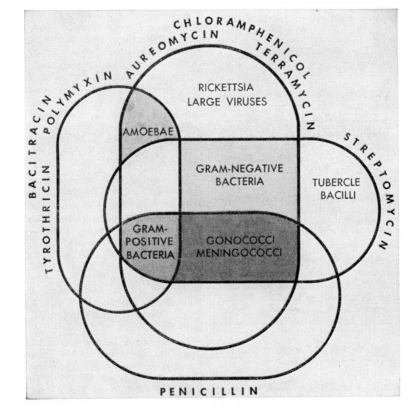

Fig. 127. Domains of the five principal antibiotics and three that are less frequently used (*left*) overlap. The three "broad-spectrum" antibiotics at the top of the page are effective against the largest group of organisms. (Raper: Scientific American, *186:* 49, 1952.)

tive bacteria become "adapted"; (c) certain cells among bacteria arise by spontaneous mutation which are resistant to the antibiotic; being resistant, they multiply freely.

Figure 127 gives a summary of the antibiotics and the organisms on which they act.

REFERENCES

Baron, Welch and Derenberg: Handbook of antibiotics, 1950; *Duggar and Singleton:* Ann. Rev. Biochem., *22:* 459, 1953 (biochemistry of antibiotics).

Immunochemistry. Kabat and Mayer: Experimental Immunochemistry, 1948, covers the field very thoroughly. See also *Haurowitz:* Biological Reviews, *27:* 247, 1952; *Tomcsik:* Ann. Rev. Biochem., *22:* 351, 1953; and the Annual Review of Microbiology.

Stacy: Proc. R. S. (London), Series B, *133:* 391, 1946, discusses the histochemistry of the Gram-staining reaction for micro-organisms.

Nungester: Bact. Rev., *15:* 105, 1951, deals with the mechanisms of man's resistance to infectious diseases. See also *Wood's* article, "White Blood Cells and Bacteria," in Scientific American, Feb., 1951, p. 48.

Reviews dealing with immunochemistry are *Grabar:* Ann. Rev. Biochem., *19:* 453, 1950; and *Mayer:* Ibid., *20:* 415, 1951.

The results of the use of gamma globulin in poliomyelitis—favorable, to some extent—are recorded by *Hammon, Coriell, and Stokes:* J. Am. Med. Assoc., *150:* 739, 1952.

For immunochemical studies with labelled antigens, see *Haurowitz, Crampton, and Sowinski:* Federation Proceedings, *10:* 560, 1951. See also *Banks, Mulligan, and Wormall:* Biochem. J., *48:* 180, 1951.

The theories dealing with antibody-antigen formation are summarized by *Porter:* Biochem. J., *46:* 31, 1950. See also *Pauling:* Baskerville Chemical Journal (City College N. Y.), 1950, p. 4; *Pardee and Pauling:* J. Am. Chem. Soc., *71:* 143, 1949.

For a discussion of "complement," see *Heidelberger:* American Scientist, *34:* 597, 1947.

For toxins, see the review by *Van Heyningen:* Annual Reports (Chemical Society), *47:* 303, 1951. See also *Pappenheimer, Jr.:* Scientific American, Oct., 1952, p. 32 (diphtheria toxin).

Dragstedt: Physiol. Rev., *21:* 563, 1941, reviews the subject of anaphylaxis.

On the subject of allergy, see Merck's Manual, 1950, p. 1; Annals N. Y. Acad. Sciences, *50:* 697–814, 1914; *Criep:* Clinical Bulletin No. 29, 1940 (Veterans' Administration); *Rose:* Annual Rev. Medicine, *2:* 155, 1951; *Kaufman:* Scientific American, Aug., 1952, p. 28 (asthma).

On the subject of histamine and antihistamine agents, see *Leonard and Huttrer:* Histamine Antagonists, 1950; Annals N. Y. Acad. Sciences, *50:* 1013–1208, 1950; *Ellis and Bundick:* J. Am. Med. Assoc., *150:* 773, 1952 (use of antihistamines); *Wyngaarden and Seevers:* Ibid., *145:* 277, 1951 (toxic effects); *Sherman:* Bull. N. Y. Acad. Med., May, 1951, p. 309 (use and abuse); *Code:* Physiol. Rev., *32:* 47, 1952 (histamine in blood); *Hoagland, Deitz, Myers, and Cosand:* J. Am. Med. Assoc., *143:* 157, 1950; Ibid., *143:* 744, 1950 (colds).

For the Rh factor, see What's New (Abbott Lab.) March, 1946; *Boyd:* Merck Report, April, 1946, p. 16; *Allen:* British Science News, 1947, p. 4; *Fisher:* American Scientist, *35:* 95, 1947.

A method of assaying hyaluronidase is described by *Jaques:* Biochem. J., *53:* 56, 1953.

Chemotherapy. See *Work and Work:* The Basis of Chemotherapy, 1948; *Ing,* in *Gilman's* Organic Chemistry, *3:* 392, 1953; *Cheney,* Ibid., *3:* 533, 1953. See also *Albert:* Selective Toxicity with Special Reference to Chemotherapy, 1951, pp. 129, 153; *Walker:* British Medical Bulletin, *5:* 361, 1948; Merck Manual, 1950, p. 828 (sulfa drugs); Merck Report, April, 1951, p. 17 (sulfa drugs).

The literature on the sulfonamides is enormous. Here are a few references: *Crossley:* Science, *91:* 369, 1940; Ind. Eng. Chem., News Edition, *18:* 385, 1940; *Marshall:* Bull. N. Y. Acad. Med., Dec., 1940, p. 723; *Blake:* Ibid., April, 1940, p. 197.

Urinary excretion products of the sulfonamides are discussed by *Scudi and Silber:* J. Biol. Chem., *156:* 343, 1944.

The interference of sulfaguanidine and succinylsulfathiazole with the synthesis of some vitamins in the intestine is discussed in Nutr. Rev., *1:* 341, 1943.

For a discussion of the antagonism of *p*-aminobenzoic acid to sulfonamides, see Nutr. Rev., *3:* 152, 1945.

For the more strictly clinical phases, see, for example, J. Am. Med. Assoc., *116:* 513, 1941; *Ottenberg:* N. Y. State J. Med., *39:* 418, 1939; *Gold:* Bull. N. Y. Acad. Med., Feb., 1943, p. 132.

For a review of the sulfonamide compounds, with emphasis on clinical applications, see New and Nonofficial Remedies (1951), p. 90.

For a survey of antimalarials, see *Burt:* J. Chem. Educ., *23:* 412, 1946.

The effectiveness of chloroquine is discussed in J. Am. Med. Assoc., *130:* 1069, 1946. For the chemistry of the substance, see *Kenyon, Wiesner, and Kwartler:* Ind. Eng. Chem., *41:* 654, 1949.

Evans, Jr.: Federation Proceedings, *3:* 390, 1946, describes the enzyme systems operating within the malarial parasite.

Northey is the author of the book: Sulfonamides and Allied Compounds, 1948.

Antibiotics. Work: Ann. Rev. Biochem., *21:* 431, 1952 (review); *Kirby:* J. Am. Med. Assoc., *144:* 233, 1950 (trends in antibiotic therapy); *Abraham and Newton:* Annual Reports (Chemical Society), *47:* 285, 1951 (progress in antibiotics); *Gray:* Scientific American, August, 1949, p. 26 (review); Annals N. Y. Acad. Sciences, *55:* 967–1284, 1952 (antibiotics in tropical diseases); *Raper:* Scientific American, April, 1952, p. 49 (progress); *Finland:* Bull. N. Y. Acad. Med., *27:* 199, 1951 (review); Chem. Eng. News, *29:* 1190, 1951 (review); *Bird:* Science, *114:* 3, 1951 (antibiotic growth stimulants); Nutr. Rev., *10:* 298, 1951 (growth stimulants).

Penicillin. Merck Manual, 1950, p. 834 (clinical review); *Peck and Lyons:* Ann. Rev. Biochem., *20:* 382, 1951 (chemistry); *Smith:* Analyst, *73:* 197, 1948 (chemistry); *Gale, etc.:* J. General Microbiology, *1:* 53, 77, 299, 314, 327, 1947; *Gale:* Ibid., *3:* 127, 1949 (how penicillin functions); *Gordon, Pan, Virgona, and Numerof:* Science, *118:* 43, 1953 (biosynthesis).

Streptomycin. Umbreit: Trans. N. Y. Acad. Sciences, *15:* 8, 1952 (mode of ac-

tion); Annals N. Y. Acad. Sciences, *52:* 625–788, 1949 (chemotherapy of tuberculosis); *Fox:* J. Chem. Educ., *29:* 29, 1952 (chemotherapy of tuberculosis); J. Am. Med. Assoc., *147:* 253 1951; Ibid., *142:* 650, 1950 (chemotherapy of tuberculosis); *Dubos:* Scientific American, Oct., 1949, p. 31 (tuberculosis); *Tempel:* J. Am. Med. Assoc., *150:* 1165, 1952 (treatment of tuberculosis); Merck Report, Jan., 1949, p. 25 (dihydrostreptomycin); J. Am. Med. Assoc., *148:* 1034, 1952; *Selikoff, Robitzek, and Ornstein:* Ibid., *150:* 973, 1952 (hydrazid therapy of tuberculosis); J. Am. Med. Assoc., *148:* 334, 1952 (neomycin); Ann. Rev. Biochem., *20:* 375, 1951 (neomycin-chemistry).

Aureomycin and Terramycin. Ann. Rev. Biochem., *19:* 500, 1950; *20:* 388, 378, 1951; *21:* 432, 1952; *Horsfall, Jr.:* Bull. N. Y. Acad. Med., Jan., 1950, p. 4 (virus infections); *Spink and Yow:* J. Am. Med. Assoc., *141:* 964, 1949 (treatment with aureomycin); *Rane:* Scientific American, April, 1949, p. 18 (aureomycin); Annals N. Y. Acad. Sciences, *51:* 175–342 (1948) (aureomycin); *Smadel:* Bull. N. Y. Acad. Med., April, 1951, p. 221 (virus infections); Annals N. Y. Acad. Sciences, *53:* 221–460, 1950 (terramycin); J. Am. Med. Assoc., *146:* 254, 1951 (terramycin); *Hochstein, Stephens, Conover, Regna, Pasternack, Brunings, and Woodword:* J. Am. Chem. Soc., *74:* 3708, 1952 (chemistry of terramycin).

Chloramphenicol. Ann. Rev. Biochem., *19:* 499, 1950; *20:* 387, 1951; *21:* 434, 1952; *Glazko, Dill, and Rebstock:* J. Biol. Chem., *183:* 679, 1950 (metabolic products); *Altemeier and Culbertson:* J. Am. Med. Assoc., *145:* 449, 1951 (clinical); *Smadel:* Ibid., *142:* 315, 1950 (clinical).

Bacitracin. Ann. Rev. Biochem., *19:* 501, 1950; *20:* 389, 1951; J. Am. Med. Assoc., *145:* 822, 1951; *Anker, Johnson, Goldberg and Meleney:* J. Bacteriology, *55:* 249, 1948; *Meleney and Johnson:* J. Am. Med. Assoc., *133:* 675, 1947 (therapy).

Bacterial Resistance to Antibiotics. Work: Ann. Rev. Biochem., *21:* 444, 1952; *Long:* Bull. N. Y. Acad. Med., Dec., 1952, p. 809; J. Am. Med. Assoc., *148:* 470, 1952.

For growth-promoting properties of antibiotics, see *Stokstad and Jukes:* Proc. Soc. Exp. Biol. Med., *73:* 523, 1950; *Elam, Jacobs, Tidwell, Gee, and Couch:* J. Nutrition, *49:* 307, 1953.

Appendix

Table 69 NUTRITIVE VALUE OF 100 GRAMS OF SELECTED FOODS, EDIBLE PORTION
(Adapted from U. S. Department of Agriculture Misc. Publ. No. 572.)

Food item	Water	Food energy	Protein	Fat	Carbohydrate	Calcium	Phosphorus	Iron	Vitamin A value	Thiamine	Riboflavin	Niacin	Ascorbic acid
	Per cent	Calories	Grams	Grams	Grams	Milligrams	Milligrams	Milligrams	International Units	Milligrams	Milligrams	Milligrams	Milligrams
MILK, CREAM, ICE CREAM, CHEESE													
Milk:													
Buttermilk; cultured	90.5	35	3.5	0.1	5.1	(118)	(93)	(0.07)	(Trace)	(0.04)	(0.18)	(0.1)	(1)
Chocolate flavored [1]	83.0	75	3.2	2.2	10.6	109	91	.07	90	.03	.16	.1	0
Condensed; sweetened	27.0	327	8.1	8.4	54.8	273	228	(.20)	(430)	(.05)	(.39)	(.2)	(1)
Dry skim	3.5	359	35.6	1.0	52.0	1,300	1,030	.58	(40)	.35	1.96	1.1	7
Dry whole	3.5	496	25.8	26.7	38.0	949	728	.58	1,400	.30	1.46	.7	6
Evaporated; unsweetened	73.7	139	7.0	7.9	9.9	243	195	.17	400	.05	.36	.2	1
Fresh skim	90.5	35	3.5	.1	5.1	(118)	(93)	(.07)	(Trace)	.04	(.18)	(.1)	1
Fresh whole	87.0	69	3.5	3.9	4.9	118	93	.07	(160)	.04	.17	.1	1
Cream; ice cream:													
Cream (20 per cent); sweet or sour	72.5	208	2.9	20.0	4.0	(97)	(77)	(.06)	(830)	(.03)	(.14)	(.1)	(1)
Ice cream; plain [1]	62.0	210	4.0	12.3	20.8	132	104	.10	540	.04	.19	.1	Trace
Cheese:													
Cheddar type	39	393	23.9	32.3	1.7	873	610	(.57)	1,740	.04	.50	(.2)	(0)
Cottage	74.0	101	19.2	.8	4.3	82	263	(.46)	(30)	.02	.29	(.1)	(0)
Cream	53.3	367	7.1	36.9	1.7	(298)	(208)	(.17)	2,210	(.01)	.14	.1	(0)
Processed; canned [2]	37.5	382	21.9	31.8	2.0	716	831	.76	1,260	.03	.43	.1	(0)
FATS, OILS													
Bacon, medium fat	20	626	9.1	65	(1.1)	13	108	.8	(0)	(.42)	(.10)	(2.1)	0
Butter	15.5	733	.6	81	.4	16	16	.2	[3]3,300	Trace	.01	.1	0
French dressing	38.3	423	.8	39	17.3	(5)	(5)	.1	0	(0)	0	0	0
Lard, other shortening	0	900	0	100	0	0	0	0	0	(0)	(0)	0	0
Margarine with vitamin A added	15.5	733	.6	81	.4	0	(15)	(.2)	[4](1,980)	(0)	0	0	0
Mayonnaise	16	720	1.5	78	3.0	(2)	(60)	(1.0)	(210)	(.04)	(.04)	(0)	(0)
Salad dressing	44.7	391	1.1	36.8	13.9	(19)	(30)	(.4)	(140)	(.02)	(.03)	(0)	(0)
Salad or cooking oil	0	900	0	100	0	0	0	0	0	0	0	0	0
Salt pork; fat	8	781	3.9	85	0	2	42	.6	(0)	(.18)	(.04)	(.9)	0
EGGS													
Egg yolk; fresh	49.4	355	16.3	31.9	.7	147	585	7.2	3,210	.32	.52	..	0
Eggs; whole; dried	2	593	(48.2)	(43.3)	(2.6)	187	800	8.7	4,450	.35	1.23	.2	0
Eggs; whole; fresh	74.0	158	12.8	11.5	.7	54	210	2.7	1,140	.12	.34	.1	0

MEAT, POULTRY, FISH												
Beef:												
Chuck roast (wholesale chuck)	65	218	18.6	16	0	11	200	2.8	(0)	.12	.15	5.0
Corned beef, canned	57.3	232	24.4	15	0	29	113	4.0	(0)	.02	.19	2.7
Corned beef, medium	54.2	288	15.8	25	0	9	170	2.4	(0)	.05	.10	1.7
Dried or chipped	47.7	194	34.3	6.3	0	20	370	5.1	(0)	.11	.22	3.7
Hamburger	55	316	16	28	0	9	172	2.4	(0)	.10	.13	4.3
Loin steaks (wholesale loin)	57	293	16.9	25	0	10	182	2.5	(0)	.10	.13	4.6
Rib roast or steak (wholesale rib)	59	277	17.4	23	0	10	188	2.6	(0)	.11	.14	4.7
Roast, canned	60.0	217	25	13	0	9	164	2.2	(0)	.02	.24	4.5
Round steak (wholesale round)	67	194	19.3	13	0	11	208	2.9	(0)	.12	.15	5.2
Rump roast (wholesale rump)	53	341	15.5	31	0	9	167	2.3	(0)	.10	.12	4.2
Soup meat (wholesale shanks)	70	162	20.3	9	0	12	219	3.0	(0)	.13	.16	5.5
Stew meat (73 per cent lean)	53	333	15.8	30	0	9	170	2.4	(0)	.10	.12	4.3
Lamb:												
Leg roast (wholesale leg)	63.7	230	18.0	17.5	0	10	194	2.7	(0)	.21	.26	5.9
Shoulder roast (wholesale 3-rib shoulder)	58.3	290	15.6	25.3	0	9	168	2.3	(0)	.18	.23	5.2
Sirloin chop (wholesale leg)	63.7	230	18.0	17.5	0	10	194	2.7	(0)	.21	.25	5.9
Pork:												
Bacon. See Fats, Oils.												
Ham, fresh	53	340	15.2	31	0	9	164	2.3	(0)	.96	.19	4.1
Ham, smoked	42	384	16.9	35	(.3)	10	182	2.5	(0)	.78	.19	3.8
Loin	58	291	16.4	25	0	10	177	2.5	(0)	1.04	.20	4.4
Pork links; sausage	41.9	446	10.8	44.8	0	6	116	1.6	(0)	.22	.15	2.3
Salt pork. See Fats, Oils.												
Spareribs	53	346	14.6	32	0	8	157	2.2	(0)	.92	.18	3.9
Veal:												
Chops (wholesale loin)	69	176	19.2	11	0	11	207	2.9	(0)	.18	.27	6.3
Cutlet (wholesale round)	70	159	19.5	9	0	11	210	2.9	(0)	.18	.28	6.4
Leg roast or steak (wholesale leg)	(68)	186	(19.1)	(12.2)	0	11	206	2.9	(0)	.17	.27	6.3
Stew meat (74 per cent lean)	64	226	18.3	17	0	11	197	2.7	(0)	.17	.26	6.0
Variety meats; meat mixtures:												
Beef and gravy, canned [5]	65.3	188	19.4	11.7	1.3	19	122	2.7	(30)	.09	.19	2.7
Bologna	62.4	217	14.8	15.9	3.6	9	160	2.2	(0)	.31	.30	3.0
Chile con carne, without beans, canned [6]	66.3	198	10.2	14.6	6.4	21	152	.7	160	.01	.10	2.1
Frankfurters	64.3	201	15.2	14.1	3.3	9	164	2.3	(0)	.19	.23	2.4

Note: Parentheses indicate imputed value.

[1] Calculated from ingredients.

[2] Cheddar type.

[3] Year-round average.

[4] Plain margarine is considered to have no vitamin A value.

[5] 90 per cent beef, 10 per cent tomato gravy.

[6] Not less than 60 per cent meat, not more than 8 per cent cereals, seasonings.

Table 69   NUTRITIVE VALUE OF 100 GRAMS OF SELECTED FOODS, EDIBLE PORTION—CONTINUED

Food item	Water	Food energy	Protein	Fat	Carbo-hydrate	Calcium	Phos-phorus	Iron	Vitamin A value	Thiamine	Ribo-flavin	Niacin	Ascorbic acid
	Per cent	Calo-ries	Grams	Grams	Grams	Milli-grams	Milli-grams	Milli-grams	Inter-national Units	Milli-grams	Milli-grams	Milli-grams	Milli-grams
MEAT, POULTRY, FISH—Continued													
Variety meats; meat mixtures—Continued:													
Ham and eggs, canned [7]	63.9	227	14.4	18.3	1.2	43	166	2.2	500	.16	.24	1.7	0
Hash, corned beef, canned [8]	69.4	143	15.1	6.1	7.0	26	(90)	1.3	(0)	.02	.13	2.4	0
Hash, meat and vegetable, canned [9]	73.3	122	10.0	5.0	9.3	14	(66)	1.2	(0)	.04	.11	2.5	6
Heart, fresh	75.4	126	(16.5)	(6.3)	(.7)	10	236	6.2	(0)	.54	.90	6.8	14
Liver, fresh	70.9	131	(19.8)	(4.2)	(3.6)	8	373	12.1	19,200	.27	2.80	16.1	31
Liver sausage	59.0	258	16.7	20.6	1.5	9	238	5.4	(5,750)	.17	1.12	4.6	(0)
Luncheon meat, canned [10]	56.3	270	15.2	22.5	1.7	21	170	1.4	(0)	.29	.21	2.7	0
Pork and gravy, canned [11]	64.9	206	15.4	15.2	1.9	16	162	1.6	(0)	.19	.24	2.7	0
Pork sausage, bulk, canned	57.0	280	16.0	24.0	0	17	131	2.2	(0)	.19	.21	2.8	0
Spaghetti with meat, canned [12]	71.0	142	9.8	6.9	10.2	38	97	1.8	480	.02	.12	2.2	...
Stew, meat and vegetable, canned [13]	72.9	127	11.6	5.5	7.8	36	(136)	1.4	1,780	.04	.12	2.4	4
Tongue, fresh, medium fat	68	202	16.4	15	.4	30	119	6.9	(0)	.22	.27	5.0	0
Vienna sausage, canned	64.1	210	16.0	16.2	0	19	(164)	.6	(0)	.07	.14	3.1	0
Poultry:													
Chicken, boned, canned	67.1	175	21.8	9.8	0	32	(218)	(1.9)	Trace	.01	.15	3.7	...
Chicken, roasters [14]	66.0	194	20.2	12.6	0	16	218	1.9	Trace	.11	.18	8.6	...
Turkey, medium fat [14]	58.3	262	20.1	20.2	0	23	320	3.8	Trace	.12	.19	7.9	...
Fish and shellfish:													
Cod	82.6	70	16.5	.4	0	18	189	.9	...	.04	.05	2.3	2
Fish, miscellaneous, medium fat	77.2	98	19.0	2.5	0	21	218	1.0	...	.07	.07	4.2	(2)
Oysters, solids and liquor	87.1	50	6.0	1.2	3.7	68	172	7.1	[15] 80	.18	.23	1.2	...
Salmon, canned	67.4	169	20.6	9.6	0	67	286	1.3	80	.03	.18	6.5	0
Sardines, canned in oil, drained solids	57.4	207	25.7	11.0	1.2	35	365	1.8	290	.06	.12	5.2	0
Sardines, canned in oil, total contents of can	47.1	331	21.1	27	1.0	29	299	1.5	710	.05	.10	4.3	0
Shrimp, canned	78.3	82	17.8	.8	.8	(75)	(210)	(2.0)	60	.01	.03	1.9	0
Tuna fish, canned, drained solids	57.7	217	27.7	11.8	0	34	290	1.7	70	.04	.13	10.6	0
Tuna fish, canned, total contents of can	51.4	294	23.9	22.1	0	30	252	1.5	130	.04	.11	9.2	0
DRY BEANS AND PEAS, NUTS													
Dry beans and peas:													
Bean soup, navy, dehydrated [16]	7.2	332	17.6	1.2	62.7	(148)	(463)	(10.3)	(0)	.46	.22	2.4	1
Beans, canned, baked	71.0	117	5.7	2.0	19.0	(49)	(154)	(3.4)	[17] 70	.05	.05	.8	[17] 4
Beans, common or kidney, dry seed	10.5	350	22.0	1.5	62.1	148	463	10.3	0	.60	.24	2.1	2

Beans, lima, dry seed	12.6	341	20.7	1.3	61.6	68	381	7.5	0	.60	.24	2.1	2
Chickpeas	10.6	369	20.8	4.7	60.9	92	375	7.1	Trace	.35	.15	1.4	(2)
Cowpeas	10.6	351	22.9	1.4	61.6	80	450	7.8	0	.83	.23	2.2	2
Pea soup, dehydrated [18]	7.2	336	20.4	1.2	60.8	(73)	(397)	(6.0)	220	.62	.21	3.1	2
Peas, split	10.0	354	24.5	1.0	61.7	73	397	6.0	370	.87	.29	3.0	2
Soybeans, whole, mature	7.5	351	34.9	18.1	[19] (12.0)	227	586	8.0	110	1.14	.31	2.1	Trace
Nuts:													
Almonds	4.7	640	18.6	54.1	19.6	254	475	4.4	0	0.25	0.67	4.6	Trace
Peanut butter	1.7	619	26.1	47.8	21.0	74	393	1.9	0	.20	.16	16.2	(0)
Peanuts, roasted	2.6	600	26.9	44.2	23.6	74	393	1.9	0	[20] .30	.16	16.2	(0)
Pecans	3.0	747	9.4	73.0	13.0	74	324	2.4	50	.72	.11	.9	2
Walnuts, English	3.3	702	15.0	64.4	15.6	83	380	2.1	30	.48	.13	1.2	3
VEGETABLES													
Fresh:													
Asparagus	93.0	26	2.2	.2	3.9	21	62	.9	1,000	.16	.17	1.2	33
Beans, lima, green	66.5	131	7.5	.8	23.5	63	158	2.3	280	.25	.14	.9	32
Beans, snap	88.9	42	2.4	.2	7.7	65	44	1.1	630	.08	.10	.6	19
Beet greens	90.4	33	2.0	.3	5.6	[21]	45	3.2	6,700	.05	.17	.3	34
Beets	87.6	46	1.6	.1	9.6	27	43	1.0	20	.03	.05	.4	10
Broccoli	89.9	37	3.3	.2	5.5	130	76	1.3	3,500	.09	.21	.9	118
Brussels sprouts	84.9	58	4.4	.5	8.9	34	78	1.3	400	.11	(.06)	(.3)	94
Cabbage	92.4	29	1.4	.2	5.3	46	31	.5	80	.07	.06	.3	52
Carrots	88.2	45	1.2	.3	9.3	39	37	.8	12,000	.07	.06	.5	6
Cauliflower	91.7	31	2.4	.2	4.9	22	72	1.1	90	.10	.11	.6	69
Celery	93.7	22	1.3	.2	3.7	50	40	.5	0	.03	.04	.3	7
Chard	91.8	25	1.4	.2	4.4	[22]	36	4.0	2,800	.06	.13	.2	38
Collards	86.6	50	3.9	.6	7.2	249	58	1.6	6,870	.22	(.20)	(.8)	100
Corn, sweet, white or yellow	73.9	108	3.7	1.2	20.5	9	120	.5	[23] 390	.15	.14	1.4	12

Note: Parentheses indicate imputed value.

7 50 per cent ham, 50 per cent whole eggs.
8 72 per cent beef, 28 per cent potatoes.
9 50 per cent meat, 48 per cent potatoes, 2 per cent onions.
10 Pork.
11 90 per cent pork, 10 per cent gravy.
12 50 per cent meat, 10 per cent dry spaghetti, 30 per cent tomato puree, 5 per cent cheese, 5 per cent onions.
13 50 per cent meat, 15 per cent potatoes, 15 per cent carrots, 8 per cent dry beans, 12 per cent tomato puree.

14 Vitamin values based on muscle meat only.
15 Based on pink salmon. Canned red salmon may have a value several times higher.
16 Navy bean meal, farinaceous flour up to 15 per cent.
17 Contributed by tomatoes.
18 Pea meal, farinaceous flour up to 15 per cent.
19 "Available" carbohydrate.
20 Based on peanuts without skins; when skins are included the thiamine value is higher.
21 118 mg.; may not be available because of presence of oxalic acid.
22 105 mg.; may not be available because of presence of oxalic acid.
23 Based on yellow corn; white corn contains only a trace.

523

Table 69   NUTRITIVE VALUE OF 100 GRAMS OF SELECTED FOODS, EDIBLE PORTION—CONTINUED

Food item	Water	Food energy	Protein	Fat	Carbo-hydrate	Calcium	Phos-phorus	Iron	Vitamin A value	Thiamine	Ribo-flavin	Niacin	Ascorbic acid
	Per cent	Calo-ries	Grams	Grams	Grams	Milli-grams	Milli-grams	Milli-grams	Inter-national Units	Milli-grams	Milli-grams	Milli-grams	Milli-grams
VEGETABLES—Continued													
Fresh—Continued:													
Cucumbers	96.1	14	.7	.1	2.7	10	21	.3	[24] 0	.04	.09	.2	8
Dandelion greens	85.8	52	2.7	.7	8.8	187	70	3.1	13,650	.19	.14	(.8)	36
Eggplant	92.7	28	1.1	.2	5.5	15	37	.4	30	.07	.06	.8	5
Kale	86.6	50	3.9	.6	7.2	225	62	2.2	7,540	.12	.35	(.8)	115
Lettuce, headed	94.8	18	1.2	.2	2.9	22	25	.5	540	.06	.07	.2	8
Lettuce, all other	94.8	18	1.2	.2	2.9	62	20	1.1	1,620	.06	.07	.2	18
Mustard greens	92.2	28	2.3	.3	4.0	220	38	2.9	6,460	.09	.20	.8	102
Okra	89.8	39	1.8	.2	7.4	82	62	.7	740	.12	.10	.7	30
Onions, mature	87.5	49	1.4	.2	10.3	32	44	.5	50	.03	.02	.1	[25] 9
Parsnips	78.6	83	1.5	.5	18.2	57	80	.7	0	.11	.09	.2	18
Peas, green	74.3	101	6.7	.4	17.7	22	122	1.9	680	.36	.18	2.1	26
Peppers, green	92.4	29	1.2	.2	5.7	11	25	.4	630	.07	.04	.4	120
Potatoes	77.8	85	2.0	.1	19.1	11	56	.7	20	.11	.04	1.2	17
Pumpkin	90.5	36	1.2	.2	7.3	21	44	.8	(3,400)	(.05)	(.08)	(.6)	8
Radishes	93.6	22	1.2	.1	4.2	37	31	1.0	30	.04	.04	.1	24
Rutabagas	89.1	41	1.1	.1	8.9	55	41	.4	330	.06	.06	.5	36
Spinach	92.7	25	2.3	.3	3.2	[26]	55	3.0	9,420	.12	.24	.7	59
Squash, summer	95.0	19	.6	.1	3.9	15	15	.4	260	.04	.05	1.1	17
Squash, winter	88.6	44	1.5	.3	8.8	19	28	.6	4,950	.05	.08	.6	8
Sweetpotatoes	68.5	125	1.8	.7	27.9	30	49	.7	[27] 7,700	.10	.06	.7	22
Tomatoes	94.1	23	1.0	.3	4.0	11	27	.6	1,100	.06	.04	.6	23
Turnip greens	89.5	37	2.9	.4	5.4	259	50	2.4	9,540	.10	.56	.8	136
Turnips	90.9	35	1.1	.2	7.1	40	34	.5	Trace	.06	.06	.5	28
Canned:													
Asparagus	93.6	21	1.6	.3	3.0	20	34	1.0	[28] 600	.06	.09	.8	15
Beans, lima	80.9	72	3.8	.3	13.5	27	73	1.7	130	.03	.05	.5	8
Beans, snap	94.0	19	1.0	0	3.8	27	19	1.4	410	.03	.05	.3	4
Beets	89.4	39	1.0	0	8.7	15	29	.6	20	.01	.03	.1	5
Carrots	92.2	30	.5	.4	6.1	22	24	.6	12,000	.03	.02	.3	2
Corn, white or yellow	80.5	77	2.0	.5	16.1	4	51	.5	[23] 200	.02	.05	.8	5
Peas, green	82.3	69	3.4	.4	12.9	25	67	1.8	540	.11	.06	.9	8
Pumpkin	90.2	38	1.0	.3	7.9	(20)	(36)	(.7)	3,400	.02	.06	.5	(0)

	Water (gm)	Calories	Protein (gm)	Fat (gm)	Carbohydrate (gm)	Calcium (mg)	Phosphorus (mg)	Iron (mg)	Vitamin A (I.U.)	Thiamine (mg)	Riboflavin (mg)	Niacin (mg)	Ascorbic acid (mg)
Sauerkraut	93.2	20	1.1	.2	3.4	(46)	(31)	(.5)	Trace	.03	.20	.2	18[29]
Spinach	92.3	25	2.3	.4	3.0	30	33	1.6	6,790	.02	.08	.3	14
Tomato catsup	69.5	110	2.0	0.4	24.5	12	18	0.8	(1,880)	0.09	0.07	2.2	11
Tomato juice	93.5	23	1.0	.2	4.3	(7)	(15)	(.4)	1,050	.05	.03	.7	16
Tomato puree	89.2	40	1.8	.5	7.2	(11)	(37)	(1.1)	1,880	.09	(.07)	1.8	28
Tomatoes	94.2	21	1.0	.2	3.9	(11)	(27)	(.6)	1,050	.05	.03	.7	16

FRUIT

Fresh:	Water (gm)	Calories	Protein (gm)	Fat (gm)	Carbohydrate (gm)	Calcium (mg)	Phosphorus (mg)	Iron (mg)	Vitamin A (I.U.)	Thiamine (mg)	Riboflavin (mg)	Niacin (mg)	Ascorbic acid (mg)
Apples	84.1	64	.3	.4	14.9	6	10	.3	90	.04	.02	.2	5
Apricots	85.4	56	1.0	.1	12.9	16	23	.5	2,790	.03	.04	.7	4
Avocadoes	65.4	265	1.7	26.4	5.1	10	38	.6	290	.12	.15	1.1	16
Bananas	74.8	99	1.2	.2	23	8	28	.6	430	.09	.06	.6	10
Berries:													
Blueberries	83.4	68	.6	.6	15.1	16	13	.8	280	(.03)	(.07)	(.3)	16
Strawberries	90.0	41	.8	.6	8.1	28	27	.8	60	.03	.07	.3	60
Other berries	84.4	65	1.2	.8	13.2	36	34	.9	320	.03	(.07)	(.3)	23
Cantaloups	94.0	23	.6	.2	4.6	17	16	.4	3,420[31]	.06	.04	.8	33
Grapefruit	88.8	4	.5	.2	10.1	17	18	.3	Trace	.04	.02	.2	40
Grapes	81.6	74	.8	.4	16.7	17	21	.6	80	.05	.03	.4	4
Lemons	89.3	44	.9	.6	8.7	(14)	(10)	(.1)	0	.04	Trace	.1	45
Limes	86.0	53	.8	.1	12.3	(14)	(10)	(.1)	0	(.04)	(Trace)	(.1)	27
Oranges	87.2	50	.9	.2	11.2	33	23	.4	(190)	.08	.03	.2	49
Peaches	86.9	51	.5	.1	12.0	8	22	.6	880	.02	.05	.9	8
Pears	82.7	70	.7	.4	15.8	13	16	.3	20	.02	.04	.1	4
Pineapples	85.3	58	.4	.2	13.7	16	11	.5	130	.08	(.02)	(.2)	24
Plums	85.7	56	.7	.1	12.9	17	20	.5	350	.15	(.03)	.6	5
Rhubarb	94.9	18	.5	.1	3.8	2	25	.5	30	.01	.01	.1	9
Tangerines; other mandarin type oranges	87.3	50	.8	.3	10.9	(33)	(23)	(.4)	(420)	.07	(.03)	(.2)	31
Watermelons	92.1	31	.5	.2	6.9	7	12	.2	590	.05	.05	.2	6
Canned:													
Apples: applesauce	79.8	80	.2	.1	19.7	(4)	(6)	(.2)	(60)	.01	.01	Trace	1
Apricots	77.3	89	.6	.1	21.4	(10)	(15)	(.3)	1,350	.02	.02	.3	4
Cherries	78.1	86	.6	.1	20.8	(11)	(14)	(.3)	(430)	.03	.02	.2	3
Cranberry sauce	48.1	209	.1	.3	51.4	(8)	(7)	(.3)	(30)	..	(.04)	..	2
Fruit cocktail	(80.6)	78	(.4)	(.2)	(18.6)	(9)	(12)	(.4)	160	.01	.01	.4	2

Note: Parentheses indicate imputed value.

²⁴ Based on pared cucumber; unpared contains about 260 I. U. vitamin A per 100 gm.
²⁵ Green bunching onions contain about 23 mg. ascorbic acid per 100 gm.
²⁶ 81 mg.; may not be available because of presence of oxalic acid.
²⁷ If pale varieties only were used, value would be very much lower.
²⁸ Based on green products; bleached products contain only a trace.
²⁹ Drained solids only.
³⁰ 90 mg.; may not be available because of presence of oxalic acid.
³¹ Based on deeply colored varieties.
³² 51 mg.; may not be available because of presence of oxalic acid.

Table 69 NUTRITIVE VALUE OF 100 GRAMS OF SELECTED FOODS, EDIBLE PORTION—CONTINUED

Food item	Water	Food energy	Protein	Fat	Carbo- hydrate	Calcium	Phos- phorus	Iron	Vitamin A value	Thiamine	Ribo- flavin	Niacin	Ascorbic acid
	Per cent	Calo- ries	Grams	Grams	Grams	Milli- grams	Milli- grams	Milli- grams	Inter- national Units	Milli- grams	Milli- grams	Milli- grams	Milli- grams
FRUIT—Continued													
Canned—Continued													
Grapefruit juice..........	89.4	41	.5	.2	9.4	8	12	.4	Trace	.03	.02	.2	35
Grapefruit segments.......	79.8	81	.6	.2	19.1	13	14	.3	Trace	.03	.02	.2	30
Orange juice.............	86	55	.6	.1	12.9	(33)	(23)	(.4)	(100)	.07	.02	.2	42
Peaches.................	80.9	75	.4	.1	18.2	(5)	(14)	(.4)	450	.01	.02	.7	4
Pears...................	81.1	75	.2	.1	18.4	(8)	(10)	(.2)	Trace	.01	.02	.1	2
Pineapple juice..........	86.2	54	.3	.1	13.0	15	8	.5	80	.05	.02	.2	9
Pineapples..............	78.0	87	.4	.1	21.1	29	7	.6	80	.07	.02	.2	9
Plums; Italian prunes....	78.6	84	.4	.1	20.4	8	12	1.1	(230)	.03	.03	.4	1
Dried:													
Apple nuggets...........	1.6	390	1.4	1.0	93.9	24	42	4.1	(0)	.05	.08	.5	11
Apricots [33]...........	24	292	5.2	.4	66.9	86	119	4.9	7,430	.01	.16	3.3	12
Cranberries.............	4.9	409	2.9	6.6	84.4	82	22	3.4	660	.19	.18	.9	33
Peaches [33]............	24	295	3.0	.6	69.4	44	126	6.9	3,250	.01	.20	5.4	19
Prunes [34].............	24	299	2.3	.6	71.0	54	85	3.9	1,890	.10	.16	1.7	3
Raisins [34]............	24	298	2.3	.5	71.2	78	129	3.3	50	.15	.08	.5	Trace
GRAIN PRODUCTS													
Baked goods:													
Bread:													
Rye, light..............	37.6	263	(6.4)	(3.4)	(51.7)	(22)	(96)	(.8)	(0)	.16	(.04)	(1.1)	0
White, enriched.........	35.9	261	8.5	2.0	52.3	(56)	(100)	(1.8)	(0)	(.24)	(.15)	(2.2)	0
Whole wheat.............	37	262	9.5	3.5	48.0	(60)	370	2.6	(0)	.28	.15	3.5	0
Cake, light batter type..	26.8	327	6.4	8.2	57.0	62	(126)	2.0	....	.03	.10	.7	0
Cookies, assorted, plain.	4.8	438	6.0	12.7	75.0	(22)	(65)	(.6)	(0)	.04	(.04)	(.5)	0
Cracker meal; crackers, assorted ...	4.5	422	9.5	10.3	72.7	22	102	1.5	(0)	(.07)	(0)	(.6)	0
Crackers, graham.......	5.5	419	8.0	10.0	74.3	20	203	1.9	(0)	.30	.12	1.5	0
Fig bars................	13.8	363	4.2	4.8	75.8	(69)	(69)	(1.3)	(0)	.02	(.06)	(.9)	0
Pie, apple..............		266	(2.9)	(9.6)	(42.0)	(11)	(22)	1.9	(0)	.05	(.04)	.4	(0)
Pie, cream..............		223	(2.8)	(9.8)	(31.0)	20	(38)	(1.8)	(0)	.03	.08	.2	(0)
Rolls, plain, enriched...	29.4	304	8.2	6.1	54.1	(56)	(100)	(1.8)	(0)	(.24)	(.15)	(2.2)	0
Rolls, sweet, unenriched..	29.6	304	7.8	5.4	56.0	(56)	(100)	.5	(0)	.08	.13	.8	0
Breakfast cereals:													
Corn flakes.............	9.3	359	7.9	.7	80.3	(10)	56	(1.0)	(0)	(.16)	.08	1.6	0
Corn flakes, restored.													
Oatmeal.................	8.3	396	14.2	7.4	68.2	54	365	5.2	(0)	.55	.14	1.1	0

Note: the nutrient column headings are not printed on this page (they appear on the preceding page). The columns are, in order: Water (%), Food energy (cal.), Protein (g.), Fat (g.), Carbohydrate (g.), Calcium (mg.), Phosphorus (mg.), Iron (mg.), Vitamin A (I.U.), Thiamine (mg.), Riboflavin (mg.), Niacin (mg.), Ascorbic acid (mg.).

Food	Water	Energy	Protein	Fat	Carb.	Ca	P	Fe	Vit. A	Thiamine	Riboflavin	Niacin	Ascorbic
Rice flakes; puffed rice	8.8	363	7.2	.4	82.6	9	(92)	.9	0	(.05)	(.03)	(1.4)	0
Rice flakes; puffed rice, restored	8.8	363	7.2	.4	82.6	9	(92)	.9	(0)	(.05)	(.03)	(1.4)	0
Wheat cereals:													
Farina	11	359	11.5	1.0	76.1	21	125	.8	(0)	.06	.06	1.0	0
Farina, enriched	11	359	11.5	1.0	76.1	21	125	(1.3)	(0)	(.37)	(.26)	(1.3)	0
Flakes; puffed wheat	6.2	372	11.9	1.5	77.7	33	353	3.7	(0)	.15	.12	4.2	0
Flakes; puffed wheat, restored	6.2	372	11.9	1.5	77.7	33	353	3.7	(0)	.15	.12	4.2	0
Shredded wheat	7.7	369	10.4	1.4	78.7	(38)	(385)	(3.8)	(0)	.20	.14	4.2	0
Whole-grain, uncooked	8.7	368	11.7	2.0	75.8	38	385	3.8	(0)	.45	.13	4.6	0
Other cereals:													
Barley, pearled, light	11.1	357	8.2	1.0	78.8	16	189	(2.0)	(0)	.12	.08	3.1	0
Hominy	11.4	357	8.5	.8	78.9	11	70	1.0	(0)	.15	.05	(.9)	0
Macaroni; spaghetti	11	360	13	1.4	73.9	22	144	1.2	(0)	.13	.08	2.1	0
Noodles	9.1	385	14.3	5.0	70.6	24	156	1.9	(200)	(.13)	(.12)	(2.1)	0
Rice:													
Brown	12.0	356	7.5	1.7	77.7	39	303	5.5	(0)	.29	.05	4.6	0
Converted	(12.3)	351	(7.6)	(.3)	(79.4)	(9)	(92)	(.7)	(0)	.23	.04	3.8	0
White	12.3	351	7.6	.3	79.4	9	92	.7	(0)	.05	.03	1.4	0
Tapioca	12.6	350	.6	.2	86.4	12	12	(1.0)	(0)	0	(0)	(0)	0
SUGARS, SWEETS													
Honey	20	319	.3	0	79.5	5	16	.9	(0)	Trace	.04	.2	4
Jams; marmalades	28	288	.5	.3	70.8	12	12	(.3)	10	.02	.02	.2	6
Jellies	34.5	261	.2	0	65.0	(12)	(12)	(.3)	(10)	(.02)	(.02)	(.2)	4
Molasses, cane	24	240	(0)	(0)	(60)	273	51	6.7	(0)	.08	.16	2.8	(0)
Sirup, table blends	25	296	(0)	(0)	(74)	46	16	4.1	0	0	.01	.1	(0)
Sugar, brown	3	382	(0)	(0)	(95.5)	[35] 76	[35] 37	2.6	(0)	(0)	(0)	(0)	(0)
Sugar, granulated or powdered	.5	398	(0)	(0)	99.5	(0)	(0)	.1	(0)	(0)	(0)	(0)	0
MISCELLANEOUS													
Bouillon cubes	(3)	259	17.7	0	47.0	40	510	9.2	(0)	0.03	0.83	[36] .6	(0)
Chocolate, unsweetened	2.3	570	(5.5)	52.9	(18)	[37]	343	2.5	(0)	Trace	.24	1.1	(0)
Cocoa	4.3	329	(9.0)	18.8	(31.0)	[38]	709	2.7	(0)	Trace	(.39)	(2.3)	(0)
Cocoanut, dry, shredded	3.3	579	3.6	39.1	53.2	43	191	3.6	0	Trace	Trace	Trace	(0)
Gelatin dessert powder	1.6	392	9.4	0	88.7	(0)	(0)	(0)	(0)	(0)	(0)	(0)	(0)
Olives, green	75.2	144	1.5	13.5	4.0	101	15	2.0	420	Trace	..	Trace	..
Pickles, cucumber	95.2	11	.5	.2	1.9	24	22	.9	190	.01	.02	.7	7
Wheat germ	11.0	389	25.2	10.0	49.5	84	1,096	8.1	(0)	2.05	.80	4.6	(0)
Yeast, compressed, baker's	70.9	109	13.3	.4	13.0	25	605	4.9	(0)	.45	2.07	28.2	(0)
Yeast, dried, brewer's	7.0	348	46.1	1.6	37.4	106	1,893	18.2	(0)	9.69	5.45	36.2	(0)

Note: Parentheses indicate imputed value.

[33] Sulfured.
[34] Unsulfured.
[35] Based on dark brown sugar; lower values for light brown sugar.
[36] Based on vegetable extract type; meat extract type may have up to 27.0 mg. of niacin per 100 gm.
[37] 95 mg.; may not be available because of presence of oxalic acid.
[38] 160 mg.; may not be available because of presence of oxalic acid.

527

SOME PROPERTIES OF SOLUTIONS

Cells contain much water; more than two-thirds the weight of the body is water. In this medium there are inorganic and organic substances, such as salt and sugar (which form solutions), and more complex organic substances, such as proteins, which form colloidal solutions. To some extent, such gases as oxygen and carbon dioxide are also dissolved in water.

Body fluids like blood, lymph, digestive juices, urine, and milk, represent varying types of solutions.

An understanding of some fundamental facts concerning solutions is essential in biochemistry. Such facts, conveniently classified under physical chemistry, may be presented as a prelude to the chapters on proteins and enzymes, which have been studied both from the angle of the physical chemist and from that of the organic chemist.

While such facts as are brought out in this chapter find their application in every field of biochemistry, their usefulness is strikingly illustrated in studies dealing with the chemistry of respiration (Chap. 10).

The theory of electrolytic dissociation, from which so much of value follows, is based upon several properties of solutions which will now be discussed.

Vapor Pressure.   When a liquid evaporates, the escaping molecules exert a pressure known as the vapor pressure. In a mixture, each component exerts its independent pressure. When 1 mole of methyl alcohol is added to 4 moles of ethyl alcohol, the partial pressure of methyl alcohol is one-fifth of the vapor pressure of pure methyl alcohol (at that temperature), and the partial pressure of ethyl alcohol is four-fifths of the vapor pressure of pure ethyl alcohol. The total pressure of the solution is the sum of these two partial pressures.

The vapor pressure of either component is lowered on the addition of the other. This is particularly important when we have a solution of a non-volatile solute, such as sugar, in a liquid such as water. The sugar is non-volatile and, for practical purposes, has zero vapor pressure. Therefore the partial pressure of the water in the solution is the total vapor pressure of the solution. The vapor pressure of the solution is therefore less than the vapor pressure of the pure solvent.

For example, if one mole of sugar is mixed with 99 moles of water, the vapor pressure of the solution is 99/100 of the vapor pressure of pure water (at that temperature). This is an example of the law discovered by Raoult.

Boiling Point.   A liquid boils when its vapor pressure equals that of the atmosphere. Since the atmospheric pressure is normally 760 mm., the boiling point of water is 100° C., because at that temperature the vapor pressure is 760 mm. When the atmospheric pressure falls to 733 mm., water boils at 99° C.

A nonvolatile solute lowers the vapor pressure of a solvent. Now the boiling point is that temperature at which the vapor pressure of the liquid reaches the atmospheric pressure; therefore solutions will not boil at the same temperatures as the pure liquids, but will require a higher temperature.

Freezing Point.   The freezing point is defined as that temperature at which the liquid is in equilibrium with the solid. A solution, with a lower vapor pressure than the pure solvent, will not be in equilibrium with the solid solvent at the normal freezing point. The system must be cooled to that temperature at which the solution and the solid solvent have the same vapor pressure. The freezing point of a solution is therefore less than that of the pure solvent.

Osmosis. If two open vessels, one containing pure water and the other an aqueous solution, are covered with a bell jar, the pure water gradually passes through the vapor state into the solution until it is all gone. The reason for this is that the solution has a smaller vapor pressure than the pure solvent.

If now the two vessels are so arranged that the liquids are in contact through a membrane permeable to the solvent but not to the solute, we find that the solvent passes through this semipermeable membrane into the solution. The number of impacts of water molecules per square centimeter is greater on the pure solvent side than on the solution side, and hence one would anticipate a flow of solvent into the solution. This flow is known as *osmosis*.

Osmosis takes place whenever a solution is separated by a semipermeable membrane from a solution of different concentration. In osmosis the solvent flows from the less concentrated solution into the more concentrated solution.

Osmotic Pressure. If the solvent is to be prevented from penetrating the semipermeable membrane (see preceding paragraph) pressure has to be applied to the solution. This pressure is equivalent to the osmotic pressure. The osmotic pressure of a dilute solution is proportional to the temperature and to the fraction of solute molecules in solution.

The Theory of Electrolytic Dissociation. Aqueous solutions of acids, bases, and salts are excellent conductors of electricity. These substances, electrolytes, constitute a large group of compounds. Sugar, alcohol, glycerol, and, in general, compounds of carbon (organic compounds) are poor conductors of electricity; they are the nonelectrolytes.

Of course, as might be anticipated, in between the excellent conductors and the poor conductors there are many gradations.

Good conductors of electricity give rise to abnormal boiling point elevations, abnormal freezing point depressions, and abnormal osmotic pressures. The poor conductors give normal values.

To explain these phenomena, Arrhenius proposed his now celebrated theory of electrolytic dissociation. He suggested that substances which when dissolved in water are good conductors, are dissociated. Sodium chloride, for example, becomes

$$NaCl \rightleftarrows Na^+ + Cl^-$$

sodium, electrically charged (a sodium ion) and chlorine, electrically charged (a chloride ion). In terms of the effects on boiling point, freezing point, and osmotic pressure, each ion behaves as if it were a molecular unit; so that when sodium chloride is dissolved, it behaves as if it were two ions ($Na^+ + Cl^-$) rather than one molecule. Hence the abnormal results.

On the other hand, nonelectrolytes dissociate very little. For example, cane sugar when dissolved in water still remains as cane sugar molecules. Cane sugar solutions would therefore show no abnormal changes in boiling point, freezing point and osmotic pressure.

From our knowledge of the structures of the atom and the crystalline substance, we know sodium chloride to be completely ionized not only in dilute solutions but also at all other concentrations. The salt is in the completely ionized state.

We can therefore rewrite Arrhenius' equation thus:

$$Na^+Cl^- \rightleftarrows Na^+ + Cl^-$$

which means that when salt is dissolved in water, or when a concentrated solution is diluted, the principal effect is an electrolytic dissociation of pre-existing ions and not an ionization of pre-existing molecules.

Acids and Bases.   The classic view—the view based on the work of Arrhenius—is that an acid yields hydrogen ions in solution and a base yields hydroxyl ions in solution. In dealing with aqueous systems, this view is still a convenient one for many purposes and will be freely used throughout the book. However, the more modern theory, due to Brønsted (and others), has wider implications. According to Brønsted, an acid is a substance which gives off protons (hydrogen ions), and a base is one which unites with protons. In general,

$$A \rightleftarrows H^+ + B$$

A representing the acid and B the base (conjugate base).

Here the definition of an acid remains essentially the same as before, but the definition of a base is less restricted. Formerly the definition of a base was formulated with the basis that water is the solvent, but of course there can be many solvents other than water. For instance, in the equation

$$HCl \rightleftarrows H^+ + Cl^-$$

HCl was considered an acid because in water solution it yielded H^+. The newer concept may be written

$$\underset{\text{(acid)}}{HCl} \rightleftarrows \underset{}{H^+} + \underset{\text{(base)}}{Cl^-}$$

And again,

$$\underset{\text{(acid)}}{CH_3COOH} \rightleftarrows \underset{}{H^+} + \underset{\text{(base)}}{CH_3COO^-}$$
$$\underset{\text{(acid)}}{H_2CO_3} \rightleftarrows \underset{}{H^+} + \underset{\text{(base)}}{HCO_3^-}$$
$$\underset{\text{(acid)}}{H_3O^+} \rightleftarrows \underset{}{H^+} + \underset{\text{(base)}}{H_2O} \text{ *}$$

These acids yield protons (H^+) and particles which combine with protons —particles which, by definition, are bases.

An acid, then, is a substance which yields a proton and a base; and a base is a substance which combines with a proton to form an acid.

Amphoteric Substances.   When a substance acts as an acid and may also act as a base, it is known as an amphoteric substance. Water, for example, may act as an acid because it yields protons:

$$HOH \rightleftarrows H^+ + OH^-$$

* The H^+ exists in aqueous solution in the hydrated form, H_3O^+, the "hydronium," or "oxonium" ion.

and it may act as a base because it combines with protons:

$$HOH + H^+ \rightleftarrows H_3O^+$$

Liquid ammonia may act as an acid:

$$NH_3 \rightleftarrows H^+ + NH_2^-$$

and also as a base:

$$NH_3 + H^+ \rightleftarrows NH_4^+$$

Dissociation of Water. While in general chemistry a discussion of acids and bases must include solvents other than water, in biochemistry, dealing with body tissues, water is the fluid of the utmost importance.

Returning to the classic, and from a practical point of view, the more convenient form for the student, water dissociates thus:

$$HOH \rightleftarrows H^+ + OH^{-*}$$

Applying the law of mass action,

$$K = \frac{[H^+][OH^-]}{[HOH]} \dagger$$

Water dissociates but slightly (one molecule in ten million), which means that the concentration of undissociated water remains practically constant.

Therefore, for K[HOH] we can substitute a new constant, K_w, and write

$$K_w = [H^+][OH^-]$$

where K_w stands for the "ion product," or "dissociation constant," of water.

We further learn from this equation that the product of $[H^+]$ and $[OH^-]$ is a constant. K_w at 25° C. is 1×10^{-14}; so that, since

$$K_w = [H^+][OH^-],$$

and $[H^+]$ is equal to $[OH^-]$

$$K_w = [H^+]^2 \text{ or } [OH^-]^2$$

or $[H^+]$ or $[OH^-] = \sqrt{K_w}$.

So that

$$[H^+] = \sqrt{K_w} = \sqrt{1 \times 10^{-14}} = 10^{-7} \text{ (moles per liter)}$$

The Meaning of pH. pH is the negative logarithm of $[H^+]$, or the logarithm to the base 10 of the reciprocal of $[H^+]$.‡

$$pH = -\log[H^+] = \log \frac{1}{[H^+]}$$

and

$$[H^+] = 10^{-pH}$$

So that if $[H^+] = 10^{-7}$, then $pH = 7.0$

if $[H^+] = 10^{-1}$, then $pH = 1.0$

* Or, more correctly, $2H_2O \rightleftarrows H_3O^+ + OH^-$.

† [ ] = moles per liter.

or K[HOH] = $[H^+][OH^-]$.

‡ For the sake of simplicity, we adhere to the "hydrogen ion," $[H^+]$ rather than to the more modern "hydronium ion," $[H_3O^+]$.

In other words, the greater the hydrogen ion concentration, the lower the pH; so that a solution with a pH of 2 is more acid than one with a pH of 6.

As an example of an interconversion, if $[H^+] = 2.73 \times 10^{-4}$, what is the pH?

$$\text{Log } 2.73 = 0.43 \text{ and log } 10^{-4} = -4$$

$$pH = \log \frac{1}{2.73 \times 10^{-4}} = \log 1 - \log (2.73 \times 10^{-4})$$

$$\text{Log } 1 = 0; \text{ then}$$

$$pH = -\log (2.73 \times 10^{-4})$$
$$= -\log 2.73 - \log 10^{-4}$$
$$= -0.43 + 4$$
$$pH = 3.57$$

If the pH is 5.41, what is $[H^+]$?

$$[H^+] = 10^{-pH}$$
$$= 10^{-5.41}$$
$$= 10^{-6+0.59}$$
$$= 10^{0.59} \times 10^{-6}$$

Antilog of $0.59 = 3.89$
Therefore $[H^+] = 3.89 \times 10^{-6}$

Some examples of pH and $[H^+]$ are given in approximate figures:

Substance	pH	[H⁺]
N HCl	0.0	1.0
0.1 N HCl	1.0	10^{-1}
0.01 N HCl	2.0	10^{-2}
N CH₃COOH	2.3	4.3×10^{-3}
0.1 N CH₃COOH	2.8	1.3×10^{-3}
N NaOH	14.0	10^{-14}
0.1 N NaOH	13.0	10^{-13}
N NH₄OH	11.7	1.7×10^{-12}
0.1 N NH₄OH	11.2	5.4×10^{-12}

Dissociation of a Weak Acid in the Presence of Its Salt.   In the body we find carbonic acid in the presence of its salt, sodium bicarbonate, and, in general, weak acids in the presence of their salts.

In the dissociation of a weak acid, $HA = H^+ + A^-$, by applying the mass action law we get the expression

$$\frac{[H^+] \times [A^-]}{[HA]} = Ka \tag{1}$$

We can titrate an acid with alkali, determining at intervals the pH of the solution (by methods to be outlined presently), and we get titration curves (Figs. 128, 129, and 130). The curve changes least when the acid is half neutralized. At this point the solution shows its maximum buffering effect, a *buffer* being a solution which resists change of pH when acid or alkali is added. From (1), we get

$$[H^+] = K_a \frac{[HA]}{[A^-]}$$

In the presence of a weak acid (acetic) and its salt, the acid is very slightly dissociated, and the anions are approximately all due to the salt. The [HA], then, represents (approximately) total acid, undissociated and dissociated; and the [A⁻] represents (approximately) total salt, undissociated and dissociated. So that we can write

$$[H^+] = K_a \frac{[Acid]}{[Salt]}$$

Fig. 128.

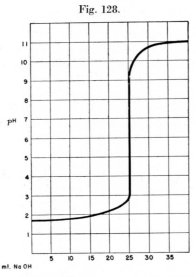

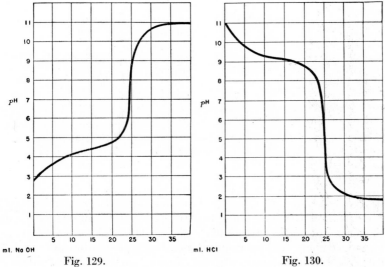

Fig. 129. Fig. 130.

Fig. 128. Titration of 25 ml. of 0.1 N hydrochloric acid with 0.1 N sodium hydroxide.
Fig. 129. Titration of 25 ml. of 0.1 N acetic acid with 0.1 N sodium hydroxide.
Fig. 130. Titration of 25 ml. of 0.1 N ammonium hydroxide with 0.1 N hydrochloric acid.

Transforming this into pH value (the usual form of the Hasselbach-Henderson equation), we get

$$pH = pK_a + \log \frac{[Salt]}{[Acid]}$$

where $pK_a = -\log K_a$

Where we have maximum buffering action (when [salt] = [acid]), then

$$pH = pK_a$$

Methods of Determining pH.   There are two common methods available: the indicator method and the method involving the use of the potentiometer. The details involved in such determinations must be left to texts devoted to laboratory methods, but a few general remarks will be made.

INDICATORS.   These substances, with which pH is often measured, change colors with change of pH. They are usually weak acids or bases wherein the dissociated ion and the undissociated molecule have different colors;

Table 70   A FEW COMMON INDICATORS
(Bertho and Grassmann: Laboratory Methods of Biochemistry.)

| | | Color in | |
Common name	Zone of color change	Acid solution	Alkaline solution
Thymol blue *	1.2– 2.8	red	yellow
Bromophenol blue	3.0– 4.6	yellow	blue
Methyl orange	3.1– 4.4	red	yellow
Methyl red	4.0– 6.0	red	yellow
Bromocresol purple	5.2– 6.8	yellow	violet
Bromothymol blue	6.0– 7.6	yellow	blue
Phenol red	6.8– 8.4	yellow	red
Naphtholphthalein	7.3– 8.7	faint pink	blue
Cresol red	7.2– 8.8	yellow	red
Cresolphthalein	8.2– 9.8	colorless	red
Phenolphthalein	8.3–10.0	colorless	red
Alizarin yellow R	10.3–11.7	yellow	red

* Thymol blue exhibits, in addition, a second zone of color change between 8.0 and 9.6 (yellow—blue). Cresol red and phenol red become pink at pH less than 2 besides changing in the zone shown in the table.

or the one has color and the other has none. The color changes take place within certain pH ranges, different indicators having different pH ranges.

As an example of the use of indicators, we will select two, methyl orange and phenolphthalein. If we examine Fig. 128, representing the titration of a strong acid with a strong base, we can see that both of these indicators can be used. This is so because both indicators undergo their color change at pH values which are very close to the stoichiometric point—to the the point at which an equivalent of reacting substance has been added. (In this connection, compare with Table 70, in which the zones of color changes, in pH values, of these and other indicators are given.)

In the titration of a weak acid with a strong base (Fig. 129), phenolphthalein, and not methyl orange, can be used as indicator. Here at the stoichiometric point, the product formed—a salt of a weak acid and a strong base—gives a slightly alkaline reaction; the *p*H is above 7; and methyl orange undergoes its color change long before the stoichiometric point is reached.

Figure 130 represents the titration of a weak base with a strong acid—the reverse of Fig. 129. Here methyl orange, and not phenolphthalein, can be used. At the stoichiometric point, the product formed—a salt of a weak base and a strong acid—gives a slightly acid reaction; and phenolphthalein undergoes its color change before the stoichiometric point is reached.

A list of several indicators, giving changes in acid and alkaline solutions, is given in Table 70. (See also Fig. 131.)

POTENTIOMETER METHOD. Aside from the indicator method of determining *p*H, there is the method which involves *electrometric measurement*, which, though not so simple to carry out, is more accurate.

A metal immersed in the solution of one of its salts gives rise to two opposing forces: the solution pressure of the metal (as the metal tends to go into solution), and the osmotic pressure of the ions in solution. Nernst has shown that the potential difference between a metal and the solution of one of its salts is given by the equation

$$E = \frac{RT}{nF} \, ln \, \frac{K}{p}$$

where E = electrode potential, F = Faraday (96,500 coulombs), ln = natural logarithm to base e, K = solution pressure of the metal, p = osmotic pressure of ions in solution, n = valence of metallic ion, R = gas constant (8.316 joules per degree), and T = absolute temperature.

At any given temperature, RT/F is a constant; so that E will vary with n and K (which depend upon the nature of the metal) and p (which depends upon the concentration of ions in solution). Using two electrodes of the *same* metal dipping into two solutions of *different* concentrations, and connecting the electrodes by wire and the solutions by a "salt bridge" (an inverted **U**-tube with salt solution), an electromotive force will be developed equal to the difference between the two electrode potentials; or

$$E = E_1 - E_2$$
$$= \frac{RT}{nF} \, ln \, \frac{K_1}{p_1} - \frac{RT}{nF} \, ln \, \frac{K_2}{p_2}$$
$$= \frac{RT}{nF} \, (ln K_1 - ln p_1 - ln K_2 + ln p_2)$$

But $K_1 = K_2$, since we are dealing with the same metal. Therefore

$$E = \frac{RT}{nF} \, ln \, \frac{p_2}{p_1}$$

Now p, the osmotic pressure, is proportional to concentration, c; so that

$$E = \frac{RT}{nF} \, ln \, \frac{c_2}{c_1} \tag{I}$$

One type of electrode which may be used is platinum black saturated with hydrogen; this acts as a hydrogen electrode. Here such electrodes are

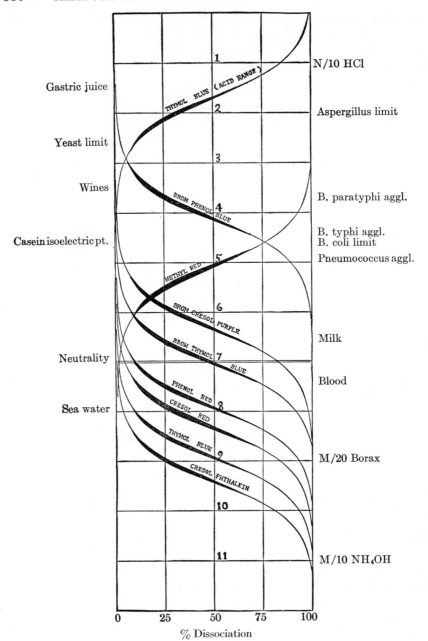

Fig. 131. Indicator curves. Shading indicates useful range. (Clark: The Determination of Hydrogen Ions. Williams and Wilkins Co.)

dipped into solutions containing different concentrations of hydrogen ions. Knowing the $[H^+]$ of one solution, the $[H^+]$ of the second solution can be determined from the electromotive force produced. Let $[H^+]$ of the known solution be normal (1); then equation (I) becomes

$$E = \frac{RT}{nF} \ln \frac{1}{[H^+]}$$

R, T, n, and F are known. The result is multiplied by 2.303 to change the natural log (ln) to $\log_{10}$. Then we get

$$E = 0.058 \log \frac{1}{[H^+]}$$
$$\text{or } E = 0.058 \, (-\log [H^+])$$
$$\text{or } E = 0.058 \, pH$$
$$\text{or } pH = \frac{E}{0.058}$$

Often, glass, calomel, and quinhydrone electrodes are used instead of the "normal" electrode; but what has been discussed illustrates the principle involved.

Colloidal Solutions.   The fact that protoplasm belongs to the group known as "colloids" makes a discussion of colloidal solutions appropriate. In a general way, the particles in suspension in a colloidal solution—where the particles do not settle—are intermediate in size between those in true solutions and coarse suspensions. The range of size of colloidal particles is approximately between $0.2 \, \mu$ (or 200 $m\mu$) and 1 $m\mu$ (where $\mu = 1$ micron $= 10^{-3}$ mm.; and $m\mu = 1$ millimicron $= 10^{-6}$ mm.). Particles larger than 200 $m\mu$ are said to be in coarse suspension and those smaller than 1 $m\mu$ are said to be in true solution.

These boundaries, chosen arbitrarily, are matters of convenience. For example, the upper limit, 200 $m\mu$, represents the resolving power of a very good microscope with proper illumination. The lower limit, 1 $m\mu$, is near the limit of visibility of the ultramicroscope.

The range of colloidal solutions is such that they show many properties in common with true solutions and coarse suspensions. There is a gradation of properties with increasing size—from true solution, up through colloidal solutions to the coarse suspensions—and at no place is there an abrupt break.

Graham, the "father of colloid chemistry," distinguished crystalloids from colloids on the basis of diffusion. Colloids, which are relatively large particles, diffuse slowly or not at all, while crystalloids, which are smaller particles, diffuse readily. In a practical way, this method is sometimes used to distinguish a colloidal solution from a true solution.

Colloidal solutions run through ordinary filters. The use of filter paper is a rough but convenient method for separating colloidal particles from those in coarse suspension.

To separate colloidal particles from those in true solution, filters with much finer pores than are found in filter paper must be used. These are available in membranes such as parchment, animal membranes, collodion, cellophane, etc. Using special techniques, membranes having pores of any desired size may be prepared. In this way colloidal particles can be separated from smaller ones, or even two different sizes of colloidal particles from each other. This operation is known as *dialysis* and is frequently used to purify colloidal solutions from dissolved impurities.

Colloidal solutions in contrast to coarse suspensions, are perfectly clear under the ordinary microscope. However, to the naked eye they often appear to be turbid, especially when examined at right angles to the path of a beam of light. This is the *Tyndall effect* and is due to the fact that the particles are large enough to scatter light. In the ultramicroscope the microscope is so arranged as to look at right angles to the beam of incident light. The light is here scattered by the colloidal particles, and each particle appears as a light spot in a dark field. This enables us to examine particles too small to be seen in the ordinary microscope. In true solutions the particles are too small even to scatter light, so that solutions appear homogeneous both in the microscope and in the ultramicroscope.

Colloidal particles in the ultramicroscope appear to be in a state of vigorous motion. It is an irregular, rapid motion and is known as the *Brownian movement*, named after Robert Brown who first observed it.

We can summarize our results thus:

Suspensions	*Colloidal solutions*	*True solutions*
Do not pass through filters	Pass through filters	Pass through filters
Do not dialyze	Do not dialyze	Do dialyze
No osmotic pressure	Little osmotic pressure	Large osmotic pressure
No depression in freezing point	Little depression in freezing point	Large depression in freezing point
No elevation in boiling point	Little elevation in boiling point	Large elevation in boiling point
Particles larger than 200 mμ	Particles between 200 mμ and 1 mμ	Particles smaller than 1 mμ
Microscopic (or larger)	Ultramicroscopic	Invisible

Surface Tension.   In the interior of a liquid the molecules are equally attracted by neighboring molecules. This is not true at the surface of a liquid, where attraction from the top is lacking. (Attraction forces due to air molecules are negligible.) Freedom of movement is, therefore, restricted at the surface, and one such result is the formation of a surface membrane. A certain force pulling the surface molecules inward is called "surface tension" (or "interfacial tension"). With colloidal particles this interfacial tension is exhibited at those points where particles and liquid meet (they meet at the interface).

Certain types of colloids—the emulsoids, in which the colloid and the liquid medium are more or less soluble in one another—tend to decrease the surface tension of liquids. The foaming of such solutions is due to the lowering of the surface tension.

The temporary emulsion formed by shaking together oil and water may be converted into a permanent one by the addition of soap, which lowers the interfacial tension existing at the interface of the oil and water droplets.

Willard Gibbs was the first to show that substances which lower the surface tension tend to concentrate at the surface (they are *adsorbed*), and various properties of colloids—those dealing with precipitation, electrical charges, viscosity, etc.—are related to such adsorption. The bearing on cellular problems becomes apparent when we remember once again that protoplasm is a colloidal system.

The extent of adsorption depends upon several factors: one such factor is the fineness of division. The finer the division—the greater the surface—the better the adsorption; and colloids are finely divided particles.

Many biological materials, usually of a protein and therefore of colloidal character, can be purified by making use of the principles of adsorption. The protein is adsorbed on some suitable material—charcoal, aluminum hydroxide, etc.—at the proper pH and "freed," or "eluted," at another pH.

REFERENCES

Physical chemistry texts for students of biochemistry and medicine are *West:* Physical Chemistry, 1942; *Bull:* Physical Chemistry, 1951; *Clark:* Topics in Physical Chemistry, 1952.

Index